W9-CFU-683

THE WORKS OF
OSCAR WILDE

Edited and introduced by
Dr Timothy Gaynor

SENATE

The Works of Oscar Wilde

This edition published in 1997 by Senate,
an imprint of Tiger Books International PLC,
26A York Street, Twickenham,
Middlesex TW1 3LJ, United Kingdom

Cover design © Tiger Books International 1997

3 5 7 9 10 8 6 4 2

All rights reserved. No part of this publication may be
reproduced, stored in a retrieval system or transmitted,
in any form or by any means, electronic, mechanical,
photocopying, recording or otherwise, without the prior
permission of the copyright owners.

ISBN 1 85170 538 4

Printed and bound in Great Britain by
Cox & Wyman, Reading, Berkshire

CONTENTS

INTRODUCTION

Oscar Fingal O'Flahertie Wills Wilde was born in Dublin on 16 October 1854 to a prosperous Anglo-Irish family. He grew up with the uncertain benefits of membership of Ireland's ruling Protestant cadre. He was the younger son of Sir William Ralph Wills, a leading oculist and ear surgeon, who was knighted by Queen Victoria for services to public health. His mother, Jane Francesca Elgee Wilde, was a more ambivalent figure who, under the name of 'Speranza', was a well-known supporter of the Young Ireland movement. It was a background of both privilege and, on his mother's side, dissent – a combination that would be fully realized in Wilde's brilliant literary career and subsequent fall from grace.

Like the young Samuel Beckett after him, Oscar Wilde was sent to Portrora Royal School in Enniskillen (1864-71) and thereafter to Trinity College, Dublin (1871-74), where he excelled in Latin and Ancient Greek. But it was the last stage of his education at Magdalen College, Oxford (1874-79), that finally forged Wilde's identity. He studied at Oxford at a time when the university was falling under the intoxicating sway of aestheticism – a modish doctrine perhaps best summarized by Walter Pater's exaltation to enjoy 'art for art's sake'. Wilde regularly attended Pater's lectures and appeared greatly affected by them. He readily adopted the attitude of the stricken aesthete and began to dress in a fashionably foppish manner. His rooms filled with the paraphernalia of the aesthete – the preferred blue china, gaudy peacock feather screens and vases of lilies and sunflowers. It was aestheticism's insistence on the implicit value of any experience which allowed Wilde a sympathetic avenue through which to explore his homosexuality.

Wilde soon emerged as the most effortlessly gifted of his contemporaries, his poem 'Ravenna' winning the prestigious Newdigate Prize for poetry in 1878. One can easily imagine the frock-coated young poet reciting the line 'Adieu, Ravenna!' to a packed Sheldonian theatre. 'Ravenna' offers an insight into his rich classical education and deft mastery of poetical form.

After graduating Wilde went to London, eventually settling in Tite Street, Chelsea. The young aesthetes in his circle became a somewhat scandalous *cause celèbre*, attracting the troubled attention of a bewildered London society. Wilde continued to dress with his same Oxford flamboyance but now without the caveat of youthful student folly to mitigate his eccentricity. He wore his hair long and preferred velvet to the more austere fabrics with which tailors dressed Victorian society. Through his dandyish behaviour, affectations and general posturing Wilde attracted a great deal of, often unfavourable, attention. He, and the painters and artists with whom he kept company, were regularly lampooned in cartoons in the satirical magazine *Punch*. In 1881 Gilbert and Sullivan wrote the light operetta *Patience* which made delightful sport of the well-known dandies and aesthetes of the day.

Aestheticism's insistence on the autonomy of art carried with it a cavalier disdain for the harsh facts of everyday life. Wilde, however, could not afford to be quite so lofty. Much of his subsequent life was determined by the banal need to earn money. He left England in 1882 for a lucrative lecture tour of the United States and Canada where the young aesthete was a valued commodity. Wilde had ambivalent feelings about Americans, however, at once lambasting what he saw as their parvenu pretensions but at the same time appreciating their unstuffiness – a quality which he found a refreshing change from the stifling conventionality of Victorian London. Returning to lecture in Britain, Wilde continued to delight and scandalize his often ambivalent audiences with his precocity and sparkling wit.

In 1884 Wilde married Constance Lloyd with whom he had two sons. The marriage would in no way resolve Wilde's conflictual homosexual desires. He spent the next few years reviewing books and editing the magazine *Woman's World* (1887-89) to earn a necessary living. During the 1880s Wilde also wrote essays and articles for, among others, *Blackwoods' Magazine* and *Fortnightly Review*. These included the essay *The Critic as Artist* in which he expounds upon the tenets of the aestheticist doctrine. During this period he also began writing short stories. *The Happy Prince and Other Tales*, an enchanting collection that has captivated generations of readers, was published in 1888. *The Happy Prince* and *The Selfish Giant* are explorations of a world impoverished by a lack of compassion, a theme he would return to in his later essays and verse after his fall from grace.

During this period Wilde also wrote the novel *The Picture of Dorian Gray*. Its publication was met with poor reviews – Wilde was widely criticized for the work's apparent immorality. Critics felt it to be an unwholesome tale of vanity, murder and self-obsession that revealed the true decadence at the heart of aestheticism. However, none of the reviewers could bring himself to mention the real cause of his concern, namely that the work was centred around a sexually ambivalent Adonis. The novel marked the problematic recurrence of Wilde's homosexual leanings, a fact that Victorian society would eventually refuse to tolerate.

It is as a playwright, however, that Wilde is now best remembered. He wrote two early plays that have been largely ignored. *Vera* (1880) and *The Duchess of Padua* (1883), which Wilde himself admitted were 'unfit for publication'. Clearly, they gave no indication of the delightful lightness of touch on which his later success depended. It was not until *Lady Windermere's Fan* was produced in 1892 that the world at large was able to appreciate Wilde's rapier wit and sharp epigrammatic style. This success was swiftly followed by *A Woman of No Importance* (1893) in which he made use of his time spent in America to sardonic effect, *An Ideal Husband* (1895), and his most celebrated work, *The Importance of Being Earnest* (1895). Acquaintances of Wilde recalled after his death that his greatest gift was perhaps his love of conversation, an evanescent art at which he was extraordinarily skilled. It is his plays, more than his poems and prose works, that best capture his laconic wit and supreme sure-fire delivery.

The final phase of Wilde's short but glittering career began with his friendship with Lord Arthur Douglas. Douglas, or 'Bosie' as he was known to his intimates, was renowned for his good looks and precocious charm, and has on occasion been suggested as the model for the dangerously compelling Dorian Gray. Wilde became deeply infatuated and insisted upon appearing everywhere in public with Bosie at his side. Wilde had frequently tested the bounds of Victorian tolerance throughout his career but had finally misjudged society's willingness to accept his libertarian nature. Bosie's father, the volatile 9th Marquess of Queensberry, objected violently to this questionable 'friendship'. Queensberry sent a note to Wilde's London club bearing one of the most renowned spelling mistakes in legal history. 'To Oscar Wilde', it read, 'posing *somdomite*'. Wilde responded to the accusation of sodomy with legal action for libel. Queensberry, however, was too powerful a public figure, or his case too strong. Wilde lost the trial and found himself under a charge for homosexual offences under the Criminal Law Amendment Act of 1885. The trial took place against a background of vilification in the press. At the trial the jury was unable to reach a verdict, but a hasty retrial found Wilde guilty. On the 25 May 1895 he was sentenced to two years' imprisonment with hard labour.

The years in prison, largely spent at Reading Gaol, were a time of great suffering and humiliation. On his release Wilde was bankrupt and disgraced. The library and contents of his house in Tite Street had been auctioned off leaving him with only the clothes he stood in. He fled to the Continent, travelling under the assumed name of Sebastian Melmoth. His flight took him to Italy and finally Paris. But this unhappy period produced some of Wilde's finest work. In 1897 Wilde wrote *De Profundis*, a long and affecting essay on sorrow and loss born out of his period of imprisonment. In 1898 'The Ballad of Reading Gaol' was published. The poem is both a moving account of his stay in prison and a passionate call for prison reform – a subject upon which he had strong views.

Wilde lived simply and in comparative poverty in Paris but continued to delight a small circle of friends with his conversation and witty letters. He died in Paris on 30 November 1900 having seen in the new century. He had lived Walter Pater's imprecation 'to burn with a hard, gem-like flame' to the letter.

DR TIMOTHY GAYNOR 1997

STORIES

THE PICTURE OF DORIAN GRAY

THE PREFACE

THE artist is the creator of beautiful things.

To reveal art and conceal the artist is art's aim.

The critic is he who can translate into another manner or a new material his impression of beautiful things.

The highest, as the lowest, form of criticism is a mode of autobiography.

Those who find ugly meanings in beautiful things are corrupt without being charming. This is a fault.

Those who find beautiful meanings in beautiful things are the cultivated. For these there is hope.

They are the elect to whom beautiful things mean only Beauty.

There is no such thing as a moral or an immoral book. Books are well written, or badly written. That is all.

The nineteenth century dislike of Realism is the rage of Caliban seeing his own face in a glass.

The nineteenth century dislike of Romanticism is the rage of Caliban not seeing his own face in a glass.

The moral life of man forms part of the subject-matter of the artist, but the morality of art consists in the perfect use of an imperfect medium.

No artist desires to prove anything. Even things that are true can be proved.

No artist has ethical sympathies. An ethical sympathy in an artist is an unpardonable mannerism of style.

No artist is ever morbid. The artist can express everything.

15

Thought and language are to the artist instruments of an art.

Vice and virtue are to the artist materials for an art.

From the point of view of form, the type of all the arts is the art of the musician. From the point of view of feeling, the actor's craft is the type.

All art is at once surface and symbol.

Those who go beneath the surface do so at their peril.

Those who read the symbol do so at their peril.

It is the spectator, and not life, that art really mirrors.

Diversity of opinion about a work of art shows that the work is new, complex, and vital.

When critics disagree the artist is in accord with himself.

We can forgive a man for making a useful thing as long as he does not admire it. The only excuse for making a useless thing is that one admires it intensely.

All art is quite useless.

OSCAR WILDE.

CHAPTER I

THE studio was filled with the rich odour of roses, and when the light summer wind stirred amidst the trees of the garden, there came through the open door the heavy scent of the lilac, or the more delicate perfume of the pink-flowering thorn. From the corner of the divan of Persian saddlebags on which he was lying, smoking, as was his custom, innumerable cigarettes, Lord Henry Wotton could just catch the gleam of the honey-sweet and honey-coloured blossoms of a laburnum, whose tremulous branches seemed hardly able to bear the burden of a beauty so flame-like as theirs ; and now and then the fantastic shadows of birds in flight flitted across the long tussore-silk curtains that were stretched in front of the huge window, producing a kind of momentary Japanese effect, and making him think of those pallid jade-faced painters of Tokio who, through the medium of an art that is necessarily immobile, seek to convey the sense of swiftness and motion. The sullen murmur of the bees shouldering their way through the long unmown grass, or circling with monotonous insistence round the dusty gilt horns of the straggling woodbine, seemed to make the stillness more oppressive. The dim roar of London was like the bourdon note of a distant organ.

In the centre of the room, clamped to an upright easel, stood the full-length portrait of a young man of extraordinary personal beauty, and in front of it, some little distance away, was sitting the artist himself, Basil Hallward, whose sudden disappearance some years ago caused, at the time, such public

excitement, and gave rise to so many strange con-
jectures.

As the painter looked at the gracious and comely
form he had so skilfully mirrored in his art, a smile of
pleasure passed across his face, and seemed about to
linger there. But he suddenly started up, and, closing
his eyes, placed his fingers upon the lids, as though he
sought to imprison within his brain some curious
dream from which he feared he might awake.

" It is your best work, Basil, the best thing you
have ever done," said Lord Henry, languidly. " You
must certainly send it next year to the Grosvenor.
The Academy is too large and too vulgar. Whenever
I have gone there, there have been either so many
people that I have not been able to see the pictures,
which was dreadful, or so many pictures that I have
not been able to see the people, which was worse.
The Grosvenor is really the only place."

" I don't think I shall send it anywhere," he
answered, tossing his head back in that odd way that
used to make his friends laugh at him at Oxford.
" No : I won't send it anywhere."

Lord Henry elevated his eyebrows, and looked at
him in amazement through the thin blue wreaths of
smoke that curled up in such fanciful whirls from his
heavy opium-tainted cigarette. " Not send it anywhere ? My dear fellow, why ? Have you any reason ?
What odd chaps you painters are ! You do anything
in the world to gain a reputation. As soon as you have
one, you seem to want to throw it away. It is silly of
you, for there is only one thing in the world worse than
being talked about, and that is not being talked about.
A portrait like this would set you far above all the
young men in England, and make the old men quite
jealous, if old men are ever capable of any emotion."

" I know you will laugh at me," he replied, " but
I really can't exhibit it. I have put too much of
myself into it."

Lord Henry stretched himself out on the divan and laughed.

"Yes, I knew you would ; but it is quite true, all the same."

"Too much of yourself in it ! Upon my word, Basil, I didn't know you were so vain ; and I really can't see any resemblance between you, with your rugged strong face and your coal-black hair, and this young Adonis, who looks as if he was made out of ivory and rose-leaves. Why, my dear Basil, he is a Narcissus, and you—well, of course you have an intellectual expression, and all that. But beauty, real beauty, ends where an intellectual expression begins. Intellect is in itself a mode of exaggeration, and destroys the harmony of any face. The moment one sits down to think, one becomes all nose, or all forehead, or something horrid. Look at the successful men in any of the learned professions. How perfectly hideous they are ! Except, of course, in the Church. But then in the Church they don't think. A bishop keeps on saying at the age of eighty what he was told to say when he was a boy of eighteen, and as a natural consequence he always looks absolutely delightful. Your mysterious young friend, whose name you have never told me, but whose picture really fascinates me, never thinks. I feel quite sure of that. He is some brainless, beautiful creature, who should be always here in winter when we have no flowers to look at, and always here in summer when we want something to chill our intelligence. Don't flatter yourself, Basil : you are not in the least like him."

"You don't understand me, Harry," answered the artist. "Of course I am not like him. I know that perfectly well. Indeed, I should be sorry to look like him. You shrug your shoulders ? I am telling you the truth. There is a fatality about all physical and intellectual distinction, the sort of fatality that seems to dog through history the faltering

steps of kings. It is better not to be different
from one's fellows. The ugly and the stupid have the
best of it in this world. They can sit at their ease
and gape at the play. If they know nothing of victory,
they are at least spared the knowledge of defeat.
They live as we all should live, undisturbed, indifferent, and without disquiet. They neither bring
ruin upon others, nor ever receive it from alien hands.
Your rank and wealth, Harry ; my brains, such
as they are—my art, whatever it may be worth ;
Dorian Gray's good looks—we shall all suffer for what
the gods have given us, suffer terribly."

"Dorian Gray ? Is that his name ? " asked Lord
Henry, walking across the studio towards Basil
Hallward.

" Yes, that is his name. I didn't intend to tell it
to you."

" But why not ? "

" Oh, I can't explain. When I like people immensely I never tell their names to any one. It is
like surrendering a part of them. I have grown to
love secrecy. It seems to be the one thing that can
make modern life mysterious or marvellous to us.
The commonest thing is delightful if one only hides
it. When I leave town now I never tell my people
where I am going. If I did, I would lose all my pleasure.
It is a silly habit, I dare say, but somehow it seems to
bring a great deal of romance into one's life. I suppose
you think me awfully foolish about it ? "

" Not at all," answered Lord Henry, " not at all,
my dear Basil. You seem to forget that I am married,
and the one charm of marriage is that it makes a life
of deception absolutely necessary for both parties.
I never know where my wife is, and my wife never
knows what I am doing. When we meet—we do
meet occasionally, when we dine out together, or go
down to the Duke's—we tell each other the most
absurd stories with the most serious faces. My wife

is very good at it—much better, in fact, than I am.
She never gets confused over her dates, and I always
do. But when she does find me out, she makes no
row at all. I sometimes wish she would ; but she merely
laughs at me."

" I hate the way you talk about your married life,
Harry," said Basil Hallward, strolling towards the
door that led into the garden. " I believe that you
are really a very good husband, but that you are
thoroughly ashamed of your own virtues. You are
an extraordinary fellow. You never say a moral
thing, and you never do a wrong thing. Your cynicism
is simply a pose."

" Being natural is simply a pose, and the most
irritating pose I know," cried Lord Henry, laughing ;
and the two young men went out into the garden
together, and ensconced themselves on a long bamboo
seat that stood in the shade of a tall laurel bush. The
sunlight slipped over the polished leaves. In the grass
white daisies were tremulous.

After a pause, Lord Henry pulled out his watch.
" I am afraid I must be going, Basil," he murmured,
" and before I go, I insist on your answering a question
I put to you some time ago."

" What is that ? " said the painter, keeping his
eyes fixed on the ground.

" You know quite well."

" I do not, Harry."

" Well, I will tell you what it is. I want you to
explain to me why you won't exhibit Dorian Gray's
picture. I want the real reason."

" I told you the real reason."

" No, you did not. You said it was because there
was too much of yourself in it. Now, that is childish."

" Harry," said Basil Hallward, looking him straight
in the face, " every portrait that is painted with
feeling is a portrait of the artist, not of the sitter.
The sitter is merely the accident, the occasion. It

is not he who is revealed by the painter ; it is rather
the painter who, on the coloured canvas, reveals
himself. The reason I will not exhibit this picture is
that I am afraid that I have shown in it the secret
of my own soul."

Lord Henry laughed. " And what is that ? " he
asked.

" I will tell you," said Hallward ; but an expression of perplexity came over his face.

" I am all expectation, Basil," continued his companion, glancing at him.

" Oh, there is really very little to tell, Harry,"
answered the painter ; " and I am afraid you will
hardly understand it. Perhaps you will hardly believe it."

Lord Henry smiled, and, leaning down, plucked a
pink-petalled daisy from the grass, and examined it.
" I am quite sure I shall understand it," he replied,
gazing intently at the little golden white-feathered
disk, " and as for believing things, I can believe
anything, provided that it is quite incredible."

The wind shook some blossoms from the trees, and
the heavy lilac-blooms, with their clustering stars,
moved to and fro in the languid air. A grasshopper
began to chirrup by the wall, and like a blue thread
a long thin dragon-fly floated past on its brown gauze
wings. Lord Henry felt as if he could hear Basil
Hallward's heart beating, and wondered what was
coming.

" The story is simply this," said the painter after
some time. " Two months ago I went to a crush at
Lady Brandon's. You know we poor artists have to
show ourselves in society from time to time, just to
remind the public that we are not savages. With an
evening coat and a white tie, as you told me once,
anybody, even a stockbroker, can gain a reputation
for being civilised. Well, after I had been in the room
about ten minutes, talking to huge overdressed

dowagers and tedious Academicians, I suddenly became conscious that some one was looking at me. I
turned half-way round, and saw Dorian Gray for the
first time. When our eyes met, I felt that I was
growing pale. A curious sensation of terror came
over me. I knew that I had come face to face with
some one whose mere personality was so fascinating
that, if I allowed it to do so, it would absorb my
whole nature, my whole soul, my very art itself. I
did not want any external influence in my life. You
know yourself, Harry, how independent I am by
nature. I have always been my own master; had
at least always been so, till I met Dorian Gray.
Then—— but I don't know how to explain it to you.
Something seemed to tell me that I was on the verge
of a terrible crisis in my life. I had a strange feeling
that Fate had in store for me exquisite joys and
exquisite sorrows. I grew afraid, and turned to
quit the room. It was not conscience that made me
do so; it was a sort of cowardice. I take no credit
to myself for trying to escape."

"Conscience and cowardice are really the same
things, Basil. Conscience is the trade-name of the
firm. That is all."

"I don't believe that, Harry, and I don't believe
you do either. However, whatever was my motive
—and it may have been pride, for I used to be very
proud—I certainly struggled to the door. There,
of course, I stumbled against Lady Brandon. 'You
are not going to run away so soon, Mr. Hallward?'
she screamed out. You know her curiously shrill
voice?"

"Yes; she is a peacock in everything but beauty,"
said Lord Henry, pulling the daisy to bits with his
long, nervous fingers.

"I could not get rid of her. She brought me up
to Royalties, and people with Stars and Garters, and
elderly ladies with gigantic tiaras and parrot noses.

She spoke of me as her dearest friend. I had only met her once before, but she took it into her head to lionise me. I believe some picture of mine had made a great success at the time, at least had been chattered about in the penny newspapers, which is the nineteenth-century standard of immortality. Suddenly I found myself face to face with the young man whose personality had so strangely stirred me. We were quite close, almost touching. Our eyes met again. It was reckless of me, but I asked Lady Brandon to introduce me to him. Perhaps it was not so reckless, after all. It was simply inevitable. We would have spoken to each other without any introduction. I am sure of that. Dorian told me so afterwards. He, too, felt that we were destined to know each other."

"And how did Lady Brandon describe this wonderful young man?" asked his companion. "I know she goes in for giving a rapid *précis* of all her guests. I remember her bringing me up to a truculent and red-faced old gentleman covered all over with orders and ribbons, and hissing into my ear, in a tragic whisper which must have been perfectly audible to everybody in the room, the most astounding details. I simply fled. I like to find out people for myself. But Lady Brandon treats her guests exactly as an auctioneer treats his goods. She either explains them entirely away, or tells one everything about them except what one wants to know."

"Poor Lady Brandon! You are hard on her, Harry!" said Hallward, listlessly.

"My dear fellow, she tried to found a *salon*, and only succeeded in opening a restaurant. How could I admire her? But tell me, what did she say about Mr. Dorian Gray?"

"Oh, something like, 'Charming boy—poor dear mother and I absolutely inseparable. Quite forget what he does—afraid he—doesn't do anything—oh, yes, plays the piano—or is it the violin, dear Mr.

Gray ?   Neither of us could help laughing, and we became friends at once."

"Laughter is not at all a bad beginning for a friendship, and it is far the best ending for one," said the young lord, plucking another daisy.

Hallward shook his head. "You don't understand what friendship is, Harry," he murmured— "or what enmity is, for that matter. You like every one ; that is to say, you are indifferent to every one."

"How horribly unjust of you ! " cried Lord Henry, tilting his hat back, and looking up at the little clouds that, like ravelled skeins of glossy white silk, were drifting across the hollowed turquoise of the summer sky. "Yes ; horribly unjust of you. I make a great difference between people. I choose my friends for their good looks, my acquaintances for their good characters, and my enemies for their good intellects. A man cannot be too careful in the choice of his enemies. I have not got one who is a fool. They are all men of some intellectual power, and consequently they all appreciate me. Is that very vain of me ? I think it is rather vain."

"I should think it was, Harry. But according to your category I must be merely an acquaintance."

"My dear old Basil, you are much more than an acquaintance."

"And much less than a friend. A sort of brother, I suppose ? "

"Oh, brothers ! I don't care for brothers. My elder brother won't die, and my younger brothers seem never to do anything else."

"Harry ! " exclaimed Hallward, frowning.

"My dear fellow, I am not quite serious. But I can't help detesting my relations. I suppose it comes from the fact that none of us can stand other people having the same faults as ourselves. I quite sympathise with the rage of the English democracy against what they call the vices of the upper orders. The masses feel that drunkenness, stupidity, and immorality should be their own special property, and that if any one of us makes an ass of himself he is poaching on their preserves. When poor Southwark got into the Divorce Court, their indignation was quite magnificent. And yet I don't suppose that ten per cent. of the proletariat live correctly."

" I don't agree with a single word that you have said, and, what is more, Harry, I feel sure you don't either."

Lord Henry stroked his pointed brown beard, and tapped the toe of his patent-leather boot with a tasselled ebony cane. " How English you are, Basil! That is the second time you have made that observation. If one puts forward an idea to a true Englishman—always a rash thing to do—he never dreams of considering whether the idea is right or wrong. The only thing he considers of any importance is whether one believes it oneself. Now, the value of an idea has nothing whatsoever to do with the sincerity of the man who expresses it. Indeed, the probabilities are that the more insincere the man is, the more purely intellectual will the idea be, as in that case it will not be coloured by either his wants, his desires, or his prejudices. However, I don't propose to discuss politics, sociology, or metaphysics with you. I like persons better than principles, and I like persons with no principles better than anything else in the world. Tell me more about Mr. Dorian Gray. How often do you see him ? "

" Every day. I couldn't be happy if I didn't see him every day. He is absolutely necessary to me."

" How extraordinary ! I thought you would never care for anything but your art."

" He is all my art to me now," said the painter, gravely. " I sometimes think, Harry, that there are only two eras of any importance in the world's history. The first is the appearance of a new medium for art, and the second is the appearance of a new personality for art also. What the invention of oil-painting was to the Venetians, the face of Antinoüs was to late Greek sculpture, and the face of Dorian Gray will some day be to me. It is not merely that I paint from him, draw from him, sketch from him. Of course I have done all that. But he is much more to me than a model or a sitter. I won't tell you that I am dissatisfied with what I have done of him, or that his beauty is such that Art cannot express it. There is nothing that Art cannot express, and I know that the work I have done, since I met Dorian Gray, is good work, is the best work of my life. But in some curious way—I wonder will you understand me ? —his personality has suggested to me an entirely new manner in art, an entirely new mode of style. I see things differently, I think of them differently. I can now recreate life in a way that was hidden from me before. ' A dream of form in days of thought : ' —who is it who says that ? I forget ; but it is what Dorian Gray has been to me. The merely visible presence of this lad—for he seems to me little more than a lad, though he is really over twenty—his merely visible presence—ah ! I wonder can you realise all that that means ? Unconsciously he defines for me the lines of a fresh school, a school that is to have in it all the passion of the romantic spirit, all the perfection of the spirit that is Greek. The harmony of soul and body—how much that is ! We in our madness have separated the two, and have invented a realism that is vulgar, an ideality that is void. Harry ! if you only knew what Dorian Gray is to me ! You remember that landscape of mine, for which Agnew offered me such a huge price, but which I would not part with ? It is one of the best things I have ever done. And why is it so ? Because, while I was painting it, Dorian Gray sat beside me. Some subtle influence passed from him to me, and for the first time in my life I saw in the plain woodland the wonder I had always looked for, and always missed."

"Basil, this is extraordinary! I must see Dorian Gray."

Hallward got up from the seat, and walked up and down the garden. After some time he came back. "Harry," he said, "Dorian Gray is to me simply a motive in art. You might see nothing in him. I see everything in him. He is never more present in my work than when no image of him is there. He is a suggestion, as I have said, of a new manner. I find him in the curves of certain lines, in the loveliness and subtleties of certain colours. That is all."

"Then why won't you exhibit his portrait?" asked Lord Henry.

"Because, without intending it, I have put into it some expression of all this curious artistic idolatry, of which, of course, I have never cared to speak to him. He knows nothing about it. He shall never know anything about it. But the world might guess it; and I will not bare my soul to their shallow prying eyes. My heart shall never be put under their microscope. There is too much of myself in the thing, Harry—too much of myself!"

"Poets are not so scrupulous as you are. They know how useful passion is for publication. Nowadays a broken heart will run to many editions."

"I hate them for it," cried Hallward. "An artist should create beautiful things, but should put nothing of his own life into them. We live in an age when men treat art as if it were meant to be a form of autobiography. We have lost the abstract sense of beauty. Some day I will show the world what it is; and for that reason the world shall never see my portrait of Dorian Gray."

"I think you are wrong, Basil, but I won't argue with you. It is only the intellectually lost who ever argue. Tell me, is Dorian Gray very fond of you?"

The painter considered for a few moments. " He likes me," he answered, after a pause ; " I know he likes me. Of course I flatter him dreadfully. I find a strange pleasure in saying things to him that I know I shall be sorry for having said. As a rule, he is charming to me, and we sit in the studio and talk of a thousand things. Now and then, however, he is horribly thoughtless, and seems to take a real delight in giving me pain. Then I feel, Harry, that I have given away my whole soul to some one who treats it as if it were a flower to put in his coat, a bit of decoration to charm his vanity, an ornament for a summer's day."

" Days in summer, Basil, are apt to linger," murmured Lord Henry. " Perhaps you will tire sooner than he will. It is a sad thing to think of, but there is no doubt that Genius lasts longer than Beauty. That accounts for the fact that we all take such pains to over-educate ourselves. In the wild struggle for existence, we want to have something that endures, and so we fill our minds with rubbish and facts, in the silly hope of keeping our place. The thoroughly well-informed man—that is the modern ideal. And the mind of the thoroughly well-informed man is a dreadful thing. It is like a bric-à-brac shop, all monsters and dust, with everything priced above its proper value. I think you will tire first, all the same. Some day you will look at your friend, and he will seem to you to be a little out of drawing, or you won't like his tone of colour, or something. You will bitterly reproach him in your own heart, and seriously think that he has behaved very badly to you. The next time he calls, you will be perfectly cold and indifferent. It will be a great pity, for it will alter you. What you have told me is quite a romance, a romance of art one might call it, and the worst of having a romance of any kind is that it leaves one so unromantic."

" Harry, don't talk like that. As long as I live

the personality of Dorian Gray will dominate me. You can't feel what I feel. You change too often."

"Ah, my dear Basil, that is exactly why I can feel it. Those who are faithful know only the trivial side of love : it is the faithless who know love's tragedies." And Lord Henry struck a light on a dainty silver case, and began to smoke a cigarette with a self-conscious and satisfied air, as if he had summed up the world in a phrase. There was a rustle of chirruping sparrows in the green lacquer leaves of the ivy, and the blue cloud-shadows chased themselves across the grass like swallows. How pleasant it was in the garden! And how delightful other people's emotions were!—much more delightful than their ideas, it seemed to him. One's own soul, and the passions of one's friends—those were the fascinating things in life. He pictured to himself with silent amusement the tedious luncheon that he had missed by staying so long with Basil Hallward. Had he gone to his aunt's he would have been sure to have met Lord Hoodbody there, and the whole conversation would have been about the feeding of the poor, and the necessity for model lodging-houses. Each class would have preached the importance of those virtues, for whose exercise there was no necessity in their own lives. The rich would have spoken on the value of thrift, and the idle grown eloquent over the dignity of labour. It was charming to have escaped all that! As he thought of his aunt, an idea seemed to strike him. He turned to Hallward, and said, " My dear fellow, I have just remembered."

" Remembered what, Harry ? "

" Where I heard the name of Dorian Gray."

" Where was it ? " asked Hallward, with a slight frown.

" Don't look so angry, Basil. It was at my aunt, Lady Agatha's. She told me she had discovered a wonderful young man, who was going to help her in

the East End, and that his name was Dorian Gray.
I am bound to state that she never told me he was
good-looking. Women have no appreciation of good
looks; at least, good women have not. She said
that he was very earnest, and had a beautiful nature.
I at once pictured to myself a creature with spectacles
and lank hair, horribly freckled, and tramping about
on huge feet. I wish I had known it was your friend."

" I am very glad you didn't, Harry."

" Why ? "

" I don't want you to meet him."

" You don't want me to meet him ? "

" No."

" Mr. Dorian Gray is in the studio, sir," said the
butler, coming into the garden.

" You must introduce me now," cried Lord Henry,
laughing.

The painter turned to his servant, who stood blinking in the sunlight. " Ask Mr. Gray to wait, Parker :
I shall be in in a few moments," the man bowed, and
went up the walk.

Then he looked at Lord Henry. " Dorian Gray is
my dearest friend," he said. " He has a simple and a
beautiful nature. Your aunt was quite right in what
she said of him. Don't spoil him. Don't try to influence him. Your influence would be bad. The
world is wide, and has many marvellous people in
it. Don't take away from me the one person who
gives to my art whatever charm it possesses ; my
life as an artist depends on him. Mind, Harry, I
trust you." He spoke very slowly, and the words
seemed wrung out of him almost against his will.

" What nonsense you talk ! " said Lord Henry,
smiling, and, taking Hallward by the arm, he almost
led him into the house.

CHAPTER II

AS they entered they saw Dorian Gray. He was seated at the piano, with his back to them, turning over the pages of a volume of Schumann's "Forest Scenes." "You must lend me these, Basil," he cried. "I want to learn them. They are perfectly charming."

"That entirely depends on how you sit to-day, Dorian."

"Oh, I am tired of sitting, and I don't want a life-sized portrait of myself," answered the lad, swinging round on the music-stool, in a wilful, petulant manner. When he caught sight of Lord Henry, a faint blush coloured his cheeks for a moment, and he started up. "I beg your pardon, Basil, but I didn't know you had any one with you."

"This is Lord Henry Wotton, Dorian, an old Oxford friend of mine. I have just been telling him what a capital sitter you were, and now you have spoiled everything."

"You have not spoiled my pleasure in meeting you, Mr. Gray," said Lord Henry, stepping forward and extending his hand. "My aunt has often spoken to me about you. You are one of her favourites, and, I am afraid, one of her victims also."

"I am in Lady Agatha's black books at present," answered Dorian, with a funny look of penitence. "I promised to go to a club in Whitechapel with her last Tuesday, and I really forgot all about it. We were to have played a duet together—three duets, I believe. I don't know what she will say to me. I am far too frightened to call."

"Oh, I will make your peace with my aunt. She is quite devoted to you. And I don't think it really matters about your not being there. The audience probably thought it was a duet. When Aunt Agatha sits down to the piano she makes quite enough noise for two people."

" That is very horrid to her, and not very nice to me," answered Dorian, laughing.

Lord Henry looked at him. Yes, he was certainly wonderfully handsome, with his finely-curved scarlet lips, his frank blue eyes, his crisp gold hair. There was something in his face that made one trust him at once. All the candour of youth was there, as well as all youth's passionate purity. One felt that he had kept himself unspotted from the world. No wonder Basil Hallward worshipped him.

" You are too charming to go in for philanthropy, Mr. Gray—far too charming." And Lord Henry flung himself down on the divan, and opened his cigarette-case.

The painter had been busy mixing his colours and getting his brushes ready. He was looking worried, and when he heard Lord Henry's last remark he glanced at him, hesitated for a moment, and then said, " Harry, I want to finish this picture to-day. Would you think it awfully rude of me if I asked you to go away ? "

Lord Henry smiled, and looked at Dorian Gray. " Am I to go, Mr. Gray ? " he asked.

" Oh, please don't, Lord Henry. I see that Basil is in one of his sulky moods ; and I can't bear him when he sulks. Besides, I want you to tell me why I should not go in for philanthropy."

" I don't know that I shall tell you that, Mr. Gray. It is so tedious a subject that one would have to talk seriously about it. But I certainly shall not run away, now that you have asked me to stop. You don't really mind, Basil, do you ? You have often told me that you liked your sitters to have some one to chat to."

Hallward bit his lip. " If Dorian wishes it, of

course you must stay. Dorian's whims are laws to everybody, except himself."

Lord Henry took up his hat and gloves. " You are very pressing, Basil, but I am afraid I must go. I have promised to meet a man at the Orleans. Goodbye, Mr. Gray. Come and see me some afternoon in Curzon Street. I am nearly always at home at five o'clock. Write to me when you are coming. I should be sorry to miss you."

" Basil," cried Dorian Gray, " if Lord Henry Wotton goes I shall go too. You never open your lips while you are painting, and it is horribly dull standing on a platform and trying to look pleasant. Ask him to stay. I insist upon it."

" Stay, Harry, to oblige Dorian, and to oblige me," said Hallward, gazing intently at his picture. " It is quite true, I never talk when I am working, and never listen either, and it must be dreadfully tedious for my unfortunate sitters. I beg you to stay."

" But what about my man at the Orleans ? "

The painter laughed. " I don't think there will be any difficulty about that. Sit down again, Harry. And now, Dorian, get up on the platform, and don't move about too much, or pay any attention to what Lord Henry says. He has a very bad influence over all his friends, with the single exception of myself."

Dorian Gray stepped up on the dais, with the air of a young Greek martyr, and made a little *moue* of discontent to Lord Henry, to whom he had rather taken a fancy. He was so unlike Basil. They made a delightful contrast. And he had such a beautiful voice. After a few moments he said to him, " Have you really a very bad influence, Lord Henry ? As bad as Basil says ? "

" There is no such thing as a good influence, Mr. Gray All influence is immoral—immoral from the scientific point of view."

" Why ? "

" Because to influence a person is to give him one's own soul. He does not think his natural thoughts or burn with his natural passions. His virtues are not real to him. His sins, if there are such things as sins, are borrowed. He becomes an echo of some one else's music, an actor of a part that has not been written for him. The aim of life is self-development. To realise one's nature perfectly—that is what each of us is here for. People are afraid of themselves, nowadays. They have forgotten the highest of all duties, the duty that one owes to one's self. Of course they are charitable. They feed the hungry, and clothe the beggar. But their own souls starve, and are naked. Courage has gone out of our race. Perhaps we never really had it. The terror of society, which is the basis of morals, the terror of God, which is the secret of religion—these are the two things that govern us. And yet——"

" Just turn your head a little more to the right, Dorian, like a good boy," said the painter, deep in his work, and conscious only that a look had come into the lad's face that he had never seen there before.

" And yet," continued Lord Henry, in his low, musical voice, and with that graceful wave of the hand that was always so characteristic of him, and that he had even in his Eton days, " I believe that if one man were to live out his life fully and completely, were to give form to every feeling, expression to every thought, reality to every dream—I believe that the world would gain such a fresh impulse of joy that we would forget all the maladies of mediæ-valism, and return to the Hellenic ideal—to some-thing finer, richer, than the Hellenic ideal, it may be. But the bravest man amongst us is afraid of himself. The mutilation of the savage has its tragic survival in the self-denial that mars our lives. We are punished for our refusals. Every impulse that we strive to strangle broods in the mind, and poisons us.

The body sins once, and has done with its sin, for action is a mode of purification. Nothing remains then but the recollection of a pleasure, or the luxury of a regret. The only way to get rid of a temptation is to yield to it. Resist it, and your soul grows sick with longing for the things it has forbidden to itself, with desire for what its monstrous laws have made monstrous and unlawful. It has been said that the great events of the world take place in the brain. It is in the brain, and the brain only, that the great sins of the world take place also. You, Mr. Gray, you yourself, with your rose-red youth and your rose-white boyhood, you have had passions that have made you afraid, thoughts that have filled you with terror, day-dreams and sleeping dreams whose mere memory might stain your cheek with shame——"

"Stop!" faltered Dorian Gray, " stop! you bewilder me. I don't know what to say. There is some answer to you, but I cannot find it. Don't speak. Let me think. Or, rather, let me try not to think."

For nearly ten minutes he stood there, motionless, with parted lips, and eyes strangely bright. He was dimly conscious that entirely fresh influences were at work within him. Yet they seemed to him to have come really from himself. The few words that Basil's friend had said to him—words spoken by chance, no doubt, and with wilful paradox in them—had touched some secret chord that had never been touched before, but that he felt was now vibrating and throbbing to curious pulses.

Music had stirred him like that. Music had troubled him many times. But music was not articulate. It was not a new world, but rather another chaos, that it created in us. Words! Mere words! How terrible they were! How clear, and vivid, and cruel! One could not escape from them. And yet what a subtle magic there was in them! They seemed to be able to give a plastic form to formless things, and to have a music of their own as sweet as that of viol or of lute. Mere words! Was there anything so real as words?

Yes; there had been things in his boyhood that he had not understood. He understood them now. Life suddenly became fiery-coloured to him. It seemed to him that he had been walking in fire. Why had he not known it?

With his subtle smile, Lord Henry watched him. He knew the precise psychological moment when to say nothing. He felt intensely interested. He was amazed at the sudden impression that his words had produced, and, remembering a book that he had read when he was sixteen, a book which had revealed to him much that he had not known before, he wondered whether Dorian Gray was passing through a similar experience. He had merely shot an arrow into the air. Had it hit the mark? How fascinating the lad was!

Hallward painted away with that marvellous bold touch of his, that had the true refinement and perfect delicacy that in art, at any rate, comes only from strength. He was unconscious of the silence.

" Basil, I am tired of standing," cried Dorian Gray, suddenly. " I must go out and sit in the garden. The air is stifling here."

" My dear fellow, I am so sorry. When I am painting, I can't think of anything else. But you never sat better. You were perfectly still. And I have caught the effect I wanted—the half-parted lips, and the bright look in the eyes. I don't know what Harry has been saying to you, but he has certainly made you have the most wonderful expression. I suppose he has been paying you compliments. You mustn't believe a word that he says."

" He has certainly not been paying me compliments Perhaps that is the reason that I don't believe any-thing he has told me."

" You know you believe it all," said Lord Henry,

looking at him with his dreamy, languorous eyes.
" I will go out to the garden with you. It is horribly
hot in the studio. Basil, let us have something iced
to drink, something with strawberries in it."

" Certainly, Harry. Just touch the bell, and when
Parker comes I will tell him what you want. I have
got to work up this background, so I will join you
later on. Don't keep Dorian too long. I have never
been in better form for painting than I am to-day.
This is going to be my masterpiece. It is my masterpiece as it stands."

Lord Henry went out to the garden, and found
Dorian Gray burying his face in the great cool lilac-
blossoms, feverishly drinking in their perfume as if
it had been wine. He came close to him, and put
his hand upon his shoulder. " You are quite right
to do that," he murmured. " Nothing can cure the
soul but the senses, just as nothing can cure the
senses but the soul."

The lad started and drew back. He was bare-
headed, and the leaves had tossed his rebellious curls
and tangled all their gilded threads. There was a
look of fear in his eyes, such as people have when
they are suddenly awakened. His finely-chiselled
nostrils quivered, and some hidden nerve shook the
scarlet of his lips and left them trembling.

" Yes," continued Lord Henry, " that is one of
the great secrets of life—to cure the soul by means
of the senses, and the senses by means of the soul.
You are a wonderful creation. You know more than
you think you know, just as you know less than you
want to know."

Dorian Gray frowned and turned his head away.
He could not help liking the tall, graceful young man
who was standing by him. His romantic olive-coloured
face and worn expression interested him. There
was something in his low, languid voice that was
absolutely fascinating. His cool, white, flower-like

hands, even, had a curious charm. They moved, as he spoke, like music, and seemed to have a language of their own. But he felt afraid of him, and ashamed of being afraid. Why had it been left for a stranger to reveal him to himself? He had known Basil Hallward for months, but the friendship between them had never altered him. Suddenly there had come some one across his life who seemed to have disclosed to him life's mystery. And, yet, what was there to be afraid of? He was not a schoolboy or a girl. It was absurd to be frightened.

" Let us go and sit in the shade," said Lord Henry. " Parker has brought out the drinks, and if you stay any longer in this glare you will be quite spoiled, and Basil will never paint you again. You really must not allow yourself to become sunburnt. It would be unbecoming."

" What can it matter? " cried Dorian Gray, laughing, as he sat down on the seat at the end of the garden.

" It should matter everything to you, Mr. Gray."

" Why? "

" Because you have the most marvellous youth, and youth is the one thing worth having."

" I don't feel that, Lord Henry."

" No, you don't feel it now. Some day, when you are old and wrinkled and ugly, when thought has seared your forehead with its lines, and passion branded your lips with its hideous fires, you will feel it, you will feel it terribly. Now, wherever you go, you charm the world. Will it always be so? . . . You have a wonderfully beautiful face, Mr. Gray. Don't frown. You have. And Beauty is a form of Genius —is higher, indeed, than Genius, as it needs no explanation. It is of the great facts of the world, like sunlight, or spring-time, or the reflection in dark waters of that silver shell we call the moon. It cannot be questioned. It has its divine right of sovereignty.

It makes princes of those who have it. You smile?
Ah! when you have lost it you won't smile . . .
People say sometimes that Beauty is only superficial. That may be so. But at least it is not so superficial as Thought is. To me Beauty is the wonder
of wonders. It is only shallow people who do not judge
by appearances. The true mystery of the world is
the visible, not the invisible. . . . Yes, Mr. Gray,
the gods have been good to you. But what the gods
give they quickly take away. You have only a few
years in which to live really, perfectly, and fully. When
your youth goes, your beauty will go with it, and then
you will suddenly discover that there are no triumphs
left for you, or have to content yourself with those
mean triumphs that the memory of your past will
make more bitter than defeats. Every month as it
wanes brings you nearer to something dreadful.
Time is jealous of you, and wars against your lilies
and your roses. You will become sallow, and hollow-
cheeked, and dull-eyed. You will suffer horribly.
. . . Ah! realise your youth while you have it. Don't
squander the gold of your days, listening to the tedious,
trying to improve the hopeless failure, or giving away
your life to the ignorant, the common, and the vulgar.
These are the sickly aims, the false ideals, of our age.
Live! Live the wonderful life that is in you! Let
nothing be lost upon you. Be always searching for
new sensations. Be afraid of nothing. . . . A new
Hedonism—that is what our century wants. You
might be its visible symbol. With your personality
there is nothing you could not do. The world belongs
to you for a season. . . . The moment I met you I
saw that you were quite unconscious of what you
really are, of what you really might be. There was
so much in you that charmed me that I felt I must
tell you something about yourself. I thought how
tragic it would be if you were wasted. For there is
such a little time that your youth will last—such a

little time. The common hill-flowers wither, but they blossom again. The laburnum will be as yellow next June as it is now. In a month there will be purple stars on the clematis, and year after year the green night of its leaves will hold its purple stars. But we never get back our youth. The pulse of joy that beats in us at twenty, becomes sluggish. Our limbs fail, our senses rot. We degenerate into hideous puppets, haunted by the memory of the passions of which we were too much afraid, and the exquisite temptations that we had not the courage to yield to. Youth! Youth! There is absolutely nothing in the world but youth!"

Dorian Gray listened, open-eyed and wondering. The spray of lilac fell from his hand upon the gravel. A furry bee came and buzzed round it for a moment. Then it began to scramble all over the oval stellated globe of the tiny blossoms. He watched it with that strange interest in trivial things that we try to develop when things of high import make us afraid, or when we are stirred by some new emotion for which we cannot find expression, or when some thought that terrifies us lays sudden siege to the brain and calls on us to yield. After a time the bee flew away. He saw it creeping into the stained trumpet of a Tyrian convolvulus. The flower seemed to quiver, and then swayed gently to and fro.

Suddenly the painter appeared at the door of the studio, and made staccato signs for them to come in. They turned to each other, and smiled.

"I am waiting," he cried. "Do come in. The light is quite perfect, and you can bring your drinks."

They rose up, and sauntered down the walk together. Two green-and-white butterflies fluttered past them, and in the pear-tree at the corner of the garden a thrush began to sing.

"You are glad you have met me, Mr. Gray," said Lord Henry, looking at him.

" Yes, I am glad now. I wonder shall I always be glad ? "'

" Always ! That is a dreadful word. It makes me shudder when I hear it. Women are so fond of using it. They spoil every romance by trying to make it last for ever. It is a meaningless word, too. The only difference between a caprice and a life-long passion is that the caprice lasts a little longer."

As they entered the studio, Dorian Gray put his hand upon Lord Henry's arm. " In that case, let our friendship be a caprice," he murmured, flushing at his own boldness, then stepped up on the platform and resumed his pose.

Lord Henry flung himself into a large wicker arm-chair, and watched him. The sweep and dash of the brush on the canvas made the only sound that broke the stillness, except when, now and then, Hallward stepped back to look at his work from a distance. In the slanting beams that streamed through the open doorway the dust danced and was golden. The heavy scent of the roses seemed to brood over every-thing.

After about a quarter of an hour Hallward stopped painting, looked for a long time at Dorian Gray, and then for a long time at the picture, biting the end of one of his huge brushes, and frowning. " It is quite finished," he cried at last, and stooping down he wrote his name in long vermilion letters on the left-hand corner of the canvas.

Lord Henry came over and examined the picture. It was certainly a wonderful work of art, and a wonder-ful likeness as well.

" My dear fellow, I congratulate you most warmly," he said. " It is the finest portrait of modern times. Mr. Gray, come over and look at yourself."

The lad started, as if awakened from some dream. " Is it really finished ? " he murmured. stepping down from the platform.

" Quite finished," said the painter. " And you have sat splendidly to-day. I am awfully obliged to you."

" That is entirely due to me," broke in Lord Henry. " Isn't it, Mr. Gray ? "

Dorian made no answer, but passed listlessly in front of his picture, and turned towards it. When he saw it he drew back, and his cheeks flushed for a moment with pleasure. A look of joy came into his eyes, as if he had recognised himself for the first time. He stood there motionless and in wonder, dimly conscious that Hallward was speaking to him, but not catching the meaning of his words. The sense of his own beauty came on him like a revelation. He had never felt it before. Basil Hallward's compliments had seemed to him to be merely the charming exaggerations of friendship. He had listened to them, laughed at them, forgotten them. They had not influenced his nature. Then had come Lord Henry Wotton with his strange panegyric on youth, his terrible warning of its brevity. That had stirred him at the time, and now, as he stood gazing at the shadow of his own loveliness, the full reality of the description flashed across him. Yes, there would be a day when his face would be wrinkled and wizen, his eyes dim and colourless, the grace of his figure broken and deformed. The scarlet would pass away from his lips, and the gold steal from his hair. The life that was to make his soul would mar his body. He would become dreadful, hideous, and uncouth.

As he thought of it, a sharp pang of pain struck through him like a knife, and made each delicate fibre of his nature quiver. His eyes deepened into amethyst, and across them came a mist of tears. He felt as if a hand of ice had been laid upon his heart.

" Don't you like it ? " cried Hallward at last, stung a little by the lad's silence, not understanding what it meant.

" Of course he likes it," said Lord Henry. " Who
wouldn't like it ? It is one of the greatest things in
modern art. I will give you anything you like to ask
for it. I must have it."

" It is not my property, Harry."

" Whose property is it ? "

" Dorian's, of course," answered the painter.

" He is a very lucky fellow."

" How sad it is ! " murmured Dorian Gray, with
his eyes still fixed upon his own portrait. " How
sad it is ! I shall grow old, and horrible, and dreadful.
But this picture will remain always young. It will
never be older than this particular day of June. . . .
If it were only the other way ! If it were I who was
to be always young, and the picture that was to grow
old ! For that—for that—I would give everything !
Yes, there is nothing in the whole world I would not
give ! I would give my soul for that ! "

" You would hardly care for such an arrangement,
Basil," cried Lord Henry, laughing. " It would be
rather hard lines on your work."

" I should object very strongly, Harry," said
Hallward.

Dorian Gray turned and looked at him. " I believe
you would, Basil. You like your art better than
your friends. I am no more to you than a green
bronze figure. Hardly as much, I dare say."

The painter stared in amazement. It was so unlike
Dorian to speak like that. What had happened ?
He seemed quite angry. His face was flushed and
his cheeks burning.

" Yes," he continued, " I am less to you than your
ivory Hermes or your silver Faun. You will like them
always. How long will you like me ? Till I have my
first wrinkle, I suppose. I know, now, that when
one loses one's good looks, whatever they may be,
one loses everything. Your picture has taught me that.
Lord Henry Wotton is perfectly right. Youth is

the only thing worth having. When I find that I am growing old, I shall kill myself."

Hallward turned pale, and caught his hand. " Dorian ! Dorian ! " he cried, " don't talk like that. I have never had such a friend as you, and I shall never have such another. You are not jealous of material things, are you ?—you who are finer than any of them ! "

" I am jealous of everything whose beauty does not die. I am jealous of the portrait you have painted of me. Why should it keep what I must lose ? Every moment that passes takes something from me, and gives something to it. Oh, if it were only the other way ! If the picture could change, and I could be always what I am now ! Why did you paint it ? It will mock me some day—mock me horribly ! " The hot tears welled into his eyes ; he tore his hand away, and, flinging himself on the divan, he buried his face in the cushions, as though he was praying.

" This is your doing, Harry," said the painter, bitterly.

Lord Henry shrugged his shoulders. " It is the real Dorian Gray—that is all."

" It is not."

" If it is not, what have I to do with it ? "

" You should have gone away when I asked you," he muttered.

" I stayed when you asked me," was Lord Henry's answer.

" Harry, I can't quarrel with my two best friends at once, but between you both you have made me hate the finest piece of work I have ever done, and I will destroy it. What is it but canvas and colour ? I will not let it come across our three lives and mar them."

Dorian Gray lifted his golden head from the pillow, and with pallid face and tear-stained eyes looked at him, as he walked over to the deal painting-table

that was set beneath the high curtained window.
What was he doing there? His fingers were
straying about among the litter of tin tubes and
dry brushes, seeking for something. Yes, it was for
the long palette-knife, with its thin blade of lithe
steel. He had found it at last. He was going to rip
up the canvas.

With a stifled sob the lad leaped from the couch,
and, rushing over to Hallward, tore the knife out of
his hand, and flung it to the end of the studio. " Don't,
Basil, don't ! " he cried. " It would be murder ! "

" I am glad you appreciate my work at last, Dorian,"
said the painter, coldly, when he had recovered from
his surprise. " I never thought you would."

" Appreciate it ? I am in love with it, Basil. It
is part of myself. I feel that."

" Well, as soon as you are dry, you shall be var-
nished, and framed, and sent home. Then you can
do what you like with yourself." And he walked across
the room and rang the bell for tea. " You will have
tea, of course, Dorian ? And so will you, Harry ?
Or do you object to such simple pleasures ? "

" I adore simple pleasures," said Lord Henry.
" They are the last refuge of the complex. But I
don't like scenes, except on the stage. What absurd
fellows you are, both of you ! I wonder who it was
defined man as a rational animal. It was the most
premature definition ever given. Man is many things,
but he is not rational. I am glad he is not, after
all : though I wish you chaps would not squabble
over the picture. You had much better let me have
it, Basil. This silly boy doesn't really want it, and
I really do."

" If you let any one have it but me, Basil, I shall
never forgive you ! " cried Dorian Gray ; " and I
don't allow people to call me a silly boy."

" You know the picture is yours, Dorian. I gave
it to you before it existed."

" And you know you have been a little silly, Mr.
Gray, and that you don't really object to being
reminded that you are extremely young."

" I should have objected very strongly this morning, Lord Henry."

" Ah ! this morning ! You have lived since then."

There came a knock at the door, and the butler
entered with a laden tea-tray and set it down upon
a small Japanese table. There was a rattle of cups
and saucers and the hissing of a fluted Georgian urn.
Two globe-shaped china dishes were brought in by
a page. Dorian Gray went over and poured out the
tea. The two men sauntered languidly to the table,
and examined what was under the covers.

" Let us go to the theatre to-night," said Lord
Henry. " There is sure to be something on, somewhere. I have promised to dine at White's but it
is only with an old friend, so I can send him a wire
to say that I am ill, or that I am prevented from
coming in consequence of a subsequent engagement.
I think that would be a rather nice excuse : it would
have all the surprise of candour."

" It is such a bore putting on one's dress-clothes,"
muttered Hallward. " And, when one has them on,
they are so horrid."

" Yes," answered Lord Henry, dreamily, " the
costume of the nineteenth century is detestable. It
is so sombre, so depressing. Sin is the only real colour-
element left in modern life."

" You really must not say things like that before
Dorian, Harry."

" Before which Dorian ? The one who is pouring
out tea for us, or the one in the picture ? "

" Before either."

" I should like to come to the theatre with you,
Lord Henry," said the lad.

" Then you shall come ; and you will come too,
Basil, won't you ? "

" I can't really. I would sooner not. I have a lot of work to do."

" Well, then, you and I will go alone, Mr. Gray."

" I should like that awfully."

The painter bit his lip and walked over, cup in hand, to the picture. " I shall stay with the real Dorian," he said, sadly.

" Is it the real Dorian ? " cried the original of the portrait, strolling across to him. " Am I really like that ? "

" Yes ; you are just like that."

" How wonderful, Basil ! "

" At least you are like it in appearance. But it will never alter," sighed Hallward. " That is something."

" What a fuss people make about fidelity ! " exclaimed Lord Henry. " Why, even in love it is purely a question for physiology. It has nothing to do with our own will. Young men want to be faithful, and are not ; old men want to be faithless, and cannot : that is all one can say."

" Don't go to the theatre to-night, Dorian," said Hallward. " Stop and dine with me."

" I can't, Basil."

" Why ? "

" Because I have promised Lord Henry Wotton to go with him."

" He won't like you the better for keeping your promises. He always breaks his own. I beg you not to go."

Dorian Gray laughed and shook his head.

" I entreat you."

The lad hesitated, and looked over at Lord Henry, who was watching them from the tea-table with an amused smile.

" I must go, Basil," he answered.

" Very well," said Hallward ; and he went over and laid down his cup on the tray. " It is rather

late, and, as you have to dress, you had better lose
no time. Good-bye, Harry. Good-bye, Dorian. Come
and see me soon. Come to-morrow."

" Certainly."

" You won't forget ? "

" No, of course not," cried Dorian.

" And . . . Harry ! "

" Yes, Basil ? "

" Remember what I asked you, when we were in
the garden this morning."

" I have forgotten it."

" I trust you."

" I wish I could trust myself," said Lord Henry,
laughing. " Come, Mr. Gray, my hansom is outside, and I can drop you at your own place. Good-
bye, Basil. It has been a most interesting afternoon."

As the door closed behind them, the painter flung
himself down on a sofa, and a look of pain came into
his face.

CHAPTER III

AT half-past twelve next day Lord Henry
Wotton strolled from Curzon Street over to
the Albany to call on his uncle, Lord Fermor,
a genial if somewhat rough-mannered old bachelor,
whom the outside world called selfish because
it derived no particular benefit from him, but who
was considered generous by Society as he fed the people
who amused him. His father had been our ambassador
at Madrid when Isabella was young, and Prim un-
thought of, but had retired from the Diplomatic Service in a capricious moment of annoyance at not
being offered the Embassy at Paris, a post to which
he considered that he was fully entitled by reason
of his birth, his indolence, the good English of his
despatches, and his inordinate passion for pleasure.
The son, who had been his father's secretary, had

resigned along with his chief, somewhat foolishly as was thought at the time, and on succeeding some months later to the title, had set himself to the serious study of the great aristocratic art of doing absolutely nothing. He had two large town houses, but preferred to live in chambers, as it was less trouble, and took most of his meals at his club. He paid some attention to the management of his collieries in the Midland counties, excusing himself for this taint of industry on the ground that the one advantage of having coal was that it enabled a gentleman to afford the decency of burning wood on his own hearth. In politics he was a Tory, except when the Tories were in office, during which period he roundly abused them for being a pack of Radicals. He was a hero to his valet, who bullied him, and a terror to most of his relations, whom he bullied in turn. Only England could have produced him, and he always said that the country was going to the dogs. His principles were out of date, but there was a good deal to be said for his prejudices.

When Lord Henry entered the room, he found his uncle sitting in a rough shooting coat, smoking a cheroot, and grumbling over *The Times*. " Well, Harry," said the old gentleman, " what brings you out so early ? I thought you dandies never got up till two, and were not visible till five."

" Pure family affection, I assure you, Uncle George. I want to get something out of you."

" Money, I suppose," said Lord Fermor, making a wry face. " Well, sit down and tell me all about it. Young people, nowadays, imagine that money is everything."

" Yes," murmured Lord Henry, settling his button-hole in his coat ; " and when they grow older they know it. But I don't want money. It is only people who pay their bills who want that, Uncle George, and I never pay mine. Credit is the capital of a younger

son, and one lives charmingly upon it. Besides, I
always deal with Dartmoor's tradesmen, and consequently they never bother me. What I want is
information ; not useful information, of course ; useless information."

" Well, I can tell you anything that is in an English
Blue-book, Harry, although those fellows nowadays
write a lot of nonsense. When I was in the Diplomatic, things were much better. But I hear they let
them in now by examination. What can you expect ?
Examinations, sir, are pure humbug from beginning
to end. If a man is a gentleman, he knows quite
enough, and if he is not a gentleman, whatever he
knows is bad for him."

" Mr. Dorian Gray does not belong to Blue-books,
Uncle George," said Lord Henry, languidly.

" Mr. Dorian Gray ? Who is he ? " asked Lord
Fermor, knitting his bushy white eyebrows.

" That is what I have come to learn, Uncle George.
Or rather, I know who he is. He is the last Lord
Kelso's grandson. His mother was a Devereux ;
Lady Margaret Devereux. I want you to tell me about
his mother. What was she like ? Whom did she
marry ? You have known nearly everybody in your
time, so you might have known her. I am very much
interested in Mr. Gray at present. I have only just
met him."

" Kelso's grandson ! " echoed the old gentleman.
—" Kelso's grandson ! . . . Of course. . . . I knew
his mother intimately. I believe I was at her christening. She was an extraordinarily beautiful girl,
Margaret Devereux ; and made all the men frantic
by running away with a penniless young fellow ; a
mere nobody, sir, a subaltern in a foot regiment, or
something of that kind. Certainly. I remember the
whole thing as if it happened yesterday. The poor
chap was killed in a duel at Spa, a few months after
the marriage. There was an ugly story about it.

They said Kelso got some rascally adventurer, some Belgian brute, to insult his son-in-law in public; paid him, sir, to do it, paid him; and that the fellow spitted his man as if he had been a pigeon. The thing was hushed up, but, egad, Kelso ate his chop alone at the club for some time afterwards. He brought his daughter back with him, I was told, and she never spoke to him again. Oh yes; it was a bad business. The girl died too; died within a year. So she left a son, did she? I had forgotten that. What sort of boy is he? If he is like his mother he must be a good-looking chap."

"He is very good-looking," assented Lord Henry.

"I hope he will fall into proper hands," continued the old man. "He should have a pot of money waiting for him if Kelso did the right thing by him. His mother had money too. All the Selby property came to her, through her grandfather. Her grandfather hated Kelso, thought him a mean dog. He was, too. Came to Madrid once when I was there. Egad, I was ashamed of him. The Queen used to ask me about the English noble who was always quarrelling with the cabmen about their fares. They made quite a story of it. I didn't dare to show my face at Court for a month. I hope he treated his grandson better than he did the jarvies."

"I don't know," answered Lord Henry. "I fancy that the boy will be well off. He is not of age yet. He has Selby, I know. He told me so. And . . . his mother was very beautiful?"

"Margaret Devereux was one of the loveliest creatures I ever saw, Harry. What on earth induced her to behave as she did, I never could understand. She could have married anybody she chose. Carlington was mad after her. She was romantic, though. All the women of that family were. The men were a poor lot, but, egad! the women were wonderful. Carlington went on his knees to her. Told me so

himself. She laughed at him, and there wasn't a
girl in London at the time who wasn't after him.
And by the way, Harry, taking about silly marriages,
what is this humbug your father tells me about Dartmoor wanting to marry an American? Ain't English
girls good enough for him? "

" It is rather fashionable to marry Americans just
now, Uncle George."

" I'll back English women against the world,
Harry," said Lord Fermor, striking the table with
his fist.

" The betting is on the Americans."

" They don't last, I am told," muttered his uncle.

" A long engagement exhausts them, but they are
capital at a steeplechase. They take things flying.
I don't think Dartmoor has a chance."

" Who are her people? " grumbled the old gentleman " Has she got any? "

Lord Henry shook his head. " American girls are
as clever at concealing their parents as English women
are at concealing their past," he said, rising to go.

" They are pork-packers, I suppose? "

" I hope so, Uncle George, for Dartmoor's sake.
I am told that pork-packing is the most lucrative
profession in America, after politics."

" Is she pretty? "

" She behaves as if she was beautiful. Most American women do. It is the secret of their charm."

" Why can't these American women stay in their
own country? They are always telling us that it is
the Paradise for women."

" It is. That is the reason why, like Eve, they
are so excessively anxious to get out of it," said
Lord Henry. " Good-bye, Uncle George. I shall be
late for lunch, if I stop any longer. Thanks for giving
me the information I wanted. I always like to know
everything about my new friends, and nothing about
my old ones."

" Where are you lunching, Harry ? "

" At Aunt Agatha's. I have asked myself and Mr. Gray. He is her latest *protégé*."

" Humph ! tell your Aunt Agatha, Harry, not to bother me any more with her charity appeals. I am sick of them. Why, the good woman thinks that I have nothing to do but to write cheques for her silly fads."

" All right, Uncle George, I'll tell her, but it won't have any effect. Philanthropic people lose all sense of humanity. It is their distinguishing characteristic."

The old gentleman growled approvingly, and rang the bell for his servant. Lord Henry passed up the low arcade into Burlington Street, and turned his steps in the direction of Berkeley Square.

So that was the story of Dorian Gray's parentage. Crudely as it had been told to him, it had yet stirred him by its suggestion of a strange, almost modern romance. A beautiful woman risking everything for a mad passion. A few wild weeks of happiness cut short by a hideous, treacherous crime. Months of voiceless agony, and then a child born in pain. The mother snatched away by death, the boy left to solitude and the tyranny of an old and loveless man. Yes ; it was an interesting background. It posed the lad, made him more perfect as it were. Behind every exquisite thing that existed, there was something tragic. Worlds had to be in travail, that the meanest flower might blow. . . . And how charming he had been at dinner the night before, as, with startled eyes and lips parted in frightened pleasure, he had sat opposite to him at the club, the red candleshades staining to a richer rose the wakening wonder of his face. Talking to him was like playing upon an exquisite violin. He answered to every touch and thrill of the bow. . . . There was something terribly enthralling in the exercise of influence. No other activity was like it. To project one's soul into some

gracious form, and let it tarry there for a moment ;
to hear one's own intellectual views echoed back to
one with all the added music of passion and youth ;
to convey one's temperament into another as though
it were a subtle fluid or a strange perfume ; there
was a real joy in that—perhaps the most satisfying
joy left to us in an age so limited and vulgar as our
own, an age grossly carnal in its pleasures, and grossly
common in its aims. . . . He was a marvellous type,
too, this lad, whom by so curious a chance he had
met in Basil's studio ; or could be fashioned into a
marvellous type, at any rate. Grace was his, and
the white purity of boyhood, and beauty such as old
Greek marbles kept for us. There was nothing that
one could not do with him. He could be made a
Titan or a toy. What a pity it was that such beauty
was destined to fade ! . . . And Basil ? From a
psychological point of view, how interesting he was !
The new manner in art, the fresh mode of looking at
life, suggested so strangely by the merely visible
presence of one who was unconscious of it all ; the
silent spirit that dwelt in dim woodland, and walked
unseen in open field, suddenly showing herself,
Dryad-like and not afraid, because in his soul who
sought for her there had been wakened that wonderful
vision to which alone are wonderful things revealed ;
the mere shapes and patterns of things becoming,
as it were, refined, and gaining a kind of symbolical
value, as though they were themselves patterns of
some other and more perfect form whose shadow
they made real : how strange it all was ! He remembered something like it in history. Was it not Plato,
that artist in thought, who had first analysed it ?
Was it not Buonarotti who had carved it in the
coloured marbles of a sonnet-sequence ? But in our
own century it was strange. . . . Yes ; he would
try to be to Dorian Gray what, without knowing it,
the lad was to the painter who had fashioned the

wonderful portrait. He would seek to dominate
him—had already, indeed, half done so. He would
make that wonderful spirit his own. There was something fascinating in this son of Love and Death.

Suddenly he stopped, and glanced up at the houses.
He found that he had passed his aunt's some distance, and, smiling to himself, turned back. When
he entered the somewhat sombre hall the butler told
him that they had gone in to lunch. He gave one of
the footmen his hat and stick, and passed into the
dining-room.

" Late as usual, Harry," cried his aunt, shaking
her head at him.

He invented a facile excuse, and having taken
the vacant seat next to her, looked round to see
who was there. Dorian bowed to him shyly from the
end of the table, a flush of pleasure stealing into his
cheek. Opposite was the Duchess of Harley ; a
lady of admirable good-nature and good temper,
much liked by every one who knew her, and of those
ample architectural proportions that in women who
are not Duchesses are described by contemporary
historians as stoutness. Next to her sat, on her right,
Sir Thomas Burdon, a Radical member of Parliament,
who followed his leader in public life, and in private
life followed the best cooks, dining with the Tories,
and thinking with the Liberals, in accordance with a
wise and well-known rule. The post on her left was
occupied by Mr. Erskine of Treadley, an old gentleman of considerable charm and culture, who had
fallen, however, into bad habits of silence, having,
as he explained once to Lady Agatha, said everything that he had to say before he was thirty. His
own neighbour was Mrs. Vandeleur, one of his aunt's
oldest friends, a perfect saint amongst women, but so
dreadfully dowdy that she reminded one of a badly
bound hymn-book. Fortunately for him she had on
the other side Lord Faudel, a most intelligent middle-

aged mediocrity, as bald as a Ministerial statement
in the House of Commons, with whom she was con-
versing in that intensely earnest manner which is
the one unpardonable error, as he remarked once
himself, that all really good people fall into, and from
which none of them ever quite escape.

"We are talking about poor Dartmoor, Lord
Henry," cried the Duchess, nodding pleasantly to
him across the table. "Do you think he will really
marry this fascinating young person?"

"I believe she has made up her mind to propose
to him, Duchess."

"How dreadful!" exclaimed Lady Agatha.
"Really, some one should interfere."

"I am told, on excellent authority, that her father
keeps an American dry-goods store," said Sir Thomas
Burdon, looking supercilious.

"My uncle has already suggested pork-packing,
Sir Thomas."

"Dry-goods! What are American dry-goods?"
asked the Duchess, raising her large hands in wonder,
and accentuating the verb.

"American novels," answered Lord Henry, helping
himself to some quail.

The Duchess looked puzzled.

"Don't mind him, my dear," whispered Lady
Agatha. "He never means anything that he says."

"When America was discovered," said the Radical
member, and he began to give some wearisome facts.
Like all people who try to exhaust a subject, he
exhausted his listeners. The Duchess sighed, and
exercised her privilege of interruption. "I wish to
goodness it never had been discovered at all!" she
exclaimed. "Really, our girls have no chance nowadays.
It is most unfair."

"Perhaps, after all, America never has been discovered," said Mr. Erskine. "I myself would say that
it had merely been detected."

"Oh! but I have seen specimens of the inhabitants," answered the Duchess, vaguely. "I must confess that most of them are extremely pretty. And they dress well, too. They get all their dresses in Paris. I wish I could afford to do the same."

"They say that when good Americans die they go to Paris," chuckled Sir Thomas, who had a large wardrobe of Humour's cast-off clothes.

"Really! And where do bad Americans go to when they die?" inquired the Duchess.

"They go to America," murmured Lord Henry.

Sir Thomas frowned. "I am afraid that your nephew is prejudiced against that great country," he said to Lady Agatha. "I have travelled all over it, in cars provided by the directors, who, in such matters, are extremely civil. I assure you that it is an education to visit it."

"But must we really see Chicago in order to be educated?" asked Mr. Erskine, plaintively. "I don't feel up to the journey."

Sir Thomas waved his hand. "Mr. Erskine of Treadley has the world on his shelves. We practical men like to see things, not to read about them. The Americans are an extremely interesting people. They are absolutely reasonable. I think that is their distinguishing characteristic. Yes, Mr. Erskine, an absolutely reasonable people. I assure you there is no nonsense about the Americans."

"How dreadful!" cried Lord Henry. "I can stand brute force, but brute reason is quite unbearable. There is something unfair about its use. It is hitting below the intellect."

"I do not understand you," said Sir Thomas, growing rather red.

"I do, Lord Henry," murmured Mr. Erskine, with a smile.

"Paradoxes are all very well in their way. . . ." rejoined the Baronet.

"Was that a paradox?" asked Mr. Erskine. "I did not think so. Perhaps it was. Well, the way of paradoxes is the way of truth. To test Reality we must see it on the tight-rope. When the Verities become acrobats we can judge them."

"Dear me!" said Lady Agatha, "how you men argue! I am sure I never can make out what you are talking about. Oh! Harry, I am quite vexed with you. Why do you try to persuade our nice Mr. Dorian Gray to give up the East End? I assure you he would be quite invaluable. They would love his playing."

"I want him to play to me," cried Lord Henry, smiling, and he looked down the table and caught a bright answering glance.

"But they are so unhappy in Whitechapel," continued Lady Agatha.

"I can sympathise with everything, except suffering," said Lord Henry, shrugging his shoulders. "I cannot sympathise with that. It is too ugly, too horrible, too distressing. There is something terribly morbid in the modern sympathy with pain. One should sympathise with the colour, the beauty, the joy of life. The less said about life's sores the better."

"Still, the East End is a very important problem," remarked Sir Thomas, with a grave shake of the head.

"Quite so," answered the young lord. "It is the problem of slavery, and we try to solve it by amusing the slaves."

The politician looked at him keenly. "What change do you propose, then?" he asked.

Lord Henry laughed. "I don't desire to change anything in England except the weather," he answered. "I am quite content with philosophic contemplation. But, as the nineteenth century has gone bankrupt through an over-expenditure of sympathy, I would suggest that we should appeal to Science to put us straight. The advantage of the emotions is that they lead us astray, and the advantage of Science is that it is not emotional."

" But we have such grave responsibilities," ventured Mrs. Vandeleur, timidly.

" Terribly grave," echoed Lady Agatha.

Lord Henry looked over at Mr. Erskine. " Humanity takes itself too seriously. It is the world's original sin. If the caveman had known how to laugh, History would have been different."

" You are really very comforting," warbled the Duchess. " I have always felt rather guilty when I came to see your dear aunt, for I take no interest at all in the East End. For the future I shall be able to look her in the face without a blush."

" A blush is very becoming, Duchess," remarked Lord Henry.

" Only when one is young," she answered. " When an old woman like myself blushes, it is a very bad sign. Ah ! Lord Henry, I wish you would tell me how to become young again."

He thought for a moment. " Can you remember any great error that you committed in your early days, Duchess ? " he asked, looking at her across the table.

" A great many, I fear," she cried.

" Then commit them over again," he said, gravely. " To get back one's youth, one has merely to repeat one's follies."

" A delightful theory ! " she exclaimed. " I must put it into practice."

" A dangerous theory ! " came from Sir Thomas's tight lips. Lady Agatha shook her head, but could not help being amused. Mr. Erskine listened.

" Yes," he continued, " that is one of the great secrets of life. Nowadays most people die of a sort of creeping common sense, and discover when it is too late that the only things one never regrets are one's mistakes."

A laugh ran round the table.

He played with the idea, and grew wilful ; tossed it into the air and transformed it ; let it escape and recaptured it ; made it iridescent with fancy, and winged it with paradox. The praise of folly, as he went on, soared into a philosophy, and Philosophy herself became young, and catching the mad music of Pleasure, wearing, one might fancy, her wine-stained robe and wreath of ivy, danced like a Bacchante over the hills of life, and mocked the slow Silenus for being sober. Facts fled before her like frightened forest things. Her white feet trod the huge press at which wise Omar sits, till the seething grape-juice rose round her bare limbs in waves of purple bubbles, or crawled in red foam over the vat's black, dripping, sloping sides. It was an extraordinary improvisation. He felt that the eyes of Dorian Gray were fixed on him, and the consciousness that amongst his audience there was one whose temperament he wished to fascinate, seemed to give his wit keenness, and to lend colour to his imagination. He was brilliant, fantastic, irresponsible. He charmed his listeners out of themselves, and they followed his pipe laughing. Dorian Gray never took his gaze off him, but sat like one under a spell, smiles chasing each other over his lips, and wonder growing grave in his darkening eyes.

At last, liveried in the costume of the age, Reality entered the room in the shape of a servant to tell the Duchess that her carriage was waiting. She wrung her hands in mock despair. " How annoying ! " she cried. " I must go. I have to call for my husband at the club, to take him to some absurd meeting at Willis's Rooms, where he is going to be in the chair. If I am late, he is sure to be furious, and I couldn't have a scene in this bonnet. It is far too fragile. A harsh word would ruin it. No, I must go, dear Agatha. Good-bye, Lord Henry, you are quite

62   THE PICTURE OF DORIAN GRAY

delightful, and dreadfully demoralising. I am sure I
don't know what to say about your views. You must
come and dine with us some night. Tuesday? Are
you disengaged Tuesday ? "

"For you I would throw over anybody, Duchess,"
said Lord Henry, with a bow.

"Ah ! that is very nice, and very wrong of you,"
she cried ; "so mind you come ; " and she swept
out of the room, followed by Lady Agatha and the
other ladies.

When Lord Henry had sat down again, Mr. Erskine
moved round, and taking a chair close to him, placed
his hand upon his arm.

"You talk books away," he said   "why don't
you write one ? "

"I am too fond of reading books to care to write
them, Mr. Erskine. I should like to write a novel
certainly ; a novel that would be as lovely as a
Persian carpet, and as unreal. But there is no literary
public in England for anything except newspapers,
primers, and encyclopædias. Of all people in the world
the English have the least sense of the beauty of
literature."

"I fear you are right," answered Mr. Erskine.
"I myself used to have literary ambitions, but I
gave them up long ago. And now, my dear young
friend, if you will allow me to call you so, may I
ask if you really meant all that you said to us at
lunch ? "

"I quite forget what I said," smiled Lord Henry.
"Was it all very bad ? "

"Very bad, indeed. In fact, I consider you extremely dangerous, and if anything happens to our
good Duchess we shall all look on you as being primarily
responsible. But I should like to talk to you about
life. The generation into which I was born was
tedious. Some day, when you are tired of London,
come down to Treadley, and expound to me your

philosophy of pleasure over some admirable Burgundy
I am fortunate enough to possess."

" I shall be charmed. A visit to Treadley would
be a great privilege. It has a perfect host, and a
perfect library."

" You will complete it," answered the old gentleman, with a courteous bow. " And now I must bid
good-bye to your excellent aunt. I am due at the
Athenæum. It is the hour when we sleep there."

" All of you, Mr. Erskine ? "

" Forty of us, in forty arm-chairs. We are prac-
tising for an English Academy of Letters."

Lord Henry laughed, and rose. " I am going to
the Park," he cried.

As he was passing out of the door Dorian Gray
touched him on the arm. " Let me come with you,"
he murmured.

" But I thought you had promised Basil Hallward to go and see him," answered Lord Henry.

" I would sooner come with you ; yes, I feel I
must come with you. Do let me. And you will promise
to talk to me all the time ? No one talks so wonderfully as you do."

" Ah ! I have talked quite enough for to-day,"
said Lord Henry, smiling. " All I want now is to
look at life. You may come and look at it with me,
if you care to."

CHAPTER IV

ONE afternoon, a month later, Dorian Gray was
reclining in a luxurious arm-chair, in the
little library of Lord Henry's house in Mayfair.
It was, in its way, a very charming room, with
its high-panelled wainscoting of olive-stained oak,
its cream-coloured frieze and ceiling of raised plaster-
work, and its brick-dust felt carpet strewn with silk

long-fringed Persian rugs. On a tiny satinwood table stood a statuette by Clodion, and beside it lay a copy of *Les Cent Nouvelles*, bound for Margaret of Valois by Clovis Eve, and powdered with the gilt daisies that Queen had selected for her device. Some large blue china jars and parrot-tulips were arranged on the mantel-shelf, and through the small leaded panels of the window streamed the apricot-coloured light of a summer day in London.

Lord Henry had not yet come in. He was always late on principle, his principle being that punctuality is the thief of time. So the lad was looking rather sulky, as with listless fingers he turned over the pages of an elaborately-illustrated edition of *Manon Lescaut* that he had found in one of the bookcases. The formal monotonous ticking of the Louis Quartorze clock annoyed him. Once or twice he thought of going away.

At last he heard a step outside, and the door opened. " How late you are, Harry ! " he murmured.

" I am afraid it is not Harry, Mr. Gray," answered a shrill voice.

He glanced quickly round, and rose to his feet. " I beg your pardon. I thought——"

" You thought it was my husband. It is only his wife. You must let me introduce myself. I know you quite well by your photographs. I think my husband has got seventeen of them."

" Not seventeen, Lady Henry ? "

" Well, eighteen, then. And I saw you with him the other night at the Opera." She laughed nervously as she spoke, and watched him with her vague forget-me-not eyes. She was a curious woman, whose dresses always looked as if they had been designed in a rage and put on in a tempest. She was usually in love with somebody, and, as her passion was never returned. she had kept all her illusions. She tried to look picturesque, but only succeeded in being untidy. Her name was Victoria, and she had a perfect mania for going to church.

"That was at ' Lohengrin,' Lady Henry, I think ? "

" Yes ; it was at dear ' Lohengrin.' I like Wagner's music better than anybody's. It is so loud that one can talk the whole time without other people hearing what one says. That is a great advantage ; don't you think so, Mr. Gray ? "

The same nervous staccato laugh broke from her thin lips, and her fingers began to play with a long tortoise-shell paper-knife.

Dorian smiled, and shook his head : " I am afraid I don't think so, Lady Henry. I never talk during music, at least, during good music. If one hears bad music, it is one's duty to drown it in conversation."

" Ah ! that is one of Harry's views, isn't it, Mr. Gray ? I always hear Harry's views from his friends. It is the only way I get to know of them. But you must not think I don't like good music. I adore it, but I am afraid of it. It makes me too romantic. I have simply worshipped pianists—two at a time, sometimes, Harry tells me. I don't know what it is about them. Perhaps it is that they are foreigners. They all are, ain't they ? Even those that are born in England become foreigners after a time, don't they ? It is so clever of them, and such a compliment to art. Makes it quite cosmopolitan, doesn't it ? You have never been to any of my parties, have you, Mr. Gray ? You must come. I can't afford orchids, but I spare no expense in foreigners. They make one's rooms look so picturesque. But here is Harry !—Harry, I came in to look for you, to ask you something—I forget what it was—and I found Mr. Gray here. We have had such a pleasant chat about music. We have quite the same ideas. No ; I think our ideas are quite different. But he has been most pleasant. I am so glad I've seen him."

" I am charmed, my love, quite charmed," said

Lord Henry, elevating his dark crescent-shaped eyebrows and looking at them both with an amused smile. " So sorry I am late, Dorian. I went to look after a piece of old brocade in Wardour Street, and had to bargain for hours for it. Nowadays people know the price of everything, and the value of nothing."

" I am afraid I must be going," exclaimed Lady Henry, breaking an awkward silence with her silly sudden laugh. " I have promised to drive with the Duchess. Good-bye, Mr. Gray. Good-bye, Harry. You are dining out, I suppose ? So am I. Perhaps I shall see you at Lady Thornbury's."

" I dare say, my dear," said Lord Henry, shutting the door behind her, as, looking like a bird of paradise that had been out all night in the rain, she flitted out of the room, leaving a faint odour of frangipanni. Then he lit a cigarette, and flung himself down on the sofa.

" Never marry a woman with straw-coloured hair, Dorian," he said, after a few puffs.

" Why, Harry ? "

" Because they are so sentimental."

" But I like sentimental people."

" Never marry at all, Dorian. Men marry because they are tired ; women, because they are curious ; both are disappointed."

" I don't think I am likely to marry, Henry. I am too much in love. That is one of your aphorisms. I am putting it into practice, as I do everything that you say."

" Who are you in love with ? " asked Lord Henry, after a pause.

" With an actress," said Dorian Gray, blushing.

Lord Henry shrugged his shoulders. " That is a rather commonplace *début*."

" You would not say so if you saw her, Harry."

" Who is she ? "

" Her name is Sibyl Vane."

" Never heard of her."

" No one has. People will some day, however, She is a genius." .

" My dear boy, no woman is a genius. Women are a decorative sex. They never have anything to say, but they say it charmingly. Women represent the triumph of matter over mind, just as men represent the triumph of mind over morals."

" Harry, how can you ? "

" My dear Dorian, it is quite true. I am analysing women at the present, so I ought to know. The subject is not so abstruse as I thought it was. I find that, ultimately, there are only two kinds of women, the plain and the coloured. The plain women are very useful. If you want to gain a reputation for respectability, you have merely to take them down to supper. The other women are very charming. They commit one mistake, however. They paint in order to try and look young. Our grandmothers painted in order to try and talk brilliantly. *Rouge* and *esprit* used to go together. That is all over now. As long as a woman can look ten years younger than her own daughter, she is perfectly satisfied. As for conversation, there are only five women in London worth talking to, and two of these can't be admitted into decent society. However, tell me about your genius. How long have you known her ? "

" Ah ! Harry, your views terrify me."

" Never mind that. How long have you known her ? "

" About three weeks."

" And where did you come across her ? "

" I will tell you, Harry ; but you mustn't be unsympathetic about it. After all, it never would have happened if I had not met you. You filled me with a wild desire to know everything about life. For days after I met you, something seemed to throb in my veins. As I lounged in the Park, or strolled down

Piccadilly, I used to look at every one who passed
me, and wonder, with a mad curiosity, what sort of
lives they led. Some of them fascinated me. Others
filled me with terror. There was an exquisite poison
in the air. I had a passion for sensations. . . . Well,
one evening about seven o'clock, I determined to go
out in search of some adventure. I felt that this
grey, monstrous London of ours, with its myriads of
people, its sordid sinners, and its splendid sins, as
you once phrased it, must have something in store
for me. I fancied a thousand things. The mere
danger gave me a sense of delight. I remembered
what you had said to me on that wonderful evening
when we first dined together, about the search for
beauty being the real secret of life. I don't know
what I expected, but I went out and wandered east-
ward, soon losing my way in a labyrinth of grimy
streets and black, grassless squares. About half-
past eight I passed by an absurd little theatre, with
great flaring gas-jets and gaudy play-bills. A hideous
Jew, in the most amazing waistcoat I ever beheld in
my life, was standing at the entrance, smoking a
vile cigar. He had greasy ringlets, and an enormous
diamond blazed in the centre of a soiled shirt. ' Have
a box, my Lord ? ' he said, when he saw me, and
he took off his hat with an air of gorgeous servility.
There was something about him, Harry, that amused
me. He was such a monster. You will laugh at me,
I know, but I really went in and paid a whole guinea
for the stage-box. To the present day I can't make out
why I did so ; and yet if I hadn't—my dear Harry,
if I hadn't, I should have missed the greatest romance
of my life. I see you are laughing. It is horrid of
you ! "

    " I am not laughing, Dorian ; at least I am not
laughing at you. But you should not say the greatest
romance of your life. You should say the first romance
of your life. You will always be loved, and you will

always be in love with love. A *grande passion* is the
privilege of people who have nothing to do. That is
the one use of the idle classes of a country. Don't be
afraid. There are exquisite things in store for you.
This is merely the beginning."

"Do you think my nature so shallow?" cried
Dorian Gray, angrily.

"No; I think your nature so deep."

"How do you mean?"

"My dear boy, the people who love only once in
their lives are really the shallow people. What they
call their loyalty, and their fidelity, I call either the
lethargy of custom or their lack of imagination.
Faithfulness is to the emotional life what consis-
tency is to the life of the intellect—simply a confession of failures. Faithfulness! I must analyse it some
day. The passion for property is in it. There are
many things that we would throw away if we were
not afraid that others might pick them up. But I
don't want to interrupt you. Go on with your story."

"Well, I found myself seated in a horrid little
private box, with a vulgar drop-scene staring me in
the face. I looked out from behind the curtain, and
surveyed the house. It was a tawdry affair, all Cupids
and cornucopias, like a third-rate wedding cake. The
gallery and pit were fairly full, but the two rows of
dingy stalls were quite empty, and there was hardly
a person in what I suppose they called the dress-circle.
Women went about with oranges and ginger-beer,
and there was a terrible consumption of nuts going
on."

"It must have been just like the palmy days of
the British Drama."

"Just like, I should fancy, and very depressing.
I began to wonder what on earth I should do, when
I caught sight of the play-bill. What do you think
the play was, Harry?"

"I should think 'The Idiot Boy, or Dumb but

O.W.STO.

Innocent.' Our fathers used to like that sort of piece,
I believe. The longer I live, Dorian, the more keenly
I feel that whatever was good enough for our fathers
is not good enough for us. In art, as in politics, *les
grandpères ont toujours tort.*"

"This play was good enough for us, Harry. It
was 'Romeo and Juliet.' I must admit that I was
rather annoyed at the idea of seeing Shakespeare
done in such a wretched hole of a place. Still, I
felt interested, in a sort of way. At any rate, I determined to wait for the first act. There was a dreadful
orchestra, presided over by a young Hebrew who
sat at a cracked piano, that nearly drove me away,
but at last the drop-scene was drawn up, and the
play began. Romeo was a stout elderly gentleman,
with corked eyebrows, a husky tragedy voice, and
a figure like a beer-barrel. Mercutio was almost
as bad. He was played by the low-comedian, who had
introduced gags of his own and was on most friendly
terms with the pit. They were both as grotesque as
the scenery, and that looked as if it had come out of
a country-booth. But Juliet! Harry, imagine a
girl, hardly seventeen years of age, with a little
flower-like face, a small Greek head with plaited coils
of dark-brown hair, eyes that were violet wells of
passion, lips that were like the petals of a rose. She
was the loveliest thing I had ever seen in my life.
You said to me once that pathos left you unmoved,
but that beauty, mere beauty, could fill your eyes with
tears. I tell you, Harry, I could hardly see this girl for
the mist of tears that came across me. And her voice
—I never heard such a voice. It was very low at first,
with deep, mellow notes, that seemed to fall singly
upon one's ear. Then it became a little louder, and
sounded like a flute or a distant hautbois. In the garden-
scene it had all the tremulous ecstasy that one hears
just before dawn when nightingales are singing. There
were moments, later on, when it had the wild passion

of violins. You know how a voice can stir one.
Your voice and the voice of Sibyl Vane are two
things that I shall never forget. When I close my
eyes, I hear them, and each of them says something
different. I don't know which to follow. Why should
I not love her? Harry, I do love her. She is everything to me in life. Night after night I go to see her
play. One evening she is Rosalind, and the next
evening she is Imogen. I have seen her die in the gloom
of an Italian tomb, sucking the poison from her
lover's lips. I have watched her wandering through
the forest of Arden, disguised as a pretty boy in
hose and doublet and dainty cap. She has been mad,
and has come into the presence of a guilty king,
and given him rue to wear, and bitter herbs to taste
of. She has been innocent, and the black hands
of jealousy have crushed her reed-like throat. I
have seen her in every age and in every costume.
Ordinary women never appeal to one's imagination.
They are limited to their century. No glamour ever
transfigures them. One knows their minds as easily
as one knows their bonnets. One can always find
them. There is no mystery in any of them. They ride
in the Park in the morning, and chatter at tea-parties
in the afternoon. They have their stereotyped smile,
and their fashionable manner. They are quite obvious.
But an actress! How different an actress is! Harry!
why didn't you tell me that the only thing worth
loving is an actress?"

"Because I have loved so many of them,
Dorian."

"Oh, yes, horrid people with dyed hair and painted
faces."

"Don't run down dyed hair and painted faces.
There is an extraordinary charm in them, sometimes,"
said Lord Henry.

"I wish now I had not told you about Sibyl Vane."

"You could not have helped telling me, Dorian.

All through your life you will tell me everything
you do."

" Yes, Harry, I believe that is true. I cannot
help telling you things. You have a curious influence
over me. If I ever did a crime, I would come and
confess it to you. You would understand me."

" People like you—the wilful sunbeams of life—
don't commit crimes, Dorian. But I am much
obliged for the compliment, all the same. And now tell
me—reach me the matches, like a good boy : thanks
—what are your actual relations with Sibyl Vane ? "

Dorian Gray leaped to his feet, with flushed cheeks
and burning eyes. " Harry ! Sibyl Vane is sacred ! "

" It is only the sacred things that are worth
touching, Dorian," said Lord Henry, with a strange
touch of pathos in his voice. " But why should you
be annoyed ? I suppose she will belong to you some
day. When one is in love, one always begins by
deceiving one's self, and one always ends by deceiving
others. That is what the world calls a romance. You
know her, at any rate, I suppose ? "

" Of course I know her. On the first night I was
at the theatre, the horrid old Jew came round to the
box after the performance was over, and offered to
take me behind the scenes and introduce me to her.
I was furious with him, and told him that Juliet
had been dead for hundreds of years, and that her
body was lying in a marble tomb in Verona. I think,
from his blank look of amazement, that he was under
the impression that I had taken too much champagne,
or something."

" I am not surprised."

" Then he asked me if I wrote for any of the newspapers. I told him I never even read them. He
seemed terribly disappointed at that, and confided
to me that all the dramatic critics were in a con-
spiracy against him, and that they were every one of
them to be bought."

"I should not wonder if he was quite right there. But, on the other hand, judging from their appearance, most of them cannot be at all expensive."

"Well, he seemed to think they were beyond his means," laughed Dorian. "By this time, however, the lights were being put out in the theatre, and I had to go. He wanted me to try some cigars that he strongly recommended. I declined. The next night, of course, I arrived at the place again. When he saw me he made me a low bow, and assured me that I was a munificent patron of art. He was a most offensive brute, though he had an extraordinary passion for Shakespeare. He told me once, with an air of pride, that his five bankruptcies were entirely due to 'The Bard,' as he insisted on calling him. He seemed to think it a distinction."

"It was a distinction, my dear Dorian—a great distinction. Most people become bankrupt through having invested too heavily in the prose of life. To have ruined one's self over poetry is an honour. But when did you first speak to Miss Sybil Vane?"

"The third night. She had been playing Rosalind. I could not help going round. I had thrown her some flowers, and she had looked at me; at least I fancied that she had. The old Jew was persistent. He seemed determined to take me behind, so I consented. It was curious my not wanting to know her, wasn't it?"

"No; I don't think so."

"My dear Harry, why?"

"I will tell you some other time. Now I want to know about the girl."

"Sibyl? Oh, she was so shy, and so gentle. There is something of a child about her. Her eyes opened wide in exquisite wonder when I told her what I thought of her performance, and she seemed quite unconscious of her power. I think we were both rather nervous. The old Jew stood grinning at the

doorway of the dusty green-room, making elaborate
speeches about us both, while we stood looking at
each other like children. He would insist on calling
me ' My Lord,' so I had to assure Sibyl that I was
not anything of the kind. She said quite simply to
me, ' You look more like a prince. I must call you
Prince Charming.' "

"Upon my word, Dorian, Miss Sibyl knows how
to pay compliments."

" You don't understand her, Harry. She regarded
me merely as a person in a play. She knows nothing
of life. She lives with her mother, a faded tired
woman who played Lady Capulet in a sort of magenta
dressing-wrapper on the first night, and looks as if
she had seen better days."

" I know that look. It depresses me," murmured
Lord Henry, examining his rings.

" The Jew wanted to tell me her history, but I
said it did not interest me."

" You were quite right. There is always something
infinitely mean about other people's tragedies.'

" Sibyl is the only thing I care about. What is
it to me where she came from ? From her little head
to her little feet, she is absolutely and entirely divine.
Every night of my life I go to see her act, and every
night she is more marvellous."

" That is the reason, I suppose, that you never
dine with me now. I thought you must have some
curious romance on hand. You have; but it is not
quite what I expected."

" My dear Harry, we either lunch or sup together
every day, and I have been to the Opera with you
several times," said Dorian, opening his blue eyes
in wonder.

" You always come dreadfully late."

" Well, I can't help going to see Sibyl play," he
cried, " even if it is only for a single act. I get hungry
for her presence ; and when I think of the wonderful

soul that is hidden away in that little ivory body,
I am filled with awe."

" You can dine with me to-night, Dorian, can't
you ? "

He shook his head. " To-night she is Imogen," he
answered, " and to-morrow night she will be Juliet."

" When is she Sibyl Vane ? "

" Never."

" I congratulate you."

" How horrid you are ! She is all the great heroines
of the world in one. She is more than an individual.
You laugh, but I tell you she has genius. I love
her, and I must make her love me. You, who know
all the secrets of life, tell me how to charm Sibyl
Vane to love me ! I want to make Romeo jealous. I
want the dead lovers of the world to hear our laughter,
and grow sad. I want a breath of our passion to stir
their dust into consciousness, to wake their ashes into
pain. My God, Harry, how I worship her ! " He
was walking up and down the room as he spoke.
Hectic spots of red burned in his cheeks. He was
terribly excited.

Lord Henry watched him with a subtle sense of
pleasure. How different he was now from the shy,
frightened boy he had met in Basil Hallward's studio.
His nature had developed like a flower, had borne
blossoms of scarlet flame. Out of its secret hiding-
place had crept his Soul, and Desire had come to meet
it on the way.

" And what do you propose to do ? " said Lord
Henry, at last.

" I want you and Basil to come with me some night
and see her act. I have not the slightest fear of the
result. You are certain to acknowledge her genius.
Then we must get her out of the Jew's hands. She
is bound to him for three years—at least for two
years and eight months—from the present time. I
shall have to pay him something, of course. When

all that is settled, I shall take a West End theatre and bring her out properly. She will make the world as mad as she has made me."

"That would be impossible, my dear boy?"

"Yes, she will. She has not merely art, consummate art-instinct, in her, but she has personality also; and you have often told me that it is personalities, not principles, that move the age."

"Well, what night shall we go?"

"Let me see. To-day is Tuesday. Let us fix to-morrow. She plays Juliet to-morrow."

"All right. The Bristol at eight o'clock; and I will get Basil."

"Not eight, Harry, please. Half-past six. We must be there before the curtain rises. You must see her in the first act, where she meets Romeo."

"Half-past six! What an hour! It will be like having a meat-tea, or reading an English novel. It must be seven. No gentleman dines before seven. Shall you see Basil between this and then? Or shall I write to him?"

"Dear Basil! I have not laid eyes on him for a week. It is rather horrid of me, as he has sent me my portrait in the most wonderful frame, specially designed by himself, and, though I am a little jealous of the picture for being a whole month younger than I am, I must admit that I delight in it. Perhaps you had better write to him. I don't want to see him alone. He says things that annoy me. He gives me good advice."

Lord Henry smiled. "People are very fond of giving away what they need most themselves. It is what I call the depth of generosity."

"Oh, Basil is the best of fellows, but he seems to me to be just a bit of a Philistine. Since I have known you, Harry, I have discovered that."

"Basil, my dear boy, puts everything that is charming in him into his work. The consequence is that he had nothing left for life but his prejudices, his principles, and his common-sense. The only artists I have ever known, who are personally delightful, are bad artists. Good artists exist simply in what they make, and consequently are perfectly uninteresting in what they are. A great poet, a really great poet, is the most unpoetical of all creatures. But inferior poets are absolutely fascinating. The worse their rhymes are, the more picturesque they look. The mere fact of having published a book of second-rate sonnets makes a man quite irresistible. He lives the poetry that he cannot write. The others write the poetry that they dare not realise."

" I wonder is that really so, Harry ? " said Dorian Gray, putting some perfume on his handkerchief out of a large gold-topped bottle that stood on the table. " It must be, if you say it. And now I am off. Imogen is waiting for me. Don't forget about to-morrow. Good-bye."

As he left the room, Lord Henry's heavy eyelids drooped, and he began to think. Certainly few people had ever interested him so much as Dorian Gray, and yet the lad's mad adoration of some one else caused him not the slightest pang of annoyance or jealousy. He was pleased by it. It made him a more interesting study. He had been always enthralled by the methods of natural science, but the ordinary subject-matter of that science had seemed to him trivial and of no import. And so he had begun by vivisecting himself, as he had ended by vivisecting others. Human life—that appeared to him the one thing worth investigating. Compared to it there was nothing else of any value. It was true that as one watched life in its curious crucible of pain and pleasure, one could not wear over one's face a mask of glass, nor keep the sulphurous fumes from troubling the brain, and making the imagination turbid with monstrous fancies and misshapen dreams. There were

poisons so subtle that to know their properties one
had to sicken of them. There were maladies so strange
that one had to pass through them if one sought to
understand their nature. And, yet, what a great reward
one received ! How wonderful the whole world became
to one ! To note the curious hard logic of passion,
and the emotional coloured life of the intellect—to
observe where they met, and where they separated,
at what point they were in unison, and at what point
they were at discord—there was a delight in that !
What matter what the cost was ? One could never
pay too high a price for any sensation.

He was conscious—and the thought brought a
gleam of pleasure into his brown agate eyes—that
it was through certain words of his, musical words
said with musical utterance, that Dorian Gray's soul
had turned to this white girl and bowed in worship
before her. To a large extent the lad was his own
creation. He had made him premature. That was
something. Ordinary people waited till life disclosed
to them its secrets, but to the few, to the elect, the
mysteries of life were revealed before the veil was
drawn away. Sometimes this was the effect of art,
and chiefly of the art of literature, which dealt immediately with the passions and the intellect. But
now and then a complex personality took the place
and assumed the office of art ; was indeed, in its
way, a real work of art, Life having its elaborate
masterpieces, just as poetry has, or sculpture, or
painting.

Yes, the lad was premature. He was gathering
his harvest while it was yet spring. The pulse and
passion of youth were in him, but he was becoming
self-conscious. It was delightful to watch him. With
his beautiful face, and his beautiful soul, he was a
thing to wonder at. It was no matter how it all
ended, or was destined to end. He was like one of
those gracious figures in a pageant or a play, whose

joys seem to be remote from one, but whose sorrows stir one's sense of beauty, and whose wounds are like red roses.

Soul and body, body and soul—how mysterious they were! There was animalism in the soul, and the body had its moments of spirituality. The senses could refine, and the intellect could degrade. Who could say where the fleshly impulse ceased, or the physical impulse began? How shallow were the arbitrary definitions of ordinary psychologists! And yet how difficult to decide between the claims of the various schools! Was the soul a shadow seated in the house of sin? Or was the body really in the soul, as Giordano Bruno thought? The separation of spirit from matter was a mystery, and the union of spirit with matter was a mystery also.

He began to wonder whether we could ever make psychology so absolute a science that each little spring of life would be revealed to us. As it was, we always misunderstood ourselves, and rarely understood others. Experience was of no ethical value. It was merely the name men gave to their mistakes. Moralists had, as a rule, regarded it as a mode of warning, had claimed for it a certain ethical efficacy in the formation of character, had praised it as something that taught us what to follow and showed us what to avoid. But there was no motive power in experience. It was as little of an active cause as conscience itself. All that it really demonstrated was that our future would be the same as our past, and that the sin we had done once, and with loathing, we would do many times, and with joy.

It was clear to him that the experimental method was the only method by which one could arrive at any scientific analysis of the passions ; and certainly Dorian Gray was a subject made to his hand, and seemed to promise rich and fruitful results. His sudden mad love for Sibyl Vane was a psychological phenomenon of no small interest. There was no doubt that curiosity had much to do with it, curiosity and the desire for new experiences ; yet it was not a simple but rather a very complex passion. What there was in it of the purely sensuous instinct of boyhood had been transformed by the workings of the imagination, changed into something that seemed to the lad himself to be remote from sense, and was for that very reason all the more dangerous. It was the passions about whose origin we deceived ourselves that tyrannised most strongly over us. Our weakest motives were those of whose nature we were conscious. It often happened that when we thought we were experimenting on others we were really experimenting on ourselves.

While Lord Henry sat dreaming on these things, a knock came to the door, and his valet entered, and reminded him it was time to dress for dinner. He got up and looked out into the street. The sunset had smitten into scarlet gold the upper windows of the houses opposite. The panes glowed like plates of heated metal. The sky above was like a faded rose. He thought of his friend's young fiery-coloured life, and wondered how it was all going to end.

When he arrived home, about half-past twelve o'clock, he saw a telegram lying on the hall table. He opened it, and found it was from Dorian Gray. It was to tell him that he was engaged to be married to Sibyl Vane.

CHAPTER V

"MOTHER, mother, I am so happy ! " whispered the girl, burying her face in the lap of the faded, tired-looking woman who, with back turned to the shrill intrusive light, was sitting in the one armchair that their dingy sitting-room contained. " I am so happy ! " she repeated, " and you must be happy too ! "

Mrs. Vane winced, and put her thin bismuth-whitened hands on her daughter's head. " Happy ! " she echoed, " I am only happy, Sibyl, when I see you act. You must not think of anything but your acting. Mr. Isaacs has been very good to us, and we owe him money."

The girl looked up and pouted. " Money, mother ? " she cried, " what does money matter ? Love is more than money."

" Mr. Isaacs has advanced us fifty pounds to pay off our debts, and to get a proper outfit for James. You must not forget that, Sibyl. Fifty pounds is a very large sum. Mr. Isaacs has been most considerate."

" He is not a gentleman, mother, and I hate the way he talks to me," said the girl, rising to her feet, and going over to the window.

" I don't know how we could manage without him," answered the elder woman, querulously.

Sibyl Vane tossed her head and laughed. " We don't want him any more, mother. Prince Charming rules life for us now." Then she paused. A rose shook in her blood, and shadowed her cheeks. Quick breath parted the petals of her lips. They trembled. Some southern wind of passion swept over her, and stirred the dainty folds of her dress. " I love him," she said, simply.

" Foolish child ! foolish child ! " was the parrot-phrase flung in answer. The waving of crooked, false-jewelled fingers gave grotesqueness to the words.

The girl laughed again. The joy of a caged bird was in her voice. Her eyes caught the melody, and echoed it in radiance ; then closed for a moment, as though to hide their secret. When they opened the mist of a dream had passed across them.

Thin-lipped wisdom spoke at her from the worn chair, hinted at prudence, quoted from that book of

cowardice whose author apes the name of common
sense. She did not listen. She was free in her prison
of passion. Her prince, Prince Charming, was with
her. She had called on Memory to remake him.
She had sent her soul to search for him, and it had
brought him back. His kiss burned again upon her
mouth. Her eyelids were warm with his breath.

Then Wisdom altered its method and spoke of
espial and discovery. This young man might be
rich. If so, marriage should be thought of. Against
the shell of her ear broke the waves of worldly cunning.
The arrows of craft shot by her. She saw the thin
lips moving, and smiled.

Suddenly she felt the need to speak. The wordy
silence troubled her. " Mother, mother," she cried,
" why does he love me so much? I know why
I love him. I love him because he is like what
Love himself should be. But what does he see
in me? I am not worthy of him. And yet—why,
I cannot tell—though I feel so much beneath him,
I don't feel humble. I feel proud, terribly proud.
Mother, did you love my father as I love Prince
Charming? "

The elder woman grew pale beneath the coarse
powder that daubed her cheeks, and her dry lips
twitched with a spasm of pain. Sibyl rushed to her,
flung her arms round her neck, and kissed her. " Forgive me, mother, I know it pains you to talk about
our father. But it only pains you because you loved
him so much. Don't look so sad. I am as happy
to-day as you were twenty years ago. Ah ! let me
be happy for ever ! "

" My child, you are far too young to think of
falling in love. Besides, what do you know of this
young man? You don't even know his name. The
whole thing is most inconvenient, and really, when
James is going away to Australia, and I have so much
to think of, I must say that you should have shown

more consideration. However, as I said before, if he is rich. . . ."

" Ah ! Mother, mother, let me be happy ! "

Mrs. Vane glanced at her, and with one of those false theatrical gestures that so often become a mode of second nature to a stage-player, clasped her in her arms. At this moment the door opened, and a young lad with rough brown hair came into the room. He was thick-set of figure, and his hands and feet were large, and somewhat clumsy in movement. He was not so finely bred as his sister. One would hardly have guessed the close relationship that existed between them. Mrs. Vane fixed her eyes on him, and intensified the smile. She mentally elevated her son to the dignity of an audience. She felt sure that the *tableau* was interesting.

" You might keep some of your kisses for me, Sibyl, I think," said the lad, with a good-natured grumble.

" Ah ! but you don't like being kissed, Jim," she cried. " You are a dreadful old bear." And she ran across the room and hugged him.

James Vane looked into his sister's face with tenderness. " I want you to come out with me for a walk, Sibyl. I don't suppose I shall ever see this horrid London again. I am sure I don't want to."

" My son, don't say such dreadful things," murmured Mrs. Vane, taking up a tawdry theatrical dress, with a sigh, and beginning to patch it. She felt a little disappointed that he had not joined the group. It would have increased the theatrical picturesqueness of the situation

" Why not, mother ? I mean it."

" You pain me, my son. I trust you will return from Australia in a position of affluence. I believe there is no society of any kind in the Colonies, nothing that I would call society ; so when you have made your fortune you must come back and assert yourself in London."

" Society ! " muttered the lad. " I don't want to know anything about that. I should like to make some money to take you and Sibyl off the stage. I hate it ! "

" Oh, Jim ! " said Sibyl, laughing, " how unkind of you ! But are you really going for a walk with me ? That will be nice ! I was afraid you were going to say good-bye to some of your friends—to Tom Hardy, who gave you that hideous pipe, or Ned Langton, who makes fun of you for smoking it. It is very sweet of you to let me have your last afternoon. Where shall we go ? Let us go to the Park."

" I am too shabby," he answered, frowning. " Only swell people go to the Park."

" Nonsense, Jim," she whispered, stroking the sleeve of his coat.

He hesitated for a moment. " Very well," he said at last, " but don't be too long dressing." She danced out of the door. One could hear her singing as she ran upstairs. Her little feet pattered overhead.

He walked up and down the room two or three times. Then he turned to the still figure in the chair. " Mother, are my things ready ? " he asked.

" Quite ready, James," she answered, keeping her eyes on her work. For some months past she had felt ill at ease when she was alone with this rough, stern son of hers. Her shallow secret nature was troubled when their eyes met. She used to wonder if he suspected anything. The silence, for he made no other observation, became intolerable to her. She began to complain. Women defend themselves by attacking, just as they attack by sudden and strange surrenders. " I hope you will be contented, James, with your sea-faring life," she said. " You must remember that it is your own choice. You might have entered a solicitor's office. Solicitors are a very respectable class, and in the country often dine with the best families."

" I hate offices, and I hate clerks," he replied.
" But you are quite right. I have chosen my own
life. All I say is, watch over Sibyl. Don't let her come
to any harm. Mother, you must watch over her."

" James, you really talk very strangely. Of course
I watch over Sibyl."

" I hear a gentleman comes every night to the
theatre, and goes behind to talk to her. Is that
right ? What about that ? "

" You are speaking about things you don't understand, James. In the profession we are accustomed
to receive a great deal of most gratifying attention.
I myself used to receive many bouquets at one time.
That was when acting was really understood. As for
Sibyl, I do not know at present whether her attachment is serious or not. But there is no doubt that the
young man in question is a perfect gentleman. He
is always most polite to me. Besides, he has the
appearance of being rich, and the flowers he sends
are lovely."

" You don't know his name, though," said the
lad, harshly.

" No," answered his mother, with a placid expression in her face. " He has not yet revealed his real
name. I think it is quite romantic of him. He is
probably a member of the aristocracy."

James Vane bit his lip. " Watch over Sibyl, mother,"
he cried, " watch over her."

" My son, you distress me very much. Sibyl is
always under my special care. Of course, if this
gentleman is wealthy, there is no reason why she
should not contract an alliance with him. I trust
he is one of the aristocracy. He has all the appearance
of it, I must say. It might be a most brilliant marriage
for Sibyl. They would make a charming couple.
His good looks are really quite remarkable ; everybody notices them."

The lad muttered something to himself, and

drummed on the window-pane with his coarse fingers.
He had just turned round to say something, when
the door opened, and Sibyl ran in.

" How serious you both are ! " she cried. " What
is the matter ? "

" Nothing," he answered. " I suppose one must
be serious sometimes. Good-bye, mother ; I will
have my dinner at five o'clock. Everything is packed,
except my shirts, so you need not trouble."

" Good-bye, my son," she answered, with a bow of
strained stateliness.

She was extremely annoyed at the tone he had
adopted with her, and there was something in his
look that had made her feel afraid.

" Kiss me, mother," said the girl. Her flower-
like lips touched the withered cheek, and warmed
its frost.

" My child ! my child ! " cried Mrs. Vane, looking
up to the ceiling in search of an imaginary gallery.

" Come, Sibyl," said her brother, impatiently.
He hated his mother's affectations.

They went out into the flickering wind-blown sunlight, and strolled down the dreary Euston Road.
The passers-by glanced in wonder at the sullen, heavy
youth, who, in coarse, ill-fitting clothes, was in the
company of such a graceful, refined-looking girl. He
was like a common gardener walking with a rose.

Jim frowned from time to time when he caught
the inquisitive glance of some stranger. He had
that dislike of being stared at which comes on geniuses
late in life, and never leaves the commonplace. Sibyl,
however, was quite unconscious of the effect she
was producing. Her love was trembling in laughter
on her lips. She was thinking of Prince Charming,
and, that she might think of him all the more, she
did not talk of him, but prattled on about the ship
in which Jim was going to sail, about the gold he was
certain to find, about the wonderful heiress whose

life he was to save from the wicked, red-shirted
bushrangers.   For he was not to remain a sailor,
or a super-cargo, or whatever he was going to be.
Oh, no ! A sailor's existence was dreadful. Fancy
being cooped up in a horrid ship, with the hoarse,
hump-backed waves trying to get in, and a black
wind blowing the masts down, and tearing the sails
into long screaming ribands ! He was to leave the
vessel at Melbourne, bid a polite good-bye to the
captain, and go off at once to the gold-fields. Before
a week was over he was to come across a large nugget
of pure gold, the largest nugget that had ever been
discovered, and bring it down to the coast in a wagon
guarded by six mounted policemen. The bushrangers were to attack them three times, and be
defeated with immense slaughter. Or, no. He was
not to go to the gold-fields at all. They were horrid
places, where men got intoxicated, and shot each
other in bar-rooms, and used bad language. He
was to be a nice sheep-farmer, and one evening,
as he was riding home, he was to see the beautiful
heiress being carried off by a robber on a black horse,
and give chase, and rescue her. Of course she would
fall in love with him, and he with her, and they would
get married, and come home, and live in an immense
house in London. Yes, there were delightful things
in store for him. But he must be very good, and not
lose his temper, or spend his money foolishly. She
was only a year older than he was, but she knew
so much more of life. He must be sure, also, to write
to her by every mail, and to say his prayers each
night before he went to sleep. God was very good,
and would watch over him. She would pray for
him, too, and in a few years he would come back
quite rich and happy.

The lad listened sulkily to her, and made no answer.
He was heart-sick at leaving home.

Yet it was not this alone that made him gloomy

and morose. Inexperienced though he was, he had
still a strong sense of the danger of Sibyl's position.
This young dandy who was making love to her could
mean her no good. He was a gentleman, and he
hated him for that, hated him through some curious
race-instinct for which he could not account, and
which for that reason was all the more dominant
within him. He was conscious also of the shallowness and vanity of his mother's nature, and in that
saw infinite peril for Sibyl and Sibyl's happiness.
Children begin by loving their parents; as they grow
older they judge them; sometimes they forgive
them.

His mother! He had something on his mind to
ask of her, something that he had brooded on for
many months of silence. A chance phrase that he
had heard at the theatre, a whispered sneer that had
reached his ears one night as he waited at the stage-
door, had set loose a train of horrible thoughts. He
remembered it as if it had been the lash of a hunting-
crop across his face. His brows knit together into
a wedge-like furrow, and with a twitch of pain he
bit his under-lip.

"You are not listening to a word I am saying,
Jim," cried Sibyl, "and I am making the most delightful plans for your future. Do say something."

"What do you want me to say?"

"Oh! that you will be a good boy, and not forget
us," she answered, smiling at him.

He shrugged his shoulders. "You are more likely
to forget me, than I am to forget you, Sibyl."

She flushed. "What do you mean, Jim?" she
asked.

"You have a new friend, I hear. Who is he?
Why have you not told me about him? He means
you no good."

"Stop, Jim!" she exclaimed. "You must not
say anything against him. I love him."

"Why, you don't even know his name," answered
the lad. "Who is he? I have a right to know."

"He is called Prince Charming. Don't you like
the name? Oh! you silly boy! you should never
forget it. If you only saw him, you would think him
the most wonderful person in the world. Some day
you will meet him : when you come back from Australia. You will like him so much. Everybody likes
him, and I . . . love him. I wish you could come
to the theatre to-night. He is going to be there, and
I am to play Juliet. Oh! how I shall play it! Fancy,
Jim, to be in love and play Juliet! To have him
sitting there! To play for his delight! I am afraid
I may frighten the company, frighten or enthrall them.
To be in love is to surpass one's self. Poor dreadful
Mr. Isaacs will be shouting 'genius' to his loafers
at the bar. He has preached me as a dogma; to-
night he will announce me as a revelation. I feel
it. And it is all his, his only, Prince Charming, my
wonderful lover, my god of graces. But I am poor
beside him. Poor? What does that matter? When
poverty creeps in at the door, love flies in through
the window. Our proverbs want re-writing. They
were made in winter, and it is summer now; spring-
time for me, I think, a very dance of blossoms in blue
skies."

"He is a gentleman," said the lad, sullenly.

"A prince!" she cried, musically. "What more
do you want?"

"He wants to enslave you."

"I shudder at the thought of being free."

"I want you to beware of him."

"To see him is to worship him, to know him is to
trust him."

"Sibyl, you are mad about him."

She laughed, and took his arm. "You dear old
Jim, you talk as if you were a hundred. Some day
you will be in love yourself. Then you will know

what it is. Don't look so sulky. Surely you should be glad to think that, though you are going away, you leave me happier than I have ever been before. Life has been hard for us both, terribly hard and difficult. But it will be different now. You are going to a new world, and I have found one. Here are two chairs : let us sit down and see the smart people go by."

They took their seats amidst a crowd of watchers. The tulip-beds across the road flamed like throbbing rings of fire. A white dust, tremulous cloud of orris-root it seemed, hung in the panting air. The brightly-coloured parasols danced and dipped like monstrous butterflies.

She made her brother talk of himself, his hopes, his prospects. He spoke slowly and with effort. They passed words to each other as players at a game pass counters. Sibyl felt oppressed. She could not communicate her joy. A faint smile curving that sullen mouth was all the echo she could win. After some time she became silent. Suddenly she caught a glimpse of golden hair and laughing lips, and in an open carriage with two ladies Dorian Gray drove past.

She started to her feet. " There he is ! " she cried.

" Who ? " said Jim Vane.

" Prince Charming," she answered, looking after the victoria.

He jumped up, and seized her roughly by the arm. " Show him to me. Which is he ? Point him out. I must see him ! " he exclaimed ; but at that moment the Duke of Berwick's four-in-hand came between, and when it had left the space clear, the carriage had swept out of the Park.

" He is gone," murmured Sibyl, sadly. " I wish you had seen him."

" I wish I had, for as sure as there is a God in heaven, if he ever does you any wrong I shall kill him."

She looked at him in horror. He repeated his words. They cut the air like a dagger. The people round began to gape. A lady standing close to her tittered.

"Come away, Jim; come away," she whispered. He followed her doggedly, as she passed through the crowd. He felt glad at what he had said.

When they reached the Achilles Statue she turned round. There was pity in her eyes that became laughter on her lips. She shook her head at him. "You are foolish, Jim, utterly foolish; a bad-tempered boy, that is all. How can you say such horrible things? You don't know what you are talking about. You are simply jealous and unkind. Ah! I wish you would fall in love. Love makes people good, and what you said was wicked.

"I am sixteen," he answered, "and I know what I am about. Mother is no help to you. She doesn't understand how to look after you. I wish now that I was not going to Australia at all. I have a great mind to chuck the whole thing up. I would, if my articles hadn't been signed."

"Oh, don't be so serious, Jim. You are like one of the heroes of those silly melodramas mother used to be so fond of acting in. I am not going to quarrel with you. I have seen him, and oh! to see him is perfect happiness. We won't quarrel. I know you would never harm any one I love, would you?"

"Not as long as you love him, I suppose," was the sullen answer.

"I shall love him for ever!" she cried.

"And he?"

"For ever, too!"

"He had better."

She shrank from him. Then she laughed and put her hand on his arm. He was merely a boy.

At the Marble Arch they hailed an omnibus, which left them close to their shabby home in the Euston

Road. It was after five o'clock, and Sibyl had to lie down for a couple of hours before acting. Jim insisted that she should do so. He said that he would sooner part with her when their mother was not present. She would be sure to make a scene, and he detested scenes of every kind.

In Sibyl's own room they parted. There was jealousy in the lad's heart, and a fierce, murderous hatred of the stranger who, as it seemed to him, had come between them. Yet, when her arms were flung round his neck, and her fingers strayed through his hair, he softened, and kissed her with real affection. There were tears in his eyes as he went downstairs.

His mother was waiting for him below. She grumbled at his unpunctuality, as he entered. He made no answer, but sat down to his meagre meal. The flies buzzed round the table, and crawled over the stained cloth. Through the rumble of omnibuses, and the clatter of street-cabs, he could hear the droning voice devouring each minute that was left to him.

After some time, he thrust away his plate, and put his head in his hands. He felt that he had a right to know. It should have been told to him before, if it was as he suspected. Leaden with fear, his mother watched him. Words dropped mechanically from her lips. A tattered lace handkerchief twitched in her fingers. When the clock struck six, he got up, and went to the door. Then he turned back, and looked at her. Their eyes met. In hers he saw a wild appeal for mercy. It enraged him.

"Mother, I have something to ask you," he said. Her eyes wandered vaguely about the room. She made no answer. "Tell me the truth. I have a right to know. Were you married to my father?"

She heaved a deep sigh. It was a sigh of relief. The terrible moment, the moment that night and day, for weeks and months, she had dreaded, had come at last, and yet she felt no terror. Indeed in some measure it was a disappointment to her. The vulgar directness of the question called for a direct answer. The situation had not been gradually led up to. It was crude. It reminded her of a bad rehearsal.

" No," she answered, wondering at the harsh simplicity of life.

" My father was a scoundrel then ? " cried the lad, clenching his fists.

She shook her head. " I knew he was not free. We loved each other very much. If he had lived, he would have made provision for us. Don't speak against him, my son. He was your father, and a gentleman. Indeed he was highly connected."

An oath broke from his lips. " I don't care for myself," he exclaimed, " but don't let Sibyl . . . It is a gentleman, isn't it, who is in love with her, or says he is ? Highly connected, too, I suppose."

For a moment a hideous sense of humiliation came over the woman. Her head drooped. She wiped her eyes with shaking hands. " Sibyl has a mother," she murmured ; " I had none."

The lad was touched. He went towards her, and stooping down he kissed her. " I am sorry if I have pained you by asking about my father," he said, " but I could not help it. I must go now. Good-bye. Don't forget that you will only have one child now to look after, and believe me that if this man wrongs my sister, I will find out who he is, track him down, and kill him like a dog. I swear it."

The exaggerated folly of the threat, the passionate gesture that accompanied it, the mad melodramatic words, made life seem more vivid to her. She was familiar with the atmosphere. She breathed more freely, and for the first time for many months she really admired her son. She would have liked to have continued the scene on the same emotional scale, but he cut her short. Trunks had to be carried down, and mufflers looked for. The lodging-house drudge bustled in and out. There was the bargaining with the cabman. The moment was lost in vulgar details. It was with a renewed feeling of disappointment that she waved the tattered lace handkerchief from the window, as her son drove away. She was conscious that a great opportunity had been wasted. She consoled herself by telling Sibyl how desolate she felt her life would be, now that she had only one child to look after. She remembered the phrase. It had pleased her. Of the threat she said nothing. It was vividly and dramatically expressed. She felt that they would all laugh at it some day.

CHAPTER VI

" I SUPPOSE you have heard the news, Basil ? " said Lord Henry, that evening, as Hallward was shown into a little private room at the Bristol where dinner had been laid for three.

" No, Harry," answered the artist, giving his hat and coat to the bowing waiter. " What is it ? Nothing about politics, I hope ? They don't interest me. There is hardly a single person in the House of Commons worth painting ; though many of them would be the better for a little white-washing."

" Dorian Gray is engaged to be married," said Lord Henry, watching him as he spoke.

Hallward started, and then frowned. " Dorian engaged to be married ! " he cried. " Impossible ! "

" It is perfectly true."

" To whom ? "

" To some little actress or other."

" I can't believe it. Dorian is far too sensible."

" Dorian is far too wise not to do foolish things now and then, my dear Basil."

" Marriage is hardly a thing that one can do now and then, Harry."

" Except in America," rejoined Lord Henry, languidly. " But I didn't say he was married. I said he was engaged to be married. There is a great difference. I have a distinct remembrance of being married, but I have no recollection at all of being engaged. I am inclined to think that I never was engaged."

" But think of Dorian's birth, and position, and wealth. It would be absurd for him to marry so much beneath him."

" If you want to make him marry this girl tell him that, Basil. He is sure to do it, then. Whenever a man does a thoroughly stupid thing, it is always from the noblest motives."

" I hope the girl is good, Harry. I don't want to see Dorian tied to some vile creature, who might degrade his nature and ruin his intellect."

" Oh, she is better than good—she is beautiful," murmured Lord Henry, sipping a glass of vermouth and orange-bitters. " Dorian says she is beautiful; and he is not often wrong about things of that kind. Your portrait of him has quickened his appreciation of the personal appearance of other people. It has had that excellent effect, amongst others. We are to see her to-night, if that boy doesn't forget his appointment."

" Are you serious ? "

" Quite serious, Basil. I should be miserable if I thought I should ever be more serious than I am at the present moment."

" But do you approve of it, Harry ? " asked the painter, walking up and down the room, and biting his lip. " You can't approve of it, possibly. It is some silly infatuation."

" I never approve, or disapprove, of anything now. It is an absurd attitude to take towards life. We are

not sent into the world to air our moral prejudices.
I never take any notice of what common people say,
and I never interfere with what charming people
do. If a personality fascinates me, whatever mode
of expression that personality selects is absolutely
delightful to me. Dorian Gray falls in love with a
beautiful girl who acts Juliet, and proposes to marry
her. Why not ? If he wedded Messalina he would
be none the less interesting. You know I am not
a champion of marriage. The real drawback to
marriage is that it makes one unselfish. And unselfish people are colourless. They lack individuality.
Still, there are certain temperaments that marriage
makes more complex. They retain their egotism,
and add to it many other egos. They are forced to
have more than one life. They become more highly
organised, and to be highly organised is, I should
fancy, the object of man's existence. Besides, every
experience is of value, and, whatever one may say
against marriage, it is certainly an experience. I
hope that Dorian Gray will make this girl his wife,
passionately adore her for six months, and then
suddenly become fascinated by some one else. He
would be a wonderful study."

" You don't mean a single word of all that, Harry ;
you know you don't. If Dorian Gray's life were
spoiled, no one would be sorrier than yourself. You
are much better than you pretend to be."

Lord Henry laughed. " The reason we all like
to think so well of others is that we are all afraid
for ourselves. The basis of optimism is sheer terror.
We think that we are generous because we credit our
neighbour with the possession of those virtues that
are likely to be a benefit to us. We praise the banker
that we may overdraw our account, and find good
qualities in the highwayman in the hope that he may
spare our pockets. I mean everything that I have said.
I have the greatest contempt for optimism. As for a

spoiled life, no life is spoiled but one whose growth is arrested. If you want to mar a nature, you have merely to reform it. As for marriage, of course that would be silly, but there are other and more interesting bonds between men and women. I will certainly encourage them. They have the charm of being fashionable. But here is Dorian himself. He will tell you more than I can."

" My dear Harry, my dear Basil, you must both congratulate me ! " said the lad, throwing off his evening cape with its satin-lined wings and shaking each of his friends by the hand in turn. " I have never been so happy. Of course it is sudden ; all really delightful things are. And yet it seems to me to be the one thing I have been looking for all my life." He was flushed with excitement and pleasure, and looked extraordinarily handsome.

" I hope you will always be very happy, Dorian," said Hallward, " but I don't quite forgive you for not having let me know of your engagement. You let Harry know.

" And I don't forgive you for being late for dinner," broke in Lord Henry, putting his hand on the lad's shoulder, and smiling as he spoke. " Come, let us sit down and try what the new *chef* here is like, and then you will tell us how it all came about."

" There is really not much to tell," cried Dorian, as they took their seats at the small round table. " What happened was simply this. After I left you yesterday evening, Harry, I dressed, had some dinner at that little Italian restaurant in Rupert Street you introduced me to, and went down at eight o'clock to the theatre. Sibyl was playing Rosalind. Of course the scenery was dreadful, and the Orlando absurd. But Sibyl ! You should have seen her ! When she came on in her boy's clothes she was perfectly wonderful. She wore a moss-coloured velvet jerkin with cinnamon sleeves, slim brown cross-gartered hose,

a dainty little green cap with a hawk's feather caught
in a jewel, and a hooded cloak lined with dull red.
She had never seemed to me more exquisite. She
had all the delicate grace of that Tanagra figurine
that you have in your studio, Basil. Her hair clustered
round her face like dark leaves round a pale rose. As
for her acting—well, you shall see her to-night. She is
simply a born artist. I sat in the dingy box absolutely enthralled. I forgot that I was in London,
and in the nineteenth century. I was away with my
love in a forest that no man had ever seen. After
the performance was over I went behind, and spoke
to her. As we were sitting together, suddenly there
came into her eyes a look that I had never seen there
before. My lips moved towards hers. We kissed
each other. I can't describe to you what I felt at
that moment. It seemed to me that all my life had
been narrowed to one perfect point of rose-coloured
joy. She trembled all over, and shook like a white
narcissus. Then she flung herself on her knees and
kissed my hands. I feel that I should not tell you
all this, but I can't help it. Of course our engagement is a dead sceret. She has not even told her own
mother. I don't know what my guardians will say.
Lord Radley is sure to be furious. I don't care. I
shall be of age in less than a year, and then I can do
what I like. I have been right, Basil, haven't I, to
take my love out of poetry, and to find my wife in
Shakespeare's plays? Lips that Shakespeare taught
to speak have whispered their secret in my ear. I
have had the arms of Rosalind around me, and kissed
Juliet on the mouth."

"Yes, Dorian, I suppose you were right," said
Hallward, slowly.

"Have you seen her to-day?" asked Lord Henry.

Dorian Gray shook his head. "I left her in the
forest of Arden, I shall find her in an orchard in
Verona."

Lord Henry sipped his champagne in a meditative manner. "At what particular point did you mention the word marriage, Dorian? And what did she say in answer? Perhaps you forgot all about it."

"My dear Harry, I did not treat it as a business transaction, and I did not make any formal proposal. I told her that I loved her, and she said she was not worthy to be my wife. Not worthy! Why, the whole world is nothing to me compared with her."

"Women are wonderfully practical," murmured Lord Henry—"much more practical than we are. In situations of that kind we often forget to say anything about marriage, and they always remind us."

Hallward laid his hand upon his arm. "Don't, Harry. You have annoyed Dorian. He is not like other men. He would never bring misery upon any one. His nature is too fine for that."

Lord Henry looked across the table. "Dorian is never annoyed with me," he answered. "I asked the question for the best reason possible, for the only reason, indeed, that excuses one for asking any question—simply curiosity. I have a theory that it is always the women who propose to us, and not we who propose to the women. Except, of course, in middle-class life. But then the middle classes are not modern."

Dorian Gray laughed, and tossed his head. "You are quite incorrigible, Harry; but I don't mind. It is impossible to be angry with you. When you see Sibyl Vane you will feel that the man who could wrong her would be a beast, a beast without a heart. I cannot understand how any one can wish to shame the thing he loves. I love Sibyl Vane. I want to place her on a pedestal of gold, and to see the world worship the woman who is mine. What is marriage? An irrevocable vow. You mock at it for that. Ah! don't mock. It is an irrevocable vow that I want

to take. Her trust makes me faithful, her belief makes
me good. When I am with her, I regret all that you
have taught me. I become different from what you
have known me to be. I am changed, and the mere
touch of Sibyl Vane's hand makes me forget you and
all your wrong, fascinating, poisonous, delightful
theories."

"And those are . . . ?" asked Lord Henry, helping himself to some salad.

"Oh, your theories about life, your theories about
love, your theories about pleasure. All your theories,
in fact, Harry."

"Pleasure is the only thing worth having a theory
about," he answered, in his slow, melodious voice.
"But I am afraid I cannot claim my theory as my
own. It belongs to Nature, not to me. Pleasure is
Nature's test, her sign of approval. When we are
happy we are always good, but when we are good we
are not always happy."

"Ah! but what do you mean by good?" cried
Basil Hallward.

"Yes," echoed Dorian, leaning back in his chair,
and looking at Lord Henry over the heavy clusters
of purple-lipped irises that stood in the centre of
the table, "what do you mean by good, Harry?"
"To be good is to be in harmony with one's self,"
he replied, touching the thin stem of his glass with
his pale, fine-pointed fingers. "Discord is to be forced
to be in harmony with others. One's own life—that is
the important thing. As for the lives of one's neighbours, if one wishes to be a prig or a Puritan, one
can flaunt one's moral views about them, but they
are not one's concern. Besides, Individualism has
really the higher aim. Modern morality consists in
accepting the standard of one's age. I consider that
for any man of culture to accept the standard of his
age is a form of the grossest immorality."

"But, surely, if one lives merely for one's self,

Harry, one pays a terrible price for doing so?"
suggested the painter.

"Yes, we are overcharged for everything nowadays.
I should fancy that the real tragedy of the poor
is that they can afford nothing but self-denial.
Beautiful sins, like beautiful things, are the privilege
of the rich."

"One has to pay in other ways but money."

"What sort of ways, Basil?"

"Oh! I should fancy in remorse, in suffering, in
. . . well, in the consciousness of degradation."

Lord Henry shrugged his shoulders. "My dear
fellow, mediæval art is charming, but mediæval
emotions are out of date. One can use them in fiction,
of course. But then the only things that one can
use in fiction are the things that one has ceased to
use in fact. Believe me, no civilised man ever regrets
a pleasure, and no uncivilised man ever knows what
a pleasure is."

"I know what pleasure is," cried Dorian Gray.
"It is to adore some one."

"That is certainly better than being adored," he
answered, toying with some fruits. "Being adored
is a nuisance. Women treat us just as Humanity
treats its gods. They worship us, and are always bother-
ing us to do something for them."

"I should have said that whatever they ask for
they had first given to us," murmured the lad, gravely.
"They create Love in our natures. They have a
right to demand it back."

"That is quite true, Dorian," cried Hallward.

"Nothing is ever quite true," said Lord Henry.

"This is," interrupted Dorian. "You must admit,
Harry, that women give to men the very gold of
their lives."

"Possibly," he sighed, "but they invariably
want it back in such very small change. That is
the worry. Women, as some witty Frenchman once

put it, inspire us with the desire to do masterpieces,
and always prevent us from carrying them out.'

" Harry, you are dreadful ! I don't know why I
like you so much."

" You will always like me, Dorian," he replied.
" Will you have some coffee, you fellows ?—Waiter,
bring coffee, and *fine-champagne,* and some cigarettes.
No : don't mind the cigarettes ; I have some. Balis,
I can't allow you to smoke cigars. You must have a
cigarette. A cigarette is the perfect type of a perfect
pleasure. It is exquisite, and it leaves one unsatisfied.
What more can one want ? Yes, Dorian, you will
always be fond of me. I represent to you all the sins
you have never had the courage to commit."

" What nonsense you talk, Harry ! " cried the lad,
taking a light from a fire-breathing silver dragon that
the waiter had placed on the table. " Let us go
down to the theatre. When Sibyl comes on the stage
you will have a new ideal of life. She will represent
something to you that you have never known.'

" I have known everything," said Lord Henry,
with a tired look in his eyes, " but I am always ready
for a new emotion. I am afraid, however, that, for
me at any rate, there is no such thing. Still, your
wonderful girl may thrill me. I love acting. It is so
much more real than life. Let us go. Dorian, you
will come with me. I am so sorry, Basil, but there is
only room for two in the brougham. You must follow
us in a hansom."

They got up and put on their coats, sipping their
coffee standing. The painter was silent and preoccupied. There was a gloom over him. He could
not bear this marriage, and yet it seemed to him
to be better than many other things that might have
happened. After a few minutes, they all passed
downstairs. He drove off by himself, as had been
arranged, and watched the flashing lights of the
little brougham in front of him. A strange sense of

loss came over him. He felt that Dorian Gray would
never again be to him all that he had been in the
past. Life had come between them. . . . His eyes
darkened, and the crowded, flaring streets became
blurred to his eyes. When the cab drew up at the
theatre, it seemed to him that he had grown years
older.

CHAPTER VII

FOR some reason or other, the house was crowded
that night, and the fat Jew manager who met
them at the door was beaming from ear to ear
with an oily, tremulous smile. He escorted them
to their box with a sort of pompous humility,
waving his fat jewelled hands, and talking at the top
of his voice. Dorian Gray loathed him more than ever.
He felt as if he had come to look for Miranda and had
been met by Caliban. Lord Henry, upon the other
hand, rather liked him. At least he declared he did,
and insisted on shaking him by the hand, and assuring
him that he was proud to meet a man who had discovered a real genius and gone bankrupt over a poet.
Hallward amused himself with watching the faces in
the pit. The heat was terribly oppressive, and the
huge sunlight flamed like a monstrous dahlia with
petals of yellow fire. The youths in the gallery
had taken off their coats and waistcoats and hung
them over the side. They talked to each other across
the theatre, and shared their oranges with the tawdry
girls who sat beside them. Some women were laughing in the pit. Their voices were horribly shrill and
discordant. The sound of the popping of corks came
from the bar.

"What a place to find one's divinity in!" said
Lord Henry.

"Yes!" answered Dorian Gray. "It was here I

found her, and she is divine beyond all living things.
When she acts you will forget everything. These
common, rough people, with their coarse faces and
brutal gestures, become quite different when she is
on the stage. They sit silently and watch her. They
weep and laugh as she wills them to do. She makes
them as responsive as a violin. She spiritualises
them, and one feels that they are of the same flesh
and blood as one's self."

" The same flesh and blood as one's self! Oh, I
hope not ! " exclaimed Lord Henry, who was scanning
the occupants of the gallery through his opera-glass.

" Don't pay any attention to him, Dorian," said
the painter. " I understand what you mean, and I
believe in this girl. Any one you love must be marvellous, and any girl that has the effect you describe
must be fine and noble. To spiritualise one's age—
that is something worth doing. If this girl can give
a soul to those who have lived without one, if she can
create the sense of beauty in people whose lives have
been sordid and ugly, if she can strip them of their
selfishness and lend them tears for sorrows that are
not their own, she is worthy of all your adoration,
worthy of the adoration of the world. This marriage
is quite right. I did not think so at first, but I admit
it now. The gods made Sibyl Vane for you. Without
her you would have been incomplete."

" Thanks, Basil," answered Dorian Gray, pressing
his hand. " I knew that you would understand me.
Harry is so cynical, he terrifies me. But here is the
orchestra. It is quite dreadful, but it only lasts for
about five minutes. Then the curtain rises, and you
will see the girl to whom I am going to give all my
life, to whom I have given everything that is good
in me."

A quarter of an hour afterwards, amidst an extraordinary turmoil of applause, Sibyl Vane stepped
on to the stage. Yes, she was certainly lovely to

look at—one of the loveliest creatures, Lord Henry
thought, that he had ever seen. There was something of the fawn in her shy grace and startled eyes.
A faint blush, like the shadow of a rose in a mirror
of silver, came to her cheeks as she glanced at the
crowded, enthusiastic house. She stepped back a
few paces, and her lips seemed to tremble. Basil
Hallward leaped to his feet and began to applaud.
Motionless, and as one in a dream, sat Dorian Gray,
gazing at her. Lord Henry peered through his glasses,
murmuring, " Charming ! charming ! "

The scene was the hall of Capulet's house, and
Romeo in his pilgrim's dress had entered with Mercutio
and his other friends. The band, such as it was, struck
up a few bars of music, and the dance began. Through
the crowd of ungainly, shabbily-dressed actors,
Sibyl Vane moved like a creature from a finer world.
Her' body swayed, while she danced, as a plant sways
in the water. The curves of her throat were the curves
of a white lily. Her hands seemed to be made of cool
ivory.

Yet she was curiously listless. She showed no sign
of joy when her eyes rested on Romeo. The few words
she had to speak—

Good pilgrim, you do wrong your hand too much,
Which mannerly devotion shows in this ;
For saints have hands that pilgrims' hands do touch,
And palm to palm is holy palmers' kiss—

with the brief dialogue that follows, were spoken in
a thoroughly artificial manner. The voice was exquisite,
but from the point of view of tone it was absolutely
false. It was wrong in colour. It took away all the
life from the verse. It made the passion unreal.

Dorian Gray grew pale as he watched her. He
was puzzled and anxious. Neither of his friends
dared to say anything to him. She seemed to them

to be absolutely incompetent. They were horribly disappointed.

Yet they felt that the true test of any Juliet is the balcony scene of the second act. They waited for that. If she failed there, there was nothing in her.

She looked charming as she came out in the moon-light. That could not be denied. But the staginess of her acting was unbearable, and grew worse as she went on. Her gestures became absurdly artificial. She over-emphasised everything that she had to say. The beautiful passage—

Thou knowest the mask of night is on my face,
Else would a maiden blush bepaint my cheek
For that which thou hast heard me speak to-night—

was declaimed with the painful precision of a school-girl who has been taught to recite by some second-rate professor of elocution. When she leaned over the balcony and came to those wonderful lines—

Although I joy in thee,
I have no joy of this contract to-night:
It is too rash, too unadvised, too sudden;
Too like the lightning, which doth cease to be
Ere one can say, " It lightens." Sweet, good-night !
This bud of love by summer's ripening breath
May prove a beauteous flower when next we meet—

she spoke the words as though they conveyed no meaning to her. It was not nervousness. Indeed, so far from being nervous, she was absolutely self-contained. It was simply bad art. She was a complete failure.

Even the common, uneducated audience of the pit and gallery lost their interest in the play. They got restless, and began to talk loudly and to whistle. The Jew manager, who was standing at the back of the dress-circle, stamped and swore with rage. The only person unmoved was the girl herself.

When the second act was over there came a storm of hisses, and Lord Henry got up from his chair and put on his coat. " She is quite beautiful, Dorian," he said, " but she can't act. Let us go."

" I am going to see the play through," answered the lad, in a hard, bitter voice. " I am awfully sorry that I have made you waste an evening, Harry. I apologise to you both."

" My dear Dorian, I should think Miss Vane was ill," interrupted Hallward. " We will come some other night."

" I wish she were ill," he rejoined. " But she seems to me to be simply callous and cold. She has entirely altered. Last night she was a great artist. This evening she is merely a commonplace, mediocre actress."

" Don't talk like that about any one you love, Dorian. Love is a more wonderful thing than Art."

" They are both simply forms of imitation," remarked Lord Henry. " But do let us go. Dorian, you must not stay here any longer. It is not good for one's morals to see bad acting. Besides, I don't suppose you will want your wife to act. So what does it matter if she plays Juliet like a wooden doll ? She is very lovely, and if she knows as little about life as she does about acting, she will be a delightful experience. There are only two kinds of people who are really fascinating—people who know absolutely everything, and people who know absolutely nothing. Good heavens, my dear boy, don't look so tragic ! The secret of remaining young is never to have an emotion that is unbecoming. Come to the club with Basil and myself. We will smoke cigarettes and drink to the beauty of Sibyl Vane. She is beautiful. What more can you want ? "

" Go away, Harry," cried the lad. " I want to be

alone. Basil, you must go. Ah! can't you see that
my heart is breaking?" The hot tears came to his
eyes. His lips trembled, and, rushing to the back of
the box, he leaned up against the wall, hiding his face
in his hands.

"Let us go, Basil," said Lord Henry, with a strange
tenderness in his voice; and the two young men
passed out together.

A few moments afterwards the footlights flared up,
and the curtain rose on the third act. Dorian Gray
went back to his seat. He looked pale, and proud,
and indifferent. The play dragged on, and seemed
interminable. Half of the audience went out, tramping
in heavy boots, and laughing. The whole thing was
a fiasco. The last act was played to almost empty
benches. The curtain went down on a titter, and some
groans.

As soon as it was over, Dorian Gray rushed behind
the scenes into the greenroom. The girl was standing
there alone, with a look of triumph on her face. Her
eyes were lit with an exquisite fire. There was a
radiance about her. Her parted lips were smiling over
some secret of their own.

When he entered, she looked at him, and an expression of infinite joy came over her. "How badly
I acted to-night, Dorian!" she cried.

"Horribly!" he answered, gazing at her in amazement—"horribly! It was dreadful. Are you ill?
You have no idea what it was. You have no idea
what I suffered."

The girl smiled. "Dorian," she answered, lingering over his name with long-drawn music in her
voice, as though it were sweeter than honey to the
red petals of her mouth—"Dorian, you should have
understood. But you understand now, don't you?"

"Understand what?" he asked, angrily.

"Why I was so bad to-night. Why I shall always
be bad. Why I shall never act well again."

He shrugged his shoulders. "You are ill, I suppose. When you are ill you shouldn't act. You make yourself ridiculous. My friends were bored. I was bored."

She seemed not to listen to him. She was transfigured with joy. An ecstasy of happiness dominated her.

"Dorian, Dorian," she cried, "before I knew you acting was the one reality of my life. It was only in the theatre that I lived. I thought that it was all true. I was Rosalind one night, and Portia the other. The joy of Beatrice was my joy, and the sorrows of Cordelia were mine also. I believed in everything. The common people who acted with me seemed to me to be godlike. The painted scenes were my world. I knew nothing but shadows, and I thought them real. You came—oh, my beautiful love!—and you freed my soul from prison. You taught me what reality really is. To-night, for the first time in my life, I saw through the hollowness, the sham, the silliness of the empty pageant in which I had always played. To-night, for the first time, I became conscious that the Romeo was hideous, and old, and painted, that the moonlight in the orchard was false, that the scenery was vulgar, and that the words I had to speak were unreal, were not my words, were not what I wanted to say. You had brought me something higher, something of which all art is but a reflection. You had made me understand what love really is. My love! my love! Prince Charming! Prince of life! I have grown sick of shadows. You are more to me than all art can ever be. What have I to do with the puppets of a play? When I came on to-night, I could not understand how it was that everything had gone from me. I thought that I was going to be wonderful. I found that I could do nothing. Suddenly it dawned on my soul what it all meant. The knowledge was exquisite to me. I heard them hissing, and I smiled. What could they know of love such as ours? Take me away, Dorian—take me away with you, where we can be quite alone. I hate the stage. I might mimic a passion that I do not feel, but I cannot mimic one that burns me like fire. Oh, Dorian, Dorian, you understand now what it signifies? Even if I could do it, it would be profanation for me to play at being in love. You have made me see that."

He flung himself down on the sofa, and turned away his face. "You have killed my love," he muttered.

She looked at him in wonder, and laughed. He made no answer. She came across to him, and with her little fingers stroked his hair. She knelt down and pressed his hands to her lips. He drew them away, and a shudder ran through him.

Then he leaped up, and went to the door. " Yes," he cried, " you have killed my love. You used to stir my imagination. Now you don't even stir my curiosity. You simply produce no effect. I loved you because you were marvellous, because you had genius and intellect, because you realised the dreams of great poets and gave shape and substance to the shadows of art. You have thrown it all away. You are shallow and stupid. My God! how mad I was to love you! What a fool I have been! You are nothing to me now. I will never see you again. I will never think of you. I will never mention your name. You don't know what you were to me, once. Why, once . . . Oh, I can't bear to think of it! I wish I had never laid eyes upon you! You have spoiled the romance of my life. How little you can know of love, if you say it mars your art! Without your art you are nothing. I would have made you famous, splendid, magnificent. The world would have worshipped you, and you would have borne my name. What are you now? A third-rate actress with a pretty face."

The girl grew white, and trembled. She clenched her hands together, and her voice seemed to catch in her throat. "You are not serious, Dorian?" she murmured. "You are acting."

"Acting! I leave that to you. You do it so well," he answered bitterly.

She rose from her knees, and, with a piteous expression of pain in her face, came across the room to him. She put her hand upon his arm, and looked into his eyes. He thrust her back. "Don't touch me!" he cried.

A low moan broke from her, and she flung herself at his feet, and lay there like a trampled flower. "Dorian, Dorian, don't leave me!" she whispered. "I am so sorry I didn't act well. I was thinking of you all the time. But I will try—indeed, I will try. It came so suddenly across me, my love for you. I think I should never have known it if you had not kissed me—if we had not kissed each other. Kiss me again, my love. Don't go away from me. I couldn't bear it. Oh! don't go away from me. My brother . . . No; never mind. He didn't mean it. He was in jest. . . . But you, oh! can't you forgive me for to-night? I will work so hard, and try to improve. Don't be cruel to me because I love you better than anything in the world. After all, it is only once that I have not pleased you. But you are quite right, Dorian. I should have shown myself more of an artist. It was foolish of me; and yet I couldn't help it. Oh, don't leave me, don't leave me." A fit of passionate sobbing choked her. She crouched on the floor like a wounded thing, and Dorian Gray, with his beautiful eyes, looked down at her, and his chiselled lips curled in exquisite disdain. There is always something ridiculous about the emotions of people whom one has ceased to love. Sibyl Vane seemed to him to be absurdly melodramatic. Her tears and sobs annoyed him.

"I am going," he said at last, in his calm, clear voice. "I don't wish to be unkind, but I can't see you again. You have disappointed me."

She wept silently, and made no answer, but crept nearer. Her little hands stretched blindly out, and appeared to be seeking for him. He turned on his heel, and left the room. In a few moments he was out of the theatre.

Where he went to he hardly knew. He remembered wandering through dimly-lit streets, past gaunt black-shadowed archways and evil-looking houses. Women with hoarse voices and harsh laughter had called after him. Drunkards had reeled by cursing, and chattering to themselves like monstrous apes. He had seen grotesque children huddled upon door-steps, and heard shrieks and oaths from gloomy courts.

As the dawn was just breaking he found himself close to Covent Garden. The darkness lifted, and, flushed with faint fires, the sky hollowed itself into a perfect pearl. Huge carts filled with nodding lilies rumbled slowly down the polished empty street. The air was heavy with the perfume of the flowers, and their beauty seemed to bring him an anodyne for his pain. He followed into the market, and watched the men unloading their waggons. A white-smocked carter offered him some cherries. He thanked him, and wondered why he refused to accept any money for them, and began to eat them listlessly. They had been plucked at midnight, and the coldness of the moon had entered into them. A long line of boys carrying crates of striped tulips, and of yellow and red roses, defiled in front of him, threading their way through the huge jade-green piles of vegetables. Under the portico, with its grey sun-bleached pillars, loitered a troop of draggled bare-headed girls, waiting for the auction to be over. Others crowded round the swinging doors of the coffee-house in the Plazza. The heavy cart-horses slipped and stamped upon the rough stones, shaking their bells and trappings. Some of the drivers were lying asleep on a pile of sacks.

THE PICTURE OF DORIAN GRAY   113

Iris-necked, and pink-footed, the pigeons ran about picking up seeds.

After a little while, he hailed a hansom, and drove home. For a few moments he loitered upon the door-step, looking round at the silent Square with its blank, close-shuttered windows, and its staring blinds. The sky was pure opal now, and the roofs of the houses glistened like silver against it. From some chimney opposite a thin wreath of smoke was rising. It curled, a violet riband, through the nacre-coloured air.

In the huge gilt Venetian lantern, spoil of some Doge's barge, that hung from the ceiling of the great oak-panelled hall of entrance, lights were still burning from three flickering jets : thin blue petals of flame they seemed, rimmed with white fire. He turned them out, and, having thrown his hat and cape on the table, passed through the library towards the door of his bedroom, a large octagonal chamber on the ground floor that, in his new-born feeling for luxury, he had just had decorated for himself, and hung with some curious Renaissance tapestries that had been discovered stored in a disused attic at Selby Royal. As he was turning the handle of the door, his eye fell upon the portrait Basil Hallward had painted of him. He started back as if in surprise. Then he went on into his own room, looking somewhat puzzled. After he had taken the buttonhole out of his coat, he seemed to hesitate. Finally he came back, went over to the picture, and examined it. In the dim arrested light that struggled through the cream-coloured silk blinds, the face appeared to him to be a little changed. The expression looked different. One would have said that there was a touch of cruelty in the mouth. It was certainly strange.

He turned round, and, walking to the window, drew up the blind. The bright dawn flooded the room, and swept the fantastic shadows into dusky corners, where they lay shuddering. But the strange expression that he had noticed in the face of the portrait seemed to linger there, to be more intensified even. The quivering, ardent sunlight showed him the lines of cruelty round the mouth as clearly as if he had been looking into a mirror after he had done some dreadful thing.

He winced, and, taking up from the table an oval glass framed in ivory Cupids, one of Lord Henry's many presents to him, glanced hurriedly into its polished depths. No line like that warped his red lips. What did it mean ?

He rubbed his eyes, and came close to the picture, and examined it again. There were no signs of any change when he looked into the actual painting, and yet there was no doubt that the whole expression had altered. It was not a mere fancy of his own. The thing was horribly apparent.

He threw himself into a chair, and began to think. Suddenly there flashed across his mind what he had said in Basil Hallward's studio the day the picture had been finished. Yes, he remembered it perfectly. He had uttered a mad wish that he himself might remain young, and the portrait grow old ; that his own beauty might be untarnished, and the face on the canvas bear the burden of his passions and his sins ; that the painted image might be seared with the lines of suffering and thought, and that he might keep all the delicate bloom and loveliness of his then just conscious boyhood. Surely his wish had not been fulfilled ? Such things were impossible. It seemed monstrous even to think of them. And, yet, there was the picture before him, with the touch of cruelty in the mouth.

Cruelty ! Had he been cruel ? It was the girl's fault, not his. He had dreamed of her as a great artist, had given his love to her because he had thought her great. Then she had disappointed him. She had been shallow and unworthy. And, yet, a feeling of infinite regret came over him, as he thought of her lying at his feet sobbing like a little child. He remembered with what callousness he had watched her. Why had he been made like that ? Why had such a soul been given to him ? But he had suffered also. During the three terrible hours that the play had lasted, he had lived centuries of pain, æon upon æon of torture. His life was well worth hers. She had marred him for a moment, if he had wounded her for an age. Besides, women were better suited to bear sorrow than men. They lived on their emotions. They only thought of their emotions. When they took lovers, it was merely to have some one with whom they could have scenes. Lord Henry had told him that, and Lord Henry knew what women were. Why should he trouble about Sibyl Vane ? She was nothing to him now.

But the picture ? What was he to say· of that ? It held the secret of his life, and told his story. It had taught him to love his own beauty. Would it teach him to loathe his own soul ? Would he ever look at it again ?

No ; it was merely an illusion wrought on the troubled senses. The horrible night that he had passed had left phantoms behind it. Suddenly there had fallen upon his brain that tiny scarlet speck that makes men mad. The picture had not changed. It was folly to think so.

Yet it was watching him, with its beautiful marred face and its cruel smile. Its bright hair gleamed in the early sunlight. Its blue eyes met his own. A sense of infinite pity, not for himself, but for the painted image of himself, came over him. It had altered already, and would alter more. Its gold would wither into grey. Its red and white roses would die. For every sin that he committed, a stain would fleck and wreck its fairness. But he would not sin. The picture, changed or unchanged, would be to him the visible emblem of conscience. He would resist temptation. He would not see Lord Henry any more —would not, at any rate, listen to those subtle poisonous theories that in Basil Hallward's garden had first stirred within him the passion for impossible things. He would go back to Sibyl Vane, make her amends, marry her, try to love her again. Yes, it was his duty to do so. She must have suffered more than he had. Poor child ! He had been selfish and cruel to her. The fascination that she had exercised over him would return. They would be happy together. His life with her would be beautiful and pure.

He got up from his chair, and drew a large screen right in front of the portrait, shuddering as he glanced at it. "How horrible ! " he murmured to himself, and he walked across to the window and opened it. When he stepped out on to the grass, he drew a deep breath. The fresh morning air seemed to drive away all his sombre passions. He thought only of Sibyl. A faint echo of his love came back to him. He repeated her name over and over again. The birds that were singing in the dew-drenched garden seemed to be telling the flowers about her.

CHAPTER VIII

IT was long past noon when he awoke. His valet had crept several times on tiptoe into the room to see if he was stirring, and had wondered what made his young master sleep so late. Finally his bell sounded, and Victor came softly in with a cup of tea, and a pile of letters, on a small tray of old Sèvres china, and drew back the olive-satin curtains, with their shimmering blue lining, that hung in front of the three tall windows.

"Monsieur has slept well this morning," he said, smiling.

" What o'clock is it, Victor ? " asked Dorian Gray, drowsily.

" One hour and a quarter, Monsieur."

How late it was ! He sat up, and, having sipped some tea, turned over his letters. One of them was from Lord Henry, and had been brought by hand that morning. He hesitated for a moment, and then put it aside. The others he opened listlessly. They contained the usual collection of cards, invitations to dinner, tickets for private views, programmes of charity concerts, and the like, that are showered on fashionable young men every morning during the season. There was a rather heavy bill, for a chased silver Louis-Quinze toilet-set, that he had not yet had the courage to send on to his guardians, who were extremely old-fashioned people and did not realise that we live in an age when unnecessary things are our only necessities ; and there were several very courteously worded communications from Jermyn Street money-lenders offering to advance any sum of money at a moment's notice and at the most reasonable rates of interest.

After about ten minutes he got up, and, throwing on an elaborate dressing-gown of silk-embroidered cashmere wool, passed into the onyx-paved bath-room. The cool water refreshed him after his long sleep. He seemed to have forgotten all that he had gone through. A dim sense of having taken part in some strange tragedy came to him once or twice, but there was the unreality of a dream about it.

As soon as he was dressed, he went into the library and sat down to a light French breakfast, that had been laid out for him on a small round table close to the open window. It was an exquisite day. The warm air seemed laden with spices. A bee flew in, and buzzed round the blue-dragon bowl that, filled with sulphur-yellow roses, stood before him. He felt perfectly happy.

Suddenly his eye fell on the screen that he had placed in front of the portrait, and he started.

" Too cold for Monsieur ? " asked his valet, putting an omelette on the table. " I shut the window ? "

Dorian shook his head. " I am not cold," he murmured.

Was it all true ? Had the portrait really changed ? Or had it been simply his own imagination that had made him see a look of evil where there had been a look of joy ? Surely a painted canvas could not alter ? The thing was absurd. It would serve as a tale to tell Basil some day. It would make him smile.

And, yet, how vivid was his recollection of the whole thing ! First in the dim twilight, and then in the bright dawn, he had seen the touch of cruelty round the warped lips. He almost dreaded his valet leaving the room. He knew that when he was alone he would have to examine the portrait. He was afraid of certainty. When the coffee and cigarettes had been brought and the man turned to go, he felt a wild desire to tell him to remain. As the door was closing behind him he called him back. The man stood waiting for his orders. Dorian looked at him for a moment. " I am not at home to any one, Victor," he said, with a sigh. The man bowed and retired.

Then he rose from the table, lit a cigarette, and flung himself down on a luxuriously-cushioned couch that stood facing the screen. The screen was an old one, of gilt Spanish leather, stamped and wrought with a rather florid Louis-Quatorze pattern. He scanned it curiously, wondering if ever before it had concealed the secret of a man's life.

Should he move it aside, after all ? Why not let it stay there ? What was the use of knowing ? If the thing was true, it was terrible. If it was not true, why trouble about it ? But what if, by some fate or deadlier chance, eyes other than his spied behind, and saw the horrible change? What should he do if Basil Hallward came and asked to look at his own picture? Basil would be sure to do that. No; the thing had to be examined, and at once. Anything would be better than this dreadful state of doubt.

He got up, and locked both doors. At least he would be alone when he looked upon the mask of his shame. Then he drew the screen aside, and saw himself face to face. It was perfectly true. The portrait had altered.

As he often remembered afterwards, and always with no small wonder, he found himself at first gazing at the portrait with a feeling of almost scientific interest. That such a change should have taken place was incredible to him. And yet it was a fact. Was there some subtle affinity between the chemical atoms, that shaped themselves into form and colour on the canvas, and the soul that was within him? Could it be that what that soul thought, they realised? —that what it dreamed, they made true? Or was there some other, more terrible reason? He shuddered, and felt afraid, and, going back to the couch, lay there, gazing at the picture in sickened horror.

One thing, however, he felt that it had done for him. It had made him conscious how unjust, how cruel, he had been to Sibyl Vane. It was not too late to make reparation for that. She could still be his wife. His unreal and selfish love would yield to some higher influence, would be transformed into some nobler passion, and the portrait that Basil Hallward had painted of him would be a guide to him through life, would be to him what holiness is to some, and conscience to others, and the fear of God to us all. There were opiates for remorse, drugs that could lull the moral sense to sleep. But here was a visible symbol of the degradation of sin. Here was an ever-present sign of the ruin men brought upon their souls.

Three o'clock struck, and four, and the half-hour rang its double chime, but Dorian Gray did not stir. He was trying to gather up the scarlet threads of life, and to weave them into a pattern ; to find his way through the sanguine labyrinth of passion through which he was wandering. He did not know what to do, or what to think. Finally, he went over to the table, and wrote a passionate letter to the girl he had loved, imploring her forgiveness, and accusing himself of madness. He covered page after page with wild words of sorrow, and wilder words of pain. There is a luxury in self-reproach. When we blame ourselves we feel that no one else has a right to blame us. It is the confession, not the priest, that gives us absolution. When Dorian had finished the letter, he felt that he had been forgiven.

Suddenly there came a knock to the door, and he heard Lord Henry's voice outside. " My dear boy, I must see you. Let me in at once. I can't bear your shutting yourself up like this."

He made no answer at first, but remained quite still. The knocking still continued, and grew louder. Yes, it was better to let Lord Henry in, and to explain to him the new life he was going to lead, to quarrel with him if it became necessary to quarrel, to part if parting was inevitable. He jumped up, drew the screen hastily across the picture, and unlocked the door.

" I am so sorry for it all, Dorian," said Lord Henry, as he entered. " But you must not think too much about it."

" Do you mean about Sibyl Vane ? " asked the lad.

" Yes, of course," answered Lord Henry, sinking into a chair, and slowly pulling off his yellow gloves. " It is dreadful, from one point of view, but it was not your fault. Tell me, did you go behind and see her, after the play was over ? "

" Yes."

" I felt sure you had. Did you make a scene with her ? "

" I was brutal, Harry—perfectly brutal. But it is all right now. I am not sorry for anything that has happened. It has taught me to know myself better."

" Ah, Dorian, I am so glad you take it in that way ! I was afraid I would find you plunged in remorse, and tearing that nice curly hair of yours."

" I have got through all that," said Dorian, shaking his head, and smiling. " I am perfectly happy now. I know what conscience is, to begin with. It is not what you told me it was. It is the divinest thing in us. Don't sneer at it, Harry, any more—at least not before me. I want to be good. I can't bear the idea of my soul being hideous."

" A very charming artistic basis for ethics, Dorian ! I congratulate you on it. But how are you going to begin ? "

" By marrying Sibyl Vane."

" Marrying Sibyl Vane ! " cried Lord Henry, standing up, and looking at him in perplexed amazement. " But, my dear Dorian——"

" Yes, Harry, I know what you are going to say. Something dreadful about marriage. Don't say it. Don't ever say things of that kind to me again. Two days ago I asked Sibyl to marry me. I am not going to break my word to her. She is to be my wife ! "

" Your wife ! Dorian ! . . . Didn't you get my letter ? I wrote to you this morning, and sent the note down, by my own man."

" Your letter ? Oh, yes, I remember. I have not read it yet, Harry. I was afraid there might be something in it that I wouldn't like. You cut life to pieces with your epigrams."

" You know nothing then ? "

" What do you mean ? "

Lord Henry walked across the room, and, sitting down by Dorian Gray, took both his hands in his own, and held them tightly. " Dorian," he said, " my letter—don't be frightened—was to tell you that Sibyl Vane is dead."

A cry of pain broke from the lad's lips, and he leaped to his feet, tearing his hands away from Lord Henry's grasp. " Dead! Sibyl dead! It is not true ! It is a horrible lie ! How dare you say it ? "

" It is quite true, Dorian," said Lord Henry, gravely. " It is in all the morning papers. I wrote down to you to ask you not to see any one till I came. There will have to be an inquest, of course, and you must not be mixed up in it. Things like that make a man fashionable in Paris. But in London people are so prejudiced. Here, one should never make one's *début* with a scandal. One should reserve that to give an interest to one's old age. I suppose they don't know your name at the theatre ? If they don't, it is all right. Did any one see you going round to her room ? That is an important point."

Dorian did not answer for a few moments. He was dazed with horror. Finally he stammered in a stifled voice, " Harry, did you say an inquest ? What did you mean by that ? Did Sibyl—— ? Oh, Harry, I can't bear it ! But be quick. Tell me everything at once."

" I have no doubt it was not an accident, Dorian, though it must be put in that way to the public. It seems that as she was leaving the theatre with her mother, about half-past twelve or so, she said she had forgotten something upstairs. They waited some time for her, but she did not come down again. They ultimately found her lying dead on the floor of her dressing-room. She had swallowed some- thing by mistake, some dreadful thing they use at theatres. I don't know what it was, but it had either prussic acid or white lead in it. I should fancy it was prussic acid, as she seems to have died instantaneously."

" Harry, Harry, it is terrible ! " cried the lad.

" Yes ; it is very tragic, of course, but you must not get yourself mixed up in it. I see by *The Standard* that she was seventeen. I should have thought she was almost younger than that. She looked such a child, and seemed to know so little about acting. Dorian, you mustn't let this thing get on your nerves. You must come and dine with me, and afterwards we will look in at the Opera. It is a Patti night, and everybody will be there. You can come to my sister's box. She has got some smart women with her."

" So I have murdered Sibyl Vane," said Dorian Gray, half to himself—" murdered her as surely as if I had cut her little throat with a knife. Yet the roses are not less lovely for all that. The birds sing just as happily in my garden. And to-night I am to dine with you, and then go on to the Opera, and sup somewhere, I suppose, afterwards. How extraordinary dramatic life is ! If I had read all this in a book, Harry, I think I would have wept over it. Somehow, now that it has happened actually, and to me, it seems far too wonderful for tears. Here is the first passionate love-letter I have ever written in my life. Strange, that my first passionate love-letter should have been addressed to a dead girl. Can they feel, I wonder, those white silent people we call the dead ? Sibyl ! Can she feel, or know, or listen ? Oh, Harry, how I loved her once ! It seems years ago to me now. She was everything to me. Then came that dreadful night—was it really only last night ?—when she played so badly, and my heart almost broke. She explained it all to me. It was terribly pathetic. But I was not moved a bit. I thought her shallow. Suddenly something happened that made me afraid. I can't tell you what it was, but it was terrible. I said I would go back to

her. I felt I had done wrong. And now she is dead.
My God! My God! Harry, what shall I do? You
don't know the danger I am in, and there is nothing
to keep me straight. She would have done that for
me. She had no right to kill herself. It was selfish
of her."

"My dear Dorian," answered Lord Henry, taking
a cigarette from his case, and producing a gold-latten
match-box, "the only way a woman can ever reform
a man is by boring him so completely that he loses
all possible interest in life. If you had married this
girl you would have been wretched. Of course, you
would have treated her kindly. One can always be
kind to people about whom one cares nothing. But she
would have soon found out that you were absolutely
indifferent to her. And when a woman finds that
out about her husband, she either becomes dreadfully
dowdy, or wears very smart bonnets that some other
woman's husband has to pay for. I say nothing about
the social mistake, which would have been abject,
which, of course, I would not have allowed, but I assure
you that in any case the whole thing would have been
an absolute failure."

"I suppose it would," muttered the lad, walking
up and down the room, and looking horribly pale.
"But I thought it was my duty. It is not my fault
that this terrible tragedy has prevented my doing
what was right. I remember your saying once that
there is a fatality about good resolutions—that they
are always made too late. Mine certainly were."

"Good resolutions are useless attempts to interfere
with scientific laws. Their origin is pure vanity.
Their result is absolutely *nil*. They give us, now and
then, some of those luxurious sterile emotions that
have a certain charm for the weak. That is all that
can be said for them. They are simply cheques that
men draw on a bank where they have no account."

"Harry," cried Dorian Gray, coming over and

sitting down beside him, " why is it that I cannot feel this tragedy as much as I want to ? I don't think I am heartless. Do you ? "

" You have done too many foolish things during the last fortnight to be entitled to give yourself that name, Dorian," answered Lord Henry, with his sweet, melancholy smile.

The lad frowned. " I don't like that explanation, Harry," he rejoined, " but I am glad you don't think I am heartless. I am nothing of the kind. I know I am not. And yet I must admit that this thing that has happened does not affect me as it should. It seems to me to be simply like a wonderful ending to a wonderful play. It has all the terrible beauty of a Greek tragedy, a tragedy in which I took a great part, but by which I have not been wounded."

" It is an interesting question," said Lord Henry, who found an exquisite pleasure in playing on the lad's unconscious egotism—" an extremely interesting question. I fancy that the true explanation is this. It often happens that the real tragedies of life occur in such an inartistic manner that they hurt us by their crude violence, their absolute incoherence, their absurd want of meaning, their entire lack of style. They affect us just as vulgarity affects us. They give us an impression of sheer brute force, and we revolt against that. Sometimes, however, a tragedy that possesses artistic elements of beauty crosses our lives. If these elements of beauty are real, the whole thing simply appeals to our sense of dramatic effect. Suddenly we find that we are no longer the actors, but the spectators of the play. Or rather we are both. We watch ourselves, and the mere wonder of the spectacle enthralls us. In the present case, what is it that has really happened ? Some one has killed herself for love of you. I wish that I had ever had such an experience. It would have made me in love with love for the rest of my life. The

people who have adored me—there have not been
very many, but there have been some—have always
insisted on living on, long after I had ceased to care
for them, or they to care for me. They have become
stout and tedious, and when I meet them they go in
at once for reminiscences. That awful memory of
woman ! What a fearful thing it is And what an
utter intellectual stagnation it reveals ! One should
absorb the colour of life, but one should never remember its details. Details are always vulgar."

" I must sow poppies in my garden," sighed Dorian.

" There is no necessity," rejoined his companion.
" Life has always poppies in her hands. Of course,
now and then things linger. I once wore nothing
but violets all through one season, as a form of artistic
mourning for a romance that would not die. Ultimately, however, it did die. I forget what killed
it. I think it was her proposing to sacrifice the whole
world for me. That is always a dreadful moment.
It fills one with the terror of eternity. Well—would
you believe it ?—a week ago, at Lady Hampshire's,
I found myself seated at dinner next the lady in question,
and she insisted on going over the whole thing
again, and digging up the past, and raking up the
future. I had buried my romance in a bed of asphodel.
She dragged it out again, and assured me that I
had spoiled her life. I am bound to state that she
ate an enormous dinner, so I did not feel any anxiety.
But what a lack of taste she showed ! The one charm
of the past is that it is the past. But women never
know when the curtain has fallen. They always want
a sixth act, and as soon as the interest of the play
is entirely over they propose to continue it. If they
were allowed their own way, every comedy would
have a tragic ending, and every tragedy would cul-
minate in a farce. They are charmingly artificial,
but they have no sense of art. You are more fortunate
than I am. I assure you, Dorian, that not one of

the women I have known would have done for me
what Sibyl Vane did for you. Ordinary women always
console themselves. Some of them do it by going
in for sentimental colours. Never trust a woman who
wears mauve, whatever her age may be, or a woman
over thirty-five who is fond of pink ribbons. It always
means that they have a history. Others find a great
consolation in suddenly discovering the good qualities
of their husbands. They flaunt their conjugal felicity
in one's face, as if it were the most fascinating of
sins. Religion consoles some. Its mysteries have all
the charm of a flirtation, a woman once told me;
and I can quite understand it. Besides, nothing
makes one so vain as being told that one is a sinner.
Conscience makes egotists of us all. Yes; there is
really no end to the consolations that women find in
modern life. Indeed, I have not mentioned the most
important one."

"What is that, Harry?" said the lad, listlessly.

"Oh, the obvious consolation. Taking some one
else's admirer when one loses one's own. In good
society that always whitewashes a woman. But really,
Dorian, how different Sibyl Vane must have been
from all the women one meets! There is something
to me quite beautiful about her death. I am glad
I am living in a century when such wonders happen. They make one believe in the reality of the
things we all play with, such as romance, passion,
and love."

"I was terribly cruel to her. You forget that."

"I am afraid that woman appreciate cruelty,
downright cruelty, more than anything else. They
have wonderfully primitive instincts. We have
emancipated them, but they remain slaves looking
for their masters, all the same. They love being
dominated. I am sure you were splendid. I have never
seen you really and absolutely angry, but I can fancy
how delightful you looked. And, after all, you said

something to me the day before yesterday that seemed to me at the time to be merely fanciful, but that I see now was absolutely true, and it holds the key to everything."

" What was that, Harry ? "

" You said to me that Sibyl Vane represented to you all the heroines of romance—that she was Desdemona one night, and Ophelia the other ; that if she died as Juliet, she came to life as Imogen."

" She will never come to life again now," muttered the lad, burying his face in his hands.

" No, she will never come to life. She has played her last part. But you must think of that lonely death in the tawdry dressing-room simply as a strange lurid fragment from some Jacobean tragedy, as a wonderful scene from Webster, or Ford, or Cyril Tourneur. The girl never really lived, and so she has never really died. To you at least, she was always a dream, a phantom that flitted through Shakespeare's plays and left them lovelier for its presence, a reed through which Shakespeare's music sounded richer and more full of joy. The moment she touched actual life, she marred it, and it marred her, and so she passed away. Mourn for Ophelia, if you like. Put ashes on your head because Cordelia was strangled. Cry out against Heaven because the daughter of Brabantio died. But don't waste your tears over Sibyl Vane. She was less real than they are."

There was a silence. The evening darkened in the room. Noiselessly, and with silver feet, the shadows crept in from the garden. The colours faded wearily out of things.

After some time Dorian Gray looked up. " You have explained me to myself, Harry," he murmured, with something of a sigh of relief. " I felt all that you have said, but somehow I was afraid of it, and I could not express it to myself. How well you know me ! But we will not talk again of what has happened. It has been a marvellous experience. That is all. I wonder if life has still in store for me anything as marvellous."

"Life has everything in store for you, Dorian. There is nothing that you, with your extraordinary good looks, will not be able to do."

"But suppose, Harry, I became haggard, and old, and wrinkled? What then?"

"Ah, then," said Lord Henry, rising to go—" then, my dear Dorian, you would have to fight for your victories. As it is, they are brought to you. No, you must keep your good looks. We live in an age that reads too much to be wise, and that thinks too much to be beautiful. We cannot spare you. And now you had better dress, and drive down to the club. We are rather late, as it is."

"I think I shall join you at the Opera, Harry. I feel too tired to eat anything. What is the number of your sister's box?"

"Twenty-seven, I believe. It is on the grand tier. You will see her name on the door. But I am sorry you won't come and dine."

"I don't feel up to it," said Dorian, listlessly. "But I am awfully obliged to you for all that you have said to me. You are certainly my best friend. No one has ever understood me as you have."

"We are only at the beginning of our friendship, Dorian," answered Lord Henry, shaking him by the hand. "Good-bye. I shall see you before nine-thirty, I hope. Remember, Patti is singing."

As he closed the door behind him, Dorian Gray touched the bell, and in a few minutes Victor appeared with the lamps and drew the blinds down. He waited impatiently for him to go. The man seemed to take an interminable time over everything.

As soon as he had left, he rushed to the screen, and drew it back. No; there was no further change in the picture. It had received the news of Sibyl Vane's death before he had known of it himself. It was conscious of the events of life as they occurred. The vicious cruelty that marred the fine lines of the mouth had, no doubt, appeared at the very moment that the girl had drunk the poison, whatever it was. Or was it indifferent to results? Did it merely take cognizance of what passed within the soul? He wondered, and hoped that some day he would see the change taking place before his very eyes, shuddering as he hoped it.

Poor Sibyl! What a romance it had all been! She had often mimicked death on the stage. Then Death himself had touched her, and taken her with him. How had she played that dreadful last scene? Had she cursed him, as she died? No; she had died for love of him, and love would always be a sacrament to him now. She had atoned for everything, by the sacrifice she had made of her life. He would not think any more of what she had made him go through, on that horrible night at the theatre. When he thought of her, it would be as a wonderful tragic figure sent on to the world's stage to show the supreme reality of Love. A wonderful tragic figure? Tears came to his eyes as he remembered her child-like look, and winsome fanciful ways, and shy tremulous grace. He brushed them away hastily, and looked again at the picture.

He felt that the time had really come for making his choice. Or had his choice already been made? Yes, life had decided that for him—life, and his own infinite curiosity about life. Eternal youth, infinite passion, pleasures subtle and secret, wild joys and wilder sins—he was to have all these things. The portrait was to bear the burden of his shame: that was all.

A feeling of pain crept over him, as he thought of the desecration that was in store for the fair face on the canvas. Once, in boyish mockery of Narcissus, he had kissed, or feigned to kiss, those painted lips that now smiled so cruelly at him. Morning after morning he had sat before the portrait, wondering at its beauty, almost enamoured of it, as it seemed to him at times. Was it to alter now with every mood to which he yielded? Was it to become a monstrous and loathsome thing, to be hidden away in a locked room, to be shut out from the sunlight that had so often touched to brighter gold the waving wonder of its hair? The pity of it! The pity of it!

For a moment he thought of praying that the horrible sympathy that existed between him and the picture might cease. It had changed in answer to a prayer; perhaps in answer to a prayer it might remain unchanged. And, yet, who, that knew anything about Life, would surrender the chance of remaining always young, however fantastic that chance might be, or with what fateful consequences it might be fraught? Besides, was it really under his control? Had it indeed been prayer that had produced the substitution? Might there not be some curious scientific reason for it all? If thought could exercise its influence upon a living organism, might not thought exercise an influence upon dead and inorganic things? Nay, without thought or conscious desire, might not things external to ourselves vibrate in unison with our moods and passions, atom calling to atom in secret love of strange affinity? But the reason was of no importance. He would never again tempt by a prayer any terrible power. If the picture was to alter, it was to alter. That was all. Why inquire too closely into it?

For there would be a real pleasure in watching it. He would be able to follow his mind into its secret places. This portrait would be to him the most magical of mirrors. As it had revealed to him his own body, so it would reveal to him his own soul. And when winter came upon it, he would still be standing where spring trembles on the verge of summer. When the blood crept from its face, and left behind a pallid mask of chalk with leaden eyes, he would keep the glamour of boyhood. Not one blossom of his loveliness would ever fade. Not one pulse of his life would ever weaken. Like the gods of the Greeks, he would be strong, and fleet, and joyous. What did it matter what happened to the coloured image on the canvas? He would be safe. That was everything.

He drew the screen back into its former place in front of the picture, smiling as he did so, and passed into his bedroom, where his valet was already waiting for him. An hour later he was at the Opera, and Lord Henry was leaning over his chair.

CHAPTER IX

AS he was sitting at breakfast next morning, Basil Hallward was shown into the room.

"I am so glad I have found you, Dorian," he said, gravely. "I called last night, and they told me you were at the Opera. Of course I knew that was impossible. But I wish you had left word where you had really gone to. I passed a dreadful evening, half afraid that one tragedy might be followed by another. I think you might have telegraphed for me when you heard of it first. I read of it quite by chance in a late edition of *The Globe* that I picked up at the club. I came here at once, and was miserable at not finding you. I can't tell you how heart-broken I am about the whole thing. I know what you must suffer. But where were you? Did you go down and see the girl's mother? For a moment I thought of following you there. They gave the address in the paper. Somewhere in the

Euston Road, isn't it ? But I was afraid of intruding
upon a sorrow that I could not lighten. Poor woman !
What a state she must be in ! And her only child,
too ! What did she say about it all ? "

"My dear Basil, how do I know ? " murmured
Dorian Gray, sipping some pale-yellow wine from
a delicate gold-beaded bubble of Venetian glass, and
looking dreadfully bored. " I was at the Opera. You
should have come on there. I met Lady Gwendolen,
Harry's sister, for the first time. We were in her
box. She is perfectly charming ; and Patti sang
divinely. Don't talk about horrid subjects. If one
doesn't talk about a thing, it has never happened.
It is simply expression, as Harry says, that gives
reality to things. I may mention that she was not
the woman's only child. There is a son, a charming
fellow, I believe. But he is not on the stage. He is
a sailor, or something. And now, tell me about yourself and what you are painting."

" You went to the Opera ? " said Hallward, speaking very slowly, and with a strained touch of pain
in his voice. " You went to the Opera while Sibyl
Vane was lying dead in some sordid lodging ? You
can talk to me of other women being charming, and
of Patti singing divinely, before the girl you loved
has even the quiet of a grave to sleep in ? Why,
man, there are horrors in store for that little white
body of hers ! "

"Stop, Basil ! I won't hear it ! " cried Dorian,
leaping to his feet. " You must not tell me about
things. What is done is done. What is past is
past."

" You call yesterday the past ? "

" What has the actual lapse of time got to do with
it ? It is only shallow people who require years to
get rid of an emotion. A man who is master of himself can end a sorrow as easily as he can invent a
pleasure. I don't want to be at the mercy of my

emotions. I want to use them, to enjoy them, and to dominate them."

"Dorian, this is horrible! Something has changed you completely. You look exactly the same wonderful boy who, day after day, used to come down to my studio to sit for his picture. But you were simple, natural, and affectionate then. You were the most unspoiled creature in the whole world. Now, I don't know what has come over you. You talk as if you had no heart, no pity in you. It is all Harry's influence. I see that."

The lad flushed up, and, going to the window, looked out for a few moments on the green, flickering, sun-lashed garden. "I owe a great deal to Harry, Basil," he said, at last—"more than I owe to you. You only taught me to be vain."

"Well, I am punished for that, Dorian—or shall be some day."

"I don't know what you mean, Basil," he exclaimed, turning round. "I don't know what you want. What do you want?"

"I want the Dorian Gray I used to paint," said the artist, sadly.

"Basil," said the lad, going over to him, and putting his hand on his shoulder, "you have come too late. Yesterday when I heard that Sibyl Vane had killed herself——"

"Killed herself! Good heavens! Is there no doubt about that?" cried Hallward, looking up at him with an expression of horror.

"My dear Basil! Surely you don't think it was a vulgar accident? Of course she killed herself."

The elder man buried his face in his hands. "How fearful," he muttered, and a shudder ran through him.

"No," said Dorian Gray, "there is nothing fearful about it. It is one of the great romantic tragedies of the age. As a rule, people who act lead the most

commonplace lives. They are good husbands, or
faithful wives, or something tedious. You know what
I mean—middle-class virtue, and all that kind of
thing. How different Sibyl was! She lived her
finest tragedy. She was always a heroine. The last
night she played—the night you saw her—she acted
badly because she had known the reality of love.
When she knew its unreality, she died, as Juliet
might have died. She passed again into the sphere
of art. There is something of the martyr about her.
Her death has all the pathetic uselessness of martyrdom, all its wasted beauty. But, as I was saying,
you must not think I have not suffered. If you had
come in yesterday at a particular moment—about
half-past five, perhaps, or a quarter to six—you
would have found me in tears. Even Harry, who
was here, who brought me the news, in fact, had no
idea what I was going through. I suffered immensely.
Then it passed away. I cannot repeat an emotion.
No one can, except sentimentalists. And you are
awfully unjust, Basil. You come down here to console me. That is charming of you. You find me
consoled, and you are furious. How like a sympathetic person! You remind me of a story Harry
told me about a certain philanthropist who spent
twenty years of his life in trying to get some grievance
redressed, or some unjust law altered—I forget
exactly what it was. Finally he succeeded, and
nothing could exceed his disappointment. He had
absolutely nothing to do, almost died of *ennui*, and
became a confirmed misanthrope. And besides, my
dear old Basil, if you really want to console me,
teach me rather to forget what has happened, or to
see it from the proper artistic point of view. Was
it not Gautier who used to write about *la consolation
des arts*? I remember picking up a little vellum-
covered book in your studio one day and chancing
on that delightful phrase. Well, I am not like that

young man you told me of when we were down at
Marlow together, the young man who used to say
that yellow satin could console one for all the miseries
of life. I love beautiful things that one can touch
and handle. Old brocades, green bronzes, lacquer-
work, carved ivories, exquisite surroundings, luxury,
pomp, there is much to be got from all these. But
the artistic temperament that they create, or at any
rate reveal, is still more to me. To become the spectator of one's own life, as Harry says, is to escape the
suffering of life. I know you are surprised at my
talking to you like this. You have not realised how
I have developed. I was a schoolboy when you knew
me. I am a man now. I have new passions, new
thoughts, new ideas. I am different, but you must
not like me less. I am changed, but you must always
be my friend. Of course I am very fond of Harry.
But I know that you are better than he is. You
are not stronger—you are too much afraid of life—
but you are better. And how happy we used to be
together! Don't leave me, Basil, and don't quarrel
with me. I am what I am. There is nothing more
to be said."

The painter felt strangely moved. The lad was
infinitely dear to him, and his personality had been
the great turning-point in his art. He could not
bear the idea of reproaching him any more. After
all, his indifference was probably merely a mood
that would pass away. There was so much in him
that was good, so much in him that was noble.

"Well, Dorian," he said, at length; with a sad
smile, "I won't speak to you again about this horrible
thing, after to-day. I only trust your name won't
be mentioned in connection with it. The inquest is
to take place this afternoon. Have they summoned
you?"

Dorian shook his head and a look of annoyance
passed over his face at the mention of the word

" inquest." There was something so crude and vulgar about everything of the kind. " They don't know my name," he answered.

" But surely she did ? '

" Only my Christian name, and that I am quite sure she never mentioned to any one. She told me once that they were all rather curious to learn who I was, and that she invariably told them my name was Prince Charming. It was pretty of her. You must do me a drawing of Sibyl, Basil. I should like to have something more of her than the memory of a few kisses and some broken pathetic words."

" I will try and do something, Dorian, if it would please you. But you must come and sit to me yourself again. I can't get on without you."

" I can never sit to you again, Basil. It is impossible ! " he exclaimed, starting back.

The painter stared at him. " My dear boy, what nonsense ! " he cried. " Do you mean to say you don't like what I did of you ? Where is it ? Why have you pulled the screen in front of it ! Let me look at it. It is the best thing I have ever done. Do take the screen away, Dorian. It is simply disgraceful of your servant hiding my work like that. I felt the room looked different as I came in."

" My servant has nothing to do with it, Basil. You don't imagine I let him arrange my room for me ? He settles my flowers for me sometimes—that is all. No ; I did it myself. The light was too strong on the portrait."

" Too strong ! Surely not, my dear fellow ? It is an admirable place for it. Let me see it." And Hallward walked towards the corner of the room.

A cry of terror broke from Dorian Gray's lips, and he rushed between the painter and the screen. " Basil," he said, looking very pale, " you must not look at it. I don't wish you to."

" Not look at my own work ! You are not serious.

Why shouldn't I look at it ? " exclaimed Hallward, laughing.

"If you try to look at it, Basil, on my word of honour I will never speak to you again as long as I live. I am quite serious. I don't offer any explanation, and you are not to ask for any. But, remember, if you touch this screen, everything is over between us."

Hallward was thunderstruck. He looked at Dorian Gray in absolute amazement. He had never seen him like this before. The lad was actually pallid with rage. His hands were clenched, and the pupils of his eyes were like disks of blue fire. He was trembling all over.

" Dorian ! "

" Don't speak ! "

" But what is the matter ? Of course I won't look at it if you don't want me to," he said, rather coldly, turning on his heel, and going over towards the window. " But, really, it seems rather absurd that I shouldn't see my own work, especially as I am going to exhibit it in Paris in the autumn. I shall probably have to give it another coat of varnish before that, so I must see it some day, and why not to-day ? "

" To exhibit it ! You want to exhibit it ? " exclaimed Dorian Gray, a strange sense of terror creeping over him. Was the world going to be shown his secret ? Were people to gape at the mystery of his life ? That was impossible. Something—he did not know what—had to be done at once.

" Yes ; I don't suppose you will object to that. George Petit is going to collect all my best pictures for a special exhibition in the Rue de Sèze, which will open the first week in October. The portrait will only be away a month. I should think you could easily spare it for that time. In fact, you are sure to be out of town. And if you keep it always behind a screen, you can't care much about it."

Dorian Gray passed his hand over his forehead. There were beads of perspiration there. He felt that he was on the brink of a horrible danger. " You told me a month ago that you would never exhibit it," he cried. " Why have you changed your mind ? You people who go in for being consistent have just as many moods as others have. The only difference is that your moods are rather meaningless. You can't have forgotten that you assured me most solemnly that nothing in the world would induce you to send it to any exhibition. You told Harry exactly the same thing." He stopped suddenly, and a gleam of light came into his eyes. He remembered that Lord Henry had said to him once, half seriously and half in jest, " If you want to have a strange quarter of an hour, get Basil to tell you why he won't exhibit your picture. He told me why he wouldn't, and it was a revelation to me." Yes, perhaps Basil, too, had his secret. He would ask him and try.

" Basil," he said, coming over quite close, and looking him straight in the face, " we have each of us a secret. Let me know yours and I shall tell you mine. What was your reason for refusing to exhibit my picture ? "

The painter shuddered in spite of himself. " Dorian, if I told you, you might like me less than you do, and you would certainly laugh at me. I could not bear you doing either of those two things. If you wish me never to look at your picture again, I am content. I have always you to look at. If you wish the best work I have ever done to be hidden from the world, I am satisfied. Your friendship is dearer to me than any fame or reputation."

" No, Basil, you must tell me," insisted Dorian Gray. " I think I have a right to know." His feeling of terror had passed away, and curiosity had taken its place. He was determined to find out Basil Hallward's mystery.

" Let us sit down, Dorian," said the painter, looking troubled. " Let us sit down. And just answer
me one question. Have you noticed in the picture
something curious ?—something that probably at
first did not strike you, but that revealed itself to you
suddenly ? "

" Basil I " cried the lad, clutching the arms of his
chair with trembling hands, and gazing at him with
wild, startled eyes.

" I see you did. Don't speak. Wait till you hear
what I have to say. Dorian, from the moment I
met you, your personality had the most extraordinary
influence over me. I was dominated, soul, brain,
and power by you. You became to me the visible
incarnation of that unseen ideal whose memory haunts
us artists like an exquisite dream. I worshipped
you. I grew jealous of every one to whom you spoke.
I wanted to have you all to myself. I was only happy
when I was with you. When you were away from me
you were still present in my art. . . . Of course
I never let you know anything about this. It would
have been impossible. You would not have understood it. I hardly understood it myself. I only knew
that I had seen perfection face to face, and that the
world had become wonderful to my eyes—too wonderful, perhaps, for in such mad worships there is
peril, the peril of losing them, no less than the peril
of keeping them.   Weeks and weeks went on,
and I grew more and more absorbed in you. Then
came a new development. I had drawn you as Paris
in dainty armour, and as Adonis with huntsman's
cloak and polished boar-spear. Crowned with heavy
lotus-blossoms you had sat on the prow of Adrian's
barge, gazing across the green turbid Nile. You
had leant over the still pool of some Greek woodland,
and seen in the water's silent silver the marvel of your
own face. And it had all been what art should be,
unconscious, ideal, and remote. One day, a fatal day

I sometimes think, I determined to paint a wonderful portrait of you as you actually are, not in the costume of dead ages, but in your own dress and in your own time. Whether it was the Realism of the method, or the mere wonder of your own personality, thus directly presented to me without mist or veil, I cannot tell. But I know that as I worked at it, every flake and film of colour seemed to me to reveal my secret. I grew afraid that others would know of my idolatry. I felt, Dorian, that I had told too much, that I had put too much of myself into it. Then it was that I resolved never to allow the picture to be exhibited. You were a little annoyed ; but then you did not realise all that it meant to me. Harry, to whom I talked about it, laughed at me. But I did not mind that. When the picture was finished, and I sat alone with it, I felt that I was right. . . . Well, after a few days the thing left my studio, and as soon as I had got rid of the intolerable fascination of its presence it seemed to me that I had been foolish in imagining that I had seen anything in it, more than that you were extremely good-looking, and that I could paint. Even now I cannot help feeling that it is a mistake to think that the passion one feels in creation is ever really shown in the work one creates. Art is always more abstract than we fancy. Form and colour tell us of form and colour—that is all. It often seems to me that art conceals the artist far more completely than it ever reveals him. And so when I got this offer from Paris I determined to make your portrait the principal thing in my exhibition. It never occurred to me that you would refuse. I see now that you were right. The picture cannot be shown. You must not be angry with me, Dorian, for what I have told you. As I said to Harry, once, you are made to be worshipped."

Dorian Gray drew a long breath. The colour came back to his cheeks, and a smile played about his

lips. The peril was over. He was safe for the time.
Yet he could not help feeling infinite pity for the
painter who had just made this strange confession
to him, and wondered if he himself would ever be
so dominated by the personality of a friend. Lord
Henry had the charm of being very dangerous. But
that was all. He was too clever and too cynical to
be really fond of. Would there ever be some one who
would fill him with a strange idolatry ? Was that
one of the things that life had in store ?

" It is extraordinary to me, Dorian," said Hallward, " that you should have seen this in the portrait.
Did you really see it ? "

" I saw something in it," he answered, " something
that seemed to me very curious."

" Well, you don't mind my looking at the thing
now ? "

Dorian shook his head. " You must not ask me
that, Basil. I could not possibly let you stand in
front of that picture."

" You will some day, surely ? "

" Never."

" Well, perhaps you are right. And now good-bye,
Dorian. You have been the one person in my life
who has really influenced my art. Whatever I have
done that is good, I owe to you. Ah ! you don't know
what it cost me to tell you all that I have told you."

" My dear Basil," said Dorian, " what have you
told me ? Simply that you felt that you admired
me too much. That is not even a compliment."

" It was not intended as a compliment. It was a
confession. Now that I have made it, something
seems to have gone out of me. Perhaps one should
never put one's worship into words."

" It was a very disappointing confession."

" Why, what did you expect, Dorian ? You didn't
see anything else in the picture, did you ? There was
nothing else to see ? "

" No; there was nothing else to see. Why do you ask ? But you mustn't talk about worship. It is foolish. You and I are friends, Basil, and we must always remain so."

" You have got Harry," said the painter, sadly.

" Oh, Harry ! " cried the lad, with a ripple of laughter. " Harry spends his days in saying what is incredible, and his evenings in doing what is improbable. Just the sort of life I would like to lead. But still I don't think I would go to Harry if I were in trouble. I would sooner go to you, Basil."

" You will sit to me again ? "

" Impossible ! "

" You spoil my life as an artist by refusing, Dorian. No man came across two ideal things. Few come across one."

" I can't explain it to you, Basil, but I must never sit to you again. There is something fatal about a portrait. It has a life of its own. I will come and have tea with you. That will be just as pleasant."

" Pleasanter for you, I am afraid," murmured Hallward, regretfully. " And now good-bye. I am sorry you won't let me look at the picture once again. But that can't be helped. I quite understand what you feel about it."

As he left the room, Dorian Gray smiled to himself. Poor Basil ! How little he knew of the true reason ! And how strange it was that, instead of having been forced to reveal his own secret, he had succeeded, almost by chance, in wresting a secret from his friend ! How much that strange confession explained to him ! The painter's absurd fits of jealousy, his wild devotion, his extravagant panegyrics, his curious reticences— he understood them all now, and he felt sorry. There seemed to him to be something tragic in a friendship so coloured by romance.

He sighed, and touched the bell. The portrait must be hidden away at all costs. He could not

run such a risk of discovery again. It had been mad
of him to have allowed the thing to remain, even
for an hour, in a room to which any of his friends
had access.

CHAPTER X

WHEN his servant entered, he looked at
him steadfastly, and wondered if he
had thought of peering behind the screen.
The man was quite impassive, and waited for
his orders. Dorian lit a cigarette, and walked over
to the glass and glanced into it. He could see the
reflection of Victor's face perfectly. It was like a
placid mask of servility. There was nothing to be
afraid of, there. Yet he thought it best to be on his
guard.

Speaking very slowly, he told him to tell the housekeeper that he wanted to see her, and then to go to
the frame-maker and ask him to send two of his men
round at once. It seemed to him that as the man
left the room his eyes wandered in the direction of the
screen. Or was that merely his own fancy?

After a few moments, in her black silk dress, with
old-fashioned thread mittens on her wrinkled hands,
Mrs. Leaf bustled into the library. He asked her for
the key of the schoolroom.

" The old schoolroom, Mr. Dorian ? " she exclaimed.
" Why, it is full of dust. I must get it arranged, and
put straight before you go into it. It is not fit for you
to see, sir. It is not, indeed."

" I don't want it put straight, Leaf. I only want
the key."

" Well, sir, you'll be covered with cobwebs if you
go into it. Why, it hasn't been opened for nearly
five years, not since his lordship died."

He winced at the mention of his grandfather. He

had hateful memories of him. "That does not matter," he aswered. "I simply want to see the place—that is all. Give me the key."

"And here is the key, sir," said the old lady, going over the contents of her bunch with tremulously uncertain hands. "Here is the key. I'll have it off the bunch in a moment. But you don't think of living up there, sir, and you so comfortable here?"

"No, no," he cried, petulantly. "Thank you, Leaf. That will do."

She lingered for a few moments, and was garrulous over some detail of the household. He sighed, and told her to manage things as she thought best. She left the room, wreathed in smiles.

As the door closed, Dorian put the key in his pocket, and looked round the room. His eye fell on a large, purple satin coverlet heavily embroidered with gold, a splendid piece of late seventeenth-century Venetian work that his grandfather had found in a convent near Bologna. Yes, that would serve to wrap the dreadful thing in. It had perhaps served often as a pall for the dead. Now it was to hide something that had a corruption of its own, worse than the corruption of death itself—something that would breed horrors and yet would never die. What the worm was to the corpse, his sins would be to the painted image on the canvas. They would mar its beauty, and eat away its grace. They would defile it, and make it shameful. And yet the thing would still live on It would be always alive.

He shuddered, and for a moment he regretted that he had not told Basil the true reason why he had wished to hide the picture away. Basil would have helped him to resist Lord Henry's influence, and the still more poisonous influences that came from his own temperament. The love that he bore him— for it was really love—had nothing in it that was not noble and intellectual. It was not that mere physical

admiration of beauty that is born of the senses, and
that dies when the senses tire. It was such love as
Michael Angelo had known, and Montaigne, and
Winckelmann, and Shakespeare himself. Yes, Basil
could have saved him. But it was too late now. The
past could always be annihilated. Regret, denial, or
forgetfulness could do that. But the future was
inevitable. There were passions in him that would
find their terrible outlet, dreams that would make the
shadow of their evil real.

He took up from the couch the great purple-and-
gold texture that covered it, and, holding it in his
hands, passed behind the screen. Was the face on
the canvas viler than before ? It seemed to him that
it was unchanged ; and yet his loathing of it was
intensified. Gold hair, blue eyes, and rose-red lips—
they all were there. It was simply the expression
that had altered. That was horrible in its cruelty.
Compared to what he saw in it of censure or rebuke,
how shallow Basil's reproaches about Sibyl Vane
had been !—how shallow, and of what little account !
His own soul was looking out at him from the canvas
and calling him to judgment. A look of pain came
across him, and he flung the rich pall over the picture.
As he did so, a knock came to the door. He passed
out as his servant entered.

" The persons are here, Monsieur."

He felt that the man must be got rid of at once.
He must not be allowed to know where the picture
was being taken to. There was something sly about
him, and he had thoughtful, treacherous eyes. Sitting
down at the writing-table, he scribbled a note to Lord
Henry, asking him to send him round something to
read, and reminding him that they were to meet at
eight-fifteen that evening.

" Wait for an answer," he said, handing it to him,
" and show the men in here."

In two or three minutes there was another knock,

and Mr. Hubbard himself, the celebrated frame-maker of South Audley Street, came in with a somewhat rough-looking young assistant. Mr. Hubbard was a florid, red-whiskered little man, whose admiration for art was considerably tempered by the inveterate impecuniosity of most of the artists who dealt with him. As a rule, he never left his shop. He waited for people to come to him. But he always made an exception in favour of Dorian Gray. There was something about Dorian that charmed everybody. It was a pleasure even to see him.

" What can I do for you, Mr. Gray ? " he said, rubbing his fat freckled hands. " I thought I would do myself the honour of coming round in person. I have just got a beauty of a frame, sir. Picked it up at a sale. Old Florentine. Came from Fonthill, I believe. Admirably suited for a religious subject, Mr Gray."

" I am so sorry you have given yourself the trouble of coming round, Mr. Hubbard. I shall certainly drop in and look at the frame—though I don't go in much at present for religious art—but to-day I only want a picture carried to the top of the house for me. It is rather heavy, so I thought I would ask you to lend me a couple of your men."

" No trouble at all, Mr. Gray. I am delighted to be of any service to you. Which is the work of art, sir ? "

" This," replied Dorian, moving the screen back. " Can you move it, covering and all, just as it is ? I don't want it to get scratched going upstairs."

" There will be no difficulty, sir," said the genial frame-maker, beginning, with the aid of his assistant, to unhook the picture from the long brass chains by which it was suspended. " And, now, where shall we carry it to, Mr. Gray ? "

" I will show you the way, Mr. Hubbard, if you will kindly follow me. Or perhaps you had better go in front. I am afraid it is right at the top of the house. We will go up by the front staircase, as it is wider."

He held the door open for them, and they passed out into the hall and began the ascent. The elaborate character of the frame had made the picture extremely bulky, and now and then, in spite of the obsequious protests of Mr. Hubbard, who had the true tradesman's spirited dislike of seeing a gentleman doing anything useful, Dorian put his hand to it so as to help them.

" Something of a load to carry, sir," gasped the little man, when they reached the top landing. And he wiped his shiny forehead.

" I am afraid it is rather heavy," murmured Dorian, as he unlocked the door that opened into the room that was to keep for him the curious secret of his life and hide his soul from the eyes of men.

He had not entered the place for more than four years—not, indeed, since he had used it first as a play-room when he was a child, and then as a study when he grew somewhat older. It was a large, well-proportioned room, which had been specially built by the last Lord Kelso for the use of the little grandson whom, for his strange likeness to his mother, and also for other reasons, he had always hated and desired to keep at a distance. It appeared to Dorian to have but little changed. There was the huge Italian *cassone*, with its fantastically-painted panels and its tarnished gilt mouldings, in which he had so often hidden himself as a boy. There the satinwood bookcase filled with his dog-eared school-books. On the wall behind it was hanging the same ragged Flemish tapestry, where a faded king and queen were playing chess in a garden, while a company of hawkers rode by, carrying hooded birds on their gauntleted wrists. How well he remembered it all! Every moment of his lonely childhood came back to him as he looked round. He recalled the stainless purity of his boyish life, and it seemed horrible to him that it was here

the fatal portrait was to be hidden away. How little
he had thought, in those dead days, of all that was in
store for him !

But there was no other place in the house so secure
from prying eyes as this. He had the key, and no
one else could enter it. Beneath its purple pall, the
face painted on the canvas could grow bestial, sodden,
and unclean. What did it matter ? No one could
see it. He himself would not see it. Why should
he watch the hideous corruption of his soul ? He
kept his youth—that was enough. And, besides,
might not his nature grow finer, after all ? There
was no reason that the future should be so full of shame.
Some love might come across his life, and purify him,
and shield him from those sins that seemed to be
already stirring in spirit and in flesh—those curious
unpictured sins whose very mystery lent them their
subtlety and their charm. Perhaps, some day, the
cruel look would have passed away from the scarlet
sensitive mouth, and he might show to the world
Basil Hallward's masterpiece.

No ; that was impossible. Hour by hour, and week
by week, the thing upon the canvas was growing old.
It might escape the hideousness of sin, but the hideousness of age was in store for it. The cheeks would
become hollow or flaccid. Yellow crow's-feet would
creep round the fading eyes and make them horrible.
The hair would lose its brightness, the mouth would
gape or droop, would be foolish or gross, as the mouths
of old men are. There would be the wrinkled throat,
the cold, blue-veined hands, the twisted body, that
he remembered in the grandfather who had been so
stern to him in his boyhood. The picture had to be
concealed. There was no help for it.

" Bring it in, Mr. Hubbard, please," he said, wearily,
turning round. " I am sorry I kept you so long. I
was thinking of something else."

" Always glad to have a rest, Mr. Gray," answered

the frame-maker, who was still gasping for breath.
" Where shall we put it, sir ? "

" Oh, anywhere. Here : this will do. I don't want
to have it hung up. Just lean it against the wall.
Thanks."

" Might one look at the work of art, sir ? "

Dorian started. " It would not interest you, Mr.
Hubbard," he said, keeping his eye on the man.
He felt ready to leap upon him and fling him to the
ground if he dared to lift the gorgeous hanging that
concealed the secret of his life. " I shan't trouble
you any more now. I am much obliged for your kindness in coming round."

" Not at all, not at all, Mr. Gray. Ever ready to
do anything for you, sir." And Mr. Hubbard tramped
downstairs, followed by the assistant, who glanced
back at Dorian with a look of shy wonder in his rough,
uncomely face. He had never seen any one so marvellous.

When the sound of their footseps had died away,
Dorian locked the door, and put the key in his pocket.
He felt safe now. No one would ever look upon the
horrible thing. No eye but his would ever see his
shame.

On reaching the library he found that it was just
after five o'clock, and that the tea had been already
brought up. On a little table of dark perfumed wood
thickly encrusted with nacre, a present from Lady
Radley, his guardian's wife, a pretty professional
invalid, who had spent the preceding winter in Cairo,
was lying a note from Lord Henry, and beside it was
a book bound in yellow paper, the cover slightly torn
and the edges soiled. A copy of the third edition of
The St. James's Gazette had been placed on the tea-
tray. It was evident that Victor had returned. He
wondered if he had met the men in the hall as they
were leaving the house, and had wormed out of them
what they had been doing. He would be sure to miss

the picture—had no doubt missed it already, while he had been laying the tea things. The screen had not been set back, and a blank space was visible on the wall. Perhaps some night he might find him creeping upstairs and trying to force the door of the room. It was a horrible thing to have a spy in one's house. He had heard of rich men who had been blackmailed all their lives by some servant who had read a letter, or overheard a conversation, or picked up a card with an address, or found beneath a pillow a withered flower or a shred of crumpled lace.

He sighed, and, having poured himself out some tea, opened Lord Henry's note. It was simply to say that he sent him round the evening paper, and a book that might interest him, and that he would be at the club at eight-fifteen. He opened *The St. James's* languidly, and looked through it. A red pencil-mark on the fifth page caught his eye. It drew attention to the following paragraph :—

" INQUEST ON AN ACTRESS.—An inquest was held this morning at the Bell Tavern, Hoxton Road, by Mr. Danby, the District Coroner, on the body of Sibyl Vane, a young actress recently engaged at the Royal Theatre, Holborn. A verdict of death by misadventure was returned. Considerable sympathy was expressed for the mother of the deceased, who was greatly affected during the giving of her own evidence, and that of Dr. Birrell, who had made the post-mortem examination of the deceased."

He frowned, and, tearing the paper in two, went across the room and flung the pieces away. How ugly it all was ! And how horribly real ugliness made things ! He felt a little annoyed with Lord Henry for having sent him the report. And it was certainly stupid of him to have marked it with red pencil. Victor might have read it. The man knew more than enough English for that.

Perhaps he had read it, and had begun to suspect something. And, yet, what did it matter? What had Dorian Gray to do with Sibyl Vane's death? There was nothing to fear. Dorian Gray had not killed her.

His eye fell on the yellow book that Lord Henry had sent him. What was it, he wondered. He went towards the little pearl-coloured octagonal stand, that had always looked to him like the work of some strange Egyptian bees that wrought in silver, and taking up the volume, flung himself into an arm-chair, and began to turn over the leaves. After a few minutes he became absorbed. It was the strangest book that he had ever read. It seemed to him that in exquisite raiment, and to the delicate sound of flutes, the sins of the world were passing in dumb show before him. Things that he had dimly dreamed of were suddenly made real to him. Things of which he had never dreamed were gradually revealed.

It was a novel without a plot, and with only one character, being, indeed, simply a psychological study of a certain young Parisian, who spent his life trying to realise in the nineteenth century all the passions and modes of thought that belonged to every century except his own, and to sum up, as it were, in himself the various moods through which the world-spirit had ever passed, loving for their mere artificiality those renunciations that men have unwisely called virtue, as much as those natural rebellions that wise men still call sin. The style in which it was written was that curious jewelled style, vivid and obscure at once, full of argot and of archaisms, of technical expressions and of elaborate paraphrases, that characterises the work of some of the finest artists of the French school of *Symbolistes*. There were in it metaphors as monstrous as orchids, and as subtle in colour. The life of the senses was described in the terms of mystical philo-sophy. One hardly knew at times whether one was reading the spiritual ecstasies of some mediæval saint or the morbid confessions of a modern sinner. It was a poisonous book. The heavy odour of incense seemed to cling about its pages and to trouble the brain. The mere cadence of the sentences, the subtle monotony of their music, so full as it was of complex refrains and movements elaborately repeated, produced in the mind of the lad, as he passed from chapter to chapter, a form of reverie, a malady of dreaming, that made him unconscious of the falling day and creeping shadows.

Cloudless, and pierced by one solitary star, a copper-green sky gleamed through the windows. He read on by its wan light till he could read no more. Then, after his valet had reminded him several times of the lateness of the hour, he got up, and, going into the next room, placed the book on the little Florentine table that always stood at his bedside, and began to dress for dinner.

It was almost nine o'clock before he reached the club, where he found Lord Henry sitting alone, in the morning-room, looking very much bored.

" I am so sorry, Harry," he cried, " but really it is entirely your fault. That book you sent me so fascinated me that I forgot how the time was going."

" Yes : I thought you would like it," replied his host, rising from his chair.

" I didn't say I liked it, Harry. I said it fascinated me. There is a great difference."

" Ah, you have discovered that ? " murmured Lord Henry. And they passed into the dining-room.

CHAPTER XI

FOR years, Dorian Gray could not free himself from the influence of this book. Or perhaps it would be more accurate to say that he never sought to free himself from it. He procured from Paris no less than nine large-paper copies of the first edition, and had them bound in different colours, so that they might suit his various moods and the changing fancies of a nature over which he seemed, at times, to have almost entirely lost control. The hero, the wonderful young Parisian, in whom the romantic and the scientific temperaments were so strangely blended, became to him a kind of prefiguring type of himself. And, indeed, the whole book seemed to him to contain the story of his own life, written before he had lived it.

In one point he was more fortunate than the novel's fantastic hero. He never knew—never, indeed, had any cause to know—that somewhat grotesque dread of mirrors, and polished metal surfaces, and still water, which came upon the young Parisian so early in his life, and was occasioned by the sudden decay of a beauty that had once, apparently, been so remarkable. It was with an almost cruel joy—and perhaps in nearly every joy, as certainly in every pleasure, cruelty has its place—that he used to read the latter part of the book, with its really tragic, if somewhat over-emphasised, account of the sorrow and despair of one who had himself lost what in others, and in the world, he had most dearly valued.

For the wonderful beauty that had so fascinated Basil Hallward, and many others besides him, seemed never to leave him. Even those who had heard the most evil things against him, and from time to time

strange rumours about his mode of life crept through
London and became the chatter of the clubs, could not
believe anything to his dishonour when they saw him.
He had always the look of one who had kept himself
unspotted from the world. Men who talked grossly
became silent when Dorian Gray entered the room.
There was something in the purity of his face that re-
buked them. His mere presence seemed to recall to
them the memory of the innocence that they had
tarnished. They wondered how one so charming
and graceful as he was could have escaped the stain of
an age that was at once sordid and sensual.

Often, on returning home from one of those mysterious and prolonged absences that gave rise to such
strange conjecture among those who were his friends,
or thought that they were so, he himself would creep
upstairs to the locked room, open the door with the
key that never left him now, and stand, with a mirror,
in front of the portrait that Basil Hallward had
painted of him, looking now at the evil and ageing
face on the canvas, and now at the fair young face that
laughed back at him from the polished glass. The
very sharpness of the contrast used to quicken his
sense of pleasure. He grew more and more enamoured
of his own beauty, more and more interested in the
corruption of his own soul. He would examine with
minute care, and sometimes with a monstrous and
terrible delight, the hideous lines that seared the
wrinkling forehead, or crawled around the heavy sensual mouth, wondering sometimes which were the
more horrible, the signs of sin or the signs of age.
He would place his white hands beside the coarse
bloated hands of the picture, and smile. He mocked
the misshapen body and the failing limbs.

There were moments, indeed, at night, when,
lying sleepless in his own delicately-scented chamber,
or in the sordid room of the little ill-famed tavern
near the Docks, which, under an assumed name, and

in disguise, it was his habit to frequent, he would
think of the ruin he had brought upon his soul, with
a pity that was all the more poignant because it
was purely selfish. But moments such as these were
rare. That curiosity about life which Lord Henry
had first stirred in him, as they sat together in the
garden of their friend, seemed to increase with gratification. The more he knew, the more he desired to
know. He had mad hungers that grew more ravenous
as he fed them.

Yet he was not really reckless, at any rate in his
relations to society. Once or twice every month
during the winter, and on each Wednesday evening
while the season lasted, he would throw open to the
world his beautiful house and have the most celebrated musicians of the day to charm his guests with
the wonders of their art. His little dinners, in the
settling of which Lord Henry always assisted him,
were noted as much for the careful selection and placing of those invited, as for the exquisite taste shown
in the decoration of the table, with its subtle symphonic arrangements of exotic flowers, and embroidered
cloths, and antique plate of gold and silver. Indeed,
there were many, especially among the very young
men, who saw, or fancied that they saw, in Dorian
Gray, the true realisation of a type of which they had
often dreamed in Eton or Oxford days, a type that was
to combine something of the real culture of the scholar
with all the grace and distinction and perfect manner
of a citizen of the world. To them he seemed to be of
the company of those whom Dante describes as having
sought to " make themselves perfect by the worship
of beauty." Like Gautier, he was one for whom " the
visible world existed."

And, certainly, to him Life itself was the first,
the greatest, of the arts, and for it all the other arts
seemed to be but a preparation. Fashion, by which
what is really fantastic becomes for a moment

universal, and Dandyism, which, in its own way, is an attempt to assert the absolute modernity of beauty, had, of course, their fascination for him. His mode of dressing, and the particular styles that from time to time he affected, had their marked influence on the young exquisites of the Mayfair balls and Pall Mall club windows, who copied him in everything that he did, and tried to reproduce the accidental charm of his graceful, though to him only half-serious, fopperies.

For, while he was but too ready to accept the position that was almost immediately offered to him on his coming of age, and found, indeed, a subtle pleasure in the thought that he might really become to the London of his own day what to imperial Neronian Rome the author of the *Satyricon* once had been, yet in his inmost heart he desired to be something more than a mere *arbiter elegantiarum*, to be consulted on the wearing of a jewel, or the knotting of a necktie, or the conduct of a cane. He sought to elaborate some new scheme of life that would have its reasoned philosophy and its ordered principles, and find in the spiritualising of the senses its highest realisation.

The worship of the senses has often, and with much justice, been decried, men feeling a natural instinct of terror about passions and sensations that seem stronger than themselves, and that they are conscious of sharing with the less highly organised forms of existence. But it appeared to Dorian Gray that the true nature of the senses had never been understood, and that they had remained savage and animal merely because the world had sought to starve them into submission or to kill them by pain, instead of aiming at making them elements of a new spirituality, of which a fine instinct for beauty was to be the dominant characteristic. As he looked back upon man moving through History, he was haunted by a feeling of loss. So much had been surrendered ! And to such little purpose ! There had been mad wilful rejections, monstrous forms of self-torture and self-denial, whose origin was fear, and whose result was a degradation infinitely more terrible than that fancied degradation from which, in their ignorance, they had sought to escape. Nature, in her wonderful irony, driving out the anchorite to feed with the wild animals of the desert and giving to the hermit the beasts of the field as his companions.

Yes: there was to be, as Lord Henry had prophesied, a new Hedonism that was to recreate life, and to save it from that harsh, uncomely puritanism that is having, in our own day, its curious revival. It was to have its service of the intellect, certainly; yet, it was never to accept any theory or system that would involve the sacrifice of any mode of passionate experience. Its aim, indeed, was to be experience itself, and not the fruits of experience, sweet or bitter as they might be. Of the asceticism that deadens the senses, as of the vulgar profligacy that dulls them, it was to know nothing. But it was to teach man to concentrate himself upon the moments of a life that is itself but a moment.

There are few of us who have not sometimes wakened before dawn, either after one of those dreamless nights that make us almost enamoured of death, or one of those nights of horror and misshapen joy, when through the chambers of the brain sweep phantoms more terrible than reality itself, and instinct with that vivid life that lurks in all grotesques, and that lends to Gothic art its enduring vitality, this art being, one might fancy, especially the art of those whose minds have been troubled with the malady of reverie. Gradually white fingers creep through the curtains, and they appear to tremble. In black fantastic shapes, dumb shadows crawl into the corners of the room, and crouch there. Outside, there is the stirring of birds among the leaves, or the sound of men going forth to their work, or the sigh and sob of the wind coming down from the hills, and wandering

round the silent house, as though it feared to wake the
sleepers, and yet must needs call forth sleep from
her purple cave. Veil after veil of thin dusky gauze
is lifted, and by degrees the forms and colours of
things are restored to them, and we watch the dawn
remaking the world in its antique pattern. The wan
mirrors get back their mimic life. The flameless
tapers stand where we had left them, and beside
them lies the half-cut book that we had been studying,
or the wired flower that we had worn at the ball, or
the letter that we had been afraid to read, or that
we had read too often. Nothing seems to us changed.
Out of the unreal shadows of the night comes back
the real life that we had known. We have to resume
it where we had left off, and there steals over us a
terrible sense of the necessity for the continuance of
energy in the same wearisome round of stereotyped
habits, or a wild longing, it may be, that our eyelids
might open some morning upon a world that had been
refashioned anew in the darkness for our pleasure,
a world in which things would have fresh shapes
and colours, and be changed, or have other secrets,
a world in which the past would have little or no
place, or survive, at any rate, in no conscious form
of obligation or regret, the remembrance even of joy
having its bitterness, and the memories of pleasure
their pain.

It was the creation of such worlds as these that
seemed to Dorian Gray to be the true object, or
amongst the true objects, of life ; and in his search
for sensations that would be at once new and delightful, and possess that element of strangeness that is
so essential to romance, he would often adopt certain
modes of thought that he knew to be really alien to
his nature, abandon himself to their subtle influences,
and then, having, as it were, caught their colour and
satisfied his intellectual curiosity, leave them with
that curious indifference that is not incompatible with

a real ardour of temperament, and that indeed, according to certain modern psychologists, is often a condition of it.

It was rumoured of him once that he was about to join the Roman Catholic communion ; and certainly the Roman ritual had always a great attraction for him. The daily sacrifice, more awful really than all the sacrifices of the antique world, stirred him as much by its superb rejection of the evidence of the senses as by the primitive simplicity of its elements and the eternal pathos of the human tragedy that it sought to symbolise. He loved to kneel down on the cold marble pavement, and watch the priest, in his stiff flowered vestment, slowly and with white hands moving aside the veil of the tabernacle, or raising aloft the jewelled lantern-shaped monstrance with that pallid wafer that at times, one would fain think, is indeed the " *panis cælestis*," the bread of angels, or, robed in the garments of the Passion of Christ, breaking the Host into the chalice, and smiting his breast for his sins. The fuming censers, that the grave boys, in their lace and scarlet, tossed into the air like great gilt flowers, had their subtle fascination for him. As he passed out, he used to look with wonder at the black confessionals, and long to sit in the dim shadow of one of them and listen to men and women whispering through the worn grating the true story of their lives.

But he never fell into the error of arresting his intellectual development by any formal acceptance of creed or system, or of mistaking, for a house in which to live, an inn that is but suitable for the sojourn of a night, or for a few hours of a night in which there are no stars and the moon is in travail. Mysticism, with its marvellous power of making common things strange to us, and the subtle antinomianism that always seems to accompany it, moved him for a season ; and for a season he inclined to the

materialistic doctrines of the *Darwinismus* movement
in Germany, and found a curious pleasure in tracing the
thoughts and passions of men to some pearly cell in
the brain, or some white nerve in the body, delighting
in the conception of the absolute dependence of the
spirit on certain physical conditions, morbid or
healthy, normal or diseased. Yet, as has been said
of him before, no theory of life seemed to him to be
of any importance compared with life itself. He felt
keenly conscious of how barren all intellectual speculation is when separated from action and experiment.
He knew that the senses, no less than the soul, have
their spiritual mysteries to reveal.

And so he would now study perfumes, and the
secrets of their manufacture, distilling heavily-scented
oils, and burning odorous gums from the East. He
saw that there was no mood of the mind that had not
its counterpart in the sensuous life, and set himself
to discover their true relation, wondering what there
was in frankincense that made one mystical, and in
ambergris that stirred one's passions, and in violets
that woke the memory of dead romances, and in musk
that troubled the brain, and in champak that stained
the imagination ; and seeking often to elaborate a
real psychology of perfumes, and to estimate the
several influences of sweet-smelling roots, and scented
pollen-laden flowers, or aromatic balms, and of dark
and fragrant woods, of spikenard that sickens, of
hovenia that makes men mad, and of aloes that are
said to be able to expel melancholy from the soul.

At another time he devoted himself entirely to
music, and in a long latticed room, with a vermilion-
and-gold ceiling and walls of olive-green lacquer, he
used to give curious concerts, in which mad gypsies
tore wild music from little zithers, or grave yellow-
shawled Tunisians plucked at the strained strings of
monstrous lutes, while grinning negroes beat mono-
tonously upon copper drums, and, crouching upon

scarlet mats, slim turbaned Indians blew through long pipes of reed or brass, and charmed, or feigned to charm, great hooded snakes and horrible horned adders. The harsh intervals and shrill discords of barbaric music stirred him at times when Schubert's grace, and Chopin's beautiful sorrows, and the mighty harmonies of Beethoven himself, fell unheeded on his ear. He collected together from all parts of the world the strangest instruments that could be found, either in the tombs of dead nations or among the few savage tribes that have survived contact with Western civilisations, and loved to touch and try them. He had the mysterious *furuparis* of the Rio Negro Indians, that women are not allowed to look at, and that even youths may not see till they have been subjected to fasting and scourging, and the earthen jars of the Peruvians that have the shrill cries of birds, and flutes of human bones such as Alfonso de Ovalle heard in Chili, and the sonorous green jaspers that are found near Cuzco and give forth a note of singular sweetness. He had painted gourds filled with pebbles that rattled when they were shaken ; the long *clarin* of the Mexicans, into which the performer does not blow, but through which he inhales the air ; the harsh *ture* of the Amazon tribes, that is sounded by the sentinels who sit all day long in high trees, and can be heard, it is said, at a distance of three leagues ; the *teponazili*, that has two vibrating tongues of wood, and is beaten with sticks that are smeared with an elastic gum obtained from the milky juice of plants ; the *yotl*-bells of the Aztecs, that are hung in clusters like grapes ; and a huge cylindrical drum, covered with the skins of great serpents, like the one that Bernal Diaz saw when he went with Cortes into the Mexican temple, and of whose doleful sound he has left us so vivid a description. The fantastic character of these instruments fascinated him, and he felt a curious delight in the thought that Art, like Nature, has her monsters, things of bestial shape and with hideous voices. Yet, after some time, he wearied of them, and would sit in his box at the Opera, either alone or with Lord Henry, listening in rapt pleasure to " Tannhäuser," and seeing in the prelude to that great work of art a presentation of the tragedy of his own soul.

On one occasion he took up the study of jewels, and appeared at a costume ball as Anne de Joyeuse, Admiral of France, in a dress covered with five hundred and sixty pearls. This taste enthralled him for years, and, indeed, may be said never to have left him. He would often spend a whole day settling and resettling in their cases the various stones that he had collected, such as the olive-green chrysoberyl that turns red by lamplight, the cymophane with its wire-like line of silver, the pistachio-coloured peridot, rose-pink and wine-yellow topazes, carbuncles of fiery scarlet with tremulous four-rayed stars, flame-red cinnamon-stones, orange and violet spinels, and amethysts with their alternate layers of ruby and sapphire. He loved the red gold of the sunstone, and the moonstone's pearly whiteness, and the broken rainbow of the milky opal. He procured from Amsterdam three emeralds of extraordinary size and richness of colour, and had a turquoise de la vieille roche that was the envy of all the connoisseurs.

He discovered wonderful stories, also, about jewels. In Alphonso's Clericalis Disciplina a serpent was mentioned with eyes of real jacinth, and in the romantic history of Alexander, the Conqueror of Emathia was said to have found in the vale of Jordon snakes " with collars of real emeralds growing in their backs." There was a gem in the brain of the dragon, Philostratus told us, and " by the exhibition of golden letters and a scarlet robe " the monster could be thrown into a magical sleep, and slain. According to the great alchemist, Pierre de Boniface, the dia-

mond rendered a man invisible, and the agate of India
made him eloquent. The cornelian appeased anger,
and the hyacinth provoked sleep, and the amethyst
drove away the fumes of wine. The garnet cast out
demons, and the hydropicus deprived the moon of her
colour. The selenite waxed and waned with the
moon, and the meloceus, that discovers thieves, could
be affected only by the blood of kids. Leonardus
Camillus had seen a white stone taken from the brain
of a newly-killed toad, that was a certain antidote
against poison. The bezoar, that was found in the
heart of the Arabian deer, was a charm that could
cure the plague. In the nests of Arabian birds was
the aspilates, that, according to Democritus, kept the
wearer from any danger by fire.

The King of Ceilan rode through his city with a
large ruby in his hand, at the ceremony of his coronation. The gates of the palace of John the Priest
were " made of sardius, with the horn of the horned
snake inwrought, so that no man might bring poison
within." Over the gable were " two golden apples,
in which were two carbuncles," so that the gold might
shine by day, and the carbuncles by night. In Lodge's
strange romance *A Margarite of America* it was
stated that in the chamber of the queen one could
behold " all the chaste ladies of the world, inchased
out of silver, looking through fair mirrours of chry-
solites, carbuncles, sapphires, and greene emeraults."
Marco Polo had seen the inhabitants of Zipangu
place rose-coloured pearls in the mouths of the dead.
A sea-monster had been enamoured of the pearl
that the diver brought to King Perozes, and had
slain the thief, and mourned for seven moons over its
loss. When the Huns lured the king into the great
pit, he flung it away—Procopius tells the story—nor
was it ever found again, though the Emperor Anas-
tasius offered five hundred-weight of gold pieces for it.
The King of Malabar had shown to a certain Venetian

a rosary of three hundred and four pearls, one for every god that he worshipped.

When the Duke de Valentinois, son of Alexander VI., visited Louis XII. of France, his horse was loaded with gold leaves, according to Brantôme, and his cap had double rows of rubies that threw out a great light. Charles of England had ridden in stirrups hung with four hundred and twenty-one diamonds. Richard II. had a coat, valued at thirty thousand marks, which was covered with balas rubies. Hall described Henry VIII., on his way to the Tower previous to his coronation, as wearing " a jacket of raised gold, the placard embroidered with diamonds and other rich stones, and a great bauderike about his neck of large balasses." The favourites of James I. wore earrings of emeralds set in gold filigrane. Edward II. gave to Piers Gaveston a suit of red-gold armour studded with jacinths, a collar of gold roses set with turquoise-stones, and a skull-cap *parsemé* with pearls. Henry II. wore jewelled gloves reaching to the elbow, and had a hawk-glove sewn with twelve rubies and fifty-two great orients. The ducal hat of Charles the Rash, the last Duke of Burgundy of his race, was hung with pear-shaped pearls, and studded with sapphires.

How exquisite life had once been ! How gorgeous in its pomp and decoration ! Even to read of the luxury of the dead was wonderful.

Then he turned his attention to embroideries, and to the tapestries that performed the office of frescoes in the chill rooms of the Northern nations of Europe. As he investigated the subject—and he always had an extraordinary faculty of becoming absolutely absorbed for the moment in whatever he took up—he was almost saddened by the reflection of the ruin that Time brought on beautiful and wonderful things. He, at any rate, had escaped that. Summer followed summer, and the yellow jonquils bloomed and died many times, and nights of horror repeated the story

of their shame, but he was unchanged. No winter
marred his face or stained his flower-like bloom.
How different it was with material things ! Where
had they passed to ? Where was the great crocus-
coloured robe, on which the gods fought against the
giants, that had been worked by brown girls for the
pleasure of Athena ? Where, the huge velarium that
Nero had stretched across the Colosseum at Rome,
that Titan sail of purple on which was represented
the starry sky, and Apollo driving a chariot drawn by
white gilt-reined steeds ? He longed to see the curious
table-napkins wrought for the Priest of the Sun,
on which were displayed all the dainties and viands
that could be wanted for a feast ; the mortuary
cloth of King Chilperic, with its three hundred golden
bees ; the fantastic robes that excited the indignation
of the Bishop of Pontus, and were figured with " lions,
panthers, bears, dogs, forests, rocks, hunters—all,
in fact, that a painter can copy from nature ; " and
the coat that Charles of Orleans once wore, on the
sleeves of which were embroidered the verses of a song
beginning " *Madame, je suis tout joyeux,*" the musical
accompaniment of the words being wrought in gold
thread, and each note, of square shape in those days,
formed with four pearls. He read of the room that
was prepared at the palace at Rheims for the use of
Queen Joan of Burgundy, and was decorated with
" Thirteen hundred and twenty-one parrots, made in
broidery, and blazoned with the king's arms, and five
hundred and sixty-one butterflies, whose wings were
similarly ornamented with the arms of the queen,
the whole worked in gold." Catherine de Médicis
had a mourning-bed made for her of black velvet
powdered with crescents and suns. Its curtains were
of damask, with leafy wreaths and garlands, figured
upon a gold and silver ground, and fringed along the
edges with broideries of pearls, and it stood in a room
hung with rows of the queens' devices in cut black

velvet upon cloth of silver. Louis XIV. had gold
embroidered caryatides fifteen feet high in his apartment. The state bed of Sobieski, King of Poland,
was made of Smyrna gold brocade embroidered in
turquoises with verses from the Koran. Its supports
were of silver gilt, beautifully chased, and profusely
set with enamelled and jewelled medallions. It had
been taken from the Turkish camp before Vienna,
and the standard of Mohammed had stood beneath
the tremulous gilt of its canopy.

And so, for a whole year, he sought to accumulate
the most exquisite specimens that he could find of
textile and embroidered work, getting the dainty
Delhi muslins, finely wrought with gold-thread palmates, and stitched over with iridescent beetles'
wings ; the Dacca gauzes, that from their trans-
parency are known in the East as " woven air," and
" running water," and " evening dew " ; strange
figured cloths from Java ; elaborate yellow Chinese
hangings ; books bound in tawny satins or fair blue
silks, and wrought with *fleurs de lys*, birds, and images ;
veils of *lacis* worked in Hungary point ; Sicilian brocades, and stiff Spanish velvets ; Georgian work with
its gilt coins, and Japanese *Foukousas* with their green-
toned golds and their marvellously-plumaged birds.

He had a special passion, also, for ecclesiastical
vestments, as indeed he had for everything connected with the service of the Church. In the long
cedar chests that lined the west gallery of his house
he had stored away many rare and beautiful specimens
of what is really the raiment of the Bride of Christ,
who must wear purple and jewels and fine linen that
she may hide the pallid macerated body that is worn
by the suffering that she seeks for, and wounded by
self-inflicted pain. He possessed a gorgeous cope of
crimson silk and gold-thread damask, figured with a
repeating pattern of golden pomegranates set in six-
petalled formal blossoms, beyond which on either side

was the pine-apple device wrought in seed-pearls.
The orphreys were divided into panels representing
scenes from the life of the Virgin, and the coronation
of the Virgin was figured in coloured silks upon the
hood. This was Italian work of the fifteenth century.
Another cope was of green velvet, embroidered with
heart-shaped groups of acanthus-leaves, from which
spread long-stemmed white blossoms, the details of
which were picked out with silver thread and coloured
crystals. The morse bore a seraph's head in gold-
thread raised work. The orphreys were woven in a
diaper of red and gold silk, and were starred with
medallions of many saints and martyrs, among whom
was St. Sebastian. He had chasubles, also, of amber-
coloured silk, and blue silk and gold brocade, and yellow
silk damask and cloth of gold, figured with repre-
sentations of the Passion and Crucifixion of Christ,
and embroidered with lions and peacocks and other
emblems ; dalmatics of white satin and pink silk
damask, decorated with tulips and dolphins and *fleurs
de lys* ; altar frontals of crimson velvet and blue
linen ; and many corporals, chalice-veils, and sudaria.
In the mystic offices to which such things were put,
there was something that quickened his imagination.

For these treasures, and everything that he collected
in his lovely house, were to be to him means of forgetfulness, modes by which he could escape, for a
season, from the fear that seemed to him at times to
be almost too great to be borne. Upon the walls of
the lonely locked room where he had spent so much of
his boyhood, he had hung with his own hands the
terrible portrait whose changing features showed him
the real degradation of his life, and in front of it had
draped the purple-and-gold pall as a curtain. For
weeks he would not go there, would forget the hideous
painted thing, and get back his light heart, his wonderful joyousness, his passionate absorption in mere
existence. Then, suddenly, some night he would creep

out of the house, go down to dreadful places near
Blue Gate Fields, and stay there, day after day, until
he was driven away. On his return he would sit in
front of the picture, sometimes loathing it and himself,
but filled, at other times, with that pride of individualism that is half the fascination of sin, and smiling
with secret pleasure, at the misshapen shadow that
had to bear the burden that should have been his own.

After a few years he could not endure to be long
out of England, and gave up the villa that he had
shared at Trouville with Lord Henry, as well as the
little white walled-in house at Algiers where they had
more than once spent the winter. He hated to be
separated from the picture that was such a part of
his life, and was also afraid that during his absence
some one might gain access to the room, in spite of the
elaborate bars that he had caused to be placed upon
the door.

He was quite conscious that this would tell them
nothing. It was true that the portrait still preserved,
under all the foulness and ugliness of the face, its
marked likeness to himself ; but what could they
learn from that ? He would laugh at any one who
tried to taunt him. He had not painted it. What
was it to him how vile and full of shame it looked ?
Even if he told them, would they believe it ?

Yet he was afraid. Sometimes when he was
down at his great house in Nottinghamshire, entertaining the fashionable young men of his own rank
who were his chief companions, and astounding the
county by the wanton luxury and gorgeous splendour
of his mode of life, he would suddenly leave his guests
and rush back to town to see that the door had not
been tampered with, and that the picture was still
there. What if it should be stolen ? The mere thought
made him cold with horror. Surely the world would
know his secret then. Perhaps the world already
suspected it.

For, while he fascinated many, there were not a few who distrusted him. He was very nearly black-balled at a West End club of which his birth and social position fully entitled him to become a member, and it was said that on one occasion when he was brought by a friend into the smoking-room of the Churchill, the Duke of Berwick and another gentleman got up in a marked manner and went out. Curious stories became current about him after he had passed his twenty-fifth year. It was rumoured that he had been seen brawling with foreign sailors in a low den in the distant parts of Whitechapel, and that he con-sorted with thieves and coiners and knew the mysteries of their trade. His extraordinary absences became notorious, and, when he used to reappear again in society, men would whisper to each other in corners, or pass him with a sneer, or look at him with cold searching eyes, as though they were determined to discover his secret.

Of such insolences and attempted slights he, of course, took no notice, and in the opinion of most people his frank debonair manner, his charming boyish smile, and the infinite grace of that wonderful youth that seemed never to leave him, were in them-selves a sufficient answer to the calumnies, for so they termed them, that were circulated about him. It was remarked, however, that some of those who had been most intimate with him appeared, after a time, to shun him. Women who had wildly adored him, and for his sake had braved all social censure and set convention at defiance, were seen to grow pallid with shame or horror if Dorian Gray entered the room.

Yet these whispered scandals only increased, in the eyes of many, his strange and dangerous charm. His great wealth was a certain element of security. Society, civilised society at least, is never very ready to believe anything to the detriment of those who are both rich and fascinating. It feels instinctively that manners are of more importance than morals, and, in its opinion, the highest respectability is of much less value than the possession of a good *chef*. And, after all, it is a very poor consolation to be told that the man who has given one a bad dinner, or poor wine, is irreproachable in his private life. Even the cardinal virtues cannot atone for half-cold *entrées*, as Lord Henry remarked once, in a discussion on the subject ; and there is possibly a good deal to be said for his view. For the canons of good society are, or should be, the same as the canons of art. Form is absolutely essential to it. It should have the dignity of a ceremony, as well as its unreality, and should combine the insincere character of a romantic play with the wit and beauty that make such plays delightful to us. Is insincerity such a terrible thing ? I think not. It is merely a method by which we can multiply our personalities.

Such, at any rate, was Dorian Gray's opinion. He used to wonder at the shallow psychology of those who conceive the Ego in man as a thing simple, permanent, reliable, and of one essence. To him, man was a being with myriad lives and myriad sensations, a complex multiform creature that bore within itself strange legacies of thought and passion, and whose very flesh was tainted with the monstrous maladies of the dead. He loved to stroll through the gaunt cold picture-gallery of his country house and look at the various portraits of those whose blood flowed in his veins. Here was Philip Herbert, described by Francis Osborne, in his *Memoires on the Reigns of Queen Elizabeth and King James*, as one who was "caressed by the Court for his handsome face, which kept him not long company." Was it young Herbert's life that he sometimes led ? Had some strange poisonous germ crept from body to body till it had reached his own ? Was it some dim sense of that ruined grace that had made him so suddenly,

and almost without cause, give utterance, in Basil Hallward's studio, to the mad prayer that had so changed
his life? Here, in gold-embroidered red doublet,
jewelled surcoat, and gilt-edged ruff and wrist-bands,
stood Sir Anthony Sherard, with his silver-and-black
armour piled at his feet. What had this man's legacy
been? Had the lover of Giovanna of Naples bequeathed him some inheritance of sin and shame?
were his own actions merely the dreams that the dead
man had not dared to realise? Here, from the fading
canvas, smiled Lady Elizabeth Devereux, in her
gauze hood, pearl stomacher, and pink slashed sleeves.
A flower was in her right hand, and her left clasped
an enamelled collar of white and damask roses. On
a table by her side lay a mandolin and an apple.
There were large green rosettes upon her little pointed
shoes. He knew her life, and the strange stories
that were told about her lovers. Had he something
of her temperament in him? These oval heavy-lidded
eyes seemed to look curiously at him. What of George
Willoughby, with his powdered hair and fantastic
patches? How evil he looked! The face was saturnine
and swarthy, and the sensual lips seemed to be twisted
with disdain. Delicate lace ruffles fell over the lean
yellow hands that were so over-laden with rings.
He had been a macaroni of the eighteenth century,
and the friend, in his youth, of Lord Ferrars. What
of the second Lord Beckenham, the companion of
the Prince Regent in his wildest days, and one of the
witnesses at the secret marriage with Mrs. Fitzherbert?
How proud and handsome he was, with his chestnut
curls and insolent pose! What passions had he bequeathed? The world had looked upon him as infamous. He had led the orgies at Carlton House.
The star of the Garter glittered upon his breast.
Beside him hung the portrait of his wife, a pallid,
thin-lipped woman in black. Her blood, also, stirred
within him. How curious it all seemed! And his

mother with her Lady Hamilton face, and her moist
wine-dashed lips—he knew what he had got from
her. He had got from her his beauty, and his passion
for the beauty of others. She laughed at him in
her loose Bacchante dress. There were vine leaves
in her hair. The purple spilled from the cup she was
holding. The carnations of the painting had withered,
but the eyes were still wonderful in their depth and
brilliancy of colour. They seemed to follow him
wherever he went.

Yet one had ancestors in literature, as well as in
one's own race, nearer perhaps in type and temperament, many of them, and certainly with an influence
of which one was more absolutely conscious. There
were times when it appeared to Dorian Gray that the
whole of history was merely the record of his own life,
not as he had lived it in act and circumstance, but
as his imagination had created it for him, as it had
been in his brain and in his passions. He felt that he
had known them all, those strange terrible figures that
had passed across the stage of the world and made
sin so marvellous, and evil so full of subtlety. It
seemed to him that in some mysterious way their
lives had been his own.

The hero of the wonderful novel that had so influenced his life had himself known this curious fancy.
In the seventh chapter he tells how, crowned with
laurel, lest lightning might strike him, he had sat, as
Tiberius, in a garden at Capri, reading the shameful
books of Elephantis, while dwarfs and peacocks
strutted round him, and the flute-player mocked the
swinger of the censer ; and, as Caligula, had caroused
with the green-shirted jockeys in their stables and
supped in an ivory manger with a jewel-frontleted
horse ; and, as Domitian, had wandered through a
corridor lined with marble mirrors, looking round
with haggard eyes for the reflection of the dagger that
was to end his days, and sick with that ennui, that

terrible *tædium vitæ*, that comes on those to whom
life denies nothing ; and had peered through a clear
emerald at the red shambles of the Circus, and then,
in a litter of pearl and purple drawn by silver-shod
mules, been carried through the Street of Pomegranates to a House of Gold, and heard men cry
on Nero Cæsar as he passed by ; and, as Elagabalus,
had painted his face with colours, and plied the distaff
among the women, and brought the Moon from
Carthage, and given her in mystic marriage to the Sun.

Over and over again Dorian used to read this
fantastic chapter, and the two chapters immediately
following, in which, as in some curious tapestries or
cunningly-wrought enamels, were pictured the awful
and beautiful forms of those whom Vice and Blood
and Weariness had made monstrous or mad : Filippo,
Duke of Milan, who slew his wife, and painted her lips
with a scarlet poison that her lover might suck death
from the dead thing he fondled ; Pietro Barbi, the
Venetian, known as Paul the Second, who sought
in his vanity to assume the title of Formosus, and
whose tiara, valued at two hundred thousand florins,
was bought at the price of a terrible sin ; Gian Maria
Visconti, who used hounds to chase living men, and
whose murdered body was covered with roses by a
harlot who had loved him ; the Borgia on his white
horse, with Fratricide riding beside him, and his
mantle stained with the blood of Perotto ; Pietro
Riario, the young Cardinal Archbishop of Florence,
child and minion of Sixtus IV., whose beauty was
equalled only by his debauchery, and who received
Leonora of Aragon in a pavilion of white and crimson
silk, filled with nymphs and centaurs, and gilded a
boy that he might serve at the feast as Ganymede or
Hylas ; Ezzelin, whose melancholy could be cured
only by the spectacle of death, and who had a passion
for red blood, as other men have for red wine—the
son of the Fiend, as was reported, and one who had

cheated his father at dice when gambling with him
for his own soul ; Giambattista Cibo, who in mockery
took the name of Innocent, and into whose torpid
veins the blood of three lads was infused by a Jewish
doctor ; Sigismondo Malatesta, the lover of Isotta,
and the lord of Rimini, whose effigy was burned at
Rome as the enemy of God and man, who strangled
Polyssena with a napkin, and gave poison to Ginevra
d'Este in a cup of emerald, and in honour of a shameful passion built a pagan church for Christian worship ; Charles VI., who had so wildly adored his
brother's wife that a leper had warned him of the
insanity that was coming on him, and who, when his
brain had sickened and grown strange, could only be
soothed by Saracen cards painted with the images of
Love and Death and Madness ; and, in his trimmed
jerkin and jewelled cap and acanthus-like curls,
Grifonetto Baglioni, who slew Astorre with his bride,
and Simonetto with his page, and whose comeliness was
such that, as he lay dying in the yellow piazza of
Perugia, those who had hated him could not choose
but weep, and Atlanta, who had cursed him, blessed
him.

There was a horrible fascination in them all. He
saw them at night, and they troubled his imagination
in the day. The Renaissance knew of strange manners
of poisoning—poisoning by a helmet and a lighted
torch, by an embroidered glove and a jewelled fan,
by a gilded pomander and by an amber chain. Dorian
Gray had been poisoned by a book. There were moments when he looked on evil simply as a mode through
which he could realise his conception of the beautiful.

CHAPTER XII

IT was on the ninth of November, the eve of his own thirty-eighth birthday, as he often remembered afterwards.

He was walking home about eleven o'clock from Lord Henry's, where he had been dining, and was wrapped in heavy furs, as the night was cold and foggy. At the corner of Grosvenor Square and South Audley Street a man passed him in the mist, walking very fast, and with the collar of his grey ulster turned up. He had a bag in his hand. Dorian recognised him. It was Basil Hallward. A strange sense of fear, for which he could not account, came over him. He made no sign of recognition, and went on quickly in the direction of his own house.

But Hallward had seen him. Dorian heard him first stopping on the pavement, and then hurrying after him. In a few moments his hand was on his arm.

"Dorian! What an extraordinary piece of luck! I have been waiting for you in your library ever since nine o'clock. Finally I took pity on your tired servant, and told him to go to bed, as he let me out. I am off to Paris by the midnight train, and I particularly wanted to see you before I left. I thought it was you, or rather your fur coat, as you passed me. But I wasn't quite sure. Didn't you recognise me?"

"In this fog, my dear Basil? Why, I can't even recognise Grosvenor Square. I believe my house is somewhere about here, but I don't feel at all certain about it. I am sorry you are going away, as I have not seen you for ages. But I suppose you will be back soon?"

"No: I am going to be out of England for six months. I intend to take a studio in Paris, and shut myself up till I have finished a great picture I have in my head. However, it wasn't about myself I wanted to talk. Here we are at your door. Let me come in for a moment. I have something to say to you."

" I shall be charmed. But won't you miss your train ? " said Dorian Gray, languidly, as he passed up the steps and opened the door with his latchkey.

The lamp-light struggled out through the fog, and Hallward looked at his watch. " I have heaps of time," he answered. " The train doesn't go till twelve-fifteen, and it is only just eleven. In fact, I was on my way to the club to look for you, when I met you. You see, I shan't have any delay about luggage, as I have sent on my heavy things. All I have with me is in this bag, and I can easily get to Victoria in twenty minutes."

Dorian looked at him and smiled. " What a way for a fashionable painter to travel ! A Gladstone bag, and an ulster ! Come in, or the fog will get into the house. And mind you don't talk about anything serious. Nothing is serious nowadays. At least nothing should be."

Hallward shook his head as he entered, and followed Dorian into the library. There was a bright wood fire blazing in the large open hearth. The lamps were lit, and an open Dutch silver spirit-case stood, with some siphons of soda-water and large cut-glass tumblers, on a little marqueterie table.

" You see your servant made me quite at home, Dorian. He gave me everything I wanted, including your best gold-tipped cigarettes. He is a most hospitable creature. I like him much better than the Frenchman you used to have. What has become of the Frenchman, by the by ? "

Dorian shrugged his shoulders. " I believe he married Lady Radley's maid, and has established her in Paris as an English dressmaker. *Anglomanie* is very fashionable over there now, I hear. It seems silly of the French, doesn't it? But—do you know? —he was not at all a bad servant. I never liked him, but I had nothing to complain about. One often imagines things that are quite absurd. He was really very devoted to me, and seemed quite sorry when he went away. Have another brandy-and-soda? Or would you like hock-and-seltzer? I always take hock-and-seltzer myself. There is sure to be some in the next room."

" Thanks, I won't have anything more," said the painter, taking his cap and coat off, and throwing them on the bag that he had placed in the corner. " And now, my dear fellow, I want to speak to you seriously. Don't frown like that. You make it so much more difficult for me."

" What is it all about? " cried Dorian, in his petulant way, flinging himself down on the sofa. " I hope it is not about myself. I am tired of myself to-night. I should like to be somebody else."

" It is about yourself," answered Hallward, in his grave, deep voice, " and I must say it to you. I shall only keep you half an hour."

Dorian sighed, and lit a cigarette. " Half an hour ! " he murmured.

" It is not much to ask of you, Dorian, and it is entirely for your own sake that I am speaking. I think it right that you should know that the most dreadful things are being said against you in London."

" I don't wish to know anything about them. I love scandals about other people, but scandals about myself don't interest me. They have not got the charm of novelty."

" They must interest you, Dorian. Every gentleman is interested in his good name. You don't want people to talk of you as something vile and degraded. Of course you have your position, and your wealth, and all that kind of thing. But position and wealth

are not everything. Mind you, I don't believe these
rumours at all. At least, I can't believe them when
I see you. Sin is a thing that writes itself across a
man's face. It cannot be concealed. People talk
sometimes of secret vices. There are no such things.
If a wretched man has a vice, it shows itself in the
lines of his mouth, the droop of his eyelids, the moulding of his hands even. Somebody—I won't mention his name, but you know him—came to me last
year to have his portrait done. I had never seen
him before, and had never heard anything about him
at the time, though I have heard a good deal since.
He offered an extravagant price. I refused him.
There was something in the shape of his fingers that I
hated. I know now that I was quite right in what I
fancied about him. His life is dreadful. But you,
Dorian, with your pure, bright, innocent face, and
your marvellous untroubled youth—I can't believe
anything against you. And yet I see you very seldom,
and you never come down to the studio now, and
when I am away from you, and I hear all these
hideous things that people are whispering about you,
I don't know what to say. Why is it, Dorian, that
a man like the Duke of Berwick leaves the room of
a club when you enter it? Why is it that so
many gentlemen in London will neither go to
your house nor invite you to theirs? You used to
be a friend of Lord Staveley. I met him at dinner
last week. Your name happened to come up in conversation, in connection with the miniatures you have
lent to the exhibition at the Dudley. Staveley curled
his lip, and said that you might have the most artistic
tastes, but that you were a man whom no pure-minded
girl should be allowed to know, and whom no chaste
woman should sit in the same room with. I reminded
him that I was a friend of yours, and asked him what
he meant. He told me. He told me right out before
everybody. It was horrible! Why is your friendship

so fatal to young men ? There was that wretched boy in the Guards who committed suicide. You were his great friend. There was Sir Henry Ashton, who had to leave England, with a tarnished name. You and he were inseparable. What about Adrian Singleton, and his dreadful end ? What about Lord Kent's only son, and his career ? I met his father yesterday in St. James's Street. He seemed broken with shame and sorrow. What about the young Duke of Perth ? What sort of life has he got now ? What gentleman would associate with him ? "

" Stop, Basil. You are talking about things of which you know nothing," said Dorian Gray, biting his lip, and with a note of infinite contempt in his voice. " You ask me why Berwick leaves a room when I enter it. It is because I know everything about his life, not because he knows anything about mine. With such blood as he has in his veins, how could his record be clean ? You ask me about Henry Ashton and young Perth. Did I teach the one his vices, and the other his debauchery ? If Kent's silly son takes his wife from the streets what is that to me ? If Adrian Singleton writes his friend's name across a bill, am I his keeper ? I know how people chatter in England. The middle classes air their moral prejudices over their gross dinner-tables, and whisper about what they call the profligacies of their betters in order to try and pretend that they are in smart society, and on intimate terms with the people they slander. In this country it is enough for a man to have distinction and brains for every common tongue to wag against him. And what sort of lives do these people, who pose as being moral, lead themselves ? My dear fellow, you forget that we are in the native land of the hypocrite."

" Dorian," cried Hallward, " that is not the question. England is bad enough, I know, and English society is all wrong. That is the reason why I want

you to be fine. You have not been fine. One had
a right to judge of a man by the effect he has over
his friends. Yours seem to lose all sense of honour,
of goodness, of purity. You have filled them with
a madness for pleasure. They have gone down into
the depths. You led them there. Yes: you led
them there, and yet you can smile, as you are smiling
now. And there is worse behind. I know you and
Harry are inseparable. Surely for that reason, if
for none other, you should not have made his
sister's name a by-word."

" Take care, Basil. You go too far."

" I must speak, and you must listen. You shall
listen. When you met Lady Gwendolen, not a breath
of scandal had ever touched her. Is there a single
decent woman in London now who would drive
with her in the Park? Why, even her children are
not allowed to live with her. Then there are other
stories—stories that you have been seen creeping
at dawn out of dreadful houses and slinking in disguise into the foulest dens in London. Are they true?
Can they be true? When I first heard them, I laughed.
I hear them now, and they make me shudder. What
about your country house, and the life that is led
there? Dorian, you don't know what is said about
you. I won't tell you that I don't want to preach
to you. I remember Harry saying once that every
man who turned himself into an amateur curate for
the moment always began by saying that, and then
proceeded to break his word. I do want to preach
to you. I want you to lead such a life as will make
the world respect you. I want you to have a clean
name and a fair record. I want you to get rid of the
dreadful people you associate with. Don't shrug
your shoulders like that. Don't be so indifferent.
You have a wonderful influence. Let it be for good,
not for evil. They say that you corrupt every one
with whom you become intimate, and that it is quite

sufficient for you to enter a house, for shame of some kind to follow after. I don't know whether it is so or not. How should I know? But it is said of you. I am told things that it seems impossible to doubt. Lord Gloucester was one of my greatest friends at Oxford. He showed me a letter that his wife had written to him when she was dying alone in her villa at Mentone. Your name was implicated in the most terrible confession I ever read. I told him that it was absurd—that I knew you thoroughly, and that you were incapable of anything of the kind. Know you? I wonder do I know you? Before I could answer that, I should have to see your soul."

" To see my soul! " muttered Dorian Gray, starting up from the sofa and turning almost white from fear.

" Yes," answered Hallward, gravely, and with deep-toned sorrow in his voice—" to see your soul. But only God can do that."

A bitter laugh of mockery broke from the lips of the younger man. " You shall see it yourself, to-night! " he cried, seizing a lamp from the table. " Come : it is your own handiwork. Why shouldn't you look at it? You can tell the world all about it afterwards, if you choose. Nobody would believe you. If they did believe you, they would like me all the better for it. I know the age better than you do, though you will prate about it so tediously. Come, I tell you. You have chattered enough about corruption. Now you shall look on it face to face."

There was the madness of pride in every word he uttered. He stamped his foot upon the ground in his boyish insolent manner. He felt a terrible joy at the thought that some one else was to share his secret, and that the man who had painted the portrait that was the origin of all his shame was to be burdened for the rest of his life with the hideous memory of what he had done.

" Yes," he continued, coming closer to him, and looking steadfastly into his stern eyes, " I shall show you my soul. You shall see the thing that you fancy only God can see."

Hallward started back. " This is blasphemy, Dorian ! " he cried. " You must not say things like that. They are horrible, and they don't mean any-thing."

" You think so ? " He laughed again.

" I know so. As for what I said to you to-night, I said it for your good. You know I have been always a staunch friend to you."

" Don't touch me. Finish what you have to say."

A twisted flash of pain shot across the painter's face. He paused for a moment, and a wild feeling of pity came over him. After all, what right had he to pry into the life of Dorian Gray ? If he had done a tithe of what was rumoured about him, how much he must have suffered ! Then he straightened himself up, and walked over to the fireplace, and stood there, looking at the burning logs with their frost-like ashes and their throbbing cores of flame.

" I am waiting, Basil," said the young man, in a hard, clear voice.

He turned round. " What I have to say is this," he cried. " You must give me some answer to these horrible charges that are made against you. If you tell me that they are absolutely untrue from begin-ning to end, I shall believe you. Deny them, Dorian, deny them ! Can't you see what I am going through ? My God ! Don't tell me that you are bad, and corrupt, and shameful."

Dorian Gray smiled. There was a curl of contempt in his lips. " Come upstairs, Basil," he said, quietly. " I keep a diary of my life from day to day, and it never leaves the room in which it is written. I shall show it to you if you come with me."

" I shall come with you, Dorian, if you wish it.

I see I have missed my train. That makes no matter.
I can go to-morrow. But don't ask me to read anything to-night. All I want is a plain answer to my
question."

" That shall be given to you upstairs. I could
not give it here. You will not have to read long."

CHAPTER XIII

HE passed out of the room, and began the ascent,
Basil Hallward following close behind. They
walked softly, as men do instinctively at
night. The lamp cast fantastic shadows on the wall
and staircase. A rising wind made some of the windows
rattle.

When they reached the top landing, Dorian set
the lamp down on the floor, and taking out the key
turned it in the lock. " You insist on knowing,
Basil ? " he asked, in a low voice.

" Yes."

" I am delighted," he answered, smiling. Then
he added, somewhat harshly, " You are the one man
in the world who is entitled to know everything about
me. You have had more to do with my life than you
think : " and, taking up the lamp, he opened the door
and went in. A cold current of air passed them, and
the light shot up for a moment in a flame of murky
orange. He shuddered. " Shut the door behind
you," he whispered, as he placed the lamp on the
table.

Hallward glanced round him, with a puzzled expression. The room looked as if it had not been
lived in for years. A faded Flemish tapestry, a curtained picture, an old Italian *cassone*, and an almost
empty bookcase—that was all that it seemed to
contain, besides a chair and a table. As Dorian

Gray was lighting a half-burned candle that was standing on the mantelshelf, he saw that the whole place was covered with dust, and that the carpet was in holes. A mouse ran scuffling behind the wainscoting. There was a damp odour of mildew.

" So you think that it is only God who sees the soul, Basil ? Draw that curtain back, and you will see mine."

The voice that spoke was cold and cruel. " You are mad, Dorian, or playing a part," muttered Hallward, frowning.

" You won't ? Then 1 must do it myself," said the young man ; and he tore the curtain from its rod, and flung it on the ground.

An exclamation of horror broke from the painter's lips as he saw in the dim light the hideous face on the canvas grinning at him. There was something in its expression that filled him with disgust and loathing. Good heavens ! It was Dorian Gray's own face that he was looking at ! The horror, whatever it was, had not yet entirely spoiled that marvellous beauty. There was still some gold in the thinning hair and some scarlet on the sensual mouth. The sodden eyes had kept something of the loveliness of their blue, the noble curves had not yet completely passed away from chiselled nostrils and from plastic throat. Yes, it was Dorian himself. But who had done it ? He seemed to recognise his own brushwork, and the frame was his own design. The idea was monstrous, yet he felt afraid. He seized the lighted candle, and held it to the picture. In the left-hand corner was his own name, traced in long letters of bright vermilion.

It was some foul parody, some infamous, ignoble satire. He had never done that. Still, it was his own picture !   He knew it, and he felt as if his blood had changed in a moment from fire to sluggish ice. His own picture ! What did it mean ? Why had it altered ?

He turned, and looked at Dorian Gray with the eyes of a sick man. His mouth twitched, and his parched tongue seemed unable to articulate. He passed his hand across his forehead. It was dank with clammy sweat.

The young man was leaning against the mantel-shelf, watching him with that strange expression that one sees on the faces of those who are absorbed in a play when some great artist is acting. There was neither real sorrow in it nor real joy. There was simply the passion of the spectator, with perhaps a flicker of triumph in his eyes. He had taken the flower out of his coat, and was smelling it, or pretending to do so.

" What does this mean ? " cried Hallward, at last. His own voice sounded shrill and curious in his ears.

" Years ago, when I was a boy," said Dorian Gray, crushing the flower in his hand, " you met me, flattered me, and taught me to be vain of my good looks. One day you introduced me to a friend of yours, who explained to me the wonder of youth, and you finished the portrait of me that revealed to me the wonder of beauty. In a mad moment, that, even now, I don't know whether I regret or not, I made a wish, perhaps you would call it a prayer . . ."

" I remember it ! Oh, how well I remember it ! No, the thing is impossible ! The room is damp. Mildew has got into the canvas. The paints I used had some wretched mineral poison in them. I tell you the thing is impossible."

" Ah, what is impossible ? " murmured the young man, going over to the window, and leaning his forehead against the cold, mist-stained glass.

" You told me you had destroyed it."

" I was wrong. It has destroyed me."

" I don't believe it is my picture."

" Can't you see your ideal in it ? " said Dorian, bitterly.

" My ideal, as you call it . . ."

" As you called it."

" There was nothing evil in it, nothing shameful. You were to me such an ideal as I shall never meet again. This is the face of a satyr."

" It is the face of my soul."

" Christ! What a thing I must have worshipped! It has the eyes of a devil."

" Each of us has Heaven and Hell in him, Basil," cried Dorian, with a wild gesture of despair.

Hallward turned again to the portrait, and gazed at it. " My God! If it is true," he exclaimed, " and this is what you have done with your life, why, you must be worse even than those who talk against you fancy you to be!" He held the light up again to the canvas, and examined it. The surface seemed to be quite undisturbed, and as he had left it. It was from within, apparently, that the foulness and horror had come. Through some strange quickening of inner life the leprosies of sin were slowly eating the thing away. The rotting of a corpse in a watery grave was not so fearful.

His hand shook, and the candle fell from its socket on the floor, and lay there sputtering. He placed his foot on it and put it out. Then he flung himself into the rickety chair that was standing by the table and buried his face in his hands.

" Good God, Dorian, what a lesson! What an awful lesson!" There was no answer, but he could hear the young man sobbing at the window. " Pray, Dorian, pray," he murmured. " What is it that one was taught to say in one's boyhood? ' Lead us not into temptation. Forgive us our sins. Wash away our iniquities.' Let us say that together. The prayer of your pride has been answered. The prayer of your repentance will be answered also. I worshipped you too much. We are both punished."

Dorian Gray turned slowly around, and looked at

him with tear-dimmed eyes. " It is too late, Basil,"
he faltered.

" It is never too late, Dorian. Let us kneel down
and try if we cannot remember a prayer. Isn't there
a verse somewhere, ' Though your sins be as scarlet,
yet I will make them as white as snow ' ? "

" Those words mean nothing to me now."

" Hush ! Don't say that. You have done enough
evil in your life. My God ! Don't you see that accursed
thing leering at us ? "

Dorian Gray glanced at the picture, and suddenly
an uncontrollable feeling of hatred for Basil Hallward
came over him, as though it had been suggested to
him by the image on the canvas, whispered into his
ear by those grinning lips. The mad passions of a
hunted animal stirred within him, and he loathed
the man who was seated at the table, more than in
his whole life he had ever loathed anything. He
glanced wildly around. Something glimmered on
the top of the painted chest that faced him. His
eye fell on it. He knew what it was. It was a knife
that he had brought up, some days before, to cut a
piece of cord, and had forgotten to take away with
him. He moved slowly towards it, passing Hallward
as he did so. As soon as he got behind him, he seized
it, and turned round. Hallward stirred in his chair
as if he was going to rise. He rushed at him, and
dug the knife into the great vein that is behind the
ear, crushing the man's head down on the table,
and stabbing again and again.

There was a stifled groan, and the horrible sound
of some one choking with blood. Three times the
outstretched arms shot up convulsively, waving
grotesque stiff-fingered hands in the air. He stabbed
him twice more, but the man did not move. Something began to trickle on the floor. He waited for
a moment, still pressing the head down. Then he
threw the knife on the table, and listened.

He could hear nothing but the drip, drip on the threadbare carpet. He opened the door and went out on the landing. The house was absolutely quiet. No one was about. For a few seconds he stood bending over the balustrade, and peering down into the black seething well of darkness. Then he took out the key and returned to the room, locking himself in as he did so.

The thing was still seated in the chair, straining over the table with bowed head, and humped back, and long fantastic arms. Had it not been for the red jagged tear in the neck, and the clotted black pool that was slowly widening on the table, one would have said that the man was simply asleep.

How quickly it had all been done ! He felt strangely calm, and, walking over to the window, opened it, and stepped out on the balcony. The wind had blown the fog away, and the sky was like a monstrous peacock's tail, starred with myriads of golden eyes. He looked down, and saw the policeman going his rounds and flashing the long beam of his lantern on the doors of the silent houses. The crimson spot of a prowling hansom gleamed at the corner, and then vanished. A woman in a fluttering shawl was creeping slowly by the railings, staggering as she went. Now and then she stopped, and peered back. Once, she began to sing in a hoarse voice. The policeman strolled over and said something to her. She stumbled away, laughing. A bitter blast swept across the Square. The gas-lamps flickered, and became blue, and the leafless trees shook their black iron branches to and fro. He shivered, and went back, closing the window behind him.

Having reached the door, he turned the key, and opened it. He did not even glance at the murdered man. He felt that the secret of the whole thing was not to realise the situation. The friend who had painted the fatal portrait to which all his misery had been due, had gone out of his life. That was enough.

Then he remembered the lamp. It was a rather curious one of Moorish workmanship, made of dull silver inlaid with arabesques of burnished steel, and studded with coarse turquoises. Perhaps it might be missed by his servant, and questions would be asked. He hesitated for a moment, then he turned back and took it from the table. He could not help seeing the dead thing. How still it was! How horribly white the long hands looked! It was like a dreadful wax image.

Having locked the door behind him, he crept quietly downstairs. The woodwork creaked, and seemed to cry out as if in pain. He stopped several times, and waited. No: everything was still. It was merely the sound of his own footsteps.

When he reached the library, he saw the bag and coat in the corner. They must be hidden away somewhere. He unlocked a secret press that was in the wainscoting, a press in which he kept his own curious disguises, and put them into it. He could easily burn them afterwards. Then he pulled out his watch. It was twenty minutes to two.

He sat down, and began to think. Every year—every month, almost—men were strangled in England for what he had done. There had been a madness of murder in the air. Some red star had come too close to the earth. . . . And yet what evidence was there against him? Basil Hallward had left the house at eleven. No one had seen him come in again. Most of the servants were at Selby Royal. His valet had gone to bed. . . . Paris! Yes. It was to Paris that Basil had gone, and by the midnight train, as he had intended. With his curious reserved habits, it would be months before any suspicions would be aroused. Months! Everything could be destroyed long before then.

A sudden thought struck him. He put on his fur coat and hat, and went out into the hall. There he paused, hearing the slow heavy tread of the policeman on the pavement outside, and seeing the flash of the bull's-eye reflected in the window. He waited, and held his breath.

After a few moments he drew back the latch, and slipped out, shutting the door very gently behind him. Then he began ringing the bell. In about five minutes his valet appeared half dressed, and looking very drowsy.

" I am sorry to have had to wake you up, Francis," he said, stepping in ; " but I had forgotten my latch-key. What time is it ? "

" Ten minutes past two, sir," answered the man, looking at the clock and blinking.

" Ten minutes past two ? How horribly late ! You must wake me at nine to-morrow. I have some work to do."

" All right, sir."

" Did any one call this evening ? "

" Mr. Hallward, sir. He stayed here till eleven, and then he went away to catch his train."

" Oh ! I am sorry I didn't see him. Did he leave any message ? "

" No sir, except that he would write to you from Paris, if he did not find you at the club."

" That will do, Francis. Don't forget to call me at nine to-morrow."

" No, sir."

The man shambled down the passage in his slippers.

Dorian Gray threw his hat and coat upon the table, and passed into the library. For a quarter of an hour he walked up and down the room biting his lip, and thinking. Then he took down the Blue Book from one of the shelves, and began to turn over the leaves. " Alan Campbell, 152, Hertford Street, Mayfair." Yes : that was the man he wanted.

CHAPTER XIV

AT nine o'clock the next morning his servant came in with a cup of chocolate on a tray, and opened the shutters. Dorian was sleeping quite peacefully, lying on his right side, with one hand underneath his cheek. He looked like a boy who had been tired out with play, or study.

The man had to touch him twice on the shoulder before he woke, and as he opened his eyes a faint smile passed across his lips, as though he had been lost in some delightful dream. Yet he had not dreamed at all. His night had been untroubled by any images of pleasure or of pain. But youth smiles without any reason. It is one of its chiefest charms.

He turned round, and, leaning upon his elbow, began to sip his chocolate. The mellow November sun came streaming into the room. The sky was bright, and there was a genial warmth in the air. It was almost like a morning in May.

Gradually the events of the preceding night crept with silent blood-stained feet into his brain, and reconstructed themselves there with terrible distinctness. He winced at the memory of all that he had suffered, and for a moment the same curious feeling of loathing for Basil Hallward that had made him kill him as he sat in the chair, came back to him, and he grew cold with passion. The dead man was still sitting there, too, and in the sunlight now. How horrible that was! Such hideous things were for the darkness, not for the day.

He felt that if he brooded on what he had gone through he would sicken or grow mad. There were sins whose fascination was more in the memory than in the doing of them; strange triumphs that gratified the pride more than the passions, and gave to the

intellect a quickened sense of joy, greater than any
joy they brought, or could ever bring, to the senses.
But this was not one of them. It was a thing to be
driven out of the mind, to be drugged with poppies,
to be strangled lest it might strangle one itself.

When the half-hour struck, he passed his hand
across his forehead, and then got up hastily, and
dressed himself with even more than his usual care,
giving a good deal of attention to the choice of his
necktie and scarf-pin, and changing his rings more
than once. He spent a long time also over breakfast,
tasting the various dishes, talking to his valet about
some new liveries that he was thinking of getting made
for the servants at Selby, and going through his
correspondence. At some of the letters he smiled.
Three of them bored him. One he read several times
over, and then tore up with a slight look of annoyance
in his face. " That awful thing, a woman's memory ! "
as Lord Henry had once said.

After he had drunk his cup of black coffee, he wiped
his lips slowly with a napkin, motioned to his servant
to wait, and going over to the table sat down and
wrote two letters. One he put in his pocket, the other
he handed to the valet.

" Take this round to 152, Hertford Street, Francis,
and if Mr. Campbell is out of town, get his address."

As soon as he was alone, he lit a cigarette, and
began sketching upon a piece of paper, drawing first
flowers, and bits of architecture, and then human
faces. Suddenly he remarked that every face that he
drew seemed to have a fantastic likeness to Basil
Hallward. He frowned, and, getting up, went over
to the bookcase and took out a volume at hazard.
He was determined that he would not think about
what had happened until it became absolutely necessary
that he should do so.

When he had stretched himself on the sofa, he
looked at the title-page of the book. It was Gautier's

Emaux et Camées, Charpentier's Japanese-paper edition, with the Jacquemart etching. The binding was of citron-green leather, with a design of gilt trellis-work and dotted pomegranates. It had been given to him by Adrian Singleton. As he turned over the pages his eye fell on the poem about the hand of Lacenaire, the cold yellow hand " *du supplice encore mal lavée,*" with its downy red hairs and its " *doigts de faune.*" He glanced at his own white taper fingers, shuddering slightly in spite of himself, and passed on, till he came to those lovely stanzas upon Venice :—

> " Sur une gamme chromatique,
>   Le sein de perles ruisselant,
>   La Vénus de l'Adriatique
>   Sort de l'eau son corps rose et blanc.

> " Les domes, sur l'azur des ondes
>   Suivant la phrase au pur contour,
>   S'enflent comme des gorges rondes
>   Que soulève un soupir d'amour.

> " L'esquif aborde et me dépose,
>   Jetant son amarre au pilier,
>   Devant une façade rose,
>   Sur le marbre d'un escalier."

How exquisite they were! As one read them, one seemed to be floating down the green water-ways of the pink and pearl city, seated in a black gondola with silver prow and trailing curtains. The mere lines looked to him like those straight lines of turquoise-blue that follow one as one pushes out to the Lido. The sudden flashes of colour reminded him of the gleam of the opal-and-iris-throated birds that flutter round the tall, honey-combed Campanile, or stalk, with such stately grace, through the dim, dust-stained arcades. Leaning back with half-closed eyes, he kept saying over and over to himself :—

> " Devant une façade rose,
>   Sur le marbre d'un escalier."

The whole of Venice was in those two lines. He remembered the autumn that he had passed there, and a wonderful love that had stirred him to mad, delightful follies. There was romance in every place. But Venice, like Oxford, had kept the background for romance, and, to the true romantic, background was everything, or almost everything. Basil had been with him part of the time, and had gone wild over Tintoret. Poor Basil ! what a horrible way for a man to die !

He sighed, and took up the volume again, and tried to forget. He read of the swallows that fly in and out of the little café at Smyrna where the Jadjis sit counting their amber beads and the turbaned merchants smoke their long tasselled pipes and talk gravely to each other ; he read of the Obelisk in the Place de la Concorde that weeps tears of granite in its lonely sunless exile, and longs to be back by the hot lotus-covered Nile, where there are Sphinxes, and rose-red ibises, and white vultures with gilded claws, and crocodiles, with small beryl eyes, that crawl over the green steaming mud ; he began to brood over those verses which, drawing music from kiss-stained marble, tell of that curious statue that Gautier compares to a contralto voice, the " *monstre charmant* " that couches in the porphyry-room of the Louvre. But after a time the book fell from his hand. He grew nervous, and a horrible fit of terror came over him. What if Alan Campbell should be out of England ? Days would elapse before he could come back. Perhaps he might refuse to come. What could he do then ? Every moment was of vital importance.

They had been great friends once, five years before
—almost inseparable, indeed. Then the intimacy
had come suddenly to an end. When they met in
society now, it was only Dorian Gray who smiled;
Alan Campbell never did.

He was an extremely clever young man, though
he had no real appreciation of the visible arts, and
whatever little sense of the beauty of poetry he
possessed he had gained entirely from Dorian. His
dominant intellectual passion was for science. At
Cambridge he had spent a great deal of his time
working in the Laboratory, and had taken a good
class in the Natural Science Tripos of his year. Indeed, he was still devoted to the study of chemistry,
and had a laboratory of his own, in which he used to
shut himself up all day long, greatly to the annoyance
of his mother, who had set her heart on his standing
for Parliament, and had a vague idea that a chemist
was a person who made up prescriptions. He was
an excellent musician, however, as well, and played
both the violin and the piano better than most
amateurs. In fact, it was music that had first brought
him and Dorian Gray together—music and that indefinable attraction that Dorian seemed to be able to
exercise whenever he wished, and indeed exercised
often without being conscious of it. They had met at
Lady Berkshire's the night that Rubinstein played
there, and after that used to be always seen together
at the Opera, and wherever good music was going
on. For eighteen months their intimacy lasted.
Campbell was always either at Selby Royal or in
Grosvenor Square. To him, as to many others,
Dorian Gray was the type of everything that is wonderful and fascinating in life. Whether or not a
quarrel had taken place between them no one ever
knew. But suddenly people remarked that they
scarcely spoke when they met, and that Campbell
seemed always to go away early from any party

at which Dorian Gray was present. He had changed. too—was strangely melancholy at times, appeared almost to dislike hearing music, and would never himself play, giving as his excuse, when he was called upon, that he was so absorbed in science that he had no time left in which to practise. And this was certainly true. Every day he seemed to become more interested in biology, and his name appeared once or twice in some of the scientific reviews, in connection with certain curious experiments.

This was the man Dorian Gray was waiting for. Every second he kept glancing at the clock. As the minutes went by he became horribly agitated. At last he got up, and began to pace up and down the room, looking like a beautiful caged thing. He took long stealthy strides. His hands were curiously cold.

The suspense became unbearable. Time seemed to him to be crawling with feet of lead, while he by monstrous winds was being swept towards the jagged edge of some black cleft of precipice. He knew what was waiting for him there ; saw it indeed, and, shuddering, crushed with dank hands his burning lids as though he would have robbed the very brain of sight, and driven the eyeballs back into their cave. It was useless. The brain had its own food on which it battened, and the imagination, made grotesque by terror, twisted and distorted as a living thing by pain, danced like some foul puppet on a stand, and grinned through moving masks. Then, suddenly, Time stopped for him. Yes : that blind, slow-breathing thing crawled no more, and horrible thoughts, Time being dead, raced nimbly on in front, and dragged a hideous future from its grave, and showed it to him. He stared at it. Its very horror made him stone.

At last the door opened, and his servant entered. He turned glazed eyes upon him.

" Mr. Campbell, sir," said the man.

O.W.-S.T.O

A sigh of relief broke from his parched lips, and the colour came back to his cheeks.

" Ask him to come in at once, Francis." He felt that he was himself again. His mood of cowardice had passed away.

The man bowed, and retired. In a few moments Alan Campbell walked in, looking very stern and rather pale, his pallor being intensified by his coal-black hair and dark eyebrows.

" Alan ! this is kind of you. I thank you for coming."

" I had intended never to enter your house again, Gray. But you said it was a matter of life and death." His voice was hard and cold. He spoke with slow deliberation. There was a look of contempt in the steady searching gaze that he turned on Dorian. He kept his hands in the pockets of his Astrakhan coat, and seemed not to have noticed the gesture with which he had been greeted.

" Yes : it is a matter of life and death, Alan, and to more than one person. Sit down."

Campbell took a chair by the table, and Dorian sat opposite to him. The two men's eyes met. In Dorian's there was infinite pity. He knew that what he was going to do was dreadful.

After a strained moment of silence, he leaned across and said, very quietly, but watching the effect of each word upon the face of him he had sent for, " Alan, in a locked room at the top of this house, a room to which nobody but myself has access, a dead man is seated at a table. He has been dead ten hours now. Don't stir, and don't look at me like that. Who the man is, why he died, how he died, are matters that do not concern you. What you have to do is this——"

" Stop, Gray. I don't want to know anything further. Whether what you have told me is true or not true, doesn't concern me. I entirely decline to be mixed up in your life. Keep your horrible secrets to yourself. They don't interest me any more."

" Alan, they will have to interest you. This one will have to interest you. I am awfully sorry for you, Alan. But I can't help myself. You are the one man who is able to save me. I am forced to bring you into the matter. I have no option. Alan, you are scientific. You know about chemistry, and things of that kind. You have made experiments. What you have got to do is to destroy the thing that is upstairs—to destroy it so that not a vestige of it will be left. Nobody saw this person come into the house. Indeed, at the present moment he is supposed to be in Paris. He will not be missed for months. When he is missed, there must be no trace of him found here. You, Alan, you must change him, and everything that belongs to him, into a handful of ashes that I may scatter in the air."

" You are mad, Dorian."

" Ah ! I was waiting for you to call me Dorian."

" You are mad, I tell you—mad to imagine that I would raise a finger to help you, mad to make this monstrous confession. I will have nothing to do with this matter, whatever it is. Do you think I am going to peril my reputation for you ? What is it to me what devil's work you are up to ? "

" It was suicide, Alan."

" I am glad of that. But who drove him to it ? You, I should fancy."

" Do you still refuse to do this for me ? "

" Of course, I refuse. I will have absolutely nothing to do with it. I don't care what shame comes on you. You deserve it all. I should not be sorry to see you disgraced, publicly disgraced. How dare you ask me, of all men in the world, to mix myself up in this horror ? I should have thought you knew more about people's characters. Your friend Lord Henry Wotton can't have taught you much about psychology, whatever else he has taught you. Nothing will induce me to stir a step to help you. You have come to the wrong man. Go to some of your friends. Don't come to me."

"Alan, it was murder. I killed him. You don't know what he had made me suffer. Whatever my life is, he had more to do with the making or the marring of it than poor Harry has had. He may not have intended it, the result was the same."

"Murder! Good God, Dorian, is that what you have come to? I shall not inform upon you. It is not my business. Besides, without my stirring in the matter, you are certain to be arrested. Nobody ever commits a crime without doing something stupid. But I will have nothing to do with it."

"You must have something to do with it. Wait, wait a moment; listen to me. Only listen, Alan. All I ask of you is to perform a certain scientific experiment. You go to hospitals and dead-houses, and the horrors that you do there don't affect you. If in some hideous dissecting-room or fetid laboratory you found this man lying on a leaden table with red gutters scooped out in it for the blood to flow through, you would simply look upon him as an admirable subject. You would not turn a hair. You would not believe that you were doing anything wrong. On the contrary, you would probably feel that you were benefiting the human race, or increasing the sum of knowledge in the world, or gratifying intellectual curiosity, or something of that kind. What I want you to do is merely what you have often done before. Indeed, to destroy a body must be far less horrible than what you are accustomed to work at. And, remember, it is the only piece of evidence against me. If it is discovered, I am lost; and it is sure to be discovered unless you help me."

"I have no desire to help you. You forget that. I am simply indifferent to the whole thing. It has nothing to do with me."

"Alan, I entreat you. Think of the position I

am in. Just before you came I almost fainted with terror.
You may know terror yourself some day. No! don't
think of that. Look at the matter purely from the
scientific point of view. You don't inquire where the
dead things on which you experiment come from. Don't
inquire now. I have told you too much as it is. But
I beg of you to do this. We were friends once, Alan."

" Don't speak about those days, Dorian : they are
dead."

" The dead linger sometimes. The man upstairs
will not go away. He is sitting at the table with
bowed head and outstretched arms. Alan! Alan!
if you don't come to my assistance I am ruined.
Why, they will hang me, Alan! Don't you understand ? They will hang me for what I have done."

" There is no good in prolonging this scene. I
absolutely refuse to do anything in the matter. It
is insane of you to ask me."

" You refuse ? "

Yes."

" I entreat you, Alan."

" It is useless."

The same look of pity came into Dorian Gray's eyes.
Then he stretched out his hand, took a piece of paper,
and wrote something on it. He read it over twice,
folded it carefully, and pushed it across the table.
Having done this, he got up, and went over to the
window.

Campbell looked at him in surprise, and then took
up the paper, and opened it. As he read it, his face
became ghastly pale, and he fell back in his chair.
A horrible sense of sickness came over him. He felt
as if his heart was beating itself to death in some
empty hollow.

After two or three minutes of terrible silence,
Dorian turned round, and came and stood behind
him, putting his hand upon his shoulder.

" I am so sorry for you, Alan," he murmured,

" but you leave me no alternative. I have a letter
written already. Here it is. You see the address.
If you don't help me, I must send it. If you don't
help me, I will send it. You know what the result
will be. But you are going to help me. It is impossible for you to refuse now. I tried to spare you.
You will do me the justice to admit that. You were
stern, harsh, offensive. You treated me as no man
has ever dared to treat me—no living man, at any
rate. I bore it all. Now it is for me to dictate terms."

Campbell buried his face in his hands, and a shudder
passed through him.

" Yes, it is my turn to dictate terms, Alan. You
know what they are. The thing is quite simple.
Come, don't work yourself into this fever. The thing
has to be done. Face it, and do it."

A groan broke from Campbell's lips, and he shivered
all over. The ticking of the clock on the mantelpiece
seemed to him to be dividing Time into separate atoms
of agony, each of which was too terrible to be borne.
He felt as if an iron ring was being slowly tightened
round his forehead, as if the disgrace with which he
was threatened had already come upon him. The
hand upon his shoulder weighed like a hand of lead.
It was intolerable. It seemed to crush him.

" Come, Alan, you must decide at once."

" I cannot do it," he said, mechanically, as though
words could alter things.

" You must. You have no choice. Don't delay."

He hesitated a moment. " Is there a fire in the
room upstairs ? "

" Yes, there is a gas-fire with asbestos."

" I shall have to go home and get some things from
the laboratory."

" No, Alan, you must not leave the house. Write
out on a sheet of note-paper what you want, and my
servant will take a cab and bring the things back to
you."

Campbell scrawled a few lines, blotted them, and addressed an envelope to his assistant. Dorian took the note up and read it carefully. Then he rang the bell and gave it to his valet, with orders to return as soon as possible, and to bring the things with him.

As the hall door shut, Campbell started nervously, and, having got up from the chair, went over to the chimney-piece. He was shivering with a kind of ague. For nearly twenty minutes, neither of the men spoke. A fly buzzed noisily about the room, and the ticking of the clock was like the beat of a hammer.

As the chime struck one, Campbell turned round, and, looking at Dorian Gray, saw that his eyes were filled with tears. There was something in the purity and refinement of that sad face that seemed to enrage him. " You are infamous, absolutely infamous ! " he muttered.

" Hush, Alan : you have saved my life," said Dorian.

" Your life ? Good heavens ! What a life that is ! You have gone from corruption to corruption, and now you have culminated in crime. In doing what I am going to do, what you force me to do, it is not of your life that I am thinking."

" Ah, Alan," murmured Dorian, with a sigh, " I wish you had a thousandth part of the pity for me that I have for you." He turned away as he spoke, and stood looking out at the garden. Campbell made no answer.

After about ten minutes a knock came to the door, and the servant entered, carrying a large mahogany chest of chemicals, with a long coil of steel and platinum wire and two rather curiously-shaped iron clamps.

" Shall I leave the things here, sir ? " he asked Campbell.

" Yes," said Dorian. " And I am afraid, Francis, that I have another errand for you. What is the name of the man at Richmond who supplies Selby with orchids ? "

" Harden, sir."

" Yes—Harden. You must go down to Richmond
at once, see Harden personally, and tell him to send
twice as many orchids as I ordered, and to have as
few white ones as possible. In fact, I don't want
any white ones. It is a lovely day, Francis, and
Richmond is a very pretty place, otherwise I wouldn't
bother you about it."

" No trouble, sir. At what time shall I be back ? "

Dorian looked at Campbell. " How long will your
experiment take, Alan ? " he said, in a calm, indifferent voice. The presence of a third person in the
room seemed to give him extraordinary courage.

Campbell frowned, and bit his lip. " It will take
about five hours," he answered.

" It will be time enough, then, if you are back at half-
past seven, Francis. Or stay : just leave my things out
for dressing. You can have the evening to yourself.
I am not dining at home, so I shall not want you."

" Thank you, sir," said the man, leaving the room

" Now, Alan, there is not a moment to be lost.
How heavy this chest is ! I'll take it for you. You
bring the other things." He spoke rapidly, and in
an authoritative manner. Campbell felt dominated
by him. They left the room together.

When they reached the top landing, Dorian took
out the key and turned it in the lock. Then he stopped,
and a troubled look came into his eyes. He shuddered.
" I don't think I can go in, Alan," he murmured.

" It is nothing to me. I don't require you," said
Campbell, coldly.

Dorian half opened the door. As he did so, he saw
the face of his portrait leering in the sunlight. On
the floor in front of it the torn curtain was lying. He
remembered that the night before he had forgotten,
for the first time in his life, to hide the fatal canvas,
and was about to rush forward, when he drew back
with a shudder

What was that loathsome red dew that gleamed, wet and glistening, on one of the hands, as though the canvas had sweated blood ? How horrible it was ! —more horrible, it seemed to him for the moment, than the silent thing that he knew was stretched across the table, the thing whose grotesque misshapen shadow on the spotted carpet showed him that it had not stirred, but was still there, as he had left it.

He heaved a deep breath, opened the door a little wider, and with half-closed eyes and averted head walked quickly in, determined that he would not look even once upon the dead man. Then, stooping down, and taking up the gold and purple hanging, he flung it right over the picture.

There he stopped, feeling afraid to turn round, and his eyes fixed themselves on the intricacies of the pattern before him. He heard Campbell bringing in the heavy chest, and the irons, and the other things that he had required for his dreadful work. He began to wonder if he and Basil Hallward had ever met, and, if so, what they had thought of each other.

" Leave me now," said a stern voice behind him.

He turned and hurried out, just conscious that the dead man had been thrust back into the chair, and that Campbell was gazing into a glistening yellow face. As he was going downstairs he heard the key being turned in the lock.

It was long after seven when Campbell came back into the library. He was pale, but absolutely calm. " I have done what you asked me to do," he muttered. " And now, good-bye. Let us never see each other again."

" You have saved me from ruin, Alan. I cannot forget that," said Dorian, simply.

As soon as Campbell had left, he went upstairs. There was a horrible smell of nitric acid in the room. But the thing that had been sitting at the table was gone.

CHAPTER XV

THAT evening, at eight-thirty, exquisitely
dressed and wearing a large button-hole of
Parma violets, Dorian Gray was ushered into
Lady Narborough's drawing-room by bowing servants.
His forehead was throbbing with maddened nerves,
and he felt wildly excited, but his manner as he
bent over his hostess's hand was as easy and graceful as ever. Perhaps one never seems so much at one's
ease as when one has to play a part. Certainly no
one looking at Dorian Gray that night could have
believed that he had passed through a tragedy as
horrible as any tragedy of our age. Those finely-
shaped fingers could never have clutched a knife for
sin, nor those smiling lips have cried out on God
and goodness. He himself could not help wondering
at the calm of his demeanour, and for a moment
felt keenly the terrible pleasure of a double life.

It was a small party, got up rather in a hurry by
Lady Narborough, who was a very clever woman,
with what Lord Henry used to describe as the remains of really remarkable ugliness. She had proved
an excellent wife to one of our most tedious am-
bassadors, and having buried her husband properly
in a marble mausoleum, which she had herself designed, and married off her daughters to some rich,
rather elderly men, she devoted herself now to the
pleasures of French fiction, French cookery, and French
esprit when she could get it.

Dorian was one of her special favourites, and she
always told him that she was extremely glad she had
not met him in early life. " I know, my dear, I should
have fallen madly in love with you," she used to say,
" and thrown my bonnet right over the mills for your
sake. It is most fortunate that you were not thought

of at the time As it was, our bonnets were so unbecoming, and the mills were so occupied in trying to
raise the wind, that I never had even a flirtation with
anybody.   However, that was all Narborough's
fault. He was dreadfully short-sighted, and there is
no pleasure in taking in a husband who never sees
anything.''

Her guests this evening were rather tedious. The
fact was, as she explained to Dorian, behind a very
shabby fan, one of her married daughters had come
up quite suddenly to stay with her, and, to make matters
worse, had actually brought her husband with her.
" I think it is most unkind of her, my dear," she
whispered.   " Of course I go and stay with them
every summer after I come from Homburg, but then
an old woman like me must have fresh air sometimes,
and besides, I really wake them up. You don't know
what an existence they lead down there. It is pure
unadulterated country life.   They get up early,
because they have so much to do, and go to bed early
because they have so little to think about. There
has not been a scandal in the neighbourhood since the
time of Queen Elizabeth, and consequently they all
fall asleep after dinner. You shan't sit next either
of them. You shall sit by me, and amuse me.''

Dorian murmured a graceful compliment, and
looked round the room. Yes : it was certainly a
tedious party. Two of the people he had never seen
before, and the others consisted of Ernest Harrowden,
one of those middle-aged mediocrities so common in
London clubs who have no enemies, but are thoroughly
disliked by their friends ; Lady Ruxton, an over-
dressed woman of forty-seven, with a hooked nose,
who was always trying to get herself compromised,
but was so peculiarly plain that to her great disappointment no one would ever believe anything against
her ; Mrs. Erlynne, a pushing nobody, with a delightful
lisp, and Venetian-red hair ; Lady Alice Chapman,

his hostess's daughter, a dowdy dull girl, with one of those characteristic British faces, that, once seen, are never remembered ; and her husband, a red-cheeked, white-whiskered creature who, like so many of his class, was under the impression that inordinate joviality can atone for an entire lack of ideas.

He was rather sorry he had come, till Lady Narborough, looking at the great ormolu gilt clock that sprawled in gaudy curves on the mauve-draped mantelshelf, exclaimed : " How horrid of Henry Wotton to be so late ! I sent round to him this morning on chance, and he promised faithfully not to disappoint me."

It was some consolation that Harry was to be there, and when the door opened and he heard his slow musical voice lending charm to some insincere apology, he ceased to feel bored.

But at dinner he could not eat anything. Plate after plate went away untasted. Lady Narborough kept scolding him for what she called " an insult to poor Adolphe, who invented the *menu* specially for you," and now and then Lord Henry looked across at him, wondering at his silence and abstracted manner. From time to time the butler filled his glass with champagne. He drank eagerly, and his thirst seemed to increase.

" Dorian," said Lord Henry, at last, as the *chaud-froid* was being handed round, " what is the matter with you to-night ? You are quite out of sorts."

" I believe he is in love," cried Lady Narborough, " and that he is afraid to tell me for fear I should be jealous. He is quite right. I certainly should."

"Dear Lady Narborough," murmured Dorian, smiling, " I have not been in love for a whole week— not, in fact, since Madame de Ferrol left town."

" How you men can fall in love with that woman ! " exclaimed the old lady. " I really cannot understand it."

" It is simply because she remembers you when you were a little girl, Lady Narborough," said Lord Henry. "She is the one link between us and your short frocks."

" She does not remember my short frocks at all, Lord Henry. But I remember her very well at Vienna thirty years ago, and how *décolletée* she was then."

" She is still *décolletée*," he answered, taking an olive in his long fingers ; "and when she is in a very smart gown she looks like an *édition de luxe* of a bad French novel. She is really wonderful, and full of surprises. Her capacity for family affection is extraordinary. When her third husband died, her hair turned quite gold from grief."

" How can you, Harry ! " cried Dorian.

" It is a most romantic explanation," laughed the hostess. "But her third husband, Lord Henry ! You don't mean to say Ferrol is the fourth."

" Certainly, Lady Narborough."

" I don't believe a word of it."

" Well, ask Mr. Gray. He is one of her most intimate friends."

" Is it true, Mr. Gray ? "

" She assures me so, Lady Narborough," said Dorian. " I asked her whether, like Marguerite de Navarre, she had their hearts embalmed and hung at her girdle. She told me she didn't, because none of them had any hearts at all."

" Four husbands ! Upon my word that is *trop de zèle*."

" *Trop d'audace*, I tell her," said Dorian.

" Oh ! she is audacious enough for anything, my dear. And what is Ferrol like ? I don't know him."

" The husbands of very beautiful women belong to the criminal classes," said Lord Henry, sipping his wine.

Lady Narborough hit him with her fan. " Lord

Henry, I am not at all surprised that the world says that you are extremely wicked."

"But what world says that?" asked Lord Henry, elevating his eyebrows. "It can only be the next world. This world and I are on excellent terms."

"Everybody I know says you are very wicked," cried the old lady, shaking her head.

Lord Henry looked serious for some moments. "It is perfectly monstrous," he said, at last, "the way people go about nowadays saying things against one behind one's back that are absolutely and entirely true."

"Isn't he incorrigible?" cried Dorian, leaning forward in his chair.

"I hope so," said his hostess, laughing. "But really if you all worship Madame de Feroll in this ridiculous way, I shall have to marry again so as to be in the fashion."

"You will never marry again, Lady Narborough," broke in Lord Henry. "You were far too happy. When a woman marries again it is because she detested her first husband. When a man marries again, it is because he adored his first wife. Women try their luck; men risk theirs."

"Narborough wasn't perfect," cried the old lady. "If he had been, you would not have loved him, my dear lady," was the rejoinder. "Women love us for our defects. If we have enough of them they will forgive us everything, even our intellects. You will never ask me to dinner again, after saying this, I am afraid, Lady Narborough; but it is quite true."

"Of course it is true, Lord Henry. If we women did not love you for your defects, where would you all be? Not one of you would ever be married. You would be a set of unfortunate bachelors. Not, however, that that would alter you much. Nowadays all the married men live like bachelors, and all the bachelors like married men."

" *Fin de siècle,*" murmured Lord Henry.

" *Fin du globe,*" answered his hostess.

" I wish it were *fin du globe,*" said Dorian with a sigh. " Life is a great disappointment."

" Ah, my dear," cried Lady Narborough, putting on her gloves, " don't tell me that you have exhausted Life. When a man says that one knows that life has exhausted him! Lord Henry is very wicked, and I sometimes wish that I had been ; but you are made to be good—you look so good. I must find you a nice wife. Lord Henry, don't you think that Mr. Gray should get married ? "

" I am always telling him so, Lady Narborough," said Lord Henry, with a bow.

" Well, we must look out for a suitable match for him. I shall go through Debrett carefully to-night, and draw out a list of all the eligible young ladies."

" With their ages, Lady Narborough ? " asked Dorian.

" Of course, with their ages, slightly edited. But nothing must be done in a hurry. I want it to be what *The Morning Post* calls a suitable alliance, and I want you both to be happy."

" What nonsense people talk about happy marriages ! " exclaimed Lord Henry. " A man can be happy with any woman, as long as he does not love her."

" Ah ! what a cynic you are ! cried the old lady, pushing back her chair, and nodding to Lady Ruxton. " You must come and dine with me soon again. You are really an admirable tonic, much better than what Sir Andrew prescribes for me. You must tell me what people you would like to meet, though. I want it to be a delightful gathering."

" I like men who have a future, and women who have a past," he answered. " Or do you think that would make it a petticoat party ? "

" I fear so," she said, laughing, as she stood up.

" A thousand pardons, my dear Lady Ruxton,'' she
added. "I didn't see you hadn't finished your
cigarette."

"Never mind, Lady Narborough. I smoke a
great deal too much. I am going to limit myself,
for the future."

" Pray don't, Lady Ruxton," said Lord Henry.
"Moderation is a fatal thing. Enough is as bad
as a meal. More than enough is as good as a feast."

Lady Ruxton glanced at him curiously. "You
must come and explain that to me some afternoon,
Lord Henry. It sounds a fascinating theory," she
murmured, as she swept out of the room.

" Now, mind you don't stay too long over your
politics and scandal," cried Lady Narborough from the
door. " If you do, we are sure to squabble upstairs."

The men laughed, and Mr. Chapman got up solemnly
from the foot of the table and came up to the top.
Dorian Gray changed his seat, and went and sat by
Lord Henry. Mr. Chapman began to talk in a loud
voice about the situation in the House of Commons.
He guffawed at his adversaries. The word *doctrinaire*
—word full of terror to the British mind—reappeared
from time to time between his explosions.   An
alliterative prefix served as an ornament of oratory.
He hoisted the Union Jack on the pinnacles of
Thought. The inherited stupidity of the race—sound
English common sense he jovially termed it—was
shown to be the proper bulwark for Society.

A smile curved Lord Henry's lips, and he turned
round and looked at Dorian.

" Are you better, my dear fellow ? " he asked.
" You seemed rather out of sorts at dinner."

"I am quite well, Harry. I am tired.   That
is all."

" You were charming last night. The little Duchess
is quite devoted to you. She tells me she is going
down to Selby."

" She has promised to come on the twentieth."

" Is Monmouth to be there too ? "

" Oh, yes, Harry."

" He bores me dreadfully, almost as much as he bores her. She is very clever, too clever for a woman. She lacks the indefinable charm of weakness. It is the feet of clay that makes the gold of the image precious. Her feet are very pretty, but they are not feet of clay. White porcelain feet, if you like. They have been through the fire, and what fire does not destroy, it hardens. She has had experiences."

" How long has she been married ? " asked Dorian.

" An eternity, she tells me. I believe, according to the peerage, it is ten years, but ten years with Monmouth must have been like eternity, with time thrown in. Who else is coming ? "

" Oh, the Willoughbys, Lord Rugby and his wife, our hostess, Geoffrey Clouston, the usual set. I have asked Lord Grotrian."

" I like him," said Lord Henry. " A great many people don't, but I find him charming. He atones for being occasionally somewhat over-dressed, by being always absolutely over-educated. He is a very modern type."

" I don't know if he will be able to come, Harry. He may have to go to Monte Carlo with his father."

" Ah ! what a nuisance people's people are ! Try and make him come. By the way, Dorian, you ran off very early last night. You left before eleven. What did you do afterwards ? Did you go straight home ? "

Dorian glanced at him hurriedly, and frowned. " No, Harry," he said at last, " I did not get home till nearly three."

" Did you go to the club ? "

" Yes," he answered. Then he bit his lip. " No, I don't mean that. I didn't go to the club.   I walked about. I forget what I did. . . . How

inquisitive you are, Harry! You always want to
know what one has been doing. I always want to
forget what I have been doing. I came in at half-
past two, if you wish to know the exact time. I
had left my latch-key at home, and my servant had
to let me in. If you want any corroborative evidence
on the subject you can ask him."

Lord Henry shrugged his shoulders. "My dear
fellow, as if I cared! Let us go up to the drawing-
room. No sherry, thank you, Mr. Chapman. Something has happened to you, Dorian. Tell me what it
is. You are not yourself to-night."

"Don't mind me, Harry. I am irritable, and out
of temper. I shall come round and see you to-morrow
or next day. Make my excuses to Lady Narborough.
I shan't go upstairs. I shall go home. I must go
home."

"All right, Dorian. I daresay I shall see you to-
morrow at tea-time. The Duchess is coming."

"I will try to be there, Harry," he said, leaving
the room. As he drove back to his own house he
was conscious that the sense of terror he thought
he had strangled had come back to him. Lord
Henry's casual questioning had made him lose his
nerves for the moment, and he wanted his nerve still.
Things that were dangerous had to be destroyed. He
winced. He hated the idea of even touching them.

Yet it had to be done. He realised that, and when
he had locked the door of his library, he opened the
secret press into which he had thrust Basil Hallward's
coat and bag. A huge fire was blazing. He piled
another log on it. The smell of the singeing clothes
and burning leather was horrible. It took him
three-quarters of an hour to consume everything. At
the end he felt faint and sick, and having lit some
Algerian pastilles in a pierced copper brazier, he bathed
his hands and forehead with a cool musk-scented
vinegar.

Suddenly he started.   His eyes grew strangely bright, and he gnawed nervously at his under-lip. Between two of the windows stood a large Florentine cabinet, made out of ebony, and inlaid with ivory and blue lapis.   He watched it as though it were a thing that could fascinate and make afraid, as though it held something that he longed for and yet almost loathed.   His breath quickened.   A mad craving came over him. He lit a cigarette and then threw it away.   His eyelids drooped till the long fringed lashes almost touched his cheek.   But he still watched the cabinet.   At last he got up from the sofa on which he had been lying, went over to it, and. having unlocked it, touched some hidden spring, A triangular drawer passed slowly out.   His fingers moved instinctively towards it, dipped in, and closed on something.   It was a small Chinese box of black and gold-dust lacquer, elaborately wrought, the sides patterned with curved waves, and the silken cords hung with round crystals and tasselled in plaited metal threads.   He opened it.   Inside was a green paste, waxy in lustre, the odour curiously heavy and persistent.

He hesitated for some moments, with a strangely immobile smile upon his face. Then shivering, though the atmosphere of the room was terribly hot, he drew himself up, and glanced at the clock. It was twenty minutes to twelve.   He put the box back, shutting the cabinet doors as he did so, and went into his bedroom.

As midnight was striking bronze blows upon the dusky air, Dorian Gray dressed commonly, and with a muffler wrapped round his throat, crept quietly out of the house.   In Bond Street he found a hansom with a good horse. He hailed it, and in a low voice gave the driver an address.

The man shook his head.   " It is too far for me," he muttered.

" Here is a sovereign for you," said Dorian. " You shall have another if you drive fast."

" All right, sir," answered the man, " you will be there in an hour," and after his fare had got in he turned his horse round, and drove rapidly towards the river.

CHAPTER XVI

A COLD rain began to fall, and the blurred street-lamps looked ghastly in the dipping mist. The public-houses were just closing and dim men and women were clustering in broken groups round their doors. From some of the bars came the sound of horrible laughter. In others, drunkards brawled and screamed.

Lying back in the hansom, with his hat pulled over his forehead, Dorian Gray watched with listless eyes the sordid shame of the great city, and now and then he repeated to himself the words that Lord Henry had said to him on the first day they had met, " To cure the soul by means of the senses, and the senses by means of the soul." Yes, that was the secret. He had often tried it, and would try it again now. There were opium-dens, where one could buy oblivion, dens of horror where the memory of old sins could be destroyed by the madness of sins that were new.

The moon hung low in the sky like a yellow skull. From time to time a huge misshapen cloud stretched a long arm across and hid it. The gas-lamps grew fewer, and the streets more narrow and gloomy. Once the man lost his way, and had to drive back half a mile. A steam rose from the horse as it splashed up the puddles. The side-windows of the hansom were clogged with a grey-flannel mist.

" To cure the soul by means of the senses, and the

senses by means of the soul ! " How the words rang
in his ears ! His soul, certainly, was sick to death.
Was it true that the senses could cure it ? Innocent
blood had been spilt. What could atone for that ?
Ah ! for that there was no atonement ; but though
forgiveness was impossible, forgetfulness was possible
still, and he was determined to forget, to stamp the
thing out, to crush it as one would crush the adder
that had stung one. Indeed, what right had Basil
to have spoken to him as he had done ? Who had made
him a judge over others ? He had said things that
were dreadful, horrible, not to be endured.

On and on plodded the hansom, going slower, it
seemed to him, at each step. He thrust up the trap,
and called to the man to drive faster. The hideous
hunger for opium began to gnaw at him. His throat
burned, and his delicate hands twitched nervously
together. He struck at the horse madly with his
stick. The driver laughed, and whipped up. He
laughed in answer, and the man was silent.

The way seemed interminable, and the streets
like the black web of some sprawling spider. The
monotony became unbearable, and, as the mist
thickened, he felt afraid.

Then they passed by lonely brickfields. The fog
was lighter here, and he could see the strange bottle-
shaped kilns with their orange fan-like tongues of fire.
A dog barked as they went by, and far away in the
darkness some wandering sea-gull screamed. The
horse stumbled in a rut, then swerved aside, and broke
into a gallop.

After some time they left the clay road, and rattled
again over rough-paven streets. Most of the windows
were dark, but now and then fantastic shadows were
silhouetted against some lamp-lit blind. He watched
them curiously. They moved like monstrous marionettes, and made gestures like live things. He hated
them. A dull rage was in his heart. As they turned

a corner a woman yelled something at them from an open door, and two men ran after the hansom for about a hundred yards.   The driver beat at them with his whip.

It is said that passion makes one think in a circle. Certainly with hideous iteration the bitten lips of Dorian Gray shaped and reshaped those subtle words that dealt with soul and sense, till he had found in them the full expression, as it were, of his mood, and justified, by intellectual approval, passions that without such justification would still have dominated his temper. From cell to cell of his brain crept the one thought ; and the wild desire to live, most terrible of all man's appetites, quickened into force each trembling nerve and fibre. Ugliness that had once been hateful to him because it made things real, became dear to him now for that very reason. Ugliness was the one reality. The coarse brawl, the loathsome den, the crude violence of disordered life, the very vileness of thief and outcast, were more vivid, in their intense actuality of impression, than all the gracious shapes of Art, the dreamy shadows of Song.   They were what he needed for forgetfulness. In three days he would be free.

Suddenly the man drew up with a jerk at the top of a dark lane. Over the low roofs and jagged chimney stacks of the houses rose the black masts of ships. Wreaths of white mist clung like ghostly sails to the yards.

" Somewhere about here, sir, ain't it ? " he asked huskily through the trap.

Dorian started, and peered round. " This will do," he answered, and, having got out hastily, and given the driver the extra fare he had promised him, he walked quickly in the direction of the quay. Here and there a lantern gleamed at the stern of some huge merchantman. The light shook and splintered in the puddles. A red glare came from an outward-bound steamer that was coaling. The slimy pavement looked like a wet mackintosh.

He hurried on towards the left, glancing back now and then to see if he was being followed. In about seven or eight minutes he reached a small shabby house, that was wedged in between two gaunt factories. In one of the top-windows stood a lamp. He stopped, and gave a peculiar knock.

After a little time he heard steps in the passage, and the chain being unhooked. The door opened quietly, and he went in without saying a word to the squat misshapen figure that flattened itself into the shadow as he passed. At the end of the hall hung a tattered green curtain that swayed and shook in the gusty wind which had followed him in from the street. He dragged it aside, and entered a long, low room which looked as if it had once been a third-rate dancing-saloon. Shrill flaring gas jets, dulled and distorted in the fly-blown mirrors that faced them, were ranged round the walls. Greasy reflectors of ribbed tin backed them, making quivering discs of light. The floor was covered with ochre-coloured sawdust, trampled here and there into mud, and stained with dark rings of spilt liquor. Some Malays were crouching by a little charcoal stove playing with bone counters, and showing their white teeth as they chattered. In one corner, with his head buried in his arms, a sailor sprawled over a table, and by the tawdrily-painted bar that ran across one complete side stood two haggard women mocking an old man who was brushing the sleeves of his coat with an expression of disgust. " He thinks he's got red ants on him," laughed one of them, as Dorian passed by. The man looked at her in terror and began to whimper.

At the end of the room there was a little staircase, leading to a darkened chamber. As Dorian hurried up its three rickety steps, the heavy odour

of opium met him.   He heaved a deep breath, and
his nostrils quivered with pleasure. When he entered,
a young man with smooth yellow hair, who was bending over a lamp, lighting a long thin pipe, looked up
at him, and nodded in a hesitating manner.

" You here, Adrian ? " muttered Dorian.

" Where else should I be ? " he answered, listlessly,
" None of the chaps will speak to me now."

" I thought you had left England."

" Darlington is not going to do anything.   My
brother paid the bill at last. George doesn't speak
to me either. . . .   I don't care," he added, with
a sigh. " As long as one has this stuff, one doesn't
want friends. I think I have had too many friends."

Dorian winced, and looked round at the grotesque
things that lay in such fantastic postures on the
ragged mattresses.   The twisted limbs, the gaping
mouths, the staring lustreless eyes, fascinated him.
He knew in what strange heavens they were suffering, and what dull hells were teaching them the
secret of some new joy.   They were better off than
he was.   He was prisoned in thought.   Memory,
like a horrible malady, was eating his soul away.
From time to time he seemed to see the eyes of Basil
Hallward looking at him.   Yet he felt he could not
stay.   The presence of Adrian Singleton troubled
him. He wanted to be where no man would know who
he was. He wanted to escape from himself.

" I am going on to the other place," he said, after
a pause.

" On the wharf ? "

" Yes."

" That mad-cat is sure to be there. They won't
have her in this place now."

Dorian shrugged his shoulders.   " I am sick of
women who love one. Women who hate one are
much more interesting. Besides, the stuff is better."

" Much the same."

" I like it better.   Come and have something to drink. I must have something."

" I don't want anything," murmured the young man.

" Never mind."

Adrian Singleton rose up wearily, and followed Dorian to the bar. A half-caste, in a ragged turban and a shabby ulster, grinned a hideous greeting as he thrust a bottle of brandy and two tumblers in front of them. The women sidled up, and began to chatter. Dorian turned his back on them, and said something in a low voice to Adrian Singleton.

A crooked smile, like a Malay crease, writhed across the face of one of the women. " We are very proud to-night," she sneered.

" For God's sake don't talk to me," cried Dorian, stamping his foot on the ground.   " What do you want ? Money ? Here it is. Don't ever talk to me again."

Two red sparks flashed for a moment in the woman's sodden eyes, then flickered out, and left them dull and glazed. She tossed her head, and raked the coins off the counter with greedy fingers. Her companion watched her enviously.

" It's no use," sighed Adrian Singleton.   " I don't care to go back. What does it matter ? I am quite happy here."

" You will write to me if you want anything, won't you ? " said Dorian, after a pause.

" Perhaps."

" Good-night, then."

" Good-night," answered the young man, passing up the steps, and wiping his parched mouth with a handkerchief.

Dorian walked to the door with a look of pain in his face.   As he drew the curtain aside a hideous laugh broke from the painted lips of the woman who had taken his money. " There goes the devil's bargain ! " she hiccoughed, in a hoarse voice.

" Curse you ! " he answered, " don't call me that."

She snapped her fingers.   " Prince Charming is what you like to be called, ain't it ? " she yelled after him.

The drowsy sailor leapt to his feet as she spoke, and looked wildly round.   The sound of the shutting of the hall door fell on his ear.   He rushed out as if in pursuit.

Dorian Gray hurried along the quay through the drizzling rain. His meeting with Adrian Singleton had strangely moved him, and he wondered if the ruin of that young life was really to be laid at his door, as Basil Hallward had said to him with such infamy of insult. He bit his lip, and for a few seconds his eyes grew sad. Yet, after all, what did it matter to him ? One's days were too brief to take the burden of another's errors on one's shoulders.   Each man lived his own life, and paid his own price for living it. The only pity was one had to pay so often for a single fault. One had to pay over and over again, indeed. In her dealings with man Destiny never closed her accounts.

There are moments, psychologists tell us, when the passion for sin, or for what the world calls sin, so dominates a nature, that every fibre of the body, as every cell of the brain, seems to be instinct with fearful impulses. Men and women at such moments lose the freedom of their will. They move to their terrible end as automatons move, Choice is taken from them, and conscience is either killed, or, if it lives at all, lives but to give rebellion its fascination, and disobedience its charm.   For all sins, as theologians weary not of reminding us, are sins of disobedience. When that high spirit, that morning-star of evil, fell from heaven, it was as a rebel that he fell.

Callous, concentrated on evil, with stained mien, and soul hungry for rebellion, Dorian Gray hastened on, quickening his step as he went, but as he darted aside into a dim archway, that had served him often as a short cut to the ill-famed place where he was going, he felt himself suddenly seized from behind, and before he had time to defend himself he was thrust back against the wall, with a brutal hand round his throat.

He struggled madly for life, and by a terrible effort wrenched the tightening fingers away. In a second he heard the click of a revolver, and saw the gleam of a polished barrel pointing straight at his head, and the dusky form of a short thick-set man facing him.

" What do you want ? " he gasped.

" Keep quiet," said the man. " If you stir, I shoot you."

" You are mad. What have I done to you ? "

" You wrecked the life of Sibyl Vane," was the answer, " and Sibyl Vane was my sister. She killed herself. I know it. Her death is at your door. I swore I would kill you in return. For years I have sought you. I had no clue, no trace. The two people who could have described you were dead. I knew nothing of you but the pet name she used to call you. I heard it to-night by chance. Make your peace with God, for to-night you are going to die."

Dorian Gray grew sick with fear. " I never knew her," he stammered. " I never heard of her. You are mad."

" You had better confess your sin, for as sure as I am James Vane, you are going to die." There was a horrible moment. Dorian did not know what to say or do. " Down on your knees ! " growled the man. " I give you one minute to make your peace— no more. I go on board to-night for India, and I must do my job first. One minute. That's all."

Dorian's arms fell to his side. Paralysed with terror, he did not know what to do. Suddenly a wild hope flashed across his brain. " Stop," he cried.

" How long ago is it since your sister died ? Quick, tell me ! "

" Eighteen years," said the man. " Why do you ask me ? What do years matter ? "

" Eighteen years," laughed Dorian Gray, with a touch of triumph in his voice. " Eighteen years ! Set me under the lamp and look at my face ! "

James Vane hesitated for a moment, not understanding what was meant. Then he seized Dorian Gray and dragged him from the archway.

Dim and wavering as was the wind-blown light, yet it served to show him the hideous error, as it seemed, into which he had fallen, for the face of the man he had sought to kill had all the bloom of boyhood, all the unstained purity of youth. He seemed little older than a lad of twenty summers, hardly older, if older indeed at all, than his sister had been when they had parted so many years ago. It was obvious that this was not the man who had destroyed her life.

He loosened his hold and reeled back. " My God ! my God ! " he cried, " and I would have murdered you ! "

Dorian Gray drew a long breath. " You have been on the brink of committing a terrible crime, my man," he said, looking at him sternly. " Let this be a warning to you not to take vengeance into your own hands."

" Forgive me, sir," muttered James Vane. " I was deceived. A chance word I heard in that damned den set me on the wrong track."

" You had better go home, and put that pistol away, or you may get into trouble," said Dorian. turning on his heel, and going slowly down the street.

James Vane stood on the pavement in horror. He was trembling from head to foot. After a little while a black shadow that had been creeping along the dripping wall, moved out into the light and

came close to him with stealthy footsteps. He felt
a hand laid on his arm and looked round with a
start. It was one of the women who had been
drinking at the bar.

" Why didn't you kill him? " she hissed out,
putting her haggard face quite close to his.   " I
knew you were following him when you rushed out
from Daly's.   You fool!   You should have killed
him.   He has lots of money, and he's as bad as
bad."

" He is not the man I am looking for," he answered,
" and I want no man's money. I want a man's life.
The man whose life I want must be nearly forty now.
This one is little more than a boy.   Thank God, I
have not got his blood upon my hands."

The woman gave a bitter laugh. " Little more
than a boy! " she sneered. " Why, man, it's nigh
on eighteen years since Prince Charming made me
what I am."

" You lie! " cried James Vane.

She raised her hand up to heaven.   " Before God
I am telling the truth," she cried.

" Before God? "

" Strike me dumb if it ain't so. He is the worst
one that comes here. They say he has sold himself to the devil for a pretty face. It's nigh on eighteen
years since I met him.   He hasn't changed much
since then. I have though," she added, with a sickly
leer.

" You swear this? "

" I swear it," came in hoarse echo from her flat
mouth.   " But don't give me away to him," she
whined ; " I am afraid of him. Let me have some
money for my night's lodging."

He broke from her with an oath, and rushed to the
corner of the street, but Dorian Gray had disappeared.
When he looked back, the woman had vanished also.

CHAPTER XVII

A WEEK later Dorian Gray was sitting in the conservatory at Selby Royal talking to the pretty Duchess of Monmouth, who with her husband, a jaded-looking man of sixty, was amongst his guests. It was tea-time, and the mellow light of the huge lace-covered lamp that stood on the table lit up the delicate china and hammered silver of the service at which the Duchess was presiding. Her white hands were moving daintily among the cups, and her full red lips were smiling at something that Dorian had whispered to her. Lord Henry was lying back in a silk-draped wicker chair looking at them. On a peach-coloured divan sat Lady Narborough pretending to listen to the Duke's description of the last Brazilian beetle that he had added to his collection. Three young men in elaborate smoking-suits were handing tea-cakes to some of the women. The house-party consisted of twelve people, and there were more expected to arrive on the next day.

"What are you two talking about?" said Lord Henry, strolling over to the table, and putting his cup down. "I hope Dorian has told you about my plan for rechristening everything, Gladys. It is a delightful idea."

"But I don't want to be rechristened, Harry," rejoined the Duchess, looking up at him with her wonderful eyes. "I am quite satisfied with my own name, and I am sure Mr. Gray should be satisfied with his."

"My dear Gladys, I would not alter either name for the world. They are both perfect. I was thinking chiefly of flowers. Yesterday I cut an orchid, for my buttonhole. It was a marvellous spotted thing, as effective as the seven deadly sins. In a thoughtless moment I asked one of the gardeners what it was called. He told me it was a fine specimen of *Robinsoniana*, or something dreadful of that kind.   It is a sad truth, but we have lost the faculty of giving lovely names to things. Names are everything. I never quarrel with actions. My one quarrel is with words. That is the reason I hate vulgar realism in literature. The man who could call a spade a spade should be compelled to use one.   It is the only thing he is fit for."

" Then what should we call you, Harry ? " she asked.

" His name is Prince Paradox," said Dorian.

" I recognise him in a flash," exclaimed the Duchess.

" I won't hear of it," laughed Lord Henry, sinking into a chair.   " From a label there is no escape! I refuse the title."

" Royalties may not abdicate," fell as a warning from pretty lips.

" You wish me to defend my throne, then ? "

" Yes."

" I give the truths of to-morrow."

" I prefer the mistakes of to-day," she answered.

" You disarm me, Gladys," he cried, catching the wilfulness of her mood.

" Of your shield, Harry : not of your spear."

" I never tilt against beauty," he said, with a wave of his hand.

" That is your error, Harry, believe me.   You value beauty far too much."

" How can you say that ?   I admit that I think that it is better to be beautiful than to be good. But on the other hand no one is more ready than I am to acknowledge that it is better to be good than to be ugly."

" Ugliness is one of the seven deadly sins, then ? " cried the Duchess.   " What becomes of your simile about the orchid ? "

" Ugliness is one of the seven deadly virtues, Gladys. You, as a good Tory, must not underrate them. Beer, the Bible, and the seven deadly virtues have made our England what she is."

" You don't like your country, then ? " she asked.

" I live in it."

" That you may censure it the better."

" Would you have me take the verdict of Europe on it ? " he inquired.

" What do they say of us ? "

" That Tartuffe has emigrated to England and opened a shop."

" Is that yours, Harry ? "

" I give it to you."

" I could not use it. It is too true."

" You need not be afraid. Our countrymen never recognise a description."

" They are practical."

" They are more cunning than practical. When they make up their ledger, they balance stupidity by wealth, and vice by hypocrisy."

" Still, we have done great things."

" Great things have been thrust on us, Gladys."

" We have carried their burden."

" Only as far as the Stock Exchange."

She shook her head. " I believe in the race," she cried.

" It represents the survival of the pushing."

" It has development."

" Decay fascinates me more."

" What of Art ? " she asked.

" It is a malady."

" Love ? "

" An illusion."

" Religion ? "

" The fashionable substitute for Belief."

" You are a sceptic."

" Never ! Scepticism is the beginning of Faith."

" What are you ? "

" To define is to limit."

" Give me a clue."

" Threads snap. You would lose your way in the labyrinth."

" You bewilder me. Let us talk of some one else."

" Our host is a delightful topic. Years ago he was christened Prince Charming."

" Ah ! don't remind me of that," cried Dorian Gray.

" Our host is rather horrid this evening," answered the Duchess, colouring. " I believe he thinks that Monmouth married me on purely scientific principles as the best specimen he could find of a modern butterfly."

" Well, I hope he won't stick pins into you, Duchess," laughed Dorian.

" Oh, my maid does that already, Mr. Gray, when she is annoyed with me."

" And what does she get annoyed with you about, Duchess ? "

" For the most trivial things, Mr. Gray, I assure you. Usually because I come in at ten minutes to nine and tell her that I must be dressed by half-past eight."

" How unreasonable of her ! You should give her warning."

" I daren't, Mr. Gray. Why, she invents hats for me. You remember the one I wore at Lady Hilstone's garden-party ? You don't, but it is nice of you to pretend that you do. Well, she made it out of nothing. All good hats are made out of nothing."

" Like all good reputations, Gladys," interrupted Lord Henry. " Every effect that one produces gives one an enemy. To be popular one must be a mediocrity."

" Not with women," said the Duchess, shaking her head ; " and women rule the world. I assure you we can't bear mediocrities. We women, as some one says, love with our ears, just as you men love with your eyes, if you ever love at all."

"It seems to me that we never do anything else," murmured Dorian.

"Ah! then, you never really love, Mr. Gray," answered the Duchess, with mock sadness.

"My dear Gladys!" cried Lord Henry. "How can you say that? Romance lives by repetition, and repetition converts an appetite into an art. Besides, each time that one loves is the only time one has ever loved. Difference of object does not alter singleness of passion. It merely intensifies it. We can have in life but one great experience at best, and the secret of life is to reproduce that experience as often as possible."

"Even when one has been wounded by it, Harry?" asked the Duchess, after a pause.

"Especially when one has been wounded by it," answered Lord Henry.

The Duchess turned and looked at Dorian Gray with a curious expression in her eyes. "What do you say to that, Mr. Gray?" she inquired.

Dorian hesitated for a moment. Then he threw his head back and laughed. "I always agree with Harry, Duchess."

"Even when he is wrong?"

"Harry is never wrong, Duchess."

"And does his philosophy make you happy?"

"I have never searched for happiness. Who wants happiness? I have searched for pleasure."

"And found it, Mr. Gray?"

"Often. Too often."

The Duchess sighed. "I am searching for peace," she said, "and if I don't go and dress, I shall have none this evening."

"Let me get you some orchids, Duchess," cried Dorian, starting to his feet, and walking down the conservatory.

" You are flirting disgracefully with him," said Lord Henry to his cousin. " You had better take care. He is very fascinating."

" If he were not, there would be no battle."

" Greek meets Greek, then ? "

" I am on the side of the Trojans They fought for a woman."

" They were defeated."

" There are worse things than capture," she answered.

" You gallop with a loose rein."

" Pace gives life," was the *riposte*.

" I shall write it in my diary to-night."

" What ? "

" That a burnt child loves the fire."

" I am not even singed. My wings are untouched."

" You can use them for everything except flight."

" Courage has passed from men to women. It is a new experience for us."

" You have a rival."

" Who ? "

He laughed. " Lady Narborough," he whispered. " She perfectly adores him."

" You fill me with apprehension. The appeal to Antiquity is fatal to us who are romanticists."

" Romanticists ! You have all the methods of science."

" Men have educated us."

" But not explained you."

" Describe us as a sex," was her challenge.

" Sphynxes without secrets."

She looked at him, smiling. " How long Mr. Gray is ! " she said. " Let us go and help him. I have not yet told him the colour of my frock."

" Ah ! you must suit your frock to his flowers, Gladys."

" That would be a premature surrender."

" Romantic Art begins with its climax."

" I must keep an opportunity for retreat."

" In the Parthian manner ? "

" They found safety in the desert.   I could not do that."

" Women are not always allowed a choice," he answered, but hardly had he finished the sentence before from the far end of the conservatory came a stifled groan, followed by the dull sound of a heavy fall.   Everybody started up.   The Duchess stood motionless in horror.   And with fear in his eyes Lord Henry rushed through the flapping palms to find Dorian Gray lying face downwards on the tiled floor in a death-like swoon.

He was carried at once into the blue drawing-room, and laid upon one of the sofas.   After a short time he came to himself, and looked round with a dazed expression.

" What has happened ? " he asked.   " Oh ! I remember.   Am I safe here, Harry ? "   He began to tremble.

" My dear Dorian," answered Lord Henry, " you merely fainted.   That was all.   You must have overtired yourself.   You had better not come down to dinner.   I will take your place."

" No, I will come down," he said, struggling to his feet.   " I would rather come down.   I must not be alone."

He went to his room and dressed.   There was a wild recklessness of gaiety in his manner as he sat at table, but now and then a thrill of terror ran through him when he remembered that, pressed against the window of the conservatory, like a white handkerchief, he had seen the face of James Vane watching him.

CHAPTER XVIII

THE next day he did not leave the house, and, indeed, spent most of the time in his own room, sick with a wild terror of dying, and yet indifferent to life itself. The consciousness of being hunted, snared, tracked down, had begun to dominate him. If the tapestry did but tremble in the wind, he shook. The dead leaves that were blown against the leaded panes seemed to him like his own wasted resolutions and wild regrets. When he closed his eyes, he saw again the sailor's face peering through the mist-stained glass, and horror seemed once more to lay its hand upon his heart.

But perhaps it had been only his fancy that had called vengeance out of the night, and set the hideous shapes of punishment before him. Actual life was chaos, but there was something terribly logical in the imagination. It was the imagination that set remorse to dog the feet of sin. It was the imagination that made each crime bear its misshapen brood. In the common world of fact the wicked were not punished, nor the good rewarded. Success was given to the strong, failure thrust upon the weak. That was all. Besides, had any stranger been prowling round the house he would have been seen by the servants or the keepers. Had any footmarks been found on the flower-beds, the gardeners would have reported it. Yes : it had been merely fancy. Sibyl Vane's brother had not come back to kill him. He had sailed away in his ship to founder in some winter sea. From him, at any rate, he was safe. Why, the man did not know who he was, could not know who he was. The mask of youth had saved him.

And yet if it had been merely an illusion, how terrible it was to think that conscience could raise such fearful phantoms, and give them visible form, and make them move before one ! What sort of life would his be, if day and night, shadows of his crime were to peer at him from silent corners, to mock him from secret places, to whisper in his ear as he sat at the feast, to wake him with icy fingers as he lay asleep ! As the thought crept through his brain, he grew pale with terror, and the air seemed to him to have become suddenly colder. Oh ! in what a wild hour of madness he had killed his friend ! How ghastly the mere memory of the scene ! He saw it all again. Each hideous detail came back to him with added horror. Out of the black cave of Time, terrible and swathed in scarlet, rose the image of his sin. When Lord Henry came in at six o'clock, he found him crying as one whose heart will break.

It was not till the third day that he ventured to go out. There was something in the clear, pine-scented air of that winter morning that seemed to bring him back his joyousness and his ardour for life. But it was not merely the physical conditions of environment that had caused the change. His own nature had revolted against the excess of anguish that had sought to maim and mar the perfection of its calm. With subtle and finely-wrought temperaments it is always so. Their strong passions must either bruise or bend. They either slay the man, or themselves die. Shallow sorrows and shallow loves live on. The loves and sorrows that are great are destroyed by their own plenitude. Besides, he had convinced himself that he had been the victim of a terror-stricken imagination, and looked back now on his fears with something of pity and not a little of contempt.

After breakfast he walked with the Duchess for an hour in the garden, and then drove across the park to join the shooting-party. The crisp frost lay like salt upon the grass. The sky was an inverted cup

of blue metal. A thin film of ice bordered the flat
reed-grown lake.

At the corner of the pine-wood he caught sight of
Sir Geoffrey Clouston, the Duchess's brother, jerking
two spent cartridges out of his gun. He jumped from
the cart, and having told the groom to take the mare
home, made his way towards his guest through the
withered bracken and rough undergrowth.

" Have you had good sport, Geoffrey ? " he
asked.

" Not very good, Dorian. I think most of the birds
have gone to the open. I dare say it will be better
after lunch, when we get to new ground."

Dorian strolled along by his side. The keen
aromatic air, the brown and red lights that glimmered
in the wood, the hoarse cries of the beaters ringing
out from time to time, and the sharp snaps of the guns
that followed, fascinated him, and filled him with a
sense of delightful freedom. He was dominated by
the carelessness of happiness, by the high indifference
of joy.

Suddenly from a lumpy tussock of old grass, some
twenty yards in front of them, with black-tipped
ears erect, and long hinder limbs throwing it forward, started a hare. It bolted for a thicket of alders.
Sir Geoffrey put his gun to his shoulder, but there was
something in the animal's grace of movement that
strangely charmed Dorian Gray, and he cried out at
once, " Don't shoot it, Geoffrey. Let it live."

" What nonsense, Dorian ! " laughed his companion,
and as the hare bounded into the thicket he fired.
There were two cries heard, the cry of a hare in pain,
which is dreadful, the cry of a man in agony, which
is worse.

" Good heavens ! I have hit a beater ! " exclaimed
Sir Geoffrey. " What an ass the man was to get in
front of the guns ! Stop shooting there ! " he called
out at the top of his voice. " A man is hurt."

The head-keeper came running up with a stick in his hand.

"Where, sir ? Where is he ? " he shouted. At the same time the firing ceased along the line.

"Here," answered Sir Geoffrey, angrily, hurrying towards the thicket. "Why on earth don't you keep your men back ? Spoiled my shooting for the day."

Dorian watched them as they plunged into the alder-clump, brushing the lithe, swinging branches aside. In a few moments they emerged, dragging a body after them into the sunlight. He turned away in horror. It seemed to him that misfortune followed wherever he went. He heard Sir Geoffrey ask if the man was really dead, and the affirmative answer of the keeper. The wood seemed to him to have become suddenly alive with faces. There was the trampling of myriad feet, and the low buzz of voices. A great copper-breasted pheasant came beating through the boughs overhead.

After a few moments, that were to him, in his perturbed state, like endless hours of pain, he felt a hand laid on his shoulder. He started, and looked round.

"Dorian," said Lord Henry, "I had better tell them that the shooting is stopped for to-day. It would not look well to go on."

"I wish it were stopped for ever, Harry," he answered bitterly. "The whole thing is hideous and cruel. Is the man . . . ? "

He could not finish the sentence.

"I am afraid so," rejoined Lord Henry. "He got the whole charge of shot in his chest. He must have died almost instantaneously. Come ; let us go home."

They walked side by side in the direction of the avenue for nearly fifty yards without speaking. Then Dorian looked at Lord Henry, and said, with a heavy sigh, "It is a bad omen, Harry, a very bad omen."

"What is?" asked Lord Henry. "Oh, this accident, I suppose. My dear fellow, it can't be helped. It was the man's own fault. Why did he get in front of the guns? Besides, it's nothing to us. It is rather awkward for Geoffrey, of course. It does not do to pepper beaters. It makes people think that one is a wild shot. And Geoffrey is not; he shoots very straight. But there is no use talking about the matter."

Dorian shook his head. "It is a bad omen, Harry. I feel as if something horrible were going to happen to some of us. To myself, perhaps," he added, passing his hand over his eyes, with a gesture of pain.

The elder man laughed. "The only horrible thing in the world is *ennui*, Dorian. That is the one sin for which there is no forgiveness. But we are not likely to suffer from it, unless these fellows keep chattering about this thing at dinner. I must tell them that the subject is to be tabooed. As for omens, there is no such thing as an omen. Destiny does not send us heralds. She is too wise or too cruel for that. Besides, what on earth could happen to you, Dorian? You have everything in the world that a man can want. There is no one who would not be delighted to change places with you."

"There is no one with whom I would not change places, Harry. Don't laugh like that. I am telling you the truth. The wretched peasant who has just died is better off than I am. I have no terror of Death. It is the coming of Death that terrifies me. Its monstrous wings seem to wheel in the leaden air around me. Good heavens! don't you see a man moving behind the trees there, watching me, waiting for me?"

Lord Henry looked in the direction in which the trembling gloved hand was pointing. "Yes," he said, smiling, "I see the gardener waiting for you. I suppose he wants to ask you what flowers you wish to have on the table to-night. How absurdly nervous you are, my dear fellow ! You must come and see my doctor, when we get back to town."

Dorian heaved a sigh of relief as he saw the gardener approaching. The man touched his hat, glanced for a moment at Lord Henry in a hesitating manner, and then produced a letter, which he handed to his master. " Her Grace told me to wait for an answer," he murmured.

Dorian put the letter into his pocket. " Tell her Grace that I am coming in," he said, coldly. The man turned round, and went rapidly in the direction of the house.

" How fond women are of doing dangerous things ! " laughed Lord Henry. " It is one of the qualities in them that I admire most. A woman will flirt with anybody in the world as long as other people are looking on."

" How fond you are of saying dangerous things, Harry !   In the present instance you are quite astray.   I like the Duchess very much, but I don't love her."

" And the Duchess loves you very much, but she likes you less, so you are excellently matched."

" You are talking scandal, Harry, and there is never any basis for scandal."

" The basis for every scandal is an immoral certainty," said Lord Henry, lighting a cigarette.

" You would sacrifice anybody, Harry, for the sake of an epigram."

" The world goes to the altar of its own accord," was the answer.

" I wish I could love," cried Dorian Gray, with a deep note of pathos in his voice.   " But I seem to have lost the passion, and forgotten the desire.   I am too much concentrated on myself.   My own personality has become a burden to me.   I want to escape, to go away, to forget. It was silly of me

to come down here at all.   I think I shall send a wire
to Harvey to have the yacht got ready. On a yacht
one is safe."

"Safe from what, Dorian?   You are in some
trouble.   Why not tell me what it is?   You know
I would help you."

"I can't tell you, Harry," he answered, sadly.
"And I dare say it is only a fancy of mine.   This
unfortunate accident has upset me. I have a horrible
presentiment that something of the kind may happen
to me."

"What nonsense!"

"I hope it is, but I can't help feeling it.   Ah!
here is the Duchess, looking like Artemis in a tailor-
made gown. You see we have come back, Duchess."

"I have heard all about it, Mr. Gray," she answered.   "Poor Geoffrey is terribly upset.   And
it seems that you asked him not to shoot the hare.
How curious!"

"Yes, it was very curious. I don't know what
made me say it. Some whim, I suppose. It looked
the loveliest of little live things.   But I am sorry
they told you about the man. It is a hideous subject."

"It is an annoying subject," broke in Lord Henry.
"It has no psychological value at all.   Now if
Geoffrey had done the thing on purpose, how interesting he would be! I should like to know some one who
had committed a real murder."

"How horrid of you, Harry!" cried the Duchess.
"Isn't it, Mr. Gray? Harry, Mr. Gray is ill again.
He is going to faint."

Dorian drew himself up with an effort, and smiled.
"It is nothing, Duchess," he murmured; "my
nerves are dreadfully out of order.   That is all. I
am afraid I walked too far this morning. I didn't
hear what Harry said Was it very bad? You must
tell me some other time. I think I must go and lie
down. You will excuse me, won't you?"

They had reached the great flight of steps that led
from the conservatory on to the terrace. As the glass
door closed behind Dorian, Lord Henry turned and
looked at the Duchess with his slumberous eyes.
" Are you very much in love with him ? " he asked.

She did not answer for some time, but stood gazing
at the landscape. " I wish I knew," she said at last.

He shook his head. " Knowledge would be fatal.
It is the uncertainty that charms one. A mist makes
things wonderful."

" One may lose one's way."

" All ways end at the same point, my dear Gladys."

" What is that ? "

" Disillusion."

" It was my *début* in life," she sighed.

" It came to you crowned."

" I am tired of strawberry leaves."

" They become you."

" Only in public."

" You would miss them," said Lord Henry.

" I will not part with a petal."

" Monmouth has ears."

" Old age is dull of hearing."

" Has he never been jealous ? "

" I wish he had been."

He glanced about as if in search of something.
" What are you looking for ? " she inquired.

" The button from your foil," he answered. " You
have dropped it."

She laughed. " I have still the mask."

" It makes your eyes lovelier," was the reply.

She laughed again. Her teeth showed like white
seeds in a scarlet fruit.

Upstairs, in his own room, Dorian Gray was lying
on a sofa, with terror in every tingling fibre of his
body. Life had suddenly become too hideous a
burden for him to bear. The dreadful death of the
unlucky beater, shot in the thicket like a wild animal,

had seemed to him to prefigure death for himself also. He had nearly swooned at what Lord Henry had said in a chance mood of cynical jesting.

At five o'clock he rang his bell for his servant and gave him orders to pack his things for the night-express to town, and to have the brougham at the door by eight-thirty. He was determined not to sleep another night at Selby Royal. It was an ill-omened place, Death walked there in the sunlight. The grass of the forest had been spotted with blood.

Then he wrote a note to Lord Henry, telling him that he was going up to town to consult his doctor, and asking him to entertain his guests in his absence. As he was putting it into the envelope, a knock came to the door, and his valet informed him that the head-keeper wished to see him. He frowned, and bit his lip. "Send him in," he muttered, after some moments' hesitation.

As soon as the man entered Dorian pulled his cheque-book out of a drawer, and spread it out before him.

" I suppose you have come about the unfortunate accident of this morning, Thornton ? " he said, taking up a pen.

" Yes, sir," answered the gamekeeper.

" Was the poor fellow married ?   Had he any people dependent on him ? " asked Dorian, looking bored. " If so, I should not like them to be left in want, and will send them any sum of money you may think necessary."

" We don't know who he is, sir. That is what I took the liberty of coming to you about."

" Don't know who he is ? " said Dorian, listlessly. " What do you mean ?   Wasn't he one of your men ?"

" No, sir.   Never saw him before.   Seems like a sailor, sir."

The pen dropped from Dorian Gray's hand, and he felt as if his heart had suddenly stopped beating. " A sailor ? " he cried out. " Did you say a sailor ? "

" Yes, sir. He looks as if he had been a sort of sailor ; tattooed on both arms, and that kind of thing."

" Was there anything found on him ? " said Dorian, leaning forward and looking at the man with startled eyes. " Anything that would tell his name ? "

" Some money, sir—not much, and a six-shooter. There was no name of any kind. A decent-looking man, sir, but rough-like. A sort of sailor, we think."

Dorian started to his feet. A terrible hope fluttered past him. He clutched at it madly. " Where is the body ? he exclaimed. " Quick ! I must see it at once."

" It is in an empty stable in the Home Farm, sir. The folk don't like to have that sort of thing in their houses. They say a corpse brings bad luck."

" The Home Farm ! Go there at once and meet me. Tell one of the grooms to bring my horse round. No. Never mind. I'll go to the stables myself. It will save time."

In less than a quarter of an hour Dorian Gray was galloping down the long avenue as hard as he could go. The trees seemed to sweep past him in spectral procession, and wild shadows to fling themselves across his path. Once the mare swerved at a white gate-post and nearly threw him. He lashed her across the neck with his crop. She cleft the dusky air like an arrow. The stones flew from her hoofs.

At last he reached the Home Farm. Two men were loitering in the yard. He leapt from the saddle and threw the reins to one of them. In the farthest stable a light was glimmering. Something seemed to tell him that the body was there, and he hurried to the door, and put his hand upon the latch.

There he paused for a moment, feeling that he was on the brink of a discovery that would either make or mar his life. Then he thrust the door open, and entered.

On a heap of sacking in the far corner was lying the dead body of a man dressed in a coarse shirt and a pair of blue trousers. A spotted handkerchief had been placed over the face. A coarse candle, stuck in a bottle, spluttered beside it.

Dorian Gray shuddered. He felt that his could not be the hand to take the handkerchief away, and called out to one of the farm-servants to come to him.

" Take that thing off the face. I wish to see it," he said, clutching at the doorpost for support.

When the farm-servant had done so, he stepped forward. A cry of joy broke from his lips. The man who had been shot in the thicket was James Vane.

He stood there for some minutes looking at the dead body. As he rode home, his eyes were full of tears, for he knew he was safe.

CHAPTER XIX

" THERE is no use your telling me that you are going to be good," cried Lord Henry, dipping his white fingers into a red copper bowl filled with rose-water. " You're quite perfect. Pray, don't change."

Dorian Gray shook his head. " No, Harry, I have done too many dreadful things in my life. I am not going to do any more. I began my good actions yesterday."

" Where were you yesterday ? "

" In the country, Harry. I was staying at a little inn by myself."

" My dear boy," said Lord Henry, smiling, " anybody can be good in the country. There are no temptations there. That is the reason why people who live out of town are so absolutely uncivilised.

Civilisation is not by any means an easy thing to attain
to.   There are only two ways by which man can reach
it.   One is by being cultured, the other by being
corrupt.   Country people have no opportunity of
being either, so they stagnate."

"Culture and corruption," echoed Dorian.   "I
have known something of both. It seems terrible
to me now that they should ever be found together.
For I have a new ideal, Harry. I am going to alter.
I think I have altered."

"You have not yet told me what your good action
was. Or did you say you had done more than one?"
asked his companion, as he spilt into his plate a little
crimson pyramid of seeded strawberries, and through
a perforated shell-shaped spoon snowed white sugar
upon them.

"I can tell you, Harry.   It is not a story I could
tell to anyone else. I spared somebody. It sounds
vain, but you understand what I mean.   She was
quite beautiful, and wonderfully like Sibyl Vane.
I think it was that which first attracted me to her.
You remember Sibyl, don't you?   How long ago
that seems ! Well, Hetty was not one of our own
class, of course.   She was simply a girl in a village.
But I really loved her. I am quite sure that I loved
her. All during this wonderful May that we have
been having, I used to run down and see her two or
three times a week. Yesterday she met me in a little
orchard. The apple-blossoms kept tumbling down on
her hair, and she was laughing. We were to have
gone away together this morning at dawn. Suddenly
I determined to leave her as flower-like as I had
found her."

"I should think the novelty of the emotion must
have given you a thrill of real pleasure, Dorian,"
interrupted Lord Henry. "But I can finish your
idyll for you. You gave her good advice, and broke her
heart. That was the beginning of your reformation."

"Harry, you are horrible! You mustn't say these dreadful things. Hetty's heart is not broken. Of course she cried, and all that. But there is no disgrace upon her. She can live, like Perdita, in her garden of mint and marigold."

"And weep over a faithless Florizel," said Lord Henry, laughing, as he leant back in his chair. "My dear Dorian, you have the most curiously boyish moods. Do you think this girl will ever be really contented now with anyone of her own rank? I suppose she will be married some day to a rough carter or a grinning ploughman. Well, the fact of having met you, and loved you, will teach her to despise her husband, and she will be wretched. From a moral point of view, I cannot say that I think much of your great renunciation. Even as a beginning, it is poor. Besides, how do you know that Hetty isn't floating at the present moment in some star-lit mill-pond, with lovely water-lilies round her, like Ophelia?"

"I can't bear this, Harry! You mock at everything, and then suggest the most serious tragedies. I am sorry I told you now. I don't care what you say to me. I know I was right in acting as I did. Poor Hetty! As I rode past the farm this morning, I saw her white face at the window, like a spray of jasmine. Don't let us talk about it any more, and don't try to persuade me that the first good action I have done for years, the first little bit of self-sacrifice I have ever known, is really a sort of sin. I want to be better. I am going to be better. Tell me something about yourself. What is going on in town? I have not been to the club for days."

"The people are still discussing poor Basil's disappearance."

"I should have thought they had got tired of that by this time," said Dorian, pouring himself out some wine, and frowning slightly.

" My dear boy, they have only been talking about it for six weeks, and the British public are really not equal to the mental strain of having more than one topic every three months. They have been very fortunate lately, however. They have had my own divorce-case, and Alan Campbell's suicide. Now they have got the mysterious disappearance of an artist. Scotland Yard still insists that the man in the grey ulster who left for Paris by the midnight train on the ninth of November was poor Basil, and the French police declare that Basil never arrived in Paris at all. I suppose in about a fortnight we shall be told that he has been seen in San Francisco. It is an odd thing, but everyone who disappears is said to be seen at San Francisco. It must be a delightful city, and possess all the attractions of the next world."

" What do you think has happened to Basil ? " asked Dorian, holding up his Burgundy against the light, and wondering how it was that he could discuss the matter so calmly.

" I have not the slightest idea. If Basil chooses to hide himself, it is no business of mine. If he is dead, I don't want to think about him. Death is the only thing that ever terrifies me. I hate it."

" Why ? " said the younger man, wearily.

" Because," said Lord Henry, passing beneath his nostrils the gilt trellis of an open vinaigrette box, " one can survive everything nowadays except that. Death and vulgarity are the only two facts in the nineteenth century that one cannot explain away. Let us have our coffee in the music-room, Dorian. You must play Chopin to me. The man with whom my wife ran away played Chopin exquisitely. Poor Victoria ! I was very fond of her. The house is rather lonely without her. Of course married life is merely a habit, a bad habit. But then one regrets the loss even of one's worst habits. Perhaps one regrets them the most.   They are such an essential part of one's personality."

Dorian said nothing, but rose from the table and, passing into the next room, sat down to the piano and let his fingers stray across the white and black ivory of the keys. After the coffee had been brought in, he stopped, and, looking over at Lord Henry, said, " Harry, did it ever occur to you that Basil was murdered ? "

Lord Henry yawned. " Basil was very popular, and always wore a Waterbury watch. Why should he have been murdered ? He was not clever enough to have enemies. Of course he had a wonderful genius for painting.   But a man can paint like Velasquez and yet be as dull as possible.   Basil was really rather dull. He only interested me once, and that was when he told me, years ago, that he had a wild adoration for you, and that you were the dominant motive of his art."

" I was very fond of Basil," said Dorian, with a note of sadness in his voice. " But don't people say that he was murdered ?

" Oh, some of the papers do. It does not seem to me to be at all probable. I know there are dreadful places in Paris, but Basil was not the sort of man to have gone to them. He had no curiosity. It was his chief defect."

" What would you say, Harry, if I told you that I had murdered Basil ? " said the younger man. He watched him intently after he had spoken.

" I would say, my dear fellow, that you were posing for a character that doesn't suit you.   All crime is vulgar, just as all vulgarity is crime. It is not in you, Dorian, to commit a murder.   I am sorry if I hurt your vanity by saying so, but I assure you it is true. Crime belongs exclusively to the lower orders.   I don't blame them in the smallest degree. I should fancy that crime was to them what art is to us, simply a method of procuring **extra**-ordinary sensations."

"A method of procuring sensations? Do you think, then, that a man who has once committed a murder could possibly do the same crime again? Don't tell me that."

"Oh! anything becomes a pleasure if one does it too often," cried Lord Henry, laughing. "That is one of the most important secrets of life. I should fancy, however, that murder is always a mistake. One should never do anything that one cannot talk about after dinner. But let us pass from poor Basil. I wish I could believe that he had come to such a really romantic end as you suggest; but I can't. I dare say he fell into the Seine off an omnibus, and that the conductor hushed up the scandal. Yes: I should fancy that was his end. I see him lying now on his back under those dull-green waters with the heavy barges floating over him, and long weeds catching in his hair. Do you know, I don't think he would have done much more good work. During the last ten years his painting had gone off very much."

Dorian heaved a sigh, and Lord Henry strolled across the room and began to stroke the head of a curious Java parrot, a large grey-plumaged bird, with pink crest and tail, that was balancing itself upon a bamboo perch. As his pointed fingers touched it, it dropped the white scurf of crinkled lids over black glass-like eyes, and began to sway backwards and forwards.

"Yes," he continued, turning round, and taking his handkerchief out of his pocket; "his painting had quite gone off. It seemed to me to have lost something. It had lost an ideal. When you and he ceased to be great friends, he ceased to be a great artist. What was it separated you? I suppose he bored you. If so, he never forgave you. It's a habit bores have. By the way, what has become of that

wonderful portrait he did of you ? I don't think I
have ever seen it since he finished it. Oh ! I remember
your telling me years ago that you had sent it down
to Selby, and that it had got mislaid or stolen on the
way. You never got it back ? What a pity ! It
was really a masterpiece. I remember I wanted to
buy it. I wish I had now. It belonged to Basil's
best period. Since then, his work was that curious
mixture of bad painting and good intentions that
always entitles a man to be called a representative
British artist. Did you advertise for it ? You
should."

"I forget," said Dorian. "I suppose I did. But
I never really liked it. I am sorry I sat for it. The
memory of the thing is hateful to me. Why do you
talk of it ? It used to remind me of those curious lines
in some play—' Hamlet,' I think—how do they
run ?—

> " ' Like the painting of a sorrow,
> A face without a heart.'

Yes : that is what it was like.

Lord Henry laughed. "If a man treats life artistically, his brain is his heart," he answered, sinking
into an arm-chair.

Dorian Gray shook his head, and struck some
soft chords on the piano. " ' Like the painting
of a sorrow,' " he repeated, " ' a face without a
heart.' "

The elder man lay back and looked at him with
half-closed eyes. "By the way, Dorian," he said,
after a pause, " ' what does it profit a man if he gain
the whole world and lose '—how does the quotation
run ?—' his own soul ' ? "

The music jarred and Dorian Gray started, and
stared at his friend. "Why do you ask me that,
Harry ? "

"My dear fellow," said Lord Henry, elevating

his eyebrows in surprise, " I asked you because I thought you might be able to give me an answer. That is all. I was going through the Park last Sunday, and close by the Marble Arch there stood a little crowd of shabby-looking people listening to some vulgar street-preacher. As I passed by, I heard the man yelling out that question to his audience. It struck me as being rather dramatic. London is very rich in curious effects of that kind. A wet Sunday, an uncouth Christian in a mackintosh, a ring of sickly white faces under a broken roof of dripping umbrellas, and a wonderful phrase flung into the air by shrill, hysterical lips—it was really very good in its way, quite a suggestion. I thought of telling the prophet that Art had a soul, but that man had not. I am afraid, however, he would not have understood me."

" Don't, Harry. The soul is a terrible reality. It can be bought, and sold, and bartered away. It can be poisoned, or made perfect. There is a soul in each one of us. I know it."

" Do you feel quite sure of that, Dorian ? "

" Quite sure."

" Ah ! then it must be an illusion. The things one feels absolutely certain about are never true. That is the fatality of Faith, and the lesson of Romance. How grave you are ! Don't be so serious. What have you or I to do with the superstitions of our age ? No : we have given up our belief in the soul. Play me something. Play me a nocturne, Dorian, and, as you play, tell me, in a low voice, how you have kept your youth. You must have some secret. I am only ten years older than you are, and I am wrinkled, and worn, and yellow. You are really wonderful, Dorian. You have never looked more charming than you do to-night. You remind me of the day I saw you first. You were rather cheeky, very shy, and absolutely extraordinary. You have changed, of course, but not in appearance. I wish you would tell me your secret. To get back my youth I would do anything in the world, except take exercise, get up early, or be respectable. Youth! There is nothing like it. It's absurd to talk of the ignorance of youth. The only people to whose opinions I listen now with any respect are people much younger than myself. They seem in front of me. Life has revealed to them her latest wonder. As for the aged, I always contradict the aged. I do it on principle. If you ask them their opinion on something that happened yesterday, they solemnly give you the opinions current in 1820, when people wore high stocks, believed in everything, and knew absolutely nothing. How lovely that thing you are playing is! I wonder did Chopin write it at Majorca, with the sea weeping round the villa, and the salt spray dashing against the panes? It is marvellously romantic. What a blessing it is that there is one art left to us that is not imitative! Don't stop. I want music to-night. It seems to me that you are the young Apollo, and that I am Marsyas listening to you. I have sorrows, Dorian, of my own, that even you know nothing of. The tragedy of old age is not that one is old, but that one is young. I am amazed sometimes at my own sincerity. Ah, Dorian, how happy you are! What an exquisite life you have had! You have drunk deeply of everything. You have crushed the grapes against your palate. Nothing has been hidden from you. And it has all been to you no more than the sound of music. It has not marred you. You are still the same."

"I am not the same, Harry."

"Yes: you are the same. I wonder what the rest of your life will be. Don't spoil it by renunciations. At present you are a perfect type. Don't make yourself incomplete. You are quite flawless now. You need not shake your head: you know you are. Besides, Dorian, don't deceive yourself.

Life is not governed by will or intention. Life is a question of nerves, and fibres, and slowly built-up cells in which thought hides itself and passion has its dreams. You may fancy yourself safe, and think yourself strong. But a chance tone of colour in a room or a morning sky, a particular perfume that you had once loved and that brings subtle memories with it, a line from a forgotten poem that you had come across again, a cadence from a piece of music that you had ceased to play—I tell you, Dorian, that it is on things like these that our lives depend. Browning writes about that somewhere ; but our own senses will imagine them for us. There are moments when the odour of *lilas blanc* passes suddenly across me, and I have to live the strangest month of my life over again. I wish I could change places with you, Dorian. The world has cried out against us both, but it has always worshipped you. It always will worship you. You are the type of what the age is searching for, and what it is afraid it has found. I am so glad that you have never done anything, never carved a statue, or painted a picture, or produced anything outside of yourself! Life has been your art. You have set yourself to music. Your days are your sonnets."

Dorian rose up from the piano, and passed his hand through his hair. " Yes, life has been exquisite," he murmured, " but I am not going to have the same life, Harry. And you must not say these extra-vagant things to me. You don't know everything .about me. I think that if you did, even you would turn from me. You laugh. Don't laugh."

" Why have you stopped playing, Dorian ? Go back and give me the nocturne over again. Look at that great honey-coloured moon that hangs in the dusky air. She is waiting for you to charm her, and if you play she will come closer to the earth. You won't ? Let us go to the club, then. It has been a charming evening, and we must end it charmingly. There is some one at White's who wants immensely to know you—young Lord Poole, Bournemouth's eldest son. He has already copied your neckties, and has begged me to introduce him to you. He is quite delightful, and rather reminds me of you."

" I hope not," said Dorian, with a sad look in his eyes. " But I am tired to-night, Harry. I shan't go to the club. It is nearly eleven, and I want to go to bed early."

" Do stay. You have never played so well as to-night. There was something in your touch that was wonderful. It had more expression than I had ever heard from it before."

" It is because I am going to be good," he answered, smiling. " I am a little changed already."

" You cannot change to me, Dorian," said Lord Henry. " You and I will always be friends."

" Yet you poisoned me with a book once. I should not forgive that. Harry, promise me that you will never lend that book to any one. It does harm."

" My dear boy, you are really beginning to moralise. You will soon be going about the converted, and the revivalist, warning people against all the sins of which you have grown tired. You are much too delightful to do that. Besides, it is no use. You and I are what we are, and will be what we will be. As for being poisoned by a book, there is no such thing as that. Art has no influence upon action. It annihilates the desire to act. It is superbly sterile. The books that the world calls immoral are books that show the world its own shame. That is all. But we won't discuss literature. Come round to-morrow. I am going to ride at eleven. We might go together, and I will take you to lunch afterwards with Lady Branksome. She is a charming woman, and wants to consult you about some tapestries she is thinking

of buying.   Mind you come.   Or shall we lunch·
with our little Duchess ?   She says she never sees
you now.   Perhaps you are tired of Gladys ?   I
thought you would be.   Her clever tongue gets on
one's nerves.   Well, in any case, be here at eleven."
  "Must I really come, Harry ? "
  "Certainly.   The Park is quite lovely now.   I
don't think there have been such lilacs since the year
I met you."
  "Very well.   I shall be here at eleven," said
Dorian.   "Good-night, Harry."   As he reached the
door he hesitated for a moment, as if he had something
more to say.   Then he sighed and went out.

CHAPTER XX

IT was a lovely night, so warm that he threw his
coat over his arm, and did not even put his silk
scarf round his throat.   As he strolled home,
smoking his cigarette, two young men in evening
dress passed him.   He heard one of them whisper to
the other, " That is Dorian Gray."   He remembered
how pleased he used to be when he was pointed out, or
stared at, or talked about.   He was tired of hearing his
own name now.   Half the charm of the little village
where he had been so often lately was that no one
knew who he was.   He had often told the girl whom he
had lured to love him that he was poor, and she had believed him.   He had told her once that he was wicked,
and she had laughed at him, and answered that
wicked people were always very old and very ugly.
What a laugh she had !—just like a thrush singing.
And how pretty she had been in her cotton dresses
and her large hats !   She knew nothing, but she
had everything that he had lost.
  When he reached home, he found his servant

waiting up for him. He sent him to bed, and threw himself down on the sofa in the library, and began to think over some of the things that Lord Henry had said to him.

Was it really true that one could never change? He felt a wild longing for the unstained purity of his boyhood—his rose-white boyhood, as Lord Henry had once called it. He knew that he had tarnished himself, filled his mind with corruption, and given horror to his fancy ; that he had been an evil influence to others, and had experienced a terrible joy in being so ; and that, of the lives that had crossed his own, it had been the fairest and the most full of promise that he had brought to shame. But was it all irretrievable ? Was there no hope for him ?

Ah ! in what a monstrous moment of pride and passion he had prayed that the portrait should bear the burden of his days, and he keep the unsullied splendour of eternal youth ! All his failure had been due to that. Better for him that each sin of his life had brought its sure, swift penalty along with it. There was purification in punishment. Not " Forgive us our sins," but " Smite us for our iniquities," should be the prayer of a man to a most just God.

The curiously carved mirror that Lord Henry had given to him, so many years ago now, was standing on the table, and the white-limbed Cupids laughed round it as of old. He took it up, as he had done on that night of horror, when he had first noted the change in the fatal picture, and with wild, tear-dimmed eyes looked into its polished shield. Once, some one who had terribly loved him had written to him a mad letter, ending with these idolatrous words : " The world is changed because you are made of ivory and gold. The curves of your lips rewrite history." The phrases came back to his memory, and he repeated them over and over to himself. Then he loathed his own beauty, and, flinging the mirror on the floor, crushed it into silver splinters beneath his heel. It was his beauty that had ruined him, his beauty and the youth that he had prayed for. But for those two things, his life might have been free from stain. His beauty had been to him but a mask, his youth but a mockery. What was youth at best? A green, an unripe time, a time of shallow moods and sickly thoughts. Why had he worn its livery? Youth had spoiled him.

It was better not to think of the past. Nothing could alter that. It was of himself, and of his own future, that he had to think. James Vane was hidden in a nameless grave in Selby Churchyard. Alan Campbell had shot himself one night in his laboratory, but had not revealed the secret that he had been forced to know. The excitement, such as it was, over Basil Hallward's disappearance would soon pass away. It was already waning. He was perfectly safe there. Nor, indeed, was it the death of Basil Hallward that weighed most upon his mind. It was the living death of his own soul that troubled him. Basil had painted the portrait that had marred his life. He could not forgive him that. It was the portrait that had done everything. Basil had said things to him that were unbearable, and that he had yet borne with patience. The murder had been simply the madness of a moment. As for Alan Campbell, his suicide had been his own act. He had chosen to do it. It was nothing to him.

A new life! That was what he wanted. That was what he was waiting for. Surely he had begun it already. He had spared one innocent thing, at any rate. He would never again tempt innocence. He would be good.

As he thought of Hetty Merton, he began to wonder if the portrait in the locked room had changed. Surely it was not still so horrible as it had been? Perhaps if his life became pure, he would be able to expel every sign of evil passion from the face. Perhaps the signs of evil had already gone away. He would go and look.

He took the lamp from the table and crept upstairs. As he unbarred the door a smile of joy flitted across his strangely young-looking face and lingered for a moment about his lips. Yes, he would be good, and the hideous thing that he had hidden away would no longer be a terror to him. He felt as if the load had been lifted from him already.

He went in quietly, locking the door behind him, as was his custom, and dragged the purple hanging from the portrait. A cry of pain and indignation broke from him. He could see no change save that in the eyes there was a look of cunning, and in the mouth the curved wrinkle of the hypocrite. The thing was still loathsome—more loathsome, if possible, than before—and the scarlet dew that spotted the hand seemed brighter, and more like blood newly spilt. Then he trembled. Had it been merely vanity that had made him do his one good deed? Or the desire for a new sensation, as Lord Henry had hinted, with his mocking laugh? Or that passion to act a part that sometimes makes us do things finer than we are ourselves? Or, perhaps, all these? And why was the red stain larger than it had been? It seemed to have crept like a horrible disease over the wrinkled fingers. There was blood on the painted feet, as though the thing had dripped—blood even on the hand that had not held the knife. Confess? Did it mean that he was to confess? To give himself up, and be put to death? He laughed. He felt that the idea was monstrous. Besides, even if he did confess, who would believe him? There was no trace of the murdered man anywhere. Everything belonging to him had been destroyed. He himself had burned what had been below-stairs. The world would simply say that he was mad. They would shut him up if he persisted in his story. . . . Yet it was his duty to confess, to suffer public shame, and to make public atonement. There was a God who called upon men to tell their sins to earth as well as to heaven. Nothing that he could do would cleanse him till he had told his own sin. His sin? He shrugged his shoulders. The death of Basil Hallward seemed very little to him. He was thinking of Hetty Merton. For it was an unjust mirror, this mirror of his soul that he was looking at. Vanity? Curiosity? Hypocrisy? Had there been nothing more in his renunciation than that? There had been something more. At least he thought so. But who could tell? . . . No. There had been nothing more. Through vanity he had spared her. In hypocrisy he had worn the mask of goodness. For curiosity's sake he had tried the denial of self. He recognised that now.

But this murder—was it to dog him all his life? Was he always to be burdened by his past? Was he really to confess? Never. There was only one bit of evidence left against him. The picture itself —that was evidence. He would destroy it. Why had he kept it so long? Once it had given him pleasure to watch it changing and growing old. Of late he had felt no such pleasure. It had kept him awake at night. When he had been away, he had been filled with terror lest other eyes should look upon it. It had brought melancholy across his passions. Its mere memory had marred many moments of joy. It had been like conscience to him. Yes, it had been conscience. He would destroy it.

He looked round, and saw the knife that had stabbed Basil Hallward. He had cleaned it many times, till there was no stain left upon it. It was bright, and glistened. As it had killed the painter, so it would kill the painter's work, and all that that meant. It would kill the past, and when that was dead he would be free. It would kill this monstrous soul-life, and, without its hideous warnings, he would be at peace. He seized the thing, and stabbed the picture with it.

There was a cry heard, and a crash. The cry was so horrible in its agony that the frightened servants woke, and crept out of their rooms. Two gentlemen, who were passing in the Square below, stopped, and looked up at the great house. They walked on till they met a policeman, and brought him back. The man rang the bell several times, but there was no answer. Except for a light in one of the top windows, the house was all dark. After a time, he went away and stood in an adjoining portico and watched.

" Whose house is that, constable ? " asked the elder of the two gentlemen.

" Mr. Dorian Gray's, sir," answered the policeman.

They looked at each other, as they walked away, and sneered. One of them was Sir Henry Ashton's uncle.

Inside, in the servants' part of the house, the half-clad domestics were talking in low whispers to each other. Old Mrs. Leaf was crying and wringing her hands. Francis was as pale as death.

After about quarter of an hour, he got the coachman and one of the footmen and crept upstairs. They knocked, but there was no reply. They called out. Everything was still. Finally, after vainly trying to force the door, they got on the roof, and dropped down on to the balcony. The windows yielded easily ; their bolts were old.

When they entered they found, hanging upon the wall, a splendid portrait of their master as they had last seen him, in all the wonder of his exquisite youth and beauty. Lying on the floor was a dead man, in evening dress, with a knife in his heart. He was withered, wrinkled, and loathsome of visage. It was not till they had examined the rings that they recognised who it was.

THE CANTERVILLE GHOST

A HYLO-IDEALISTIC ROMANCE

I

WHEN Mr. Hiram B. Otis, the American minister, bought Canterville Chase, every one told him he was doing a very foolish thing, as there was no doubt at all that the place was haunted. Indeed, Lord Canterville himself, who was a man of the most punctilious honour, had felt it his duty to mention the fact to Mr. Otis, when they came to discuss terms.

" We have not cared to live in the place ourselves," said Lord Canterville, " since my grand-aunt, the Dowager Duchess of Bolton, was frightened into a fit, from which she never really recovered, by two skeleton hands being placed on her shoulders as she was dressing for dinner, and I feel bound to tell you, Mr. Otis, that the ghost has been seen by several living members of my family, as well as by the rector of the parish, the Rev. Augustus Dampier, who is a fellow of King's College, Cambridge. After the unfortunate accident to the Duchess, none of our younger servants would stay with us, and Lady Canterville often got very little sleep at night, in consequence of the mysterious noises that came from the corridor and the library."

" My Lord," answered the Minister, " I will take the furniture and the ghost at a valuation. I come from a modern country, where we have everything that money can buy ; and with all our spry young fellows painting the Old World red, and carrying off your best actresses and prima-donnas, I reckon that if there were such a thing as a ghost in Europe, we'd have it at home in a

very short time in one of our public museums, or on
the road as a show."

" I fear that the ghost exists," said Lord Canterville,
smiling, " though it may have resisted the overtures of
your enterprising impresarios. It has been well known
for three centuries, since 1584 in fact, and always
makes its appearance before the death of any member
of our family."

" Well, so does the family doctor for that matter,
Lord Canterville. But there is no such thing, sir, as a
ghost, and I guess the laws of nature are not going to
be suspended for the British aristocracy."

" You are certainly very natural in America,"
answered Lord Canterville, who did not quite understand Mr. Otis's last observation, "and if you don't
mind a ghost in the house, it is all right. Only you
must remember I warned you."

A few weeks after this, the purchase was completed,
and at the close of the season the Minister and his
family went down to Canterville Chase. Mrs. Otis,
who, as Miss Lucretia R. Tappan, of West 53rd Street,
had been a celebrated New York belle, was now a very
handsome middle-aged woman, with fine eyes, and a
superb profile. Many American ladies on leaving their
native land adopt an appearance of chronic ill-health,
under the impression that it is a form of European
refinement, but Mrs. Otis had never fallen into this
error. She had a magnificent constitution, and a
really wonderful amount of animal spirits. Indeed, in
many respects, she was quite English, and was an
excellent example of the fact that we have really
everything in common with America nowadays,
except, of course, language. Her eldest son, christened
Washington by his parents in a moment of patriotism,
which he never ceased to regret, was a fair-haired,
rather good-looking young man, who had qualified
himself for American diplomacy by leading the
German at the Newport Casino for three successive

seasons, and even in London was well known as an excellent dancer. Gardenias and the peerage were his only weaknesses. Otherwise he was extremely sensible. Miss Virginia E. Otis was a little girl of fifteen, lithe and lovely as a fawn, and with a fine freedom in her large blue eyes. She was a wonderful amazon, and had once raced old Lord Bilton on her pony twice round the park, winning by a length and a half, just in front of Achilles statue, to the huge delight of the young Duke of Cheshire, who proposed for her on the spot, and was sent back to Eton that very night by his guardians, in floods of tears. After Virginia came the twins, who were usually called " The Stars and Stripes " as they were always getting swished. They were delightful boys, and with the exception of the worthy Minister the only true republicans of the family.

As Canterville Chase is seven miles from Ascot, the nearest railway station, Mr. Otis had telegraphed for a waggonette to meet them, and they started on their drive in high spirits. It was a lovely July evening, and the air was delicate with the scent of the pinewoods. Now and then they heard a wood pigeon brooding over its own sweet voice, or saw, deep in the rustling fern, the burnished breast of the pheasant. Little squirrels peered at them from the beech-trees as they went by, and the rabbits scudded away through the brushwood and over the mossy knolls, with their white tails in the air. As they entered the avenue of Canterville Chase, however, the sky became suddenly overcast with clouds, a curious stillness seemed to hold the atmosphere, a great flight of rooks passed silently over their heads, and, before they reached the house, some big drops of rain had fallen.

Standing on the steps to receive them was an old woman, neatly dressed in black silk, with a white cap and apron. This was Mrs. Umney, the housekeeper, whom Mrs. Otis, at Lady Canterville's earnest request, had consented to keep on in her former position. She made them each a low curtsey as they alighted, and said in a quaint, old-fashioned manner, " I bid you welcome to Canterville Chase." Following her, they passed through the fine Tudor hall into the library, a long, low room, panelled in black oak, at the end of which was a large stained-glass window. Here they found tea laid out for them, and, after taking off their wraps, they sat down and began to look round, while Mrs. Umney waited on them.

Suddenly Mrs. Otis caught sight of a dull red stain on the floor just by the fireplace and, quite unconscious of what it really signified, said to Mrs. Umney, " I am afraid something has been spilt there."

" Yes, madam," replied the old housekeeper in a low voice, " blood has been spilt on that spot."

" How horrid," cried Mrs. Otis ; " I don't at all care for blood-stains in a sitting-room. It must be removed at once."

The old woman smiled, and answered in the same low, mysterious voice, " It is the blood of Lady Eleanore de Canterville, who was murdered on that very spot by her own husband, Sir Simon de Canterville, in 1575. Sir Simon survived her nine years, and disappeared suddenly under very mysterious circumstances. His body has never been discovered, but his guilty spirit still haunts the Chase. The blood-stain has been much admired by tourists and others, and cannot be removed."

" That is all nonsense," cried Washington Otis ; " Pinkerton's Champion Stain Remover and Paragon Detergent will clean it up in no time," and before the terrified housekeeper could interfere he had fallen upon his knees, and was rapidly scouring the floor with a small stick of what looked like a black cosmetic. In a few moments no trace of the blood-stain could be seen.

" I knew Pinkerton would do it," he exclaimed triumphantly, as he looked round at his admiring family but no sooner had he said these words than a terrible flash of lightning lit up the sombre room, a fearful peal of thunder made them all start to their feet, and Mrs. Umney fainted.

"What a monstrous climate!" said the American Minister calmly, as he lit a long cheroot. "I guess the old country is so overpopulated that they have not enough decent weather for everybody. I have always been of opinion that emigration is the only thing for England."

"My dear Hiram," cried Mrs. Otis, "what can we do with a woman who faints?"

"Charge it to her like breakages," answered the Minister; "she won't faint after that"; and in a few moments Mrs. Umney certainly came to. There was no doubt, however, that she was extremely upset, and she sternly warned Mr. Otis to beware of some trouble coming to the house.

"I have seen things with my own eyes, sir," she said, "that would make any Christian's hair stand on end, and many and many a night I have not closed my eyes in sleep for the awful things that are done here." Mr. Otis, however, and his wife warmly assured the honest soul that they were not afraid of ghosts, and, after invoking the blessings of Providence on her new master and mistress, and making arrangements for an increase of salary, the old housekeeper tottered off to her own room.

II

THE storm raged fiercely all that night, but nothing of particular note occurred. The next morning, however, when they came down to breakfast, they found the terrible stain of blood once again on the floor. "I don't think it can be the fault of the Paragon Detergent," said Washington, "for I have tried it with everything. It must be the ghost." He accordingly rubbed out the

stain a second time, but the second morning it appeared
again. The third morning also it was there, though the
library had been locked up at night by Mr. Otis himself,
and the key carried upstairs. The whole family were
now quite interested ; Mr. Otis began to suspect that he
had been too dogmatic in his denial of the existence of
ghosts, Mrs. Otis expressed her intention of joining the
Psychical Society, and Washington prepared a long
letter to Messrs. Myers and Podmore on the subject
of the Permanence of Sanguineous Stains when
connected with crime. That night all doubts about the
objective existence of phantasmata were removed
for ever.

The day had been warm and sunny ; and, in the
cool of the evening, the whole family went out for a
drive. They did not return home till nine o'clock,
when they had a light supper. The conversation in no
way turned upon ghosts, so there were not even those
primary conditions of receptive expectation which so
often precede the presentation of psychical phenomena.
The subjects discussed, as I have since learned from
Mr. Otis, were merely such as form the ordinary
conversation of cultured Americans of the better
class, such as the immense superiority of Miss Fanny
Davenport over Sarah Bernhardt as an actress ; the
difficulty of obtaining green corn, buckwheat cakes,
and hominy, even in the best English houses ; the
importance of Boston in the development of the world-
soul ; the advantages of the baggage check system in
railway travelling ; and the sweetness of the New
York accent as compared to the London drawl. No
mention at all was made of the supernatural, nor was
Sir Simon de Canterville alluded to in any way. At
eleven o'clock the family retired, and by half-past all
the lights were out. Some time after, Mr. Otis was
awakened by a curious noise in the corridor, outside
his room. It sounded like the clank of metal, and
seemed to be coming nearer every moment. He got

up at once, struck a match, and looked at the time.
It was exactly one o'clock. He was quite calm, and
felt his pulse, which was not at all feverish. The
strange noise still continued, and with it he heard
distinctly the sound of footsteps. He put on his
slippers, took a small oblong phial out of his dressing-
case, and opened the door. Right in front of him he
saw, in the wan moonlight, an old man of terrible
aspect. His eyes were as red as burning coals ; long
grey hair fell over his shoulders in matted coils ; his
garments, which were of antique cut, were soiled and
ragged, and from his wrists and ankles hung heavy
manacles and rusty gyves.

" My dear sir," said Mr. Otis, " I really must insist
on your oiling those chains, and have brought you for
that purpose a small bottle of the Tammany Rising
Sun Lubricator. It is said to be completely efficacious
upon one application, and there are several testi-
monials to that effect on the wrapper from some of our
most eminent native divines. I shall leave it here for
you by the bedroom candles, and will be happy to
supply you with more should you require it." With
these words the United States Minister laid the bottle
down on a marble table, and, closing his door, retired
to rest.

For a moment the Canterville ghost stood quite
motionless in natural indignation ; then, dashing the
bottle violently upon the polished floor, he fled down
the corridor, uttering hollow groans, and emitting
a ghastly green light. Just, however, as he reached the
top of the great oak staircase, a door was flung open,
two little white-robed figures appeared, and a large
pillow whizzed past his head ! There was evidently
no time to be lost, so, hastily adopting the Fourth
Dimension of Space as a means of escape, he vanished
through the wainscoting, and the house became
quite quiet.

On reaching a small secret chamber in the left

wing, he leaned up against a moonbeam to recover
his breath, and began to try and realise his position.
Never, in a brilliant and uninterrupted career of three
hundred years, had he been so grossly insulted. He
thought of the Dowager Duchess, whom he had
frightened into a fit as she stood before the glass in her
lace and diamonds ; of the four housemaids, who had
gone off into hysterics when he merely grinned at them
through the curtains of one of the spare bedrooms ;
of the rector of the parish, whose candle he had blown
out as he was coming late one night from the library,
and who had been under the care of Sir William Gull
ever since, a perfect martyr to nervous disorders ; and
of old Madame de Tremouillac, who, having wakened
up one morning early and seen a skeleton seated in an
arm-chair by the fire reading her diary, had been
confined to her bed for six weeks with an attack of
brain fever, and, on her recovery, had become reconciled
to the Church, and had broken off her connection with
that notorious sceptic Monsieur de Voltaire. He
remembered the terrible night when the wicked
Lord Canterville was found choking in his dressing-
room, with the knave of diamonds half-way down his
throat, and confessed, just before he died, that he had
cheated Charles James Fox out of £50,000 at Crock-
ford's by means of that very card, and swore that the
ghost had made him swallow it. All his great achievements came back to him again, from the butler who
had shot himself in the pantry because he had seen a
green hand tapping at the window pane, to the beautiful Lady Stutfield, who was always obliged to wear
a black velvet band round her throat to hide the mark
of five fingers burnt upon her white skin, and who
drowned herself at last in the carp-pond at the end of
the King's Walk. With the enthusiastic egotism of
the true artist he went over his most celebrated
performances, and smiled bitterly to himself as he
recalled to mind his last appearance as " Red Ruben,

or the Strangled Babe," his *début* as " Gaunt Gibeon,
the Blood-sucker of Bexley Moor," and the *furore* he
had excited one lovely June evening by merely playing
ninepins with his own bones upon the lawn-tennis
ground. And after all this, some wretched modern
Americans were to come and offer him the Rising Sun
Lubricator, and throw pillows at his head ! It was quite
unbearable. Besides, no ghosts in history had ever been
treated in this manner. Accordingly, he determined
to have vengeance, and remained till daylight in an
attitude of deep thought.

III

THE next morning when the Otis family met
at breakfast, they discussed the ghost at
some length. The United States Minister was
naturally a little annoyed to find that his present
had not been accepted. " I have no wish," he said,
" to do the ghost any personal injury, and I must say
that, considering the length of time he has been in the
house, I don't think it is at all polite to throw pillows at
him "—a very just remark, at which, I am sorry to say,
the twins burst into shouts of laughter. " Upon the
other hand," he continued, " if he really declines to use
the Rising Sun Lubricator, we shall have to take his
chains from him. It would be quite impossible to sleep,
with such a noise going on outside the bedrooms."
    For the rest of the week, however, they were undis-
turbed, the only thing that excited any attention
being the continual renewal of the blood-stain on the
library floor. This certainly was very strange, as the
door was always locked at night by Mr. Otis, and the
windows kept closely barred. The chameleon-like
colour, also, of the stain excited a good deal of comment. Some mornings it was a dull (almost Indian)
red, then it would be vermilion, then a rich purple,

and once when they came down for family prayers,
according to the simple rites of the Free American
Reformed Episcopalian Church, they found it a bright
emerald-green. These kaleidoscopic changes naturally
amused the party very much, and bets on the subject
were freely made every evening. The only person who
did not enter into the joke was little Virginia, who, for
some unexplained reason, was always a good deal
distressed at the sight of the blood-stain, and very
nearly cried the morning it was emerald-green.

The second appearance of the ghost was on Sunday
night. Shortly after they had gone to bed they were
suddenly alarmed by a fearful crash in the hall. Rushing downstairs, they found that a large suit of old
armour had become detached from its stand, and had
fallen on the stone floor, while, seated in a high-backed
chair, was the Canterville ghost, rubbing his knees
with an expression of acute agony on his face. The
twins, having brought their peashooters with them,
at once discharged two pellets on him, with that
accuracy of aim which can only be attained by long
and careful practice on a writing-master, while the
United States Minister covered him with his revolver,
and called upon him, in accordance with Californian
etiquette, to hold up his hands! The ghost started
up with a wild shriek of rage, and swept through them
like a mist, extinguishing Washington Otis's candle
as he passed, and so leaving them all in total darkness.
On reaching the top of the staircase he recovered
himself, and determined to give his celebrated peal of
demoniac laughter. This he had on more than one
occasion found extremely useful. It was said to have
turned Lord Raker's wig grey in a single night, and
had certainly made three of Lady Canterville's French
governesses give warning before their month was up.
He accordingly laughed his most horrible laugh, till
the old vaulted roof rang and rang again, but hardly
had the fearful echo died away when a door opened,

and Mrs. Otis came out in a light blue dressing-gown. " I am afraid you are far from well," she said, " and have brought you a bottle of Dr. Dobell's tincture. If it is indigestion, you will find it a most excellent remedy." The ghost glared at her in fury, and began at once to make preparations for turning himself into a large black dog, an accomplishment for which he was justly renowned, and to which the family doctor always attributed the permanent idiocy of Lord Canterville's uncle, the Hon. Thomas Horton. The sound of approaching footsteps, however, made him hesitate in his fell purpose, so he contented himself with becoming faintly phosphorescent, and vanished with a deep church-yard groan, just as the twins had come up to him.

On reaching his room he entirely broke down, and became a prey to the most violent agitation. The vulgarity of the twins, and the gross materialism of Mrs. Otis, were naturally extremely annoying, but what really distressed him most was, that he had been unable to wear the suit of mail. He had hoped that even modern Americans would be thrilled by the sight of a Spectre In Armour, if for no more sensible reason, at least out of respect for their national poet Long-fellow, over whose graceful and attractive poetry he himself had whiled away many a weary hour when the Cantervilles were up in town. Besides, it was his own suit. He had worn it with success at the Kenil-worth tournament, and had been highly complimented on it by no less a person than the Virgin Queen herself. Yet when he had put it on, he had been completely overpowered by the weight of the huge breastplate and steel casque, and had fallen heavily on the stone pavement, barking both his knees severely, and bruising the knuckles of his right hand.

For some days after this he was extremely ill, and hardly stirred out of his room at all, except to keep the blood-stain in proper repair. However, by taking

great care of himself, he recovered, and resolved to
make a third attempt to frighten the United States
Minister and his family. He selected Friday, the 17th
of August, for his appearance, and spent most of that
day in looking over his wardrobe, ultimately deciding
in favour of a large slouched hat with a red feather, a
winding-sheet frilled at the wrists and neck, and a
rusty dagger. Towards evening a violent storm of
rain came on, and the wind was so high that all the
windows and doors in the old house shook and rattled.
In fact, it was just such weather as he loved. His plan
of action was this. He was to make his way quietly to
Washington Otis's room, gibber at him from the foot
of the bed, and stab himself three times in the throat
to the sound of slow music. He bore Washington a
special grudge, being quite aware that it was he
who was in the habit of removing the famous
Canterville blood-stain, by means of Pinkerton's
Paragon Detergent. Having reduced the reckless
and foolhardy youth to a condition of abject terror, he
was then to proceed to the room occupied by the
United States Minister and his wife, and there to
place a clammy hand on Mrs. Otis's forehead, while he
hissed into her trembling husband's ear the awful
secrets of the charnel-house. With regard to little
Virginia, he had not quite made up his mind. She had
never insulted him in any way, and was pretty and
gentle. A few hollow groans from the wardrobe, he
thought, would be more than sufficient, or, if that
failed to wake her, he might grabble at the counterpane
with palsy-twitching fingers. As for the twins, he was
quite determined to teach them a lesson. The first
thing to be done was, of course, to sit upon their chests,
so as to produce the stifling sensation of nightmare.
Then, as their beds were quite close to each other,
to stand between them in the form of a green, icy-cold
corpse, till they became paralysed with fear, and finally,
to throw off the winding-sheet, and crawl round the

room, with white bleached bones and one rolling eye-
ball, in the character of " Dumb Daniel, or the Suicide's
Skeleton," a *rôle* in which he had on more than one
occasion produced a great effect, and which he considered quite equal to his famous part of " Martin the
Maniac, or the Masked Mystery."

At half-past ten he heard the family going to bed.
For some time he was disturbed by wild shrieks of
laughter from the twins, who, with the light-hearted
gaiety of schoolboys, were evidently amusing themselves before they retired to rest, but at a quarter past
eleven all was still, and, as midnight sounded, he sallied
forth. The owl beat against the window panes, the
raven croaked from the old yew-tree, and the wind
wandered moaning round the house like a lost soul ;
but the Otis family slept unconscious of their doom,
and high above the rain and storm he could hear the
steady snoring of the Minister for the United States.
He stepped stealthily out of the wainscoting, with an
evil smile on his cruel, wrinkled mouth, and the moon
hid her face in a cloud as he stole past the great oriel
window, where his own arms and those of his murdered
wife were blazoned in azure and gold. On and on he
glided, like an evil shadow, the very darkness seeming
to loathe him as he passed. Once he thought he heard
something call, and stopped ; but it was only the
baying of a dog from the Red Farm, and he went on,
muttering strange sixteenth-century curses, and ever
and anon brandishing the rusty dagger in the midnight
air. Finally he reached the corner of the passage that
led to luckless Washington's room. For a moment he
paused there, the wind blowing his long grey locks
about his head, and twisting into grotesque and fantastic folds the nameless horror of the dead man's
shroud. Then the clock struck the quarter, and he
felt the time was come. He chuckled to himself, and
turned the corner ; but no sooner had he done so, than,
with a piteous wail of terror, he fell back, and hid his

blanched face in his long, bony hands. Right in front of him was standing a horrible spectre, motionless as a carven image, and monstrous as a madman's dream! Its head was bald and burnished; its face round, and fat, and white; and hideous laughter seemed to have writhed its features into an eternal grin. From the eyes streamed rays of scarlet light, the mouth was a wide well of fire, and a hideous garment, like to his own, swathed with its silent snows the Titan form. On its breast was a placard with strange writing in antique characters, some scroll of shame it seemed, some record of wild sins, some awful calendar of crime, and, with its right hand, it bore aloft a falchion of gleaming steel.

Never having seen a ghost before, he naturally was terribly frightened, and, after a second hasty glance at the awful phantom, he fled back to his room, tripping up in his long winding-sheet as he sped down the corridor, and finally dropping the rusty dagger into the Minister's jack-boots, where it was found in the morning by the butler. Once in the privacy of his own apartment, he flung himself down on a small pallet-bed, and hid his face under the clothes. After a time, however, the brave old Canterville spirit asserted itself, and he determined to go and speak to the other ghost as soon as it was daylight. Accordingly, just as the dawn was touching the hills with silver, he returned towards the spot where he had first laid eyes on the grisly phantom, feeling that, after all, two ghosts were better than one, and that, by the aid of his new friend, he might safely grapple with the twins. On reaching the spot, however, a terrible sight met his gaze. Something had evidently happened to the spectre, for the light had entirely faded from its hollow eyes, the gleaming falchion had fallen from its hand, and it was leaning up against the wall in a strained and uncomfortable attitude. He rushed forward and seized it in his arms, when, to his horror, the head slipped off and rolled on

the floor, the body assumed a recumbent posture, and
he found himself clasping a white dimity bed-curtain,
with a sweeping-brush, a kitchen cleaver, and a hollow
turnip lying at his feet !   Unable to understand this
curious transformation, he clutched the placard with
feverish haste, and there, in the grey morning light, he
read these fearful words :—

> **YE OTIS GHOSTE.**
>
> **Ye Onlie True and Originale Spook.**
>
> **Beware of Ye Imitationes.**
>
> **All others are Counterfeite.**

The whole thing flashed across him. He had been
tricked, foiled, and outwitted ! The old Canterville
look came into his eyes ; he ground his toothless gums
together ; and, raising his withered hands high above
his head, swore, according to the picturesque phrase-
ology of the antique school, that when Chanticleer had
sounded twice his merry horn, deeds of blood would
be wrought, and Murder walk abroad with silent feet.
    Hardly had he finished this awful oath when, from
the red-tiled roof of a distant homestead, a cock crew.
He laughed a long, low, bitter laugh, and waited.
Hour after hour he waited, but the cock, for some
strange reason, did not crow again. Finally, at half-
past seven, the arrival of the housemaids made him
give up his fearful vigil, and he stalked back to his
room, thinking of his vain hope and baffled purpose.
There he consulted several books of ancient chivalry,
of which he was exceedingly fond, and found that, on
every occasion on which his oath had been used,
Chanticleer had always crowed a second time. " Perdi-
tion seize the naughty fowl," he muttered, " I have

seen the day when, with my stout spear, I would have run him through the gorge, and made him crow for me an 'twere in death ! " He then retired to a comfortable lead coffin, and stayed there till evening

IV

THE next day the ghost was very weak and tired. The terrible excitement of the last four weeks was beginning to have its effect. His nerves were completely shattered, and he started at the slightest noise. For five days he kept his room, and at last made up his mind to give up the point of the blood-stain on the library floor. If the Otis family did not want it, they clearly did not deserve it. They were evidently people on a low, material plane of existence, and quite incapable of appreciating the symbolic value of sensuous phenomena. The question of phantasmic apparitions, and the development of astral bodies, was of course quite a different matter, and really not under his control. It was his solemn duty to appear in the corridor once a week, and to gibber from the large oriel window on the first and third Wednesday in every month, and he did not see how he could honourably escape from his obligations. It is quite true that his life had been very evil, but, upon the other hand, he was most conscientious in all things connected with the supernatural. For the next three Saturdays, accordingly, he traversed the corridor as usual between midnight and three o'clock, taking every possible precaution against being either heard or seen. He removed his boots, trod as lightly as possible on the old worm-eaten boards, wore a large black velvet cloak, and was careful to use the Rising Sun Lubricator for oiling his chains. I am bound to acknowledge that it was with a good deal of difficulty that he brought himself to adopt this last

mode of protection. However, one night, while the
family were at dinner, he slipped into Mr. Otis's bedroom and carried off the bottle. He felt a little humil-
iated at first, but afterwards was sensible enough to see
that there was a great deal to be said for the invention,
and, to a certain degree, it served his purpose. Still,
in spite of everything, he was not left unmolested.
Strings were continually being stretched across the
corridor, over which he tripped in the dark, and on one
occasion, while dressed for the part of " Black Isaac,
or the Huntsman of Hogley Woods," he met with a
severe fall, through treading on a butter-slide, which
the twins had constructed from the entrance of the
Tapestry Chamber to the top of the oak staircase.
This last insult so enraged him, that he resolved to
make one final effort to assert his dignity and social
position, and determined to visit the insolent young
Etonians the next night in his celebrated character of
" Reckless Rupert, or the Headless Earl."

He had not appeared in this disguise for more than
seventy years ; in fact, not since he had so frightened
pretty Lady Barbara Modish by means of it, that she
suddenly broke off her engagement with the present
Lord Canterville's grandfather, and ran away to
Gretna Green with handsome Jack Castleton, declaring
that nothing in the world would induce her to marry
into a family that allowed such a horrible phantom to
walk up and down the terrace at twilight. Poor Jack
was afterwards shot in a duel by Lord Canterville on
Wandsworth Common, and Lady Barbara died of a
broken heart at Tunbridge Wells before the year was
out, so, in every way, it had been a great success. It
was, however, an extremely difficult " make-up," if I
may use such a theatrical expression in connection
with one of the greatest mysteries of the supernatural,
or, to employ a more scientific term, the higher-
natural world, and it took him fully three hours to
make his preparations. At last everything was ready,

and he was very pleased with his appearance. The big leather riding-boots that went with the dress were just a little too large for him, and he could only find one of the two horse-pistols, but, on the whole, he was quite satisfied, and at a quarter past one he glided out of the wainscoting and crept down the corridor. On reaching the room occupied by the twins, which I should mention was called the Blue Bed Chamber, on account of the colour of its hangings, he found the door just ajar. Wishing to make an effective entrance, he flung it wide open, when a heavy jug of water fell right down on him, wetting him to the skin, and just missing his left shoulder by a couple of inches. At the same moment he heard stifled shrieks of laughter proceeding from the four-post bed. The shock to his nervous system was so great that he fled back to his room as hard as he could go, and the next day he was laid up with a severe cold. The only thing that at all consoled him in the whole affair was the fact that he had not brought his head with him, for, had he done so, the consequences might have been very serious.

He now gave up all hope of ever frightening this rude American family, and contented himself, as a rule, with creeping about the passages in list slippers, with a thick red muffler round his throat for fear of draughts, and a small arquebuse, in case he should be attacked by the twins. The final blow he received occurred on the 19th of September. He had gone downstairs to the great entrance-hall, feeling sure that there, at any rate, he would be quite unmolested, and was amusing himself by making satirical remarks on the large Saroni photographs of the United States Minister and his wife, which had now taken the place of the Canterville family pictures. He was simply but neatly clad in a long shroud, spotted with churchyard mould, had tied up his jaw with a strip of yellow linen, and carried a small lantern and a sexton's spade. In fact, he was dressed for the character of " Jonas the Graveless, or the Corpse-Snatcher of Chertsey Barn," one of his most remarkable impersonations, and one which the Cantervilles had every reason to remember, as it was the real origin of their quarrel with their neighbour, Lord Rufford. It was about a quarter past two o'clock in the morning, and, as far as he could ascertain, no one was stirring. As he was strolling towards the library, however, to see if there were any traces left of the blood-stain, suddenly there leaped out on him from a dark corner two figures, who waved their arms wildly above their heads, and shrieked out " BOO ! " in his ear.

Seized with a panic, which, under the circumstances, was only natural, he rushed for the staircase, but found Washington Otis waiting for him there with the big garden-syringe ; and being thus hemmed in by his enemies on every side, and driven almost to bay, he vanished into the great iron stove, which, fortunately for him, was not lit, and had to make his way home through the flues and chimneys, arriving at his own room in a terrible state of dirt, disorder, and despair.

After this he was not seen again on any nocturnal expedition. The twins lay in wait for him on several occasions, and strewed the passages with nutshells every night to the great annoyance of their parents and the servants, but it was of no avail. It was quite evident that his feelings were so wounded that he would not appear. Mr. Otis consequently resumed his great work on the history of the Democratic Party, on which he had been engaged for some years ; Mrs. Otis organised a wonderful clambake, which amazed the whole county ; the boys took to lacrosse, euchre, poker, and other American national games ; and Virginia rode about the lanes on her pony, accompanied by the young Duke of Cheshire, who had come to spend the last week of his holidays at Canterville Chase. It was generally assumed that the ghost had gone away, and, in fact, Mr. Otis wrote a letter to that effect to Lord Canterville, who, in reply, expressed his great pleasure at the news, and sent his best congratulations to the Minister's worthy wife.

The Otises, however, were deceived, for the ghost was still in the house, and though now almost an invalid, was by no means ready to let matters rest, particularly as he heard that among the guests was the young Duke of Cheshire, whose grand-uncle, Lord Francis Stilton, had once bet a hundred guineas with Colonel Carbury that he would play dice with the Canterville ghost, and was found the next morning lying on the floor of the card-room in such a helpless paralytic state, that though he lived on to a great age, he was never able to say anything again but " Double Sixes." The story was well known at the time, though, of course, out of respect to the feelings of the two noble families, every attempt was made to hush it up : and a full account of all the circumstances connected with it will be found in the third volume of Lord Tattle's *Recollections of the Prince Regent and his Friends.* The ghost, then, was naturally very anxious to show that he had not lost his influence over the Stiltons, with whom, indeed, he was distantly connected, his own first cousin having been married *en secondes noces* to the Sieur de Bulkeley, from whom, as every one knows, the Dukes of Cheshire are lineally descended. Accordingly, he made arrangements for appearing to Virginia's little lover in his celebrated impersonation of " The Vampire Monk, or, the Bloodless Benedictine," a performance so horrible that when old Lady Startup saw it, which she did on one fatal New Year's Eve, in the year 1764, she went off into the most piercing shrieks, which culminated in violent apoplexy, and died in three days, after disinheriting the Cantervilles, who were her nearest relations, and leaving all her money to her London apothecary. At the last moment, however, his terror of the twins prevented his leaving his room, and the little Duke slept in peace under the great feathered canopy in the Royal Bedchamber, and dreamed of Virginia.

V

A FEW days after this, Virginia and her curly-haired cavalier went out riding on Brockley meadows, where she tore her habit so badly in getting through a hedge, that, on her return home, she made up her mind to go up by the back staircase so as not to be seen. As she was running past the Tapestry Chamber, the door of which happened to be open, she fancied she saw some one inside, and thinking it was her mother's maid, who sometimes used to bring her work there, looked in to ask her to mend her habit. To her immense surprise, however, it was the Canterville Ghost himself! He was sitting by the window, watching the ruined gold of the yellow trees fly through the air, and the red leaves dancing madly down the long avenue. His head was leaning on his hand, and his whole attitude was one of extreme depression. Indeed, so forlorn, and so much out of repair did he look, that little Virginia, whose first idea had been to run away and lock herself in her room, was filled with pity, and determined to try and comfort him. So light was her footfall, and so deep his melancholy, that he was not aware of her presence till she spoke to him.

" I am so sorry for you," she said," but my brothers are going back to Eton to-morrow, and then, if you behave yourself, no one will annoy you."

" It is absurd asking me to behave myself," he answered, looking round in astonishment at the pretty little girl who had ventured to address him, " quite absurd. I must rattle my chains, and groan through keyholes, and walk about at night, if that is what you mean. It is my only reason for existing."

" It is no reason at all for existing, and you know you have been very wicked. Mrs. Umney told us, the first day we arrived here, that you had killed your wife."

" Well, I quite admit it," said the Ghost petulantly, " but it was a purely family matter, and concerned no one else."

" It is very wrong to kill any one," said Virginia, who at times had a sweet Puritan gravity, caught from some old New England ancestor.

" Oh, I hate the cheap severity of abstract ethics! My wife was very plain, never had my ruffs properly starched, and knew nothing about cookery. Why, there was a buck I had shot in Hogley Woods, a magnificent pricket, and do you know how she had it sent up to table? However, it is no matter now, for it is all over, and I don't think it was very nice of her brothers to starve me to death, though I did kill her."

" Starve you to death? Oh, Mr. Ghost, I mean Sir Simon, are you hungry? I have a sandwich in my case. Would you like it? "

" No, thank you, I never eat anything now; but it is very kind of you, all the same, and you are much nicer than the rest of your horrid, rude, vulgar, dishonest family."

" Stop! " cried Virginia, stamping her foot, " it is you who are rude, and horrid, and vulgar; and as for dishonesty, you know you stole the paints out of my box to try and furbish up that ridiculous blood-stain in the library. First you took all my reds, including the vermilion, and I couldn't do any more sunsets, then you took the emerald-green and the chrome-yellow, and finally I had nothing left but indigo and Chinese white, and could only do moonlight scenes, which are always depressing to look at, and not at all easy to paint. I never told on you, though I was very much annoyed, and it was most ridiculous, the whole thing; for who ever heard of emerald-green blood? "

" Well, really," said the Ghost, rather meekly,
" what was I to do ? It is a very difficult thing to get
real blood nowadays, and, as your brother began it all
with his Paragon Detergent, I certainly saw no reason
why I should not have your paints. As for colour,
that is always a matter of taste : the Cantervilles
have blue blood, for instance, the very bluest in
England ; but I know you Americans don't care for
things of this kind."

" You know nothing about it, and the best thing
you can do is to emigrate and improve your mind.
My father will be only too happy to give you a free
passage, and though there is a heavy duty on spirits
of every kind, there will be no difficulty about the
Custom House, as the officers are all Democrats. Once
in New York, you are sure to be a great success. I
know lots of people there who would give a hundred
thousand dollars to have a grandfather, and much
more than that to have a family Ghost."

" I don't think I should like America."

" I suppose because we have no ruins and no curiosities," said Virginia satirically.

" No ruins ! no curiosities ! " answered the Ghost ;
" you have your navy and your manners."

" Good evening ; I will go and ask papa to get the
twins an extra week's holiday."

" Please don't go, Miss Virginia," he cried ; " I
am so lonely and so unhappy, and I really don't
know what to do. I want to go to sleep and I
cannot."

" That's quite absurd ! You have merely to go to
bed and blow out the candle. It is very difficult
sometimes to keep awake, especially at church, but
there is no difficulty at all about sleeping. Why, even
babies know how to do that, and they are not very
clever."

" I have not slept for three hundred years," he
said sadly, and Virginia's beautiful blue eyes opened

284 THE CANTERVILLE GHOST

in wonder; "for three hundred years I have not slept, and I am so tired."

Virginia grew quite grave, and her little lips trembled like rose-leaves. She came towards him, and kneeling down at his side, looked up into his old withered face.

"Poor, poor Ghost," she murmured; "have you no place where you can sleep?"

"Far away beyond the pine-woods," he answered, in a low dreamy voice, "there is a little garden. There the grass grows long and deep, there are the great white stars of the hemlock flower, there the nightingale sings all night long. All night long he sings, and the cold, crystal moon looks down, and the yew-tree spreads out its giant arms over the sleepers."

Virginia's eyes grew dim with tears, and she hid her face in her hands.

"You mean the Garden of Death," she whispered.

"Yes, Death. Death must be so beautiful. To lie in the soft brown earth, with the grasses waving above one's head, and listen to silence. To have no yesterday, and no to-morrow. To forget time, to forgive life, to be at peace. You can help me. You can open for me the portals of Death's house, for Love is always with you, and Love is stronger than Death is."

Virginia trembled, a cold shudder ran through her, and for a few moments there was silence. She felt as if she was in a terrible dream.

Then the Ghost spoke again, and his voice sounded like the sighing of the wind.

"Have you ever read the old prophecy on the library window?"

' "Oh, often," cried the little girl, looking up; "I know it quite well. It is painted in curious black letters, and it is difficult to read. There are only six lines:

When a golden girl can win
Prayer from out the lips of sin,
When the barren almond bears,
And a little child gives away its tears,
Then shall all the house be still
And peace come to Canterville.

But I don't know what they mean."

" They mean," he said sadly, " that you must weep
for me for my sins, because I have no tears, and pray
with me for my soul, because I have no faith, and then,
if you have always been sweet, and good, and gentle,
the Angel of Death will have mercy on me. You will
see fearful shapes in darkness, and wicked voices will
whisper in your ear, but they will not harm you, for
against the purity of a little child the powers of Hell
cannot prevail."

Virginia made no answer, and the Ghost wrung his
hands in wild despair as he looked down at her bowed
golden head. Suddenly she stood up, very pale, and
with a strange light in her eyes. " I am not afraid,"
she said firmly, " and I will ask the Angel to have mercy
on you."

He rose from his seat with a faint cry of joy, and
taking her hand bent over it with old-fashioned grace
and kissed it. His fingers were as cold as ice, and his
lips burned like fire, but Virginia did not falter, as he
led her across the dusky room. On the faded green
tapestry were broidered little huntsmen. They blew
their tasselled horns and with their tiny hands waved
to her to go back. " Go back! little Virginia," they
cried, " go back!" but the Ghost clutched her hand
more tightly, and she shut her eyes against them.
Horrible animals with lizard tails, and goggle eyes,
blinked at her from the carven chimney-piece, and
murmured " Beware! little Virginia, beware! we may
never see you again," but the Ghost glided on more
swiftly, and Virginia did not listen. When they reached

the end of the room he stopped, and muttered some words she could not understand. She opened her eyes, and saw the wall slowly fading away like a mist, and a great black cavern in front of her. A bitter cold wind swept round them, and she felt something pulling at her dress. " Quick, quick," cried the Ghost, " or it will be too late," and, in a moment, the wainscoting had closed behind them, and the Tapestry Chamber was empty.

VI

ABOUT ten minutes later, the bell rang for tea, and, as Virginia did not come down, Mrs. Otis sent up one of the footmen to tell her. After a little time he returned and said that he could not find Miss Virginia anywhere. As she was in the habit of going out to the garden every evening to get flowers for the dinner-table, Mrs. Otis was not at all alarmed at first, but when six o'clock struck, and Virginia did not appear, she became really agitated, and sent the boys out to look for her, while she herself and Mr. Otis searched every room in the house. At half-past six the boys came back and said that they could find no trace of their sister anywhere. They were all now in the greatest state of excitement, and did not know what to do, when Mr. Otis suddenly remembered that, some few days before, he had given a band of gypsies per-mission to camp in the park. He accordingly at once set off for Blackfell Hollow, where he knew they were, accompanied by his eldest son and two of the farm-servants. The little Duke of Cheshire, who was perfectly frantic with anxiety, begged hard to be allowed to go too, but Mr. Otis would not allow him, as he was afraid there might be a scuffle. On arriving at the spot, however, he found that the gypsies had gone, and it was evident that their departure had been rather sudden, as the fire was still burning, and some plates were lying on the grass. Having sent off Washington and the two men to scour the district, he ran home, and despatched telegrams to all the police inspectors in the county, telling them to look out for a little girl who had been kidnapped by tramps or gypsies. He then ordered his horse to be brought round, and, after insisting on his wife and the three boys sitting down to dinner, rode off down the Ascot Road with a groom. He had hardly, however, gone a couple of miles when he heard somebody galloping after him, and, looking round, saw the little Duke coming up on his pony, with his face very flushed and no hat. "I'm awfully sorry, Mr. Otis," gasped out the boy, "but I can't eat any dinner as long as Virginia is lost. Please, don't be angry with me; if you had let us be engaged last year, there would never have been all this trouble. You won't send me back, will you? I can't go! I won't go!"

The Minister could not help smiling at the handsome young scapegrace, and was a good deal touched at his devotion to Virginia, so leaning down from his horse, he patted him kindly on the shoulders, and said, "Well, Cecil, if you won't go back I suppose you must come with me, but I must get you a hat at Ascot."

"Oh, bother my hat! I want Virginia!" cried the little Duke, laughing, and they galloped on to the railway station. There Mr. Otis inquired of the station-master if any one answering the description of Virginia had been seen on the platform, but could get no news of her. The station-master, however, wired up and down the line, and assured him that a strict watch would be kept for her, and, after having bought a hat for the little Duke from a linen-draper, who was just putting up his shutters, Mr. Otis rode off to Bexley, a village about four miles away, which he was told was a well-known haunt of the gypsies, as there was a large common next to it. Here they roused

up the rural policeman, but could get no information
from him, and, after riding all over the common, they
turned their horses' heads homewards, and reached
the Chase about eleven o'clock, dead-tired and almost
heart-broken. They found Washington and the twins
waiting for them at the gate-house with lanterns, as
the avenue was very dark. Not the slightest trace of
Virginia had been discovered. The gypsies had been
caught on Broxley meadows, but she was not with
them, and they had explained their sudden departure
by saying that they had mistaken the date of Chorton
Fair, and had gone off in a hurry for fear they might be
late. Indeed, they had been quite distressed at hearing
of Virginia's disappearance, as they were very grateful
to Mr. Otis for having allowed them to camp in his
park, and four of their number had stayed behind to
help in the search. The carp-pond had been dragged,
and the whole Chase thoroughly gone over, but
without any result. It was evident that, for that night
at any rate, Virginia was lost to them ; and it was in
a state of the deepest depression that Mr. Otis and the
boys walked up to the house, the groom following
behind with the two horses and the pony. In the hall
they found a group of frightened servants, and lying
on a sofa in the library was poor Mrs. Otis, almost out
of her mind with terror and anxiety, and having her
forehead bathed with eau-de-cologne by the old housekeeper. Mr. Otis at once insisted on her having
something to eat, and ordered up supper for the
whole party. It was a melancholy meal, as hardly any
one spoke, and even the twins were awestruck and
subdued, as they were very fond of their sister. When
they had finished, Mr. Otis, in spite of the entreaties of
the little Duke, ordered them all to bed, saying that
nothing more could be done that night, and that he
would telegraph in the morning to Scotland Yard for
some detectives to be sent down immediately. Just
as they were passing out of the dining-room, midnight

began to boom from the clock tower, and when the
last stroke sounded they heard a crash and a sudden
shrill cry ; a dreadful peal of thunder shook the house,
a strain of unearthly music floated through the air,
a panel at the top of the staircase flew back with a
loud noise, and out on the landing, looking very pale
and white, with a little casket in her hand, stepped
Virginia. In a moment they had all rushed up to her.
Mrs. Otis clasped her passionately in her arms, the
Duke smothered her with violent kisses, and the twins
executed a wild war-dance round the group.

"Good heavens ! child, where have you been ? "
said Mr. Otis, rather angrily, thinking that she had been
playing some foolish trick on them. " Cecil and I have
been riding all over the country looking for you, and
your mother has been frightened to death. You must
never play these practical jokes any more."

"Except on the Ghost ! except on the Ghost ! "
shrieked the twins, as they capered about.

"My own darling, thank God you are found ; you
must never leave my side again," murmured Mrs.
Otis, as she kissed the trembling child, and smoothed
the tangled gold of her hair.

"Papa," said Virginia quietly, " I have been with
the Ghost. He is dead, and you must come and see
him. He had been very wicked, but he was really
sorry for all that he had done, and he gave me this
box of beautiful jewels before he died."

The whole family gazed at her in mute amazement,
but she was quite grave and serious ; and, turning
round, she led them through the opening in the wainscoting down a narrow secret corridor, Washington
following with a lighted candle, which he had caught
up from the table. Finally, they came to a great oak
door, studded with rusty nails. When Virginia touched
it, it swung back on its heavy hinges, and they found
themselves in a little low room, with a vaulted ceiling,
and one tiny grated window. Imbedded in the wall

was a huge iron ring, and chained to it was a gaunt skeleton, that was stretched out at full length on the stone floor, and seemed to be trying to grasp with its long fleshless fingers an old-fashioned trencher and ewer, that were placed just out of its reach. The jug had evidently been once filled with water, as it was covered inside with green mould. There was nothing on the trencher but a pile of dust. Virginia knelt down beside the skeleton, and, folding her little hands together, began to pray silently, while the rest of the party looked on in wonder at the terrible tragedy whose secret was now disclosed to them.

" Hallo ! " suddenly exclaimed one of the twins, who had been looking out of the window to try and discover in what wing of the house the room was situated. " Hallo ! the old withered almond-tree has blossomed. I can see the flowers quite plainly in the moonlight."

" God has forgiven him," said Virginia gravely, as she rose to her feet, and a beautiful light seemed to illumine her face.

" What an angel you are ! " cried the young Duke, and he put his arm round her neck and kissed her.

VII

FOUR days after these curious incidents a funeral started from Canterville Chase at about eleven o'clock at night. The hearse was drawn by eight black horses, each of which carried on its head a great tuft of nodding ostrich-plumes, and the leaden coffin was covered by a rich purple pall, on which was embroidered in gold the Canterville coat-of-arms. By the side of the hearse and the coaches walked the servants with lighted torches, and the whole procession was wonderfully impressive. Lord Canterville was the chief mourner, having come up

specially from Wales to attend the funeral, and sat
in the first carriage along with little Virginia. Then
came the United States Minister and his wife, then
Washington and the three boys, and in the last carriage
was Mrs. Umney. It was generally felt that, as she
had been frightened by the ghost for more than fifty
years of her life, she had a right to see the last of him.
A deep grave had been dug in the corner of the churchyard, just under the old yew-tree, and the service was
read in the most impressive manner by the Rev.
Augustus Dampier. When the ceremony was over,
the servants, according to an old custom observed in
the Canterville family, extinguished their torches,
and, as the coffin was being lowered into the grave,
Virginia stepped forward and laid on it a large cross
made of white and pink almond-blossoms. As she did
so, the moon came out from behind a cloud, and
flooded with its silent silver the little churchyard, and
from a distant copse a nightingale began to sing.
She thought of the ghost's description of the Garden
of Death, her eyes became dim with tears, and she
hardly spoke a word during the drive home.

The next morning, before Lord Canterville went up
to town, Mr. Otis had an interview with him on the
subject of the jewels the ghost had given to Virginia.
They were perfectly magnificent, especially a certain
ruby necklace with old Venetian setting, which was
really a superb specimen of sixteenth-century work,
and their value was so great that Mr. Otis felt considerable scruples about allowing his daughter to
accept them.

" My Lord," he said, " I know that in this country
mortmain is held to apply to trinkets as well as to
land, and it is quite clear to me that these jewels are,
or should be, heirlooms in your family. I must beg
you, accordingly, to take them to London with you,
and to regard them simply as a portion of your property
which has been restored to you under certain strange

conditions. As for my daughter, she is merely a child, and has as yet, I am glad to say, but little interest in such appurtenances of idle luxury. I am also informed by Mrs. Otis, who, I may say, is no mean authority upon Art—having had the privilege of spending several winters in Boston when she was a girl—that these gems are of great monetary worth, and if offered for sale would fetch a tall price. Under these circumstances, Lord Canterville, I feel sure that you will recognise how impossible it would be for me to allow them to remain in the possession of any member of my family ; and, indeed, all such vain gauds and toys, however suitable or necessary to the dignity of the British aristocracy, would be completely out of place among those who have been brought up on the severe, and I believe immortal, principles of republican simplicity. Perhaps I should mention that Virginia is very anxious that you should allow her to retain the box as a memento of your unfortunate but misguided ancestor. As it is extremely old, and consequently a good deal out of repair, you may perhaps think fit to comply with her request. For my own part, I confess I am a good deal surprised to find a child of mine expressing sympathy with mediævalism in any form, and can only account for it by the fact that Virginia was born in one of your London suburbs shortly after Mrs. Otis had returned from a trip to Athens."

Lord Canterville listened very gravely to the worthy Minister's speech, pulling his grey moustache now and then to hide an involuntary smile, and when Mr. Otis had ended, he shook him cordially by the hand, and said, "My dear sir, your charming little daughter rendered my unlucky ancestor, Sir Simon, a very important service, and I and my family are much indebted to her for her marvellous courage and pluck. The jewels are clearly hers, and, egad, I believe that if I were heartless enough to take them from her, the wicked old fellow would be out of his grave in a fort-

night, leading me the devil of a life. As for their being
heirlooms, nothing is an heirloom that is not so
mentioned in a will or legal document, and the existence
of these jewels has been quite unknown. I assure you I
have no more claim on them than your butler, and
when Miss Virginia grows up I daresay she will be
pleased to have pretty things to wear. Besides, you
forget, Mr. Otis, that you took the furniture and the
ghost at a valuation, and anything that belonged
to the ghost passed at once into your possession,
as, whatever activity Sir Simon may have shown in
the corridor at night, in point of law he was really
dead, and you acquired his property by purchase."

Mr. Otis was a good deal distressed at Lord Canterville's refusal, and begged him to reconsider his
decision, but the good-natured peer was quite firm,
and finally induced the Minister to allow his daughter
to retain the present the ghost had given her, and
when, in the spring of 1890, the young Duchess of
Cheshire was presented at the Queen's first drawing-
room on the occasion of her marriage, her jewels
were the universal theme of admiration. For Virginia
received the coronet, which is the reward of all good
little American girls, and was married to her boy-lover
as soon as he came of age. They were both so charming,
and they loved each other so much, that every one
was delighted at the match, except the old Marchioness
of Dumbleton, who had tried to catch the Duke for
one of her seven unmarried daughters, and had given
no less than three expensive dinner-parties for that
purpose, and, strange to say, Mr. Otis himself. Mr.
Otis was extremely fond of the young Duke personally,
but, theoretically, he objected to titles, and, to use
his own words, "was not without apprehension lest,
amid the enervating influences of a pleasure-loving
aristocracy, the true principles of republican simplicity
should be forgotten." His objections, however, were
completely overruled, and I believe that when he

walked up the aisle of St. George's, Hanover Square, with his daughter leaning on his arm, there was not a prouder man in the whole length and breadth of England.

The Duke and Duchess, after the honeymoon was over, went down to Canterville Chase, and on the day after their arrival they walked over in the afternoon to the lonely churchyard by the pine-woods. There had been a great deal of difficulty at first about the inscription on Sir Simon's tombstone, but finally it had been decided to engrave on it simply the initials of the old gentleman's name, and the verse from the library window. The Duchess had brought with her some lovely roses, which she strewed upon the grave, and after they had stood by it for some time they strolled into the ruined chancel of the old abbey. There the Duchess sat down on a fallen pillar, while her husband lay at her feet smoking a cigarette and looking up at her beautiful eyes. Suddenly he threw his cigarette away, took hold of her hand, and said to her, " Virginia, a wife should have no secrets from her husband."

" Dear Cecil ! I have no secrets from you."

" Yes, you have," he answered, smiling, " you have never told me what happened to you when you were locked up with the ghost."

" I have never told any one, Cecil," said Virginia gravely.

" I know that, but you might tell me."

" Please don't ask me, Cecil, I cannot tell you. Poor Sir Simon ! I owe him a great deal. Yes, don't laugh, Cecil, I really do. He made me see what Life is, and what Death signifies, and why Love is stronger than both."

The Duke rose and kissed his wife lovingly.

" You can have your secret as long as I have your heart," he murmured.

" You have always had that, Cecil."

"And you will tell our children some day, won't you?" Virginia blushed.

THE HAPPY PRINCE

HIGH above the city, on a tall column, stood the statue of the Happy Prince. He was gilded all over with thin leaves of fine gold, for eyes he had two bright sapphires, and a large red ruby glowed on his sword-hilt.

He was very much admired indeed. " He is as beautiful as a weathercock," remarked one of the Town Councillors who wished to gain a reputation for having artistic tastes ; " only not quite so useful," he added, fearing lest people should think him unpractical, which he really was not.

" Why can't you be like the Happy Prince ? " asked a sensible mother of her little boy who was crying for the moon. " The Happy Prince never dreams of crying for anything."

" I am glad there is some one in the world who is quite happy," muttered a disappointed man as he gazed at the wonderful statue.

" He looks just like an angel," said the Charity Children as they came out of the cathedral in their bright scarlet cloaks and their clean white pinafores.

" How do you know ? " said the Mathematical Master, " you have never seen one."

" Ah ! but we have, in our dreams," answered the children ; and the Mathematical Master frowned and looked very severe, for he did not approve of children dreaming.

One night there flew over the city a little Swallow. His friends had gone away to Egypt six weeks before, but he had stayed behind, for he was in love with the most beautiful Reed. He had met her early in the spring as he was flying down the river after a big yellow moth, and had been so attracted by her slender waist that he had stopped to talk to her.

"Shall I love you?" said the Swallow, who liked to come to the point at once, and the Reed made him a low bow. So he flew round and round her, touching the water with his wings, and making silver ripples. This was his courtship, and it lasted all through the summer.

"It is a ridiculous attachment," twittered the other Swallows; "she has no money, and far too many relations;" and indeed the river was quite full of Reeds. Then, when the autumn came they all flew away.

After they had gone he felt lonely, and began to tire of his lady-love. "She has no conversation," he said, "and I am afraid that she is a coquette, for she is always flirting with the wind." And certainly, whenever the wind blew, the Reed made the most graceful curtseys. "I admit that she is domestic," he continued, "but I love travelling, and my wife, consequently, should love travelling also."

"Will you come away with me?" he said finally to her, but the Reed shook her head, she was so attached to her home.

"You have been trifling with me," he cried. "I am off to the Pyramids. Good-bye!" and he flew away.

All day long he flew, and at night-time he arrived at the city. "Where shall I put up?" he said; "I hope the town has made preparations."

Then he saw the statue on the tall column.

"I will put up there," he cried; "it is a fine position, with plenty of fresh air." So he alighted just between the feet of the Happy Prince.

"I have a golden bedroom," he said softly to himself as he looked round, and he prepared to go to sleep; but just as he was putting his head under his wing a large drop of water fell on him. "What a curious thing!" he cried; "there is not a single cloud in the sky, the stars are quite clear and bright, and yet it is raining. The climate in the north of Europe is really dreadful. The Reed used to like the rain, but that was merely her selfishness."

Then another drop fell.

" What is the use of a statue if it cannot keep the rain off ? " he said ; " I must look for a good chimney-pot," and he determined to fly away.

But before he had opened his wings, a third drop fell, and he looked up, and saw—— Ah ! what did he see ?

The eyes of the Happy Prince were filled with tears, and tears were running down his golden cheeks. His face was so beautiful in the moonlight that the little Swallow was filled with pity.

" Who are you ? " he said.

" I am the Happy Prince."

" Why are you weeping then ? " asked the Swallow ; " you have quite drenched me."

" When I was alive and had a human heart," answered the statue, " I did not know what tears were, for I lived in the Palace of Sans-Souci, where sorrow is not allowed to enter. In the daytime I played with my companions in the garden, and in the evening I led the dance in the Great Hall. Round the garden ran a very lofty wall, but I never cared to ask what lay beyond it, everything about me was so beautiful. My courtiers called me the Happy Prince, and happy indeed I was, if pleasure be happiness. So I lived, and so I died. And now that I am dead they have set me up here so high that I can see all the ugliness and all the misery of my city, and though my heart is made of lead yet I cannot choose but weep."

" What ! is he not solid gold ? " said the Swallow to himself. He was too polite to make any personal remarks out loud.

" Far away," continued the statue in a low musical

voice, " far away in a little street there is a poor house.
One of the windows is open, and through it I can see
a woman seated at a table. Her face is thin and worn,
and she has coarse, red hands, all pricked by the
needle, for she is a seamstress. She is embroidering
passion-flowers on a satin gown for the loveliest of
the Queen's maids-of-honour to wear at the next
Court-ball. In a bed in the corner of the room her
little boy is lying ill. He has a fever, and is asking
for oranges. His mother has nothing to give him but
river water, so he is crying. Swallow, Swallow, little
Swallow, will you not bring her the ruby out of my
sword-hilt ? My feet are fastened to this pedestal
and I cannot move."

" I am waited for in Egypt," said the Swallow.
" My friends are flying up and down the Nile, and
talking to the large lotus-flowers. Soon they will go
to sleep in the tomb of the great King. The King is
there himself in his painted coffin. He is wrapped in
yellow linen, and embalmed with spices. Round his
neck is a chain of pale green jade, and his hands are
like withered leaves."

" Swallow, Swallow, little Swallow," said the Prince,
" will you not stay with me for one night, and be my
messenger ? The boy is so thirsty, and the mother
so sad."

" I don't think I like boys," answered the Swallow.
" Last summer, when I was staying on the river,
there were two rude boys, the miller's sons, who were
always throwing stones at me. They never hit me, of
course ; we swallows fly far too well for that, and
besides, I come of a family famous for its agility ; but
still, it was a mark of disrespect."

But the Happy Prince looked so sad that the little
Swallow was sorry. " It is very cold here," he said ;
" but I will stay with you for one night, and be your
messenger."

" Thank you, little Swallow," said the Prince.

So the Swallow picked out the great ruby from the Prince's sword, and flew away with it in his beak over the roofs of the town.

He passed by the cathedral tower, where the white marble angels were sculptured. He passed by the palace and heard the sound of dancing. A beautiful girl came out on the balcony with her lover. " How wonderful the stars are," he said to her, " and how wonderful is the power of love ! "

" I hope my dress will be ready in time for the State-ball," she answered ; " I have ordered passion-flowers to be embroidered on it ; but the seamstresses are so lazy."

He passed over the river, and saw the lanterns hanging to the masts of the ships. He passed over the Ghetto, and saw the old Jews bargaining with each other, and weighing out money in copper scales. At last he came to the poor house and looked in. The boy was tossing feverishly on his bed, and the mother had fallen asleep, she was so tired. In he hopped, and laid the great ruby on the table beside the woman's thimble. Then he flew gently round the bed, fanning the boy's forehead with his wings. " How cool I feel ! " said the boy, " I must be getting better : " and he sank into a delicious slumber.

Then the Swallow flew back to the Happy Prince, and told him what he had done. " It is curious," he remarked, " but I feel quite warm now, although it is so cold."

" That is because you have done a good action," said the Prince. And the little Swallow began to think, and then he fell asleep. Thinking always made him sleepy.

When day broke he flew down to the river and had a bath. " What a remarkable phenomenon ! " said the Professor of Ornithology as he was passing over the bridge. " A swallow in winter ! " And he wrote a long letter about it to the local newspaper. Every one quoted it, it was full of so many words that they could not understand.

"To-night I go to Egypt," said the Swallow, and he was in high spirits at the prospect. He visited all the public monuments, and sat a long time on top of the church steeple. Wherever he went the Sparrows chirruped, and said to each other, "What a distinguished stranger!" so he enjoyed himself very much.

When the moon rose he flew back to the Happy Prince. "Have you any commissions for Egypt?" he cried; "I am just starting."

"Swallow, Swallow, little Swallow," said the Prince, "will you not stay with me one night longer?"

"I am waited for in Egypt," answered the Swallow. "To-morrow my friends will fly up to the Second Cataract. The river-horse couches there among the bulrushes, and on a great granite throne sits the God Memnon. All night long he watches the stars, and when the morning star shines he utters one cry of joy, and then he is silent. At noon the yellow lions come down to the water's edge to drink. They have eyes like green beryls, and their roar is louder than the roar of the cataract."

"Swallow, Swallow, little Swallow," said the Prince, "far away across the city I see a young man in a garret. He is leaning over a desk covered with papers, and in a tumbler by his side there is a bunch of withered violets. His hair is brown and crisp, and his lips are red as a pomegranate, and he has large and dreamy eyes. He is trying to finish a play for the Director of the Theatre, but he is too cold to write any more. There is no fire in the grate, and hunger has made him faint."

"I will wait with you one night longer," said the Swallow, who really had a good heart. "Shall I take him another ruby?"

"Alas! I have no ruby now," said the Prince,

" my eyes are all that I have left. They are made of rare sapphires, which were brought out of India a thousand years ago. Pluck out one of them and take it to him. He will sell it to the jeweller, and buy fire-wood, and finish his play."

" Dear Prince," said the Swallow, " I cannot do that " ; and he began to weep.

" Swallow, Swallow, little Swallow," said the Prince, " do as I command you."

So the Swallow plucked out the Prince's eye, and flew away to the student's garret. It was easy enough to get in, as there was a hole in the roof. Through this he darted, and came into the room. The young man had his head buried in his hands, so he did not hear the flutter of the bird's wings, and when he looked up he found the beautiful sapphire lying on the withered violets.

" I am beginning to be appreciated," he cried ; "this is from some great admirer. Now I can finish my play," and he looked quite happy.

The next day the Swallow flew down to the harbour. He sat on the mast of a large vessel and watched the sailors hauling big chests out of the hold with ropes. " Heave a-hoy ! " they shouted as each chest came up. " I am going to Egypt ! " cried the Swallow, but nobody minded, and when the moon rose he flew back to the Happy Prince.

" I am come to bid you good-bye," he cried.

" Swallow, Swallow, little Swallow," said the Prince, " will you not stay with me one night longer ? "

" It is winter," answered the Swallow, " and the chill snow will soon be here. In Egypt the sun is warm on the green palm-trees, and the crocodiles lie in the mud and look lazily about them. My companions are building a nest in the Temple of Baalbec, and the pink and white doves are watching them, and cooing to each other. Dear Prince, I must leave you, but I will never forget you, and next spring I will bring you back two beautiful jewels in place of those you have given away. The ruby shall be redder than a red rose, and the sapphire shall be as blue as the great sea."

" In the square below," said the Happy Prince, " there stands a little match-girl. She has let her matches fall in the gutter, and they are all spoiled. Her father will beat her if she does not bring home some money, and she is crying. She has no shoes or stockings, and her little head is bare. Pluck out my other eye, and give it to her, and her father will not beat her."

" I will stay with you one night longer," said the Swallow, " but I cannot pluck out your eye. You would be quite blind then."

" Swallow, Swallow, little Swallow," said the Prince, " do as I command you."

So he plucked out the Prince's other eye, and darted down with it. He swooped past the match-girl, and slipped the jewel into the palm of her hand. " What a lovely bit of glass ! " cried the little girl ; and she ran home, laughing.

Then the Swallow came back to the Prince. " You are blind now," he said, " so I will stay with you always."

" No, little Swallow," said the poor prince, " you must go away to Egypt."

" I will stay with you always," said the Swallow, and he slept at the Prince's feet.

All the next day he sat on the Prince's shoulder, and told him stories of what he had seen in strange lands. He told him of the red ibises, who stand in long rows on the banks of the Nile, and catch gold-fish in their beaks ; of the Sphinx, who is as old as the world itself, and lives in the desert, and knows every-thing ; of the merchants, who walk slowly by the side of their camels and carry amber beads in their hands ; of the King of the Mountains of the Moon, who is as black as ebony, and worships a large crystal ;

of the great green snake that sleeps in a palm-tree, and has twenty priests to feed it with honey-cakes ; and of the pygmies who sail over a big lake on large flat leaves, and are always at war with the butterflies.

" Dear little Swallow," said the Prince, " you tell me of marvellous things, but more marvellous than anything is the suffering of men and of women. There is no Mystery so great as Misery. Fly over my city, little Swallow, and tell me what you see there."

So the Swallow flew over the great city, and saw the rich making merry in their beautiful houses, while the beggars were sitting at the gates. He flew into dark lanes, and saw the white faces of starving children looking out listlessly at the black streets. Under the archway of a bridge two little boys were lying in one another's arms to try and keep themselves warm. " How hungry we are ! " they said. " You must not lie here," shouted the watchman, and they wandered out into the rain.

Then he flew back and told the Prince what he had seen.

" I am covered with fine gold," said the Prince, " you must take it off, leaf by leaf, and give it to my poor ; the living always think that gold can make them happy."

Leaf after leaf of the fine gold the Swallow picked off, till the Happy Prince looked quite dull and grey. Leaf after leaf of the fine gold he brought to the poor, and the children's faces grew rosier, and they laughed and played games in the street. " We have bread now ! " they cried.

Then the snow came, and after the snow came the frost. The streets looked as if they were made of silver, they were so bright and glistening ; long icicles like crystal daggers hung down from the eaves of the houses, everybody went about in furs, and the little boys wore scarlet caps and skated on the ice.

The poor little Swallow grew colder and colder,

but he would not leave the Prince, he loved him too well. He picked up crumbs outside the baker's door when the baker was not looking, and tried to keep himself warm by flapping his wings.

But at last he knew that he was going to die. He had just enough strength to fly up to the Prince's shoulder once more. "Good-bye, dear Prince!" he murmured, "will you let me kiss your hand?"

"I am glad that you are going to Egypt at last, little Swallow," said the Prince, "you have stayed too long here; but you must kiss me on the lips, for I love you."

"It is not to Egypt that I am going," said the Swallow. "I am going to the House of Death. Death is the brother of Sleep, is he not?"

And he kissed the Happy Prince on the lips, and fell down dead at his feet.

At that moment a curious crack sounded inside the statue, as if something had broken. The fact is that the leaden heart had snapped right in two. It certainly was a dreadfully hard frost.

Early the next morning the Mayor was walking in the square below in company with the Town Councillors. As they passed the column he looked up at the statue: "Dear me! how shabby the Happy Prince looks!" he said.

"How shabby, indeed!" cried the Town Councillors, who always agreed with the Mayor; and they went up to look at it.

"The ruby has fallen out of his sword, his eyes are gone, and he is golden no longer," said the Mayor; "in fact, he is little better than a beggar!"

"Little better than a beggar," said the Town Councillors.

"And here is actually a dead bird at his feet!" continued the Mayor. "We must really issue a proclamation that birds are not to be allowed to die here." And the Town Clerk made a note of the suggestion.

So they pulled down the statue of the Happy Prince. " As he is no longer beautiful he is no longer useful," said the Art Professor at the University.

Then they melted the statue in a furnace, and the Mayor held a meeting of the Corporation to decide what was to be done with the metal. " We must have another statue, of course," he said, " and it shall be a statue of myself."

" Of myself," said each of the Town Councillors, and they quarrelled. When I last heard of them they were quarrelling still.

" What a strange thing ! " said the overseer of the workmen at the foundry. " This broken lead heart will not melt in the furnace. We must throw it away." So they threw it on a dust-heap where the dead Swallow was also lying.

" Bring me the two most precious things in the city," said God to one of His Angels ; and the Angel brought Him the leaden heart and the dead bird.

" You have rightly chosen," said God, " for in my garden of Paradise this little bird shall sing for ever-more, and in my city of gold the Happy Prince shall praise me."

THE NIGHTINGALE AND THE ROSE

"SHE said that she would dance with me if I brought her red roses," cried the young Student "but in all my garden there is no red rose."

From her nest in the holm-oak tree the Nightingale heard him, and she looked out through the leaves and wondered.

"No red rose in all my garden!" he cried, and his beautiful eyes filled with tears. "Ah on what little things does happiness depend! I have read all that the wise men have written, and all the secrets of philosophy are mine, yet for want of a red rose is my life made wretched."

"Here at last is a true lover," said the Nightingale. "Night after night have I sung of him, though I knew him not: night after night have I told his story to the stars and now I see him. His hair is dark as the hyacinth-blossom, and his lips are red as the rose of his desire; but passion has made his face like pale ivory, and sorrow has set her seal upon his brow."

"The Prince gives a ball to-morrow night," murmured the young student, "and my love will be of the company. If I bring her a red rose she will dance with me till dawn. If I bring her a red rose, I shall hold her in my arms, and she will lean her head upon my shoulder, and her hand will be clasped in mine. But there is no red rose in my garden, so I shall sit lonely, and she will pass me by. She will have no heed of me, and my heart will break."

"Here, indeed, is the true lover," said the Nightingale. "What I sing of, he suffers: what is joy to me, to him is pain. Surely love is a wonderful thing. It is more precious than emeralds, and dearer than

306

fine opals. Pearls and pomegranates cannot buy it, nor is it set forth in the market-place. It may not be purchased of the merchants, nor can it be weighed out in the balance for gold."

"The musicians will sit in their gallery," said the young Student, "and play upon their stringed instruments, and my love will dance to the sound of the harp and the violin. She will dance so lightly that her feet will not touch the floor, and the courtiers in their gay dresses will throng round her. But with me she will not dance, for I have no red rose to give her;" and he flung himself down on the grass, and buried his face in his hands, and wept.

"Why is he weeping?" asked a little Green Lizard, as he ran past him with his tail in the air.

"Why, indeed?" said a Butterfly, who was fluttering about after a sunbeam.

"Why, indeed?" whispered a Daisy to his neighbour, in a soft, low voice.

"He is weeping for a red rose," said the Nightingale.

"For a red rose?" they cried; "how very ridiculous!" and the little Lizard, who was something of a cynic, laughed outright.

But the Nightingale understood the secret of the Student s sorrow, and she sat silent in the oak-tree, and thought about the mystery of Love.

Suddenly she spread her brown wings for flight, and soared into the air. She passed through the grove like a shadow and like a shadow she sailed across the garden.

In the centre of the grass-plot was standing a beautiful rose-tree, and when she saw it she flew over to it, and lit upon a spray.

"Give me a red rose," she cried, "and I will sing you my sweetest song."

But the Tree shook its head.

"My roses are white," it answered; "as white as the foam of the sea, and whiter than the snow upon the mountain. But go to my brother who grows round the old sun-dial, and perhaps he will give you what you want."

So the Nightingale flew over to the Rose-tree that was growing round the old sun-dial.

" Give me a red rose," she cried, " and I will sing you my sweetest song."

But the Tree shook its head.

" My roses are yellow," it answered ; " as yellow as the hair of the mermaiden who sits upon an amber throne, and yellower than the daffodil that blooms in the meadow before the mower comes with his scythe. But go to my brother who grows beneath the Student's window, and perhaps he will give you what you want."

So the Nightingale flew over to the Rose-tree that was growing beneath the Student's window.

" Give me a red rose," she cried, " and I will sing you my sweetest song."

But the Tree shook its head.

" My roses are red," it answered, " as red as the feet of the dove, and redder than the great fans of coral that wave and wave in the ocean-cavern. But the winter has chilled my veins, and the frost has nipped my buds, and the storm has broken my branches, and I shall have no roses at all this year."

" One red rose is all I want," cried the Nightingale, " only one red rose ! Is there no way by which I can get it ? "

" There is a way," answered the Tree ; " but it is so terrible that I dare not tell it to you."

"Tell it to me," said the Nightingale, "I am not afraid."

" If you want a red rose," said the Tree, " you must build it out of music by moonlight, and stain it with your own heart's-blood. You must sing to me with your breast against a thorn, All night long you must sing to me, and the thorn must pierce your heart, and your life-blood must flow into my veins, and become mine."

" Death is a great price to pay for a red rose," cried the Nightingale, " and Life is very dear to all. It is pleasant to sit in the green wood, and to watch the Sun in his chariot of gold, and the Moon in her chariot of pearl. Sweet is the scent of the hawthorn, and sweet are the bluebells that hide in the valley, and the heather that blows on the hill. Yet Love is better than Life, and what is the heart of a bird compared to the heart of a man ? "

So she spread her brown wings for flight, and soared into the air. She swept over the garden like a shadow, and like a shadow she sailed through the grove.

The young Student was still lying on the grass, where she had left him, and the tears were not yet dry in his beautiful eyes.

" Be happy," cried the Nightingale, " be happy ; you shall have your red rose. I will build it out of music by moonlight, and stain it with my own heart's-blood. All that I ask of you in return is that you will be a true lover, for Love is wiser than Philosophy, though he is wise, and mightier than Power, though he is mighty. Flame-coloured are his wings, and coloured like flame is his body. His lips are sweet as honey, and his breath is like frankincense."

The Student looked up from the grass, and listened, but he could not understand what the Nightingale was saying to him, for he only knew the things that are written down in books.

But the Oak-tree understood, and felt sad, for he was very fond of the little Nightingale who had built her nest in his branches.

" Sing me one last song," he whispered ; " I shall feel lonely when you are gone."

So the Nightingale sang to the Oak-tree, and her voice was like water bubbling from a silver jar.

When she had finished her song, the Student got up, and pulled a note-book and a lead-pencil out of his pocket.

"She has form," he said to himself, as he walked away through the grove—"that cannot be denied to her ; but has she got feeling ? I am afraid not. In fact, she is like most artists ; she is all style without any sincerity. She would not sacrifice herself for others. She thinks merely of music, and everybody knows that the arts are selfish. Still, it must be admitted that she has some beautiful notes in her voice. What a pity it is that they do not mean anything, or do any practical good ! " And he went into his room, and lay down on his little pallet-bed, and began to think of his love ; and, after a time, he fell asleep.

And when the moon shone in the heavens the Nightingale flew to the Rose-tree, and set her breast against the thorn. All night long she sang, with her breast against the thorn, and the cold crystal Moon leaned down and listened. All night long she sang, and the thorn went deeper and deeper into her breast, and her life-blood ebbed away from her.

She sang first of the birth of love in the heart of a boy and a girl. And on the topmost spray of the Rose-tree there blossomed a marvellous rose, petal following petal, as song followed song. Pale was it, at first, as the mist that hangs over the river—pale as the feet of the morning, and silver as the wings of the dawn. As the shadow of a rose in a mirror of silver, as the shadow of a rose in a water-pool, so was the rose that blossomed on the topmost spray of fhe Tree.

But the Tree cried to the Nightingale to press closer against the thorn. " Press closer, little Nightingale," cried the Tree, " or the Day will come before the rose is finished."

So the Nightingale pressed closer against the thorn, and louder and louder grew her song, for she sang of the birth of passion in the soul of a man and a maid.

And a delicate flush of pink came into the leaves of the rose, like the flush in the face of the bridegroom when he kisses the lips of the bride. But the thorn had not yet reached her heart, so the rose's heart remained white, for only a Nightingale's heart's-blood can crimson the heart of a rose.

And the Tree cried to the Nightingale to press closer against the thorn. " Press closer, little Nightingale," cried the Tree, " or the Day will come before the rose is finished."

So the Nightingale pressed closer against the thorn, and the thorn touched her heart, and a fierce pang of pain shot through her. Bitter, bitter was the pain, and wilder and wilder grew her song, for she sang of the Love that is perfected by Death, of the Love that dies not in the tomb.

And the marvellous rose became crimson, like the rose of the eastern sky. Crimson was the girdle of petals, and crimson as a ruby was the heart.

But the Nightingale's voice grew fainter, and her little wings began to beat, and a film came over her eyes. Fainter and fainter grew her song, and she felt something choking her in her throat.

Then she gave one last burst of music. The white Moon heard it, and she forgot the dawn, and lingered on in the sky. The red rose heard it, and it trembled all over with ecstasy, and opened its petals to the cold morning air. Echo bore it to her purple cavern in the hills, and woke the sleeping shepherds from their dreams. It floated through the reeds of the river, and they carried its message to the sea.

" Look, look ! " cried the Tree, " the rose is finished now ; " but the Nightingale made no answer, for she was lying dead in the long grass, with the thorn in her heart.

And at noon the Student opened his window and looked out.

" Why, what a wonderful piece of luck ! " he cried ; " here is a red rose ! I have never seen any rose like it in all my life. It is so beautiful that I am sure it has

312 THE NIGHTINGALE AND THE ROSE

a long Latin name ; " and he leaned down and plucked
it.

Then he put on his hat, and ran up to the Professor's
house with the rose in his hand.

The daughter of the Professor was sitting in the
doorway winding blue silk on a reel, and her little
dog was lying at her feet.

" You said that you would dance with me if I
brought you a red rose," cried the Student. " Here
is the reddest rose in all the world. You will wear it
to-night next your heart, and as we dance together
it will tell you how I love you."

But the girl frowned.

" I am afraid it will not go with my dress," she
answered ; " and, besides, the Chamberlain's nephew
has sent me some real jewels, and everybody knows
that jewels cost far more than flowers."

" Well, upon my word, you are very ungrateful,"
said the Student angrily ; and he threw the rose into
the street, where it fell into the gutter, and a cart-
wheel went over it.

" Ungrateful ! " said the girl. " I tell you what,
you are very rude ; and, after all, who are you ?
Only a Student. Why, I don't believe you have even
got silver buckles to your shoes as the Chamberlain's
nephew has ; " and she got up from her chair and
went into the house.

" What a silly thing Love is ! " said the Student as
he walked away. " It is not half as useful as Logic,
for it does not prove anything, and it is always telling
one of things that are not going to happen, and making
one believe things that are not true. In fact, it is
quite unpractical, and, as in this age to be practical
is everything, I shall go back to Philosophy and study
Metaphysics."

So he returned to his room and pulled out a great
dusty book, and began to read.

THE SELFISH GIANT

EVERY afternoon, as they were coming from school, the children used to go and play in the Giant's garden.

It was a large lovely garden, with soft green grass. Here and there over the grass stood beautiful flowers like stars, and there were twelve peach-trees that in the spring-time broke out into delicate blossoms of pink and pearl, and in the autumn bore rich fruit. The birds sat on the trees and sang so sweetly that the children used to stop their games in order to listen to them. " How happy we are here ! " they cried to each other.

One day the Giant came back. He had been to visit his friend the Cornish ogre, and had stayed with him for seven years. After the seven years were over he had said all that he had to say, for his conversation was limited, and he determined to return to his own castle. When he arrived he saw the children playing in the garden.

" What are you doing here ? " he cried in a very gruff voice, and the children ran away.

" My own garden is my own garden," said the Giant ; " any one can understand that, and I will allow nobody to play in it but myself." So he built a high wall all round it, and put up a notice-board.

> TRESPASSERS
> WILL BE
> PROSECUTED.

He was a very selfish Giant.

The poor children had now nowhere to play. They tried to play on the road, but the road was very dusty and full of hard stones, and they did not like it. They used to wander round the high walls when their lessons were over, and talk about the beautiful garden inside. " How happy we were there ! " they said to each other.

Then the Spring came, and all over the country there were little blossoms and little birds. Only in the garden of the Selfish Giant it was still winter. The birds did not care to sing in it as there were no children, and the trees forgot to blossom. Once a beautiful flower put its head out from the grass, but when it saw the notice-board it was so sorry for the children that it slipped back into the ground again, and went off to sleep. The only people who were pleased were the Snow and the Frost. " Spring has forgotten this garden," they cried, " so we will live here all the year round." The Snow covered up the grass with her great white cloak, and the Frost painted all the trees silver. Then they invited the North Wind to stay with them, and he came. He was wrapped in furs, and he roared all day about the garden, and blew the chimney-pots down. " This is a delightful spot," he said, " we must ask the Hail on a visit." So the Hail came. Every day for three hours he rattled on the roof of the castle till he broke most of the slates, and then he ran round and round the garden as fast as he could go. He was dressed in grey, and his breath was like ice.

" I cannot understand why the Spring is so late in coming," said the Selfish Giant, as he sat at the window and looked out at his cold, white garden ; " I hope there will be a change in the weather."

But the Spring never came, nor the Summer. The Autumn gave golden fruit to every garden, but to the Giant's garden she gave none. " He is too selfish," she said. So it was always Winter there, and the North

Wind and the Hail, and the Frost, and the Snow danced about through the trees.

One morning the Giant was lying awake in bed when he heard some lovely music. It sounded so sweet to his ears that he thought it must be the King's musicians passing by. It was really only a little linnet singing outside his window, but it was so long since he had heard a bird sing in his garden that it seemed to him to be the most beautiful music in the world. Then the Hail stopped dancing over his head, and the North Wind ceased roaring, and a delicious perfume came to him through the open casement. " I believe the Spring has come at last," said the Giant ; and he jumped out of bed and looked out.

What did he see ?

He saw a most wonderful sight. Through a little hole in the wall the children had crept in, and they were sitting in the branches of the trees. In every tree that he could see there was a little child. And the trees were so glad to have the children back again that they had covered themselves with blossoms, and were waving their arms gently above the children's heads. The birds were flying about and twittering with delight, and the flowers were looking up through the green grass and laughing. It was a lovely scene, only in one corner it was still winter. It was the farthest corner of the garden, and in it was standing a little boy. He was so small that he could not reach up to the branches of the tree, and he was wandering all round it, crying bitterly. The poor tree was still covered with frost and snow, and the North Wind was blowing and roaring above it. " Climb up I little boy," said the Tree, and it bent its branches down as low as it could ; but the boy was too tiny.

And the Giant's heart melted as he looked out. " How selfish I have been I " he said ; " now I know why the Spring would not come here. I will put that poor little boy on the top of the tree, and then I will knock down the wall, and my garden shall be the children's playground for ever and ever." He was really very sorry for what he had done.

So he crept downstairs and opened the front door quite softly, and went out into the garden. But when the children saw him they were so frightened that they all ran away, and the garden became winter again. Only the little boy did not run for his eyes were so full of tears that he did not see the Giant coming. And the Giant stole up behind him and took him gently in his hand, and put him up into the tree. And the tree broke at once into blossom, and the birds came and sang on it, and the little boy stretched out his two arms and flung them round the Giant's neck, and kissed him. And the other children when they saw that the Giant was not wicked any longer, came running back, and with them came the Spring. "It is your garden now, little children," said the Giant, and he took a great axe and knocked down the wall. And when the people were going to market at twelve o'clock they found the Giant playing with the children in the most beautiful garden they had ever seen.

All day long they played, and in the evening they came to the Giant to bid him good-bye.

"But where is your little companion?" he said: "the boy I put into the tree." The Giant loved him the best because he had kissed him.

"We don't know," answered the children. "he has gone away."

"You must tell him to be sure and come to-morrow," said the Giant. But the children said that they did not know where he lived, and had never seen him before ; and the Giant felt very sad.

Every afternoon, when school was over, the children came and played with the Giant. But the little boy whom the Giant loved was never seen again. The Giant was very kind to all the children, yet he longed for his first little friend, and often spoke of him. " How I would like to see him ! " he used to say.

Years went over, and the Giant grew very old and feeble. He could not play about any more, so he sat in a huge arm-chair, and watched the children at their games, and admired his garden. " I have many beautiful flowers," he said ; " but the children are the most beautiful flowers of all."

One winter morning he looked out of his window as he was dressing. He did not hate the Winter now, for he knew that it was merely the Spring asleep, and that the flowers were resting.

Suddenly he rubbed his eyes in wonder and looked and looked. It certainly was a marvellous sight. In the farthest corner of the garden was a tree quite covered with lovely white blossoms. Its branches were golden, and silver fruit hung down from them, and underneath it stood the little boy he had loved.

Downstairs ran the Giant in great joy, and out into the garden. He hastened across the grass, and came near to the child. And when he came quite close his face grew red with anger, and he said, " Who hath dared to wound thee ? " For on the palms of the child's hands were the prints of two nails, and the prints of two nails were on the little feet.

" Who hath dared to wound thee ? " cried the Giant ; " tell me, that I may take my big sword and slay him."

" Nay " answered the child : " but these are the wounds of Love."

" Who art thou ? " said the Giant, and a strange awe fell on him, and he knelt before the little child.

And the child smiled on the Giant, and said to him, " You let me play once in your garden, to-day you shall come with me to my garden, which is Paradise."

And when the children ran in that afternoon, they found the Giant lying dead under the tree, all covered with white blossoms.

PLAYS

LADY WINDERMERE'S FAN

TO
THE DEAR MEMORY
OF
ROBERT EARL OF LYTTON
IN AFFECTION
AND
ADMIRATION

THE PERSONS OF THE PLAY

LORD WINDERMERE
LORD DARLINGTON
LORD AUGUSTUS LORTON
MR. DUMBY
MR. CECIL GRAHAM
MR. HOPPER
PARKER, Butler

LADY WINDERMERE
THE DUCHESS OF BERWICK
LADY AGATHA CARLISLE
LADY PLYMDALE
LADY STUTFIELD
LADY JEDBURGH
MRS. COWPER-COWPER
MRS. ERLYNNE
ROSALIE, Maid

THE SCENES OF THE PLAY

ACT   I.   *Morning-room in Lord Windermere's house.*
ACT II.   *Drawing-room in Lord Windermere's house.*
ACT III.   *Lord Darlington's rooms.*
ACT IV.   *Same as Act I.*

TIME : *The Present.*
PLACE : *London.*

The action of the play takes place within twenty-four hours, beginning on a Tuesday afternoon at five o'clock, and ending the next day at 1.30 p.m.

LONDON : ST. JAMES'S THEATRE

Lessee and Manager : Mr. George Alexander
February 22nd, 1892.

LORD WINDERMERE	*Mr. George Alexander.*
LORD DARLINGTON	*Mr. Nutcombe Gould.*
LORD AUGUSTUS LORTON	*Mr. H. H. Vincent.*
MR. CECIL GRAHAM	*Mr. Ben Webster.*
MR. DUMBY	*Mr. Vane-Tempest.*
MR. HOPPER	*Mr. Alfred Holles.*
PARKER (*Butler*)	*Mr. V. Sansbury.*
LADY WINDERMERE	*Miss Lily Hanbury.*
THE DUCHESS OF BERWICK	*Miss Fanny Coleman.*
LADY AGATHA CARLISLE	*Miss Laura Graves.*
LADY PLYMDALE	*Miss Granville.*
LADY JEDBURGH	*Miss B. Page.*
LADY STUTFIELD	*Miss Madge Girdlestone*
MRS. COWPER-COWPER	*Miss A. de Winton.*
MRS. ERLYNNE	*Miss Marion Terry.*
ROSALIE (*Maid*)	*Miss Winifred Dolan.*

FIRST ACT

SCENE

Morning-room of Lord Windermere's house in Carlton House Terrace. Doors C. and R. Bureau with books and papers R. Sofa with small tea-table L. Window opening on to terrace L. Table R.

LADY WINDERMERE *is at table R., arranging roses in a blue bowl.*

Enter PARKER.

Parker : Is your ladyship at home this afternoon ?
Lady Windermere : Yes—who has called ?
Parker : Lord Darlington, my lady.
Lady Windermere (hesitates for a moment) : Show him up—and I'm at home to any one who calls.
Parker : Yes, my lady. (*Exit C.*)
Lady Windermere : It's best for me to see him before to-night. I'm glad he's come.

Enter PARKER *C.*

Parker : Lord Darlington.

Enter LORD DARLINGTON *C.*
Exit PARKER.

Lord Darlington : How do you do, Lady Windermere ?
Lady Windermere : How do you do, Lord Darlington ? No, I can't shake hands with you. My hands are all wet with these roses. Aren't they lovely ? They came up from Selby this morning.
Lord Darlington : They are quite perfect. (*Sees a fan lying on the table.*) And what a wonderful fan ! May I look at it ?

Lady Windermere : Do. Pretty, isn't it ! It's got my name on it, and everything. I have only just seen it myself. It's my husband's birthday present to me. You know to-day is my birthday ?

Lord Darlington : No ? Is it really ?

Lady Windermere : Yes, I'm of age to-day. Quite an important day in my life, isn't it ? That is why I am giving this party to-night. Do sit down. (*Still arranging flowers.*)

Lord Darlington (sitting down) : I wish I had known it was your birthday, Lady Windermere. I would have covered the whole street in front of your house with flowers for you to walk on. They are made for you. (*A short pause.*)

Lady Windermere : Lord Darlington, you annoyed me last night at the Foreign Office. I am afraid you are going to annoy me again.

Lord Darlington : I, Lady Windermere ?

Enter PARKER *and* FOOTMAN *C., with tray and tea things.*

Lady Windermere : Put it there, Parker. That will do. (*Wipes her hands with her pocket-handkerchief, goes to tea-table L., and sits down.*) Won't you come over, Lord Darlington ?

Exit PARKER *C.*

Lord Darlington (takes chair and goes across L.C.) : I am quite miserable, Lady Windermere. You must tell me what I did. (*Sits down at table L.*)

Lady Windermere : Well, you kept paying me elaborate compliments the whole evening.

Lord Darlington (smiling) : Ah, nowadays we are all of us so hard up, that the only pleasant things to pay are compliments. They're the only things we *can* pay.

Lady Windermere (shaking her head) : No, I am talking very seriously. You mustn't laugh, I am quite serious. I don't like compliments, and I don't see why a man should think he is pleasing a woman enormously when he says to her a whole heap of things that he doesn't mean.

Lord Darlington : Ah, but I did mean them. (*Takes tea which she offers him.*)

Lady Windermere (*gravely*) *:* I hope not. I should be sorry to have to quarrel with you, Lord Darlington. I like you very much, you know that. But I shouldn't like you at all if I thought you were what most other men are. Believe me, you are better than most other men, and I sometimes think you pretend to be worse.

Lord Darlington : We all have our little vanities, Lady Windermere.

Lady Windermere : Why do you make that your special one ? (*Still seated at table L.*)

Lord Darlington (*still seated L.C.*) *:* Oh, nowadays so many conceited people go about Society pretending to be good, that I think it shows rather a sweet and modest disposition to pretend to be bad. Besides, there is this to be said. If you pretend to be good, the world takes you very seriously. If you pretend to be bad, it doesn't. Such is the astounding stupidity of optimism.

Lady Windermere : Don't you *want* the world to take you seriously then, Lord Darlington ?

Lord Darlington : No, not the world. Who are the people the world takes seriously ? All the dull people one can think of, from the Bishops down to the bores. I should like *you* to take me very seriously, Lady Windermere, *you* more than any one else in life.

Lady Windermere : Why—why me ?

Lord Darlington (*after a slight hesitation*) *:* Because I think we might be great friends. Let us be great friends. You may want a friend some day.

Lady Windermere : Why do you say that ?

Lord Darlington : Oh !—we all want friends at times.

Lady Windermere : I think we're very good friends already, Lord Darlington. We can always remain so as long as you don't——

Lord Darlington : Don't what ?

Lady Windermere : Don't spoil it by saying extra-vagant silly things to me. You think I am a Puritan, I suppose ? Well, I have something of the Puritan in me. I was brought up like that. I am glad of it. My mother died when I was a mere child. I lived always with Lady Julia, my father's elder sister, you know. She was stern to me, but she taught me what the world is forgetting, the difference that there is between what is right and what is wrong. *She* allowed of no compromise. *I* allow of none.

Lord Darlington : My dear Lady Windermere !

Lady Windermere (leaning back on the sofa) : You look on me as being behind the age.—Well, I am ! I should be sorry to be on the same level as an age like this.

Lord Darlington : You think the age very bad ?

Lady Windermere : Yes. Nowadays people seem to look on life as a speculation. It is not a speculation. It is a sacrament. Its ideal is Love. Its purification is sacrifice.

Lord Darlington (smiling) : Oh, anything is better than being sacrificed !

Lady Windermere (leaning forward) : Don't say that.

Lord Darlington : I do say it. I felt it—I know it.

Enter PARKER *C.*

Parker : The men want to know if they are to put the carpets on the terrace for to-night, my lady ?

Lady Windermere : You don't think it will rain, Lord Darlington, do you ?

Lord Darlington : I won't hear of its raining on your birthday.

Lady Windermere : Tell them to do it at once, Parker.

Exit PARKER *C.*

Lord Darlington (still seated) : Do you think then— of course I am only putting an imaginary instance—

do you think that in the case of a young married couple,
say about two years married, if the husband suddenly
becomes the intimate friend of a woman of—well, more
than doubtful character—is always calling upon her,
lunching with her, and probably paying her bills—do
you think that the wife should not console herself ?

Lady Windermere (*frowning*) : Console herself ?

Lord Darlington : Yes, I think she should—I think
she has the right.

Lady Windermere : Because the husband is vile—
should the wife be vile also ?

Lord Darlington : Vileness is a terrible word, Lady
Windermere.

Lady Windermere : It is a terrible thing, Lord
Darlington.

Lord Darlington : Do you know I am afraid that
good people do a great deal of harm in this world.
Certainly the greatest harm they do is that they make
badness of such extraordinary importance. It is absurd
to divide people into good and bad. People are either
charming or tedious. I take the side of the charming,
and you, Lady Windermere, can't help belonging to
them.

Lady Windermere : Now, Lord Darlington. (*Rising
and crossing R., front of him.*) Don't stir, I am merely
going to finish my flowers. (*Goes to table R.C.*)

Lord Darlington (*rising and moving chair*) : And I
must say I think you are very hard on modern life,
Lady Windermere. Of course there is much against
it, I admit. Most women, for instance, nowadays,
are rather mercenary.

Lady Windermere : Don't talk about such people.

Lord Darlington : Well then, setting mercenary people
aside, who, of course, are dreadful, do you think
seriously that women who have committed what the
world calls a fault should never be forgiven ?

Lady Windermere (*standing at table*) : I think they
should never be forgiven.

Lord Darlington: And men? Do you think that there should be the same laws for men as there are for women?

Lady Windermere: Certainly!

Lord Darlington: I think life too complex a thing to be settled by these hard and fast rules.

Lady Windermere: If we had " these hard and fast rules," we should find life much more simple.

Lord Darlington: You allow of no exceptions?

Lady Windermere: None!

Lord Darlington: Ah, what a fascinating Puritan you are, Lady Windermere!

Lady Windermere: The adjective was unnecessary, Lord Darlington.

Lord Darlington: I couldn't help it. I can resist everything except temptation.

Lady Windermere: You have the modern affectation of weakness.

Lord Darlington (looking at her): It's only an affectation, Lady Windermere.

Enter PARKER C.

Parker: The Duchess of Berwick and Lady Agatha Carlisle.

Enter *the* DUCHESS OF BERWICK *and* LADY AGATHA CARLISLE C.

Exit PARKER C.

Duchess of Berwick (coming down C. and shaking hands): Dear Margaret, I am so pleased to see you. You remember Agatha, don't you? (*Crossing L.C.*) How do you do, Lord Darlington? I won't let you know my daughter, you are far too wicked.

Lord Darlington: Don't say that, Duchess. As a wicked man I am a complete failure. Why, there are lots of people who say I have never really done anything wrong in the whole course of my life. Of course they only say it behind my back.

Duchess of Berwick : Isn't he dreadful ? Agatha,
this is Lord Darlington. Mind you don't believe a word
he says. (LORD DARLINGTON *crosses R.C.*) No, no tea,
thank you, dear. (*Crosses and sits on sofa.*) We have
just had tea at Lady Markby's. Such bad tea, too.
It was quite undrinkable. I wasn't at all surprised. Her
own son-in-law supplies it. Agatha is looking forward
so much to your ball to-night, dear Margaret.

Lady Windermere (seated L.C.) : Oh, you mustn't
think it is going to be a ball, Duchess. It is only a
dance in honour of my birthday. A small and early.

Lord Darlington (standing L.C.) : Very small, very
early, and very select, Duchess.

Duchess of Berwick (on sofa L.) : Of course it's going
to be select. But we know *that*, dear Margaret, about
your house. It is really one of the few houses in London
where I can take Agatha, and where I feel perfectly
secure about dear Berwick. I don't know what society
is coming to. The most dreadful people seem to go
everywhere. They certainly come to my parties—the
men get quite furious if one doesn't ask them. Really,
some one should make a stand against it.

Lady Windermere : *I* will, Duchess. I will have no
one in my house about whom there is any scandal.

Lord Darlington (R.C.) : Oh, don't say that, Lady
Windermere. I should never be admitted ! (*Sitting.*)

Duchess of Berwick : Oh, men don't matter. With
women it is different. We're good. Some of us are, at
least. But we are positively getting elbowed into the
corner. Our husbands would really forget our existence
if we didn't nag at them from time to time, just to
remind them that we have a perfect legal right to do so.

Lord Darlington : It's a curious thing, Duchess,
about the game of marriage—a game, by the way,
that is going out of fashion—the wives hold all the
honours, and invariably lose the odd trick.

Duchess of Berwick : The odd trick ? Is that the
husband, Lord Darlington ?

Lord Darlington : It would be rather a good name for the modern husband.

Duchess of Berwick : Dear Lord Darlington, how thoroughly depraved you are !

Lady Windermere : Lord Darlington is trivial.

Lord Darlington : Ah, don't say that, Lady Windermere.

Lady Windermere : Why do you *talk* so trivially about life, then ?

Lord Darlington : Because I think that life is far too important a thing ever to talk seriously about it. (*Moves up C.*)

Duchess of Berwick : What does he mean ? Do, as a concession to my poor wits, Lord Darlington, just explain to me what you really mean.

Lord Darlington (*coming down back of table*) *:* I think I had better not, Duchess. Nowadays to be intelligible is to be found out. Good-bye ! (*Shakes hands with* DUCHESS.) And now—(*goes up stage*)—Lady Windermere, good-bye. I may come to-night, mayn't I ? Do let me come.

Lady Windermere (*standing up stage with* LORD DARLINGTON) *:* Yes, certainly. But you are not to say foolish, insincere things to people.

Lord Darlington (*smiling*) *:* Ah ! you are beginning to reform me. It is a dangerous thing to reform any one, Lady Windermere. (*Bows, and exit C.*)

Duchess of Berwick (*who has risen, goes C.*) *:* What a charming, wicked creature ! I like him so much. I'm quite delighted he's gone ! How sweet you're looking ! Where *do* you get your gowns ? And now I must tell you how sorry I am for you, dear Margaret. (*Crosses to sofa and sits with* LADY WINDERMERE.) Agatha, darling !

Lady Agatha : Yes, mamma. (*Rises.*)

Duchess of Berwick : Will you go and look over the photograph album that I see there ?

Lady Agatha : Yes, mamma. (*Goes to table up L.*)

Duchess of Berwick : Dear girl ! She is so fond of

photographs of Switzerland. Such a pure taste, I think. But I really am so sorry for you, Margaret.

Lady Windermere (smiling) : Why, Duchess ?

Duchess of Berwick : Oh, on account of that horrid woman. She dresses so well, too, which makes it much worse, sets such a dreadful example. Augustus—you know my disreputable brother—such a trial to us all —well, Augustus is completely infatuated about her. It is quite scandalous, for she is absolutely inadmissible into society. Many a woman has a past, but I am told that she has at least a dozen, and that they all fit.

Lady Windermere : Whom are you talking about, Duchess ?

Duchess of Berwick : About Mrs. Erlynne.

Lady Windermere : Mrs. Erlynne ? I never heard of her, Duchess. And what *has* she to do with me ?

Duchess of Berwick : My poor child ! Agatha, darling !

Lady Agatha : Yes, mamma.

Duchess of Berwick : Will you go out on the terrace and look at the sunset ?

Lady Agatha : Yes, mamma. (*Exit through window L.*)

Duchess of Berwick : Sweet girl ! So devoted to sunsets ! Shows such refinement of feeling, does it not ? After all, there is nothing like Nature, is there ?

Lady Windermere : But what is it, Duchess ? Why do you talk to me about this person ?

Duchess of Berwick : Don't you really know? I assure you we're all so distressed about it. Only last night at dear Lady Jansen's every one was saying how extraordinary it was that, of all men in London, Windermere should behave in such a way.

Lady Windermere : My husband—what has *he* got to do with any woman of that kind ?

Duchess of Berwick : Ah, what indeed, dear ? That is the point. He goes to see her continually, and stops for hours at a time, and while he is there she is not at home to any one. Not that many ladies call on her, dear, but she has a great many disreputable men friends—my own brother particularly, as I told you— and that is what makes it so dreadful about Winder- mere. We looked upon *him* as being such a model husband, but I am afraid there is no doubt about it. My dear nieces—you know the Saville girls, don't you ?—such nice domestic creatures—plain, dread- fully plain, but so good—well, they're always at the window doing fancy work, and making ugly things for the poor, which I think so useful of them in these dreadful socialistic days, and this terrible woman has taken a house in Curzon Street, right opposite them —such a respectable street, too ! I don't know what we're coming to ! And they tell me that Windermere goes there four and five times a week—they *see* him. They can't help it—and although they never talk scandal, they—well, of course—they remark on it to every one. And the worst of it all is that I have been told that this woman has got a great deal of money out of somebody, for it seems that she came to London six months ago without anything at all to speak of, and now she has this charming house in Mayfair, drives her ponies in the Park every afternoon and all—well, all—since she has known poor dear Windermere.

Lady Windermere : Oh, I can't believe it !

Duchess of Berwick : But it's quite true, my dear. The whole of London knows it. That is why I felt it was better to come and talk to you, and advise you to take Windermere away at once to Homburg or to Aix, where he'll have something to amuse him, and where you can watch him all day long. I assure you, my dear, that on several occasions after I was first married, I had to pretend to be very ill, and was obliged to drink the most unpleasant mineral waters, merely to get Berwick out of town. He was so extremely susceptible. Though I am bound to say he never gave

away any large sums of money to anybody. He is
far too high-principled for that !

Lady Windermere (interrupting) : Duchess, Duchess,
it's impossible ! (*Rising and crossing stage to C.*) :
We are only married two years. Our child is but six
months old. (*Sits in chair R. of L. table.*)

Duchess of Berwick : Ah, the dear pretty baby !
How is the little darling ? Is it a boy or a girl ? I hope
a girl—ah, no, I remember it's a boy ! I'm so sorry.
Boys are so wicked. My boy is excessively immoral.
You wouldn't believe at what hours he comes home.
And he's only left Oxford a few months—I really don't
know what they teach them there.

Lady Windermere : Are *all* men bad ?

Duchess of Berwick : Oh, all of them, my dear, all
of them, without any exception. And they never grow
any better. Men become old, but they never become
good.

Lady Windermere : Windermere and I married for
love.

Duchess of Berwick : Yes, we begin like that. It
was only Berwick's brutal and incessant threats of
suicide that made me accept him at all, and before the
year was out, he was running after all kinds of petti-
coats, every colour, every shape, every material. In
fact, before the honeymoon was over, I caught him
winking at my maid, a most pretty, respectable girl.
I dismissed her at once without a character.—No, I
remember I passed her on to my sister ; poor dear Sir
George is so short-sighted, I thought it wouldn't
matter. But it did, though—it was most unfortunate.
(*Rises.*) And now, my dear child, I must go, as we are
dining out. And mind you don't take this little
aberration of Windermere's too much to heart. Just
take him abroad, and he'll come back to you all right.

Lady Windermere : Come back to me ? (*C.*)

Duchess of Berwick (L.C.) : Yes, dear, these wicked
women get our husbands away from us, but they

always come back, slightly damaged, of course. And
don't make scenes, men hate them !

Lady Windermere : It is very kind of you, Duchess,
to come and tell all this. But I can't believe that my
husband is untrue to me.

Duchess of Berwick : Pretty child ! I was like that
once. Now I know that all men are monsters. (LADY
WINDERMERE *rings bell.*) The only thing to do is to
feed the wretches well. A good cook does wonders, and
that I know you have. My dear Margaret, you are not
going to cry ?

Lady Windermere : You needn't be afraid, Duchess,
I never cry.

Duchess of Berwick : That's quite right, dear. Crying
is the refuge of plain women but the ruin of pretty
ones. Agatha, darling !

Lady Agatha (entering L.) : Yes, mamma. (*Stands
back of table L.C.*)

Duchess of Berwick : Come and bid good-bye to
Lady Windermere, and thank her for your charming
visit. (*Coming down again*) : And by the way, I must
thank you for sending a card to Mr. Hopper—he's
that rich young Australian people are taking such
notice of just at present. His father made a great
fortune by selling some kind of food in circular tins—
most palatable, I believe—I fancy it is the thing the
servants always refuse to eat. But the son is quite
interesting. I think he's attracted by dear Agatha's
clever talk. Of course, we should be very sorry to lose
her, but I think that a mother who doesn't part with a
daughter every season has no real affection. We're
coming to-night, dear. (PARKER *opens C. doors.*) And
remember my advice, take the poor fellow out of town
at once, it is the only thing to do. Good-bye, once
more ; come, Agatha.

Exeunt DUCHESS *and* LADY AGATHA *C.*

Lady Windermere : How horrible ! I understand

now what Lord Darlington meant by the imaginary instance of the couple not two years married. Oh! it can't be true—she spoke of enormous sums of money paid to this woman. I know where Arthur keeps his bank book—in one of the drawers of that desk. I might find out by that. I *will* find out. (*Opens drawer.*) No, it is some hideous mistake. (*Rises and goes C.*) Some silly scandal! He loves *me*! He loves *me*! But why should I not look? I am his wife, I have a right to look! (*Returns to bureau, takes out book and examines it page by page, smiles and gives a sigh of relief.*) I knew it! there is not a word of truth in this stupid story. (*Puts book back in drawer. As she does so, starts and takes out another book.*) A second book—private—locked! (*Tries to open it, but fails. Sees paper knife on bureau, and with it cuts cover from book. Begins to start at the first page.*) " Mrs. Erlynne—£600—Mrs. Erlynne—£700—Mrs. Erlynne—£400." Oh! it is true! It is true! How horrible! (*Throws book on floor.*)

Enter LORD WINDERMERE *C.*

Lord Windermere: Well, dear, has the fan been sent home yet? (*Going R.C. Sees book.*) Margaret, you have cut open my bank book. You have no right to do such a thing!

Lady Windermere: You think it wrong that you are found out, don't you?

Lord Windermere: I think it wrong that a wife should spy on her husband.

Lady Windermere: I did not spy on you. I never knew of this woman's existence till half an hour ago. Some one who pitied me was kind enough to tell me what every one in London knows already—your daily visits to Curzon Street, your mad infatuation, the monstrous sums of money you squander on this infamous woman! (*Crossing L.*)

Lord Windermere: Margaret! don't talk like that of Mrs. Erlynne, you don't know how unjust it is!

Lady Windermere (turning to him) : You are very jealous of Mrs. Erlynne's honour. I wish you had been as jealous of mine.

Lord Windermere: Your honour is untouched, Margaret. You don't think for a moment that—— (*Puts book back into desk.*)

Lady Windermere: I think that you spend your money strangely. That is all. Oh, don't imagine I mind about the money. As far as I am concerned, you may squander everything we have. But what I *do* mind is that you who have loved me, you who have taught me to love you, should pass from the love that is given to the love that is bought. Oh, it's horrible ! (*Sits on sofa.*) And it is I who feel degraded ! *you* don't feel anything. I feel stained, utterly stained. You can't realise how hideous the last six months seems to me now—every kiss you have given me is tainted in my memory.

Lord Windermere (crossing to her) : Don't say that, Margaret. I never loved any one in the whole world but you.

Lady Windermere (rises) : Who is this woman, then ? Why do you take a house for her ?

Lord Windermere: I did not take a house for her.

Lady Windermere: You gave her the money to do it, which is the same thing.

Lord Windermere: Margaret, as far as I have known Mrs. Erlynne——

Lady Windermere: Is there a Mr. Erlynne—or is he a myth ?

Lord Windermere: Her husband died many years ago. She is alone in the world.

Lady Windermere: No relations ? (*A pause.*)

Lord Windermere: None.

Lady Windermere: Rather curious, isn't it ? (*L.*)

Lord Windermere (L.C.) : Margaret, I was saying to you—and I beg you to listen to me—that as far as I

have known Mrs. Erlynne, she has conducted herself
well. If years ago——

Lady Windermere : Oh ! (*Crossing R.C.*) *:* I don't
want details about her life !

Lord Windermere (*C.*) *:* I am not going to give you
any details about her life. I tell you simply this—
Mrs. Erlynne was once honoured, loved, respected.
She was well born, she had position—she lost everything—threw it away, if you like. That makes it all
the more bitter. Misfortunes one can endure—they
come from outside, they are accidents. But to suffer
for one's own faults—ah !—there is the sting of life.
It was twenty years ago, too. She was little more than
a girl then. She had been a wife for even less time than
you have.

Lady Windermere : I am not interested in her—
and—you should not mention this woman and me
in the same breath. It is an error of taste. (*Sitting
R. at desk.*)

Lord Windermere : Margaret, you could save this
woman. She wants to get back into society, and she
wants you to help her. (*Crossing to her.*)

Lady Windermere : Me !

Lord Windermere : Yes, you.

Lady Windermere : How impertinent of her ! (*A
pause.*)

Lord Windermere : Margaret, I came to ask you a
great favour, and I still ask it of you, though you have
discovered what I had intended you should never
have known, that I have given Mrs. Erlynne a large
sum of money. I want you to send her an invitation
for our party to-night. (*Standing L. of her.*)

Lady Windermere : You are mad ! (*Rises.*)

Lord Windermere : I entreat you. People may chatter
about her, do chatter about her, of course, but they
don't know anything definite against her. She has
been to several houses—not to houses where you
would go, I admit, but still to houses where women

who are in what is called Society nowadays do go. That does not content her. She wants you to receive her once.

Lady Windermere : As a triumph for her, I suppose ?

Lord Windermere : No ; but because she knows that you are a good woman—and that if she comes here once she will have a chance of a happier, a surer life than she has had. She will make no further effort to know you. Won't you help a woman who is trying to get back ?

Lady Windermere : No ! If a woman really repents, she never wishes to return to the society that has made or seen her ruin.

Lord Windermere : I beg of you.

Lady Windermere (crossing to door R.) : I am going to dress for dinner, and don't mention the subject again this evening. Arthur—(*going to him C.*)—you fancy because I have no father or mother that I am alone in the world, and that you can treat me as you choose. You are wrong, I have friends, many friends.

Lord Windermere (L.C.) : Margaret, you are talking foolishly, recklessly. I won't argue with you, but I insist upon your asking Mrs. Erlynne to-night.

Lady Windermere (R.C.) : I shall do nothing of the kind. (*Crossing L.C.*)

Lord Windermere : You refuse ? (*C.*)

Lady Windermere : Absolutely !

Lord Windermere : Ah, Margaret, do this for my sake; it is her last chance.

Lady Windermere : What has that to do with me ?

Lord Windermere : How hard good women are !

Lady Windermere : How weak bad men are !

Lord Windermere : Margaret, none of us men may be good enough for the women we marry—that is quite true—but you don't imagine I would ever—oh, the suggestion is monstrous !

Lady Windermere : Why should *you* be different from other men ? I am told that there is hardly a husband in London who does not waste his life over *some* shameful passion.

Lord Windermere : I am not one of them.

Lady Windermere : I am not sure of that !

Lord Windermere : You are sure in your heart. But don't make chasm after chasm between us. God knows the last few minutes have thrust us wide enough apart. Sit down and write the card.

Lady Windermere : Nothing in the whole world would induce me.

Lord Windermere (crossing to bureau) : Then I will ! (*Rings electric bell, sits and writes card.*)

Lady Windermere : You are going to invite this woman ? (*Crossing to him.*)

Lord Windermere : Yes.

Pause. Enter PARKER.

Parker !

Parker : Yes, my lord. (*Comes down L.C.*)

Lord Windermere : Have this note sent to Mrs. Erlynne at No. 84A Curzon Street. (*Crossing to L.C. and giving note to* PARKER.) There is no answer !

Exit PARKER *C.*

Lady Windermere : Arthur, if that woman comes here, I shall insult her.

Lord Windermere : Margaret, don't say that.

Lady Windermere : I mean it.

Lord Windermere : Child, if you did such a thing, there's not a woman in London who wouldn't pity you.

Lady Windermere : There is not a *good* woman in London who would not applaud me. We have been too lax. We must make an example. I propose to begin to-night. (*Picking up fan.*) Yes, you gave me this fan to-day ; it was your birthday present. If that woman crosses my threshold, I shall strike her across the face with it.

Lord Windermere : Margaret, you couldn't do such a thing.

Lady Windermere : You don't know me ! (*Moves R.*)

Enter PARKER.

Parker !

Parker : Yes, my lady.

Lady Windermere : I shall dine in my own room. I don't want dinner, in fact. See that everything is ready by half-past ten. And, Parker, be sure you pronounce the names of the guests very distinctly to-night. Sometimes you speak so fast that I miss them. I am particularly anxious to hear the names quite clearly, so as to make no mistake. You understand, Parker ?

Parker : Yes, my lady.

Lady Windermere : That will do !

Exit PARKER *C.*

(*Speaking to* LORD WINDERMERE) : Arthur, if that woman comes here—I warn you——

Lord Windermere : Margaret, you'll ruin us !

Lady Windermere : Us ! From this moment my life is separate from yours. But if you wish to avoid a public scandal, write at once to this woman, and tell her that I forbid her to come here !

Lord Windermere : I will not—I cannot—she must come !

Lady Windermere : Then I shall do exactly as I have said. (*Goes R.*) You leave me no choice. (*Exit R.*)

Lord Windermere (*calling after her*) : Margaret ! Margaret ! (*A pause.*) My God ! What shall I do ? I dare not tell her who this woman really is. The shame would kill her. (*Sinks down into a chair and buries his face in his hands.*)

ACT DROP.

SECOND ACT

SCENE

Drawing-room in Lord Windermere's house. Door R.U. opening into ball-room, where band is playing. Door L. through which guests are entering. Door L.U. opens on to illuminated terrace. Palms, flowers, and brilliant lights. Room crowded with guests. Lady Windermere is receiving them.

Duchess of Berwick (up C.) : So strange Lord Windermere isn't here. Mr. Hopper is very late, too. You have kept those five dances for him, Agatha ? (*Comes down.*)

Lady Agatha : Yes, mamma.

Duchess of Berwick (sitting on sofa) : Just let me see your card. I'm so glad Lady Windermere has revived cards.—They're a mother's only safeguard. You dear simple little thing ! (*Scratches out two names.*) No nice girl should ever waltz with such particularly younger sons ! It looks so fast ! The last two dances you might pass on the terrace with Mr. Hopper.

Enter MR. DUMBY *and* LADY PLYMDALE *from the ball-room.*

Lady Agatha : Yes, mamma.

Duchess of Berwick (fanning herself) : The air is so pleasant there.

Parker : Mrs. Cowper-Cowper. Lady Stutfield. Sir James Royston. Mr. Guy Berkeley.

These people enter as announced.

343

Dumby : Good evening, Lady Stutfield. I suppose this will be the last ball of the season ?

Lady Stutfield : I suppose so, Mr. Dumby. It's been a delightful season, hasn't it ?

Dumby : Quite delightful ! Good evening, Duchess. I suppose this will be the last ball of the season ?

Duchess of Berwick : I suppose so, Mr. Dumby. It has been a very dull season, hasn't it ?

Dumby : Dreadfully dull ! Dreadfully dull !

Mrs. Cowper-Cowper : Good evening, Mr. Dumby. I suppose this will be the last ball of the season ?

Dumby : Oh, I think not. There'll probably be two more. (*Wanders back to* LADY PLYMDALE.)

Parker : Mr. Rufford. Lady Jedburgh and Miss Graham. Mr. Hopper.

These people enter as announced.

Hopper : How do you do, Lady Windermere ? How do you do, Duchess ? (*Bows to* LADY AGATHA.)

Duchess of Berwick : Dear Mr. Hopper, how nice of you to come so early. We all know how you are run after in London.

Hopper : Capital place, London ! They are not nearly so exclusive in London as they are in Sydney.

Duchess of Berwick : Ah ! we know your value, Mr. Hopper. We wish there were more like you. It would make life so much easier. Do you know, Mr. Hopper, dear Agatha and I are so much interested in Australia. It must be so pretty with all the dear little kangaroos flying about. Agatha has found it on the map. What a curious shape it is ! Just like a large packing case. However, it is a very young country, isn't it ?

Hopper : Wasn't it made at the same time as the others, Duchess ?

Duchess of Berwick : How clever you are, Mr. Hopper. You have a cleverness quite of your own. Now I mustn't keep you.

Hopper : But I should like to dance with Lady Agatha, Duchess.

Duchess of Berwick : Well, I *hope* she has a dance left. Have you a dance left, Agatha ?

Lady Agatha : Yes, mamma.

Duchess of Berwick : The next one ?

Lady Agatha : Yes, mamma.

Hopper : May I have the pleasure ? (LADY AGATHA *bows.*)

Duchess of Berwick : Mind you take great care of my little chatter-box, Mr. Hopper.

LADY AGATHA *and* MR. HOPPER *pass into ball-room.*

Enter LORD WINDERMERE *L.*

Lord Windermere : Margaret, I want to speak to you.

Lady Windermere : In a moment. (*The music stops.*)

Parker : Lord Augustus Lorton.

Enter LORD AUGUSTUS.

Lord Augustus : Good evening, Lady Windermere.

Duchess of Berwick : Sir James, will you take me into the ball-room ? Augustus has been dining with us to-night. I really have had quite enough of dear Augustus for the moment.

SIR JAMES ROYSTON *gives the* DUCHESS *his arm and escorts her into the ball-room.*

Parker : Mr. and Mrs. Arthur Bowden. Lord and Lady Paisley. Lord Darlington.

These people enter as announced.

Lord Augustus (*coming up to* LORD WINDERMERE) :

Want to speak to you particularly, dear boy. I'm
worn to a shadow. Know I don't look it. None of us
men do look what we really are. Demmed good thing,
too. What I want to know is this. Who is she?
Where does she come from? Why hasn't she got any
demmed relations! Demmed nuisance, relations! But
they make one so demmed respectable.

Lord Windermere : You are talking of Mrs. Erlynne,
I suppose? I only met her six months ago. Till then,
I never knew of her existence.

Lord Augustus : You have seen a good deal of her
since then.

Lord Windermere (coldly) : Yes, I have seen a good
deal of her since then. I have just seen her.

Lord Augustus : Egad! the women are very down
on her. I have been dining with Arabella this evening!
By Jove! you should have heard what she said
about Mrs. Erlynne. She didn't leave a rag on her.
. . . *(Aside.)* Berwick and I told her that didn't matter
much, as the lady in question must have an extremely
fine figure. You should have seen Arabella's expression
. . . But, look here, dear boy. I don't know what to
do about Mrs. Erlynne. Egad! I might be married
to her; she treats me with such demmed indifference.
She's deuced clever, too! She explains everything.
Egad! she explains you. She has got any amount
of explanations for you—and all of them different.

Lord Windermere : No explanations are necessary
about my friendship with Mrs. Erlynne.

Lord Augustus : Hem! Well, look here, dear old
fellow. Do you think she will ever get into this demmed
thing called Society? Would you introduce her to
your wife? No use beating about the confounded
bush. Would you do that?

Lord Windermere : Mrs. Erlynne is coming here
to-night.

Lord Augustus : Your wife has sent her a card?

Lord Windermere : Mrs. Erlynne has received a card.

Lord Augustus : Then she's all right, dear boy. But why didn't you tell me that before ? It would have saved me a heap of worry and demmed mis-under-standings !

LADY AGATHA *and* MR. HOPPER *cross and exit on terrace L.U.E.*

Parker : Mr. Cecil Graham !

Enter MR. CECIL GRAHAM.

Cecil Graham (bows to LADY WINDERMERE, *passes over and shakes hands with* LORD WINDERMERE) :* Good evening, Arthur. Why don't you ask me how I am ? I like people to ask me how I am. It shows a wide-spread interest in my health. Now, to-night I am not at all well. Been dining with my people. Wonder why it is one's people are always so tedious ? My father would talk morality after dinner. I told him he was old enough to know better. But my ex-perience is that as soon as people are old enough to know better, they don't know anything at all. Hullo, Tuppy ! Hear you're going to be married again ; thought you were tired of that game.

Lord Augustus : You're excessively trivial, my dear boy, excessively trivial !

Cecil Graham : By the way, Tuppy, which is it ? Have you been twice married and once divorced, or twice divorced and once married ? I say you've been twice divorced and once married. It seems so much more probable.

Lord Augustus : I have a very bad memory. I really don't remember which. (*Moves away R.*)

Lady Plymdale : Lord Windermere, I've something most particular to ask you.

Lord Windermere : I am afraid—if you will excuse me—I must join my wife.

Lady Plymdale : Oh, you mustn't dream of such a thing. It's most dangerous nowadays for a husband to pay any attention to his wife in public. It always makes people think that he beats her when they're alone. The world has grown so suspicious of anything that looks like a happy married life. But I'll tell you what it is at supper. (*Moves towards door of ball-room.*)

Lord Windermere (C.): Margaret! I *must* speak to you.

Lady Windermere: Will you hold my fan for me, Lord Darlington? Thanks. (*Comes down to him.*)

Lord Windermere (crossing to her): Margaret, what you said before dinner was, of course, impossible?

Lady Windermere: That woman is not coming here to-night.

Lord Windermere (R.C.): Mrs. Erlynne is coming here, and if you in any way annoy or wound her, you will bring shame and sorrow on us both. Remember that! Ah, Margaret, only trust me! A wife should trust her husband!

Lady Windermere (C.): London is full of women who trust their husbands. One can always recognise them. They look so thoroughly unhappy. I am not going to be one of them. (*Moves up.*) Lord Darlington, will you give me back my fan, please? Thanks. . . . A useful thing a fan, isn't it? . . . I want a friend to-night, Lord Darlington; I didn't know I would want one so soon.

Lord Darlington: Lady Windermere! I knew the time would come some day; but why to-night?

Lord Windermere: I *will* tell her. I must. It would be terrible if there were any scene. Margaret . . .

Parker: Mrs. Erlynne!

LORD WINDERMERE *starts.* MRS. ERLYNNE *enters, very beautifully dressed and very dignified.* LADY WINDERMERE *clutches at her fan, then lets it drop on the floor. She bows coldly to* MRS. ERLYNNE, *who bows to her sweetly in turn, and sails into the room.*

Lord Darlington : You have dropped your fan, Lady Windermere. (*Picks it up and hands it to her.*)

Mrs. Erlynne (C.) : How do you do, again, Lord Windermere ? How charming your sweet wife looks ! Quite a picture !

Lord Windermere (*in a low voice*) : It was terribly rash of you to come !

Mrs. Erlynne (*smiling*) : The wisest thing I ever did in my life. And, by the way, you must pay me a good deal of attention this evening. I am afraid of the women. You must introduce me to some of them. The men I can always manage. How do you do, Lord Augustus ? You have quite neglected me lately. I have not seen you since yesterday. I am afraid you're faithless. Every one told me so.

Lord Augustus (R.) : Now really, Mrs. Erlynne, allow me to explain.

Mrs. Erlynne (R.C.) : No, dear Lord Augustus, you can't explain anything. It is your chief charm.

Lord Augustus : Ah ! if you find charms in me, Mrs. Erlynne——

> *They converse together.* LORD WINDERMERE *moves uneasily about the room watching* MRS. ERLYNNE.

Lord Darlington (*to* LADY WINDERMERE) : How pale you are !

Lady Windermere : Cowards are always pale !

Lord Darlington : You look faint. Come out on the terrace.

Lady Windermere : Yes. (*To* PARKER) : Parker, send my cloak out.

Mrs. Erlynne (*crossing to her*) : Lady Windermere, how beautifully your terrace is illuminated. Reminds me of Prince Doria's at Rome.

> LADY WINDERMERE *bows coldly, and goes off with* LORD DARLINGTON.

Oh, how do you do, Mr. Graham? Isn't that your
aunt, Lady Jedburgh? I should so much like to know
her.

Cecil Graham (*after a moment's hesitation and em-
barrassment*): Oh, certainly, if you wish it. Aunt
Caroline, allow me to introduce Mrs. Erlynne.

Mrs. Erlynne: So pleased to meet you, Lady
Jedburgh. (*Sits beside her on the sofa.*) Your nephew and
I are great friends. I am so much interested in his
political career. I think he's sure to be a wonderful
success. He thinks like a Tory, and talks like a Radical,
and that's so important nowadays. He's such a
brilliant talker, too. But we all know from whom he
inherits that. Lord Allandale was saying to me only
yesterday, in the park, that Mr. Graham talks almost
as well as his aunt.

Lady Jedburgh (*R.*): Most kind of you to say these
charming things to me! (MRS. ERLYNNE *smiles, and
continues conversation.*)

Dumby (*to* CECIL GRAHAM): Did you introduce Mrs.
Erlynne to Lady Jedburgh?

Cecil Graham: Had to, my dear fellow. Couldn't
help it! That woman can make one do anything
she wants. How, I don't know.

Dumby: Hope to goodness she won't speak to me!
(*Saunters towards* LADY PLYMDALE.)

Mrs. Erlynne (*C. To* LADY JEDBURGH): On
Thursday? With great pleasure. (*Rises, and speaks
to* LORD WINDERMERE, *laughing.*) What a bore it is
to have to be civil to these old dowagers! But they
always insist on it!

Lady Plymdale (*to* MR. DUMBY): Who is that well-
-dressed woman talking to Windermere?

Dumby: Haven't got the slightest idea! Looks like
an *édition de luxe* of a wicked French novel, meant
specially for the English market.

Mrs. Erlynne: So that is poor Dumby with Lady
Plymdale? I hear she is frightfully jealous of him. He

doesn't seem anxious to speak to me to-night. I suppose he is afraid of her. Those straw-coloured women have dreadful tempers. Do you know, I think I'll dance with you first, Windermere. (LORD WINDER-MERE *bites his lip and frowns*.) It will make Lord Augustus so jealous ! Lord Augustus ! (LORD AUGUSTUS *comes down*.) Lord Windermere insists on my dancing with him first, and, as it's his own house, I can't well refuse. You know I would much sooner dance with you.

Lord Augustus (with a low bow) : I wish I could think so, Mrs. Erlynne.

Mrs. Erlynne : You know it far too well. I can fancy a person dancing through life with you and finding it charming.

Lord Augustus (placing his hand on his white waist-coat) : Oh, thank you, thank you. You are the most adorable of all ladies !

Mrs. Erlynne : What a nice speech ! So simple and so sincere ! Just the sort of speech I like. Well, you shall hold my bouquet. (*Goes towards ball-room on* LORD WINDERMERE'S *arm*.) Ah, Mr. Dumby, how are you ? I am so sorry I have been out the last three times you have called. Come and lunch on Friday.

Dumby (with perfect nonchalance) : Delighted !

LADY PLYMDALE *glares with indignation at* MR. DUMBY. LORD AUGUSTUS *follows* MRS. ERLYNNE *and* LORD WINDERMERE *into the ball-room holding bouquet*.

Lady Plymdale (to MR. DUMBY) *:* What an absolute brute you are ! I never can believe a word you say ! Why did you tell me you didn't know her ? What do you mean by calling on her three times running ? You are not to go to lunch there ; of course you understand that ?

Dumby : My dear Laura, I wouldn't dream of going !

Lady Plymdale : You haven't told me her name yet ! Who is she ?

Dumby (coughs slightly and smooths his hair) : She's a Mrs. Erlynne.

Lady Plymdale : That woman !

Dumby : Yes ; that is what every one calls her.

Lady Plumdale : How very interesting ! How intensely interesting ! I really must have a good stare at her. (*Goes to door of ball-room and looks in.*) I have heard the most shocking things about her. They say she is ruining poor Windermere. And Lady Windermere, who goes in for being so proper, invites her ! How extremely amusing ! It takes a thoroughly good woman to do a thoroughly stupid thing. You are to lunch there on Friday !

Dumby : Why ?

Lady Plymdale : Because I want you to take my husband with you. He has been so attentive lately, that he has become a perfect nuisance. Now, this woman is just the thing for him. He'll dance attendance upon her as long as she lets him, and won't bother me. I assure you, women of that kind are most useful. They form the basis of other people's marriages.

Dumby : What a mystery you are !

Lady Plymdale (looking at him) : I wish *you* were !

Dumby : I am—to myself. I am the only person in the world I should like to know thoroughly ; but I don't see any chance of it just at present.

> *They pass into the ball-room, and* LADY WINDERMERE *and* LORD DARLINGTON *enter from the terrace.*

Lady Windermere : Yes. Yes. Her coming here is monstrous, unbearable. I know now what you meant to-day at tea time. Why didn't you tell me right out ? You should have !

Lord Darlington : I couldn't ! A man can't tell these things about another man ! But if I had known he was

going to make you ask her here to-night, I think I
would have told you. That insult, at any rate, you
would have been spared.

Lady Windermere : I did not ask her. He insisted
on her coming—against my entreaties—against my
commands. Oh ! the house is tainted for me ! I feel
that every woman here sneers at me as she dances by
with my husband. What have I done to deserve this ?
I gave him all my life. He took it—used it—spoiled
it ! I am degraded in my own eyes, and I lack courage
—I am a coward ! (*Sits down on sofa.*)

Lord Darlington : If I know you at all, I know that
you can't live with a man who treats you like this !
What sort of life would you have with him ? You
would feel that he was lying to you every moment of
the day. You would feel that the look in his eyes was
false, his voice false, his touch false, his passion false.
He would come to you when he was weary of others ;
you would have to comfort him. He would come to
you when he was devoted to others ; you would have
to charm him. You would have to be to him the mask
of his real life, the cloak to hide his secret.

Lady Windermere : You are right—you are terribly
right. But where am I to turn ? You said you would
be my friend, Lord Darlington.—Tell me, what am
I to do ? Be my friend now.

Lord Darlington : Between men and women there is
no friendship possible. There is passion, enmity,
worship, love, but no friendship. I love you——

Lady Windermere : No, no ! (*Rises.*)

Lord Darlington : Yes, I love you ! You are more to
me than anything in the whole world. What does your
husband give you ? Nothing. Whatever is in him he
gives to this wretched woman, whom he has thrust
into your society, into your home, to shame you before
every one. I offer you my life——

Lady Windermere : Lord Darlington !

Lord Darlington : My life—my whole life. Take it,

and do with it what you will. . . . I love you—love you as I have never loved any living thing. From the moment I met you I loved you, loved you blindly, adoringly, madly ! You did not know it then—you know it now ! Leave this house to-night. I won't tell you that the world matters nothing, or the world's voice, or the voice of society. They matter a great deal. They matter far too much. But there are moments when one has to choose between living one's own life, fully, entirely, completely—or dragging out some false, shallow, degrading existence that the world in its hypocrisy demands. You have that moment now. Choose ! Oh, my love, choose.

Lady Windermere (*moving slowly away from him, and looking at him with startled eyes*) : I have not the courage.

Lord Darlington (*following her*) : Yes ; you have the courage. There may be six months of pain, of disgrace even, but when you no longer bear his name, when you bear mine, all will be well. Margaret, my love, my wife that shall be some day—yes, my wife ! You know it ! What are you now ? This woman has the place that belongs by right to you. Oh ! go—go out of this house, with head erect, with a smile upon your lips, with courage in your eyes. All London will know why you did it ; and who will blame you ? No one. If they do, what matter ? Wrong ? What is wrong ? It's wrong for a man to abandon his wife for a shameless woman. It is wrong for a wife to remain with a man who so dishonours her. You said once you would make no compromise with things. Make none now. Be brave ! Be yourself !

Lady Windermere : I am afraid of being myself. Let me think. Let me wait ! My husband may return to me. (*Sits down on sofa.*)

Lord Darlington : And you would take him back ! You are not what I thought you were. You are just the same as every other woman. You would stand anything rather than face the censure of a world, whose praise you would despise. In a week you will be driving with this woman in the Park. She will be your constant guest—your dearest friend. You would endure anything rather than break with one blow this monstrous tie. You are right. You have no courage ; none !

Lady Windermere : Ah, give me time to think. I cannot answer you now. (*Passes her hand nervously over her brow.*)

Lord Darlington : It must be now or not at all.

Lady Windermere (*rising from the sofa*) : Then, not at all ! (*A pause.*)

Lord Darlington : You break my heart !

Lady Windermere : Mine is already broken. (*A pause.*)

Lord Darlington : To-morrow I leave England. This is the last time I shall ever look on you. You will never see me again. For one moment our lives met— our souls touched. They must never meet or touch again. Good-bye, Margaret. (*Exit.*)

Lady Windermere : How alone I am in life. How terribly alone !

> *The music stops. Enter the* DUCHESS OF BERWICK *and* LORD PAISLEY *laughing and talking. Other guests come in from ball-room.*

Duchess of Berwick : Dear Margaret, I've just been having such a delightful chat with Mrs. Erlynne. I am so sorry for what I said to you this afternoon about her. Of course, she must be all right if *you* invite her. A most attractive woman, and has such sensible views on life. Told me she entirely disapproved of people marrying more than once, so I feel quite safe about poor Augustus. Can't imagine why people speak against her. It's those horrid nieces of mine—the Saville girls—they're always talking scandal. Still, I should go to Homburg, dear, I really should. She is just a little too attractive. But where is Agatha ? Oh, there she is. (LADY AGATHA *and* MR. HOPPER *enter from terrace L.U.E.*) Mr. Hopper, I am very very angry with you. You have taken Agatha out on the terrace, and she is so delicate.

Hopper (L.C.) : Awfully sorry, Duchess. We went out for a moment and then got chatting together.

Duchess of Berwick (C.) : Ah, about dear Australia, I suppose ?

Hopper : Yes !

Duchess of Berwick : Agatha, darling ! (*Beckons her over.*)

Lady Agatha : Yes, mamma !

Duchess of Berwick (aside) : Did Mr. Hopper definitely——

Lady Agatha : Yes, mamma.

Duchess of Berwick : And what answer did you give him, dear child ?

Lady Agatha : Yes, mamma.

Duchess of Berwick (affectionately) : My dear one ! You always say the right thing. Mr. Hopper ! James ! Agatha has told me everything. How cleverly you have both kept your secret.

Hopper : You don't mind my taking Agatha off to Australia, then, Duchess ?

Duchess of Berwick (indignantly) : To Australia ? Oh, don't mention that dreadful vulgar place.

Hopper : But she said she'd like to come with me.

Duchess of Berwick (severely) : Did you say that, Agatha ?

Lady Agatha : Yes, mamma.

Duchess of Berwick : Agatha, you say the most silly things possible. I think on the whole that Grosvenor Square would be a more healthy place to reside in. There are lots of vulgar people live in Grosvenor Square, but at any rate there are no horrid kangaroos crawling about. But we'll talk about that to-morrow.

James, you can take Agatha down. You'll come to lunch, of course, James. At half-past one, instead of two. The Duke will wish to say a few words to you, I am sure.

Hopper : I should like to have a chat with the Duke, Duchess. He has not said a single word to me yet.

Duchess of Berwick : I think you'll find he will have a great deal to say to you to-morrow. (*Exit* LADY AGATHA *with* MR. HOPPER.) And now good-night, Margaret. I'm afraid it's the old, old story, dear. Love —well, not love at first sight, but love at the end of the season, which is so much more satisfactory.

Lady Windermere : Good-night, Duchess.

Exit *the* DUCHESS OF BERWICK *on* LORD PAISLEY'S *arm.*

Lady Plymdale : My dear Margaret, what a handsome woman your husband has been dancing with ! I should be quite jealous if I were you ! Is she a great friend of yours ?

Lady Windermere : No !

Lady Plymdale : Really ? Good-night, dear. (*Looks at* MR. DUMBY *and exit.*)

Dumby : Awful manners young Hopper has !

Cecil Graham : Ah ! Hopper is one of Nature's gentlemen, the worst type of gentleman I know.

Dumby : Sensible woman, Lady Windermere. Lots of wives would have objected to Mrs. Erlynne coming. But Lady Windermere has that uncommon thing called common sense.

Cecil Graham : And Windermere knows that nothing looks so like innocence as an indiscretion.

Dumby : Yes ; dear Windermere is becoming almost modern. Never thought he would. (*Bows to* LADY WINDERMERE *and exit.*)

Lady Jedburgh : Good-night, Lady Windermere.

What a fascinating woman Mrs. Erlynne is! She is
coming to lunch on Thursday, won't you come too?
I expect the Bishop and dear Lady Merton.

Lady Windermere : I am afraid I am engaged, Lady
Jedburgh.

Lady Jedburgh : So sorry. Come, dear.

> *Exeunt* LADY JEDBURGH *and* MISS GRAHAM.
> *Enter* MRS. ERLYNNE *and* LORD WINDERMERE.

Mrs. Erlynne : Charming ball it has been! Quite
reminds me of old days. (*Sits on sofa.*) And I see that
there are just as many fools in society as there used to
be. So pleased to find that nothing has altered!
Except Margaret. She's grown quite pretty. The last
time I saw her—twenty years ago, she was a fright in
flannel. Positive fright, I assure you. The dear
Duchess! and that sweet Lady Agatha! Just the
type of girl I like! Well, really, Windermere, if I
am to be the Duchess's sister-in-law——

Lord Windermere (*sitting L. of her*) : But are you——?

> *Exit* MR. CECIL GRAHAM *with rest of guests.*
> LADY WINDERMERE *watches, with a look of scorn
> and pain,* MRS. ERLYNNE *and her husband. They
> are unconscious of her presence.*

Mrs. Erlynne : Oh, yes! He's to call to-morrow at
twelve o'clock! He wanted to propose to-night. In
fact he did. He kept on proposing. Poor Augustus, you
know how he repeats himself. Such a bad habit! But
I told him I wouldn't give him an answer till to-morrow.
Of course I am going to take him. And I dare say I'll
make him an admirable wife, as wives go. And there
is a great deal of good in Lord Augustus. Fortunately
it is all on the surface. Just where good qualities should
be. Of course you must help me in this matter.

Lord Windermere : I am not called on to encourage
Lord Augustus, I suppose?

Mrs. Erlynne : Oh, no ! I do the encouraging. But you will make me a handsome settlement, Windermere, won't you ?

Lord Windermere (frowning) : Is that what you want to talk to me about to-night ?

Mrs. Erlynne : Yes.

Lord Windermere (with a gesture of impatience) : I will not talk of it here.

Mrs. Erlynne (laughing) : Then we will talk of it on the terrace. Even business should have a picturesque background. Should it not, Windermere ? With a proper background women can do anything.

Lord Windermere : Won't to-morrow do as well ?

Mrs. Erlynne : No ; you see, to-morrow I am going to accept him. And I think it would be a good thing if I was able to tell him that I had—well, what shall I say ?—£2000 a year left to me by a third cousin —or a second husband—or some distant relative of that kind. It would be an additional attraction, wouldn't it ? You have a delightful opportunity now of paying me a compliment, Windermere. But you are not very clever at paying compliments. I am afraid Margaret doesn't encourage you in that excellent habit. It's a great mistake on her part. When men give up saying what is charming, they give up thinking what is charming. But seriously, what do you say to £2000 ? £2500, I think. In modern life margin is everything. Windermere, don't you think the world an intensely amusing place ? I do !

Exit on terrace with LORD WINDERMERE. *Music strikes up in ball-room.*

Lady Windermere : To stay in this house any longer is impossible. To-night a man who loves me offered me his whole life. I refused it. It was foolish of me. I will offer him mine now. I will give him mine. I will go to him ! (*Puts on cloak and goes to the door, then turns back. Sits down at table and writes a letter, puts it into an envelope, and leaves it on table.*) Arthur has never understood me. When he reads this, he will. He may do as he chooses now with his life. I have done with mine as I think best, as I think right. It is he who has broken the bond of marriage—not I. I only break its bondage. (*Exit.*)

PARKER *enters L. and crosses towards the ball-room R. Enter* MRS. ERLYNNE.

Mrs. Erlynne : Is Lady Windermere in the ball-room ?
Parker : Her ladyship has just gone out.
Mrs. Erlynne : Gone out ? She's not on the terrace ?
Parker : No, madam. Her ladyship has just gone out of the house.
Mrs. Erlynne (starts, and looks at the servant with a puzzled expression in her face) : Out of the house ?
Parker : Yes, madam—her ladyship told me she had left a letter for his lordship on the table.
Mrs. Erlynne : A letter for Lord Windermere ?
Parker : Yes, madam.
Mrs. Erlynne : Thank you.

Exit PARKER. *The music in the ball-room stops.*

Gone out of her house ! A letter addressed to her husband ! (*Goes over to bureau and looks at letter. Takes it up and lays it down again with a shudder of fear.*) No, no ! It would be impossible ! Life doesn't repeat its tragedies like that ! Oh, why does this horrible fancy come across me ? Why do I remember now the one moment of my life I most wish to forget ? Does life repeat its tragedies ? (*Tears letter open and reads it, then sinks down into a chair with a gesture of anguish.*) Oh, how terrible ! The same words that twenty years ago I wrote to her father ! and how bitterly I have been punished for it ! No ; my punishment, my real punishment is to-night, is now ! (*Still seated R.*)

Enter LORD WINDERMERE *L.U.E.*

Lord Windermere : Have you said good-night to my wife ? (*Comes C.*)

Mrs. Erlynne (*crushing letter in her hand*) *:* Yes.

Lord Windermere : Where is she ?

Mrs. Erlynne : She is very tired. She has gone to bed. She said she had a headache.

Lord Windermere : I must go to her. You'll excuse me ?

Mrs. Erlynne (*rising hurriedly*) *:* Oh, no ! It's nothing serious. She's only very tired, that is all. Besides, there are people still in the supper-room. She wants you to make her apologies to them. She said she didn't wish to be disturbed. (*Drops letter.*) She asked me to tell you !

Lord Windermere (*picks up letter*) *:* You have dropped something.

Mrs. Erlynne : Oh yes, thank you, that is mine. (*Puts out her hand to take it.*)

Lord Windermere (*still looking at letter*) *:* But it's my wife's hand-writing, isn't it ?

Mrs. Erlynne (*takes the letter quickly*) *:* Yes, it's— an address. Will you ask them to call my carriage, please ?

Lord Windermere : Certainly. (*Goes L. and Exit.*)

Mrs. Erlynne : Thanks ! What can I do ? What can I do ? I feel a passion awakening within me that I never felt before. What can it mean ? The daughter must not be like the mother—that would be terrible. How can I save her ? How can I save my child ? A moment may ruin a life. Who knows that better than I ? Windermere must be got out of the house ; that is absolutely necessary. (*Goes L.*) But how shall I do it ? It must be done somehow. Ah !

Enter LORD AUGUSTUS *R.U.E. carrying bouquet.*

Lord Augustus : Dear lady, I am in such suspense !
May I not have an answer to my request ?

Mrs. Erlynne : Lord Augustus, listen to me. You
are to take Lord Windermere down to your club at
once, and keep him there as long as possible. You
understand ?

Lord Augustus : But you said you wished me to keep
early hours !

Mrs. Erlynne (nervously) : Do what I tell you. Do
what I tell you.

Lord Augustus : And my reward ?

Mrs. Erlynne : Your reward ? Your reward ? Oh !
ask me that to-morrow. But don't let Windermere out
of your sight to-night. If you do I will never forgive
you. I will never speak to you again. I'll have nothing
to do with you. Remember you are to keep Windermere at your club, and don't let him come back to-night.
(*Exit L.*)

Lord Augustus : Well, really, I might be her husband
already, Positively I might. (*Follows her in a bewildered
manner.*)

ACT DROP.

THIRD ACT

SCENE

Lord Darlington's Rooms. A large sofa is in front of fireplace R. At the back of the stage a curtain is drawn across the window. Doors L. and R. Table R. with writing materials. Table C. with syphons, glasses, and Tantalus frame. Table L. with cigar and cigarette box. Lamps lit.

Lady Windermere (standing by the fireplace) : Why doesn't he come ? This waiting is horrible. He should be here. Why is he not here, to wake by passionate words some fire within me ? I am cold—cold as a loveless thing. Arthur must have read my letter by this time. If he cared for me, he would have come after me, would have taken me back by force. But he doesn't care. He's entrammelled by this woman—fascinated by her—dominated by her. If a woman wants to hold a man, she has merely to appeal to what is worst in him. We make gods of men and they leave us. Others make brutes of them and they fawn and are faithful. How hideous life is ! . . . Oh ! it was mad of me to come here, horribly mad. And yet, which is the worst, I wonder, to be at the mercy of a man who loves one, or the wife of a man who in one's own house dishonours one ? What woman knows ? What woman in the whole world ? But will he love me always, this man to whom I am giving my life ? What do I bring him ? Lips that have lost the note of joy, eyes that are blinded by tears, chill hands and icy heart. I bring him nothing. I must go back—no ; I can't go back, my letter has put me in their power—Arthur would

not take me back! That fatal letter! No! Lord
Darlington leaves England to-morrow. I will go with
him—I have no choice. (*Sits down for a few moments.
Then starts up and puts on her cloak.*) No, no! I will
go back, let Arthur do with me what he pleases. I can't
wait here. It has been madness my coming. I must
go at once. As for Lord Darlington.—Oh! here he
is! What shall I do? What can I say to him? Will he
let me go away at all? I have heard that men are
brutal, horrible. . . . Oh! (*Hides her face in her hands.*)

Enter MRS. ERLYNNE *L.*

Mrs. Erlynne : Lady Windermere! (LADY WINDER-
MERE *starts and looks up. Then recoils in contempt.*)
Thank Heaven I am in time. You must go back to
your husband's house immediately.
Lady Windermere : Must?
Mrs. Erlynne (authoritatively) : Yes, you must!
There is not a second to be lost. Lord Darlington may
return at any moment.
Lady Windermere : Don't come near me!
Mrs. Erlynne : Oh! You are on the brink of ruin,
you are on the brink of a hideous precipice. You must
leave this place at once, my carriage is waiting at the
corner of the street. You must come with me and
drive straight home.

LADY WINDERMERE *throws off her cloak and
flings it on the sofa.*

What are you doing?
Lady Windermere : Mrs. Erlynne—if you had not
come here, I would have gone back. But now that
I see you, I feel that nothing in the whole world
would induce me to live under the same roof as Lord
Windermere. You fill me with horror. There is something about you that stirs the wildest—rage within me.

And I know why you are here. My husband sent you
to lure me back that I might serve as a blind to whatever relations exist between you and him.

Mrs. Erlynne: Oh ! You don't think that—you
can't.

Lady Windermere: Go back to my husband, Mrs.
Erlynne. He belongs to you and not to me. I suppose
he is afraid of a scandal. Men are such cowards. They
outrage every law of the world, and are afraid of the
world's tongue. But he had better prepare himself.
He shall have a scandal. He shall have the worst
scandal there has been in London for years. He shall
see his name in every vile paper, mine on every
hideous placard.

Mrs. Erlynne: No—no——

Lady Windermere: Yes ! he shall. Had he come
himself, I admit I would have gone back to the life
of degradation you and he had prepared for me—I
was going back—but to stay himself at home, and to
send you as his messenger—oh ! it was infamous—
infamous.

Mrs. Erlynne (C.): Lady Windermere, you wrong
me horribly—you wrong your husband horribly. He
doesn't know you are here—he thinks you are safe in
your own house. He thinks you are asleep in your
own room. He never read the mad letter vou wrote
to him !

Lady Windermere (R.): Never read it !

Mrs. Erlynne: No—he knows nothing about it.

Lady Windermere: How simple you think me !
(Going to her): You are lying to me !

Mrs. Erlynne (restraining herself): I am not. I am
telling you the truth.

Lady Windermere: If my husband didn't read my
letter, how is it that you are here ? Who told you I
had left the house you were shameless enough to enter ?
Who told you where I had gone to ? My husband told
you, and sent you to decoy me back. *(Crosses L.)*

Mrs. Erlynne (R.C.) : You husband has never seen the letter. I—saw it, I opened it. I—read it.

Lady Windermere (turning to her) : You opened a letter of mine to my husband ? You wouldn't dare !

Mrs. Erlynne : Dare ! Oh ! to save you from the abyss into which you are falling, there is nothing in the world I would not dare, nothing in the whole world. Here is the letter. Your husband has never read it. He never shall read it. (*Going to fireplace.*) It should never have been written. (*Tears it and throws it into the fire.*)

Lady Windermere (with infinite contempt in her voice and look) : How do I know that that was my letter after all ? You seem to think the commonest device can take me in !

Mrs. Erlynne : Oh ! why do you disbelieve everything I tell you ? What object do you think I have in coming here, except to save you from utter ruin, to save you from the consequence of a hideous mistake ? That letter that is burnt now *was* your letter. I swear it to you !

Lady Windermere (slowly) : You took good care to burn it before I had examined it. I cannot trust you. You, whose whole life is a lie, how could you speak the truth about anything ? (*Sits down.*)

Mrs. Erlynne (hurriedly) : Think as you like about me—say what you choose against me, but go back, go back to the husband you love.

Lady Windermere (sullenly) : I do *not* love him !

Mrs. Erlynne : You do, and you know that he loves you.

Lady Windermere : He does not understand what love is. He understands it as little as you do—but I see what you want. It would be a great advantage for you to get me back. Dear Heaven ! what a life I would have then ! Living at the mercy of a woman who has neither mercy nor pity in her, a woman whom it is an infamy to meet, a degradation to know, a vile woman, a woman who comes between husband and wife!

Mrs. Erlynne (*with a gesture of despair*): Lady Windermere, Lady Windermere, don't say such terrible things. You don't know how terrible they are, how terrible and how unjust. Listen, you must listen! Only go back to your husband, and I promise you never to communicate with him again on any pretext—never to see him—never to have anything to do with his life or yours. The money that he gave me, he gave me not through love, but through hatred, not in worship, but in contempt. The hold I have over him——

Lady Windermere (*rising*): Ah! you admit you have a hold!

Mrs. Erlynne: Yes, and I will tell you what it is. It is his love for you, Lady Windermere.

Lady Windermere: You expect me to believe that?

Mrs. Erlynne: You must believe it! it is true. It is his love for you that has made him submit to—oh! call it what you like, tyranny, threats, anything you choose. But it is his love for you. His desire to spare you—shame, yes, shame and disgrace.

Lady Windermere: What do you mean? You are insolent! What have I to do with you?

Mrs. Erlynne (*humbly*): Nothing. I know it—but I tell you that your husband loves you—that you may never meet with such love again in your whole life—that such love you will never meet—and that if you throw it away, the day may come when you will starve for love and it will not be given to you, beg for love and it will be denied you.—Oh! Arthur loves you!

Lady Windermere: Arthur? And you tell me there is nothing between you?

Mrs. Erlynne: Lady Windermere, before Heaven your husband is guiltless of all offence towards you! And I—I tell you that had it ever occurred to me that such a monstrous suspicion would have entered your mind, I would have died rather than have crossed your life or his—oh ! died, gladly died ! (*Moves away to sofa R.*)

Lady Windermere : You talk as if you had a heart. Women like you have no hearts. Heart is not in you. You are bought and sold. (*Sits L.C.*)

Mrs. Erlynne (*starts, with a gesture of pain. Then restrains herself, and comes over to where* LADY WINDERMERE *is sitting. As she speaks, she stretches out her hands towards her, but does not dare to touch her*) : Believe what you choose about me. I am not worth a moment's sorrow. But don't spoil your beautiful young life on my account ! You don't know what may be in store for you, unless you leave this house at once. You don't know what it is to fall into the pit, to be despised, mocked, abandoned, sneered at—to be an outcast ! to find the door shut against one, to have to creep in by hideous byways, afraid every moment least the mask should be stripped from one's face, and all the while to hear the laughter, the horrible laughter of the world, a thing more tragic than all the tears the world has ever shed. You don't know what it is. One pays for one's sin, and then one pays again, and all one's life one pays. You must never know that.—As for me, if suffering be an expiation, then at this moment I have expiated all my faults, whatever they have been ; for to-night you have made a heart in one who had it not, made it and broken it.—But let that pass. I may have wrecked my own life, but I will not let you wreck yours. You—why, you are a mere girl, you would be lost. You haven't got the kind of brains that enables a woman to get back. You have neither the wit nor the courage. You couldn't stand dishonour ! No ! Go back, Lady Windermere, to the husband who loves you, whom you love. You have a child, Lady Windermere. Go back to that child who even now, in pain or in joy, may be calling to you. (LADY WINDERMERE *rises.*) God gave you that child. He will require from you that you make his life fine, that you watch over him. What answer will you make to God if his life is ruined through you? Back to your house, Lady Windermere—your husband loves you! He has never swerved for a moment from the love he bears you. But even if he had a thousand loves, you must stay with your child. If he was harsh to you, you must stay with your child. If he ill-treated you, you must stay with your child. If he abandoned you, your place is with your child.

> LADY WINDERMERE *bursts into tears and buries her face in her hands.*

(*Rushing to her*): Lady Windermere!

Lady Windermere (*holding out her hands to her, helplessly, as a child might do*): Take me home. Take me home.

Mrs. Erlynne (*is about to embrace her. Then restrains herself. There is a look of wonderful joy in her face*): Come! Where is your cloak? (*Getting it from sofa*): Here. Put it on. Come at once!

> *They go to the door.*

Lady Windermere: Stop! Don't you hear voices?

Mrs. Erlynne: No, no! There is no one!

Lady Windermere: Yes, there is! Listen! Oh! that is my husband's voice! He is coming in! Save me! Oh, it's some plot! You have sent for him.

> *Voices outside.*

Mrs. Erlynne: Silence! I'm here to save you, if I can. But I fear it is too late! There! (*Points to the curtain across the window.*) The first chance you have slip out, if you ever get a chance!

Lady Windermere: But you?

Mrs. Erlynne: Oh! never mind me. I'll face them.

LADY WINDERMERE *hides herself behind the curtain.*

Lord Augustus (outside) : Nonsense, dear Windermere, you must not leave me !

Mrs. Erlynne : Lord Augustus ! Then it is I who am lost ! (*Hesitates for a moment, then looks round and sees door R., and exit through it.*)

Enter LORD DARLINGTON, MR. DUMBY, LORD WINDERMERE, LORD AUGUSTUS LORTON, *and* MR. CECIL GRAHAM.

Dumby : What a nuisance their turning us out of the club at this hour ! It's only two o'clock. (*Sinks into a chair.*) The lively part of the evening is only just beginning. (*Yawns and closes his eyes.*)

Lord Windermere : It is very good of you, Lord Darlington, allowing Augustus to force our company on you, but I'm afraid I can't stay long.

Lord Darlington : Really ! I am so sorry ! You'll take a cigar, won't you ?

Lord Windermere : Thanks ! (*Sits down.*)

Lord Augustus (*to* LORD WINDERMERE) *:* My dear boy, you must not dream of going. I have a great deal to talk to you about, of demmed importance, too. (*Sits down with him at L. table.*)

Cecil Graham : Oh ! We all know what that is ! Tuppy can't talk about anything but Mrs. Erlynne.

Lord Windermere : Well, that is no business of yours, is it, Cecil ?

Cecil Graham : None ! That is why it interests me. My own business always bores me to death. I prefer other people's.

Lord Darlington : Have something to drink, you fellows. Cecil, you'll have a whisky and soda?

Cecil Graham : Thanks. (*Goes to table with* LORD DARLINGTON) *:* Mrs. Erlynne looked very handsome to-night, didn't she ?

Lord Darlington : I am not one of her admirers.

Cecil Graham : I usen't to be, but I am now. Why ! she actually made me introduce her to poor dear Aunt Caroline. I believe she is going to lunch there.

Lord Darlington (in surprise) : No ?

Cecil Graham : She is, really.

Lord Darlington : Excuse me, you fellows. I'm going away to-morrow. And I have to write a few letters. (*Goes to writing-table and sits down.*)

Dumby : Clever woman, Mrs. Erlynne.

Cecil Graham : Hallo, Dumby ! I thought you were asleep.

Dumby : I am, I usually am !

Lord Augustus : A very clever woman. Knows perfectly well what a demmed fool I am—knows it as well as I do myself.

CECIL GRAHAM *comes towards him laughing.*

Ah, you may laugh, my boy, but it is a great thing to come across a woman who thoroughly understands one.

Dumby : It is an awfully dangerous thing. They always end by marrying one.

Cecil Graham : But I thought, Tuppy, you were never going to see her again ! Yes ! you told me so yesterday evening at the club. You said you'd heard——

Whispering to him.

Lord Augustus : Oh, she's explained that.

Cecil Graham : And the Wiesbaden affair ?

Lord Augustus : She's explained that too.

Dumby : And her income, Tuppy? Has she explained that ?

Lord Augustus (in a very serious voice) : She's going to explain that to-morrow.

CECIL GRAHAM *goes back to C. table.*

Dumby : Awfully commercial, women nowadays. Our grandmothers threw their caps over the mills, of course, but, by Jove, their grand-daughters only throw their caps over mills that can raise the wind for them.

Lord Augustus : You want to make her out a wicked woman. She is not !

Cecil Graham : Oh ! Wicked women bother one. Good women bore one. That is the only difference between them.

Lord Augustus (puffing a cigar) : Mrs. Erlynne has a future before her.

Dumby : Mrs. Erlynne has a past before her.

Lord Augustus : I prefer women with a past. They're always so demmed amusing to talk to.

Cecil Graham : Well, you'll have lots of topics of conversation with *her*, Tuppy. (*Rising and going to him.*)

Lord Augustus : You're getting annoying, dear boy ; you're getting demmed annoying.

Cecil Graham (puts his hands on his shoulders) : Now, Tuppy, you've lost your figure and you've lost your character. Don't lose your temper ; you have only got one.

Lord Augustus : My dear boy, if I wasn't the most good-natured man in London——

Cecil Graham : We'd treat you with more respect, wouldn't we, Tuppy ? (*Strolls away.*)

Dumby : The youth of the present day are quite monstrous. They have absolutely no respect for dyed hair.

LORD AUGUSTUS *looks round angrily.*

Cecil Graham : Mrs. Erlynne has a very great respect for dear Tuppy.

Dumby : Then Mrs. Erlynne sets an admirable

example to the rest of her sex. It is perfectly brutal the way most women nowadays behave to men who are not their husbands.

Lord Windermere : Dumby, you are ridiculous, and Cecil, you let your tongue run away with you. You must leave Mrs. Erlynne alone. You don't really know anything about her, and you're always talking scandal against her.

Cecil Graham (coming towards him L.C.) . My dear Arthur, I never talk scandal. *I* only talk gossip.

Lord Windermere : What is the difference between scandal and gossip ?

Cecil Graham : Oh ! gossip is charming ! History is merely gossip. But scandal is gossip made tedious by morality. Now, I never moralise. A man who moralises is usually a hypocrite, and a woman who moralises is invariably plain. There is nothing in the whole world so unbecoming to a woman as a Non-conformist conscience. And most women know it, I'm glad to say.

Lord Augustus : Just my sentiments, dear boy, just my sentiments.

Cecil Graham : Sorry to hear it, Tuppy ; whenever people agree with me, I always feel I must be wrong.

Lord Augustus : My dear boy, when I was your age——

Cecil Graham : But you never were, Tuppy, and you never will be. *(Goes up C.)* I say, Darlington, let us have some cards. You'll play, Arthur, won't you ?

Lord Windermere : No, thanks, Cecil.

Dumby (with a sigh) : Good heavens ! how marriage ruins a man ! It's as demoralising as cigarettes, and far more expensive.

Cecil Graham : You'll play, of course, Tuppy ?

Lord Augustus (pouring himself out a brandy and soda at table) : Can't, dear boy. Promised Mrs. Erlynne never to play or drink again.

Cecil Graham : Now, my dear Tuppy, don't be led

astray into the paths of virtue. Reformed, you would be perfectly tedious. That is the worst of women. They always want one to be good. And if we are good, when they meet us, they don't love us at all. They like to find us quite irretrievably bad, and to leave us quite unattractively good.

Lord Darlington (*rising from R. table, where he has been writing letters*) : They always do find us bad !

Dumby : I don't think we are bad. I think we are all good, except Tuppy.

Lord Darlington : No, we are all in the gutter, but some of us are looking at the stars. (*Sits down at C. table.*)

Dumby : We are all in the gutter, but some of us are looking at the stars ? Upon my word, you are very romantic to-night, Darlington.

Cecil Graham : Too romantic ! You must be in love. Who is the girl ?

Lord Darlington : The woman I love is not free, or thinks she isn't. (*Glances instinctively at* Lord Winder-mere *while he speaks.*)

Cecil Graham : A married woman, then ! Well, there's nothing in the world like the devotion of a married woman. It's a thing no married man knows anything about.

Lord Darlington : Oh ! she doesn't love me. She is a good woman. She is the only woman I have ever met in my life.

Cecil Graham : The only good woman you have ever met in your life ?

Lord Darlington : Yes !

Cecil Graham (*lighting a cigarette*) : Well, you are a lucky fellow ! Why, I have met hundreds of good women. I never seem to meet any but good women. The world is perfectly packed with good women. To know them is a middle-class education.

Lord Darlington : This woman has purity and in-nocence. She has everything we men have lost.

Cecil Graham : My dear fellow, what on earth should we men do going about with purity and innocence ? A carefully thought-out buttonhole is much more effective.

Dumby : She doesn't really love you then ?

Lord Darlington : No, she does not !

Dumby : I congratulate you, my dear fellow. In this world there are only two tragedies. One is not getting what one wants, and the other is getting it. The last is much the worst ; the last is a real tragedy ! But I am interested to hear she does not love you. How long could you love a woman who didn't love you, Cecil ?

Cecil Graham : A woman who didn't love me ? Oh, all my life !

Dumby : So could I. But it's so difficult to meet one.

Lord Darlington : How can you be so conceited Dumby ?

Dumby : I didn't say it as a matter of conceit. I said it as a matter of regret. I have been wildly, madly adored. I am sorry I have. It has been an immense nuisance. I should like to be allowed a little time to myself now and then.

Lord Augustus (looking round) : Time to educate yourself, I suppose.

Dumby : No, time to forget all I have learned. That is much more important, dear Tuppy.

LORD AUGUSTUS *moves uneasily in his chair.*

Lord Darlington : What cynics you fellows are !

Cecil Graham : What is a cynic ? (*Sitting on the back of the sofa.*)

Lord Darlington : A man who knows the price of everything and the value of nothing.

Cecil Graham : And a sentimentalist, my dear Darlington, is a man who sees an absurd value in everything, and doesn't know the market price of any single thing.

Lord Darlington : You always amuse me, Cecil. You talk as if you were a man of experience.

Cecil Graham : I am. (*Moves up to front of fireplace.*)

Lord Darlington : You are far too young!

Cecil Graham : That is a great error. Experience is a question of instinct about life. I have got it. Tuppy hasn't. Experience is the name Tuppy gives to his mistakes. That is all.

LORD AUGUSTUS *looks round indignantly.*

Dumby : Experience is the name every one gives to their mistakes.

Cecil Graham (standing with his back to the fireplace) : One shouldn't commit any. (*Sees* LADY WINDERMERE'S *fan on sofa.*)

Dumby : Life would be very dull without them.

Cecil Graham : Of course you are quite faithful to this woman you are in love with, Darlington, to this good woman?

Lord Darlington : Cecil, if one really loves a woman, all other women in the world become absolutely meaningless to one. Love changes one—*I* am changed.

Cecil Graham : Dear me! How very interesting! Tuppy, I want to talk to you.

LORD AUGUSTUS *takes no notice.*

Dumby : It's no use talking to Tuppy. You might just as well talk to a brick wall.

Cecil Graham : But I like talking to a brick wall— it's the only thing in the world that never contradicts me! Tuppy!

Lord Augustus : Well, what is it? What is it? (*Rising and going over to* CECIL GRAHAM.)

Cecil Graham : Come over here. I want you particularly. (*Aside*): Darlington has been moralising and talking about the purity of love, and that sort of

thing, and he has got some woman in his rooms all
the time.

Lord Augustus : No, really ! really !

Cecil Graham (in a low voice) : Yes, here is her fan.
(Points to the fan.)

Lord Augustus (chuckling) : By Jove ! By Jove !

Lord Windermere (up by door) : I am really off now,
Lord Darlington. I am sorry you are leaving England
so soon. Pray call on us when you come back ! My
wife and I will be charmed to see you !

Lord Darlington (up stage with LORD WINDERMERE*) :*
I am afraid I shall be away for many years. Good-
night !

Cecil Graham : Arthur !

Lord Windermere : What ?

Cecil Graham : I want to speak to you for a moment.
No, do come !

Lord Windermere (putting on his coat) : I can't—
I'm off.

Cecil Graham : It is something very particular. It
will interest you enormously.

Lord Windermere (smiling) : It is some of your
nonsense, Cecil.

Cecil Graham : It isn't ! It isn't really.

Lord Augustus (going to him) : My dear fellow, you
mustn't go yet. I have a lot to talk to you about. And
Cecil has something to show you.

Lord Windermere (walking over) : Well, what is it ?

Cecil Graham : Darlington has got a woman here in
his rooms. Here is her fan. Amusing, isn't it ? *(A
pause.)*

Lord Windermere : **Good** God ! *(Seizes the fan—*
DUMBY *rises.)*

Cecil Graham : What is the matter ?

Lord Windermere : Lord Darlington !

Lord Darlington (turning round) : Yes !

Lord Windermere : What is my wife's fan doing here
in your rooms ? Hands off, Cecil. Don't touch me.

Lord Darlington : Your wife's fan ?

Lord Windermere : Yes, here it is ?

Lord Darlington (walking towards him) : I don't know !

Lord Windermere : You must know. I demand an explanation. Don't hold me, you fool. (*To* CECIL GRAHAM.)

Lord Darlington (aside) : She is here after all !

Lord Windermere : Speak, sir ! Why is my wife's fan here ? Answer me ! By God ! I'll search your rooms, and if my wife's here, I'll—— (*Moves.*)

Lord Darlington : You shall not search my rooms. You have no right to do so. I forbid you !

Lord Windermere : You scoundrel ! I'll not leave your room till I have searched every corner of it ! What moves behind that curtain ? (*Rushes towards the curtain C.*)

Mrs. Erlynne (enters behind R.) : Lord Windermere !

Lord Windermere : Mrs. Erlynne !

Every one starts and turns round. LADY WINDERMERE *slips out from behind the curtain and glides from the room L.*

Mrs. Erlynne : I am afraid I took your wife's fan in mistake for my own, when I was leaving your house to-night. I am so sorry. (*Takes fan from him.* LORD WINDERMERE *looks at her in contempt.* LORD DARLINGTON *in mingled astonishment and anger.* LORD AUGUSTUS *turns away. The other men smile at each other.*)

ACT DROP.

FOURTH ACT

SCENE

Same as in Act I.

Lady Windermere (lying on sofa): How can I tell
him? I can't tell him. It would kill me. I wonder
what happened after I escaped from that horrible
room. Perhaps she told them the true reason of her
being there, and the real meaning of that—fatal fan
of mine. Oh, if he knows—how can I look him in the
face again? He would never forgive me. (*Touches
bell.*) How securely one thinks one lives—out of reach
of temptation, sin, folly. And then suddenly—Oh!
Life is terrible. It rules us, we do not rule it.

Enter ROSALIE *R.*

Rosalie: Did your ladyship ring for me?
Lady Windermere: Yes. Have you found out at
what time Lord Windermere came in last night?
Rosalie: His lordship did not come in till five
o'clock.
Lady Windermere: Five o'clock? He knocked at
my door this morning, didn't he?
Rosalie: Yes, my lady—at half-past nine. I told
him your ladyship was not awake yet.
Lady Windermere: Did he say anything?
Rosalie: Something about your ladyship's fan. I
didn't quite catch what his lordship said. Has the fan
been lost, my lady? I can't find it, and Parker says
it was not left in any of the rooms. He has looked in
all of them and on the terrace as well.

Lady Windermere : It doesn't matter. Tell Parker not to trouble. That will do.

Exit Rosalie.

Lady Windermere (rising) : She is sure to tell him. I can fancy a person doing a wonderful act of self-sacrifice, doing it spontaneously, recklessly, nobly— and afterwards finding out that it costs too much. Why should she hesitate between her ruin and mine ? . . . How strange ! I would have publicly disgraced her in my own house. She accepts public disgrace in the house of another to save me. . . . There is a bitter irony in things, a bitter irony in the way we talk of good and bad women. . . . Oh, what a lesson ! and what a pity that in life we only get our lessons when they are of no use to us ! For even if she doesn't tell, I must. Oh ! the shame of it, the shame of it. To tell it is to live through it all again. Actions are the first tragedy in life, words are the second. Words are perhaps the worst. Words are merciless. . . . Oh ! (*Starts as* LORD WINDERMERE *enters.*)

Lord Windermere (kisses her) : Margaret—how pale you look !

Lady Windermere : I slept very badly.

Lord Windermere (sitting on sofa with her) : I am so sorry. I came in dreadfully late, and didn't like to wake you. You are crying, dear.

Lady Windermere : Yes, I am crying, for I have something to tell you, Arthur.

Lord Windermere : My dear child, you are not well. You've been doing too much. Let us go away to the country. You'll be all right at Selby. The season is almost over. There is no use staying on. Poor darling ! We'll go away to-day, if you like. (*Rises.*) We can easily catch the 3.40. I'll send a wire to Fannen. (*Crosses and sits down at table to write a telegram.*)

Lady Windermere : Yes ; let us go away to-day.

No ; I can't go to-day, Arthur. There is some one I must see before I leave town—some one who has been kind to me.

Lord Windermere (rising and leaning over sofa) : Kind to you ?

Lady Windermere : Far more than that. (*Rises and goes to him.*) I will tell you, Arthur, but only love me, love me as you used to love me.

Lord Windermere : Used to ? You are not thinking of that wretched woman who came here last night ? (*Coming round and sitting R. of her*) : You don't still imagine—no, you couldn't.

Lady Windermere : I don't. I know now I was wrong and foolish.

Lord Windermere : It was very good of you to receive her last night—but you are never to see her again.

Lady Windermere : Why do you say that ? (*A pause.*)

Lord Windermere (holding her hand) : Margaret, I thought Mrs. Erlynne was a woman more sinned against than sinning, as the phrase goes. I thought she wanted to be good, to get back into a place that she had lost by a moment's folly, to lead again a decent life. I believed what she told me—I was mistaken in her. She is bad—as bad as a woman can be.

Lady Windermere : Arthur, Arthur, don't talk so bitterly about any woman. I don't think now that people can be divided into the good and the bad as though they were two separate races or creations. What are called good women may have terrible things in them, mad moods of recklessness, assertion, jealousy, sin. Bad women, as they are termed, may have in them sorrow, repentance, pity, sacrifice. And I don't think Mrs. Erlynne a bad woman—I know she's not.

Lord Windermere : My dear child, the woman's impossible. No matter what harm she tries to do us, you must never see her again. She is inadmissible anywhere.

Lady Windermere : But I want to see her. I want her to come here.

Lord Windermere : Never !

Lady Windermere : She came here once as *your* guest. She must come now as *mine.* That is but fair.

Lord Windermere : She should never have come here.

Lady Windermere (rising) : It is too late, Arthur, to say that now. (*Moves away.*)

Lord Windermere (rising) : Margaret, if you knew where Mrs. Erlynne went last night, after she left this house, you would not sit in the same room with her. It was absolutely shameless, the whole thing.

Lady Windermere : Arthur, I can't bear it any longer. I must tell you. Last night——

> *Enter* PARKER *with a tray on which lie* LADY WINDERMERE'S *fan and a card.*

Parker : Mrs. Erlynne has called to return your ladyship's fan which she took away by mistake last night. Mrs. Erlynne has written a message on the card.

Lady Windermere : Oh, ask Mrs. Erlynne to be kind enough to come up. (*Reads card.*) Say I shall be very glad to see her.

> *Exit* PARKER.

She wants to see me, Arthur.

Lord Windermere (takes card and looks at it) : Margaret, I *beg* you not to. Let me see her first, at any rate. She's a dangerous woman. She is the most dangerous woman I know. You don't realise what you're doing.

Lady Windermere : It is right that I should see her.

Lord Windermere : My child, you may be on the brink of a great sorrow. Don't go to meet it. It is absolutely necessary that I should see her before you do.

Lady Windermere : Why should it be necessary ?

Enter PARKER.

Parker : Mrs. Erlynne.

Enter MRS. ERLYNNE. *Exit* PARKER.

Mrs. Erlynne : How do you do, Lady Windermere ? (*To* LORD WINDERMERE) : How do you do ? Do you know, Lady Windermere, I am so sorry about your fan. I can't imagine how I made such a silly mistake. Most stupid of me. And as I was driving in your direction, I thought I would take the opportunity of returning your property in person with many apologies for my carelessness, and of bidding you good-bye.

Lady Windermere : Good-bye ? (*Moves towards sofa with* MRS. ERLYNNE *and sits down beside her.*) Are you going away, then, Mrs. Erlynne ?

Mrs. Erlynne : Yes ; I am going to live abroad again. The English climate doesn't suit me. My—heart is affected here, and that I don't like. I prefer living in the south. London is too full of fogs and —and serious people, Lord Windermere. Whether the fogs produce the serious people or whether the serious people produce the fogs, I don't know, but the whole thing rather gets on my nerves, and so I'm leaving this afternoon by the Club Train.

Lady Windermere : This afternoon ? But I wanted so much to come and see you.

Mrs. Erlynne : How kind of you ! But I am afraid I have to go.

Lady Windermere : Shall I never see you again, Mrs. Erynne ?

Mrs. Erlynne : I am afraid not. Our lives lie too far apart. But there is a little thing I would like you to do for me. I want a photograph of you, Lady Windermere—would you give me one ? You don't know how gratified I should be.

Lady Windermere : Oh, with pleasure. There is one on that table. I'll show it to you. (*Goes across to the table.*)

Lord Windermere (*coming up to* MRS. ERLYNNE *and speaking in a low voice*) *:* It is monstrous your intruding yourself here after your conduct last night.

Mrs. Erlynne (*with an amused smile*) *:* My dear Windermere, manners before morals !

Lady Windermere (*returning*) *:* I'm afraid it is very flattering—I am not so pretty as that. (*Showing photograph.*)

Mrs. Erlynne : You are much prettier. But haven't you got one of yourself with your little boy ?

Lady Windermere : I have. Would you prefer one of those ?

Mrs. Erlynne : Yes.

Lady Windermere : I'll go and get it for you, if you'll excuse me for a moment. I have one upstairs.

Mrs. Erlynne : So sorry, Lady Windermere, to give you so much trouble.

Lady Windermere (*moves to door R.*) *:* No trouble at all, Mrs. Erlynne.

Mrs. Erlynne : Thanks so much.

Exit LADY WINDERMERE *R.*

You seem rather out of temper this morning, Windermere. Why should you be ? Margaret and I get on charmingly together.

Lord Windermere : I can't bear to see you with her. Besides, you have not told me the truth, Mrs. Erlynne.

Mrs. Erlynne : I have not told *her* the truth, you mean.

Lord Windermere (*standing C.*) *:* I sometimes wish you had. I should have been spared then the misery, the anxiety, the annoyance of the last six months. But rather than my wife should know—that the mother whom she was taught to consider as dead, the

mother whom she has mourned as dead, is living—a
divorced woman, going about under an assumed name,
a bad woman preying upon life, as I know you now to
be—rather than that, I was ready to supply you with
money to pay bill after bill, extravagance after extra-
vagance, to risk what occurred yesterday, the first
quarrel I have ever had with my wife. You don't
understand what that means to me. How could you?
But I tell you that the only bitter words that ever
came from those sweet lips of hers were on your
account, and I hate to see you next her. You sully
the innocence that is in her. (*Moves L.C.*) And then
I used to think that with all your faults you were
frank and honest. You are not.

Mrs. Erlynne: Why do you say that?

Lord Windermere: You made me get you an
invitation to my wife's ball.

Mrs. Erlynne: For my daughter's ball—yes.

Lord Windermere: You came, and within an hour
of your leaving the house you are found in a man's
rooms—you are disgraced before every one. (*Goes up
stage C.*)

Mrs. Erlynne: Yes.

Lord Windermere (*turning round on her*): Therefore
I have a right to look upon you as what you are—a
worthless, vicious woman. I have the right to tell
you never to enter this house, never to attempt to come
near my wife——

Mrs. Erlynne (*coldly*): My daughter, you mean.

Lord Windermere: You have no right to claim her
as your daughter. You left her, abandoned her when
she was but a child in the cradle, abandoned her for
your lover, who abandoned you in turn.

Mrs. Erlynne (*rising*): Do you count that to his
credit, Lord Windermere—or to mine?

Lord Windermere: To his, now that I know you.

Mrs. Erlynne: Take care—you had better be
careful.

Lord Windermere : Oh, I am not going to mince words for you. I know you thoroughly.

Mrs. Erlynne (looking steadily at him) : I question that.

Lord Windermere : I *do* know you. For twenty years of your life you lived without your child, without a thought of your child. One day you read in the papers that she had married a rich man. You saw your hideous chance. You knew that to spare her the ignominy of learning that a woman like you was her mother, I would endure anything. You began your blackmailing.

Mrs. Erlynne (shrugging her shoulders) : Don't use ugly words, Windermere. They are vulgar. I saw my chance, it is true, and took it.

Lord Windermere : Yes, you took it—and spoiled it all last night by being found out.

Mrs. Erlynne (with a strange smile) : You are quite right, I spoiled it all last night.

Lord Windermere : And as for your blunder in taking my wife's fan from here and then leaving it about in Darlington's rooms, it is unpardonable. I can't bear the sight of it now. I shall never let my wife use it again. The thing is soiled for me. You should have kept it and not brought it back.

Mrs. Erlynne : I think I *shall* keep it. (*Goes up.*) It's extremely pretty. (*Takes up fan.*) I shall ask Margaret to give it to me.

Lord Windermere : I hope my wife will give it you.

Mrs. Erlynne : Oh, I'm sure she will have no objection.

Lord Windermere : I wish that at the same time she would give you a miniature she kisses every night before she prays.—It's the miniature of a young innocent-looking girl with beautiful *dark* hair.

Mrs. Erlynne : Ah, yes, I remember. How long ago that seems ! (*Goes to sofa and sits down.*) It was done before I was married. Dark hair and an innocent expression were the fashion then, Windermere ! (*A pause.*)

Lord Windermere : What do you mean by coming here this morning ? What is your object ? (*Crossing L.C. and sitting.*)

Mrs. Erlynne (*with a note of irony in her voice*) : To bid good-bye to my dear daughter, of course.

> LORD WINDERMERE *bites his under lip in anger.* MRS. ERLYNNE *looks at him, and her voice and manner become serious. In her accents as she talks there is a note of deep tragedy. For a moment she reveals herself.*

Oh, don't imagine I am going to have a pathetic scene with her, weep on her neck and tell her who I am, and all that kind of thing. I have no ambition to play the part of a mother. Only once in my life have I known a mother's feelings. That was last night. They were terrible—they made me suffer—they made me suffer too much. For twenty years, as you say, I have lived childless—I want to live childless still. (*Hiding her feelings with a trivial laugh.*) Besides, my dear Windermere, how on earth could I pose as a mother with a grown-up daughter ? Margaret is twenty-one, and I have never admitted that I am more than twenty-nine, or thirty at the most. Twenty-nine when there are pink shades, thirty when there are not. So you see what difficulties it would involve. No, as far as I am concerned, let your wife cherish the memory of this dead, stainless mother. Why should I interfere with her illusions ? I find it hard enough to keep my own. I lost one illusion last night. I thought I had no heart. I find I have, and a heart doesn't suit me, Windermere. Somehow it doesn't go with modern dress. It makes one look old. (*Takes up hand-mirror from table and looks into it.*) And it spoils one's career at critical moments.

Lord Windermere : You fill me with horror—with absolute horror.

Mrs. Erlynne (rising) : I suppose, Windermere, you would like me to retire into a convent, or become a hospital nurse, or something of that kind, as people do in silly modern novels. That is stupid of you, Arthur ; in real life we don't do such things—not as long as we have any good looks left, at any rate. No— what consoles one nowadays is not repentance, but pleasure. Repentance is quite out of date. And besides, if a woman really repents, she has to go to a bad dressmaker, otherwise no one believes in her. And nothing in the world would induce me to do that. No ; I am going to pass entirely out of your two lives. My coming into them has been a mistake—I discovered that last night.

Lord Windermere : A fatal mistake.

Mrs. Erlynne (smiling) : Almost fatal.

Lord Windermere : I am sorry now I did not tell my wife the whole thing at once.

Mrs. Erlynne : I regret my bad actions. You regret your good ones—that is the difference between us.

Lord Windermere : I don't trust you. I *will* tell my wife. It's better for her to know, and from me. It will cause her infinite pain—it will humiliate her terribly, but it's right that she should know.

Mrs. Erlynne : You propose to tell her ?

Lord Windermere : I am going to tell her.

Mrs. Erlynne (going up to him) : If you do, I will make my name so infamous that it will mar every moment of her life. It will ruin her, and make her wretched. If you dare to tell her, there is no depth of degradation I will not sink to, no pit of shame I will not enter. You shall not tell her—I forbid you.

Lord Windermere : Why ?

Mrs. Erlynne (after a pause) : If I said to you that I cared for her, perhaps loved her even—you would sneer at me, wouldn't you ?

Lord Windermere : I should feel it was not true. A mother's love means devotion, unselfishness, sacrifice. What could you know of such things?

Mrs. Erlynne : You are right. What could I know of such things? Don't let us talk any more about it —as for telling my daughter who I am, that I do not allow. It is my secret, it is not yours. If I make up my mind to tell her, and I think I will, I shall tell her before I leave the house—if not, I shall never tell her.

Lord Windermere (angrily) : Then let me beg of you to leave our house at once. I will make your excuses to Margaret.

Enter LADY WINDERMERE *R. She goes over to* MRS. ERLYNNE *with the photograph in her hand.* LORD WINDERMERE *moves to back of sofa, and anxiously watches* MRS. ERLYNNE *as the scene progresses.*

Lady Windermere : I am so sorry, Mrs. Erlynne, to have kept you waiting. I couldn't find the photograph anywhere. At last I discovered it in my husband's dressing-room—he had stolen it.

Mrs. Erlynne (takes the photograph from her and looks at it) : I am not surprised—it is charming. (*Goes over to sofa with* LADY WINDERMERE, *and sits down beside her. Looks again at the photograph.*) And so that is your little boy ! What is he called?

Lady Windermere : Gerard, after my dear father.

Mrs. Erlynne (laying the photograph down) : Really?

Lady Windermere : Yes. If it had been a girl, I would have called it after my mother. My mother had the same name as myself, Margaret.

Mrs. Erlynne : My name is Margaret too.

Lady Windermere : Indeed !

Mrs. Erlynne : Yes. (*Pause.*) You are devoted to your mother's memory, Lady Windermere, your husband tells me.

Lady Windermere : We all have ideals in life. At least we all should have. Mine is my mother.

Mrs. Erlynne : Ideals are dangerous things. Realities are better. They wound, but they're better.

Lady Windermere (shaking her head) : If I lost my ideals, I should lose everything.

Mrs. Erlynne : Everything ?

Lady Windermere : Yes. *(Pause.)*

Mrs. Erlynne : Did your father often speak to you of your mother ?

Lady Windermere : No, it gave him too much pain. He told me how my mother had died a few months after I was born. His eyes filled with tears as he spoke. Then he begged me never to mention her name to him again. It made him suffer even to hear it. My father—my father really died of a broken heart. His was the most ruined life I know.

Mrs. Erlynne (rising) : I am afraid I must go now, Lady Windermere.

Lady Windermere (rising) : Oh no, don't.

Mrs. Erlynne : I think I had better. My carriage must have come back by this time. I sent it to Lady Jedburgh's with a note.

Lady Windermere : Arthur, would you mind seeing if Mrs. Erlynne's carriage has come back ?

Mrs. Erlynne : Pray don't trouble, Lord Windermere.

Lady Windermere : Yes, Arthur, do go, please.

LORD WINDERMERE *hesitates for a moment and looks at* MRS. ERLYNNE. *She remains quite impassive. He leaves the room.*

(To MRS. ERLYNNE*) :* Oh ! What am I to say to you ? You saved me last night ? *(Goes towards her.)*

Mrs. Erlynne : Hush—don't speak of it.

Lady Windermere : I must speak of it. I can't let you think that I am going to accept this sacrifice. I

am not. It is too great. I am going to tell my husband
everything. It is my duty.

Mrs. Erlynne : It is not your duty—at least you
have duties to others besides him. You say you owe
me something ?

Lady Windermere : I owe you everything.

Mrs. Erlynne : Then pay your debt by silence. That
is the only way in which it can be paid. Don't spoil
the one good thing I have done in my life by telling
it to any one. Promise me that what passed last night
will remain a secret between us. You must not bring
misery into your husband's life. Why spoil his love ?
You must not spoil it. Love is easily killed. Oh ! how
easily love is killed. Pledge me your word, Lady
Windermere, that you will *never* tell him. I insist
upon it.

Lady Windermere (with bowed head) : It is your will,
not mine.

Mrs. Erlynne : Yes, it is my will. And never forget
your child—I like to think of you as a mother. I
like you to think of yourself as one.

Lady Windermere (looking up) : I always will now.
Only once in my life I have forgotten my own mother
—that was last night. Oh, if I had remembered her I
should not have been so foolish, so wicked.

Mrs. Erlynne (with a slight shudder) : Hush, last
night is quite over.

Enter LORD WINDERMERE.

Lord Windermere : Your carriage has not come back
yet, Mrs. Erlynne.

Mrs. Erlynne : It makes no matter. I'll take a
hansom. There is nothing in the world so respectable
as a good Shrewsbury and Talbot. And now, dear
Lady Windermere, I am afraid it is really good-bye.
(*Moves up C.*) Oh, I remember. You'll think me
absurd, but do you know I've taken a great fancy to

this fan that I was silly enough to run away with last night from your ball. Now, I wonder would you give it to me ? Lord Windermere says you may. I know it is his present.

Lady Windermere : Oh, certainly, if it will give you any pleasure. But it has my name on it. It has " Margaret " on it.

Mrs. Erlynne : But we have the same Christian name.

Lady Windermere : Oh, I forgot. Of course, do have it. What a wonderful chance our names being the same !

Mrs. Erlynne : Quite wonderful. Thanks—it will always remind me of you. (*Shakes hands with her.*)

Enter PARKER.

Parker : Lord Augustus Lorton. Mrs. Erlynne's carriage has come.

Enter LORD AUGUSTUS.

Lord Augustus : Good-morning, dear boy. Good-morning, Lady Windermere. (*Sees* MRS. ERLYNNE.) Mrs. Erlynne !

Mrs. Erlynne : How do you do, Lord Augustus ? Are you quite well this morning ?

Lord Augustus (*coldly*) : Quite well, thank you, Mrs. Erlynne.

Mrs. Erlynne : You don't look at all well, Lord Augustus. You stop up too late—it is so bad for you. You really should take more care of yourself. Good-bye, Lord Windermere. (*Goes towards door with a bow to* LORD AUGUSTUS. *Suddenly smiles and looks back at him.*) Lord Augustus ! Won't you see me to my carriage ? You might carry the fan.

Lord Windermere : Allow me !

Mrs. Erlynne : No ; I want Lord Augustus. I have

a special message for the dear Duchess. Won't you carry the fan, Lord Augustus?

Lord Augustus : If you really desire it, Mrs. Erlynne.

Mrs. Erlynne (laughing) : Of course I do. You'll carry it so gracefully. You would carry off anything gracefully, dear Lord Augustus. (*When she reaches the door she looks back for a moment at* LADY WINDERMERE. *Their eyes meet. Then she turns, and exit C. followed by* LORD AUGUSTUS.)

Lady Windermere : You will never speak against Mrs. Erlynne again, Arthur, will you?

Lord Windermere (gravely) : She is better than one thought her.

Lady Windermere : She is better than I am.

Lord Windermere (smiling as he strokes her hair) : Child, you and she belong to different worlds. Into your world evil has never entered.

Lady Windermere : Don't say that, Arthur. There is the same world for all of us, and good and evil, sin and innocence, go through it hand in hand. To shut one's eyes to half of life that one may live securely is as though one blinded oneself that one might walk with more safety in a land of pit and precipice.

Lord Windermere (moves down with her) : Darling why do you say that?

Lady Windermere (sits on sofa) : Because I, who had shut my eyes to life, came to the brink. And one who had separated us——

Lord Windermere : We were never separated.

Lady Windermere : We never must be again. O Arthur, don't love me less, and I will trust you more. I will trust you absolutely. Let us go to Selby. In the Rose Garden at Selby the roses are white and red.

Enter LORD AUGUSTUS *C.*

Lord Augustus : Arthur, she has explained everything!

LADY WINDERMERE looks horribly frightened at this. LORD WINDERMERE starts. LORD AUGUSTUS takes WINDERMERE by the arm and brings him to front of stage. He talks rapidly and in a low voice. LADY WINDERMERE stands watching them in terror.

My dear fellow, she has explained every demmed thing. We all wronged her immensely. It was entirely for my sake she went to Darlington's rooms. Called first at the Club—fact is, wanted to put me out of suspense —and being told I had gone on—followed—naturally frightened when she heard a lot of us coming in— retired to another room—I assure you, most gratifying to me, the whole thing. We all behaved brutally to her. She is just the woman for me. Suits me down to the ground. All the conditions she makes are that we live entirely out of England. A very good thing too. Demmed clubs, demmed climate, demmed cooks, demmed everything. Sick of it all!

Lady Windermere (frightened): Has Mrs. Erlynne—— ?

Lord Augustus (advancing towards her with a low bow): Yes, Lady Windermere—Mrs. Erlynne has done me the honour of accepting my hand.

Lord Windermere: Well, you are certainly marrying a very clever woman!

Lady Windermere (taking her husband's hand): Ah, you're marrying a very good woman!

CURTAIN.

A WOMAN OF NO IMPORTANCE

TO
GLADYS
COUNTESS DE GREY

THE PERSONS OF THE PLAY

LORD ILLINGWORTH
SIR JOHN PONTEFRACT
LORD ALFRED RUFFORD
MR. KELVIL, M.P.
THE VEN. ARCHDEACON DAUBENY, D.D.
GERALD ARBUTHNOT
FARQUHAR, Butler
FRANCIS, Footman

LADY HUNSTANTON
LADY CAROLINE PONTEFRACT
LADY STUTFIELD
MRS. ALLONBY
MISS HESTER WORSLEY
ALICE, Maid
MRS. ARBUTHNOT

THE SCENES OF THE PLAY

ACT   I. *The Terrace at Hunstanton Chase.*
ACT II. *The Drawing-room at Hunstanton Chase.*
ACT III. *The Hall at Hunstanton Chase.*
ACT IV. *Sitting-room in Mrs. Arbuthnot's House at
          Wrockley.*
TIME :   *The Present.*
PLACE : *The Shires.*

*The action of the play takes place within
twenty-four hours.*

397

LONDON: HAYMARKET THEATRE

Lessee and Manager: Mr. H. Beerbohm Tree
April, 19th, 1893

LORD ILLINGWORTH	*Mr. Tree.*
SIR JOHN PONTEFRACT	*Mr. E. Holman Clark.*
LORD ALFRED RUFFORD	*Mr. Ernest Lawford.*
MR. KELVIL, M.P.	*Mr. Charles Allan.*
THE VEN. ARCHDEACON.	
DAUBENY, D.D.	*Mr. Kemble.*
GERALD ARBUTHNOT	*Mr. Terry.*
FARQUHAR (*Butler*)	*Mr. Hay.*
FRANCIS (*Footman*)	*Mr. Montague.*
LADY HUNSTANTON	*Miss Rose Leclercq.*
LADY CAROLINE PONTEFRACT	*Miss Le Thèire.*
LADY STUTFIELD	*Miss Blanche Horlock.*
MRS. ALLONBY	*Mrs. Tree.*
MISS HESTER WORSLEY	*Miss Julia Neilson.*
ALICE (*Maid*)	*Miss Kelly.*
MRS. ARBUTHNOT	*Mrs. Bernard-Beere.*

FIRST ACT

SCENE

Lawn in front of the terrace at Hunstanton.

SIR JOHN *and* LADY CAROLINE PONTEFRACT, MISS WORSLEY, *on chairs under large yew tree.*

Lady Caroline : I believe this is the first English country house you have stayed at, Miss Worsley ?

Hester : Yes, Lady Caroline.

Lady Caroline : You have no country houses, I am told, in America ?

Hester : We have not many.

Lady Caroline : Have you any country ? What we should call country ?

Hester (smiling) : We have the largest country in the world, Lady Caroline. They used to tell us at school that some of our states are as big as France and England put together.

Lady Caroline : Ah ! you must find it very draughty, I should fancy. (*To* SIR JOHN) : John, you should have your muffler. What is the use of my always knitting mufflers for you if you won't wear them ?

Sir John : I am quite warm, Caroline, I assure you.

Lady Caroline : I think not, John. Well, you couldn't come to a more charming place than this, Miss Worsley, though the house is excessively damp, quite unpardonably damp, and dear Lady Hunstanton is sometimes a little lax about the people she asks down here. (*To* SIR JOHN) : Jane mixes too much. Lord Illingworth, of course, is a man of high distinction. It is a privilege to meet him. And that member of Parliament, Mr. Kettle——

399

Sir John : Kelvil, my love, Kelvil.

Lady Caroline : He must be quite respectable. One has never heard his name before in the whole course of one's life, which speaks volumes for a man, nowadays. But Mrs. Allonby is hardly a very suitable person.

Hester : I dislike Mrs. Allonby. I dislike her more than I can say.

Lady Caroline : I am not sure, Miss Worsley, that foreigners like yourself should cultivate likes or dislikes about the people they are invited to meet. Mrs. Allonby is very well born. She is a niece of Lord Brancaster's. It is said, of course, that she ran away twice before she was married. But you know how unfair people often are. I myself don't believe she ran away more than once.

Hester : Mr. Arbuthnot is very charming.

Lady Caroline : Ah, yes ! the young man who has a post in a bank. Lady Hunstanton is most kind in asking him here, and Lord Illingworth seems to have taken quite a fancy to him. I am not sure, however, that Jane is right in taking him out of his position. In my young days, Miss Worsley, one never met any one in society who worked for their living. It was not considered the thing.

Hester : In America those are the people we respect most.

Lady Caroline : I have no doubt of it.

Hester : Mr. Arbuthnot has a beautiful nature ! He is so simple, so sincere. He has one of the most beatuiful natures I have ever come across. It is a privilege to meet *him*.

Lady Caroline : It is not customary in England, Miss Worsley, for a young lady to speak with such enthusiasm of any person of the opposite sex. English women conceal their feelings till after they are married. They show them then.

Hester : Do you, in England, allow no friendship to exist between a young man and a young girl ?

Enter LADY HUNSTANTON, *followed by* FOOTMAN *with shawls and a cushion.*

Lady Caroline : We think it very inadvisable. Jane, I was just saying what a pleasant party you have asked us to meet. You have a wonderful power of selection. It is quite a gift.

Lady Hunstanton : Dear Caroline, how kind of you ! I think we all do fit in very nicely together. And I hope our charming American visitor will carry back pleasant recollections of our English country life. (*To Footman*) *:* The cushion, there, Francis. And my shawl. The Shetland. Get the Shetland.

Exit Footman for shawl.

Enter GERALD ARBUTHNOT.

Gerald : Lady Hunstanton, I have such good news to tell you. Lord Illingworth has just offered to make me his secretary.

Lady Hunstanton : His secretary ? That is good news indeed, Gerald. It means a very brilliant future in store for you. Your dear mother will be delighted. I really must try and induce her to come up here to-night. Do you think she would, Gerald ? I know how difficult it is to get her to go anywhere.

Gerald : Oh ! I am sure she would, Lady Hunstanton, if she knew Lord Illingworth had made me such an offer.

Enter Footman with shawl.

Lady Hunstanton : I will write and tell her about it, and ask her to come up and meet him. (*To Footman*) *:* Just wait, Francis. (*Writes letter.*)

Lady Caroline : That is a very wonderful opening for so young a man as you are. Mr. Arbuthnot.

Gerald : It is indeed, Lady Caroline. I trust I shall be able to show myself worthy of it.

Lady Caroline : I trust so.

Gerald (to HESTER) *:* You have not congratulated me yet, Miss Worsley.

Hester : Are you very pleased about it ?

Gerald : Of course I am. It means everything to me—things that were out of the reach of hope before may be within hope's reach now.

Hester : Nothing should be out of the reach of hope. Life is a hope.

Lady Hunstanton : I fancy, Caroline, that Diplomacy is what Lord Illingworth is aiming at. I heard that he was offered Vienna. But that may not be true.

Lady Caroline : I don't think that England should be represented abroad by an unmarried man, Jane. It might lead to complications.

Lady Hunstanton : You are too nervous, Caroline. Believe me, you are too nervous. Besides, Lord Illingworth may marry any day. I was in hopes he would have married Lady Kelso. But I believe he said her family was too large. Or was it her feet ? I forget which. I regret it very much. She was made to be an ambassador's wife.

Lady Caroline : She certainly has a wonderful faculty of remembering people's names, and forgetting their faces.

Lady Hunstanton : Well, that is very natural, Caroline, is it not ? *(To Footman) :* Tell Henry to wait for an answer. I have written a line to your dear mother, Gerald, to tell her your good news, and to say she really must come to dinner.

Exit Footman.

Gerald : That is awfully kind of you, Lady Hunstanton. *(To* HESTER) *:* Will you come for a stroll, Miss Worsley ?

Hester : With pleasure. (*Exit with* GERALD.)

Lady Hunstanton : I am very much gratified at Gerald Arbuthnot's good fortune. He is quite a *protégé* of mine. And I am particularly pleased that Lord Illingworth should have made the offer of his own accord without my suggesting anything. Nobody likes to be asked favours. I remember poor Charlotte Pagden making herself quite unpopular one season, because she had a French governess she wanted to recommend to every one.

Lady Caroline : I saw the governess, Jane. Lady Pagden sent her to me. It was before Eleanor came out. She was far too good-looking to be in any respectable household. I don't wonder Lady Pagden was so anxious to get rid of her.

Lady Hunstanton : Ah, that explains it.

Lady Caroline : John, the grass is too damp for you. You had better go and put on your overshoes at once.

Sir John : I am quite comfortable, Caroline, I assure you.

Lady Caroline : You must allow me to be the best judge of that, John. Pray do as I tell you.

SIR JOHN *gets up and goes off.*

Lady Hunstanton : You spoil him, Caroline, you do indeed !

Enter MRS. ALLONBY *and* LADY STUTFIELD.

(*To* MRS. ALLONBY) : Well, dear, I hope you like the park. It is said to be well timbered.

Mrs. Allonby : The trees are wonderful, Lady Hunstanton.

Lady Stutfield : Quite, quite wonderful.

Mrs. Allonby : But somehow, I feel sure that if I lived in the country for six months, I should become so unsophisticated that no one would take the slightest notice of me.

Lady Hunstanton : I assure you, dear, that the country has not that effect at all. Why, it was from Melthorpe, which is only two miles from here, that Lady Belton eloped with Lord Fethersdale. I remember the occurrence perfectly. Poor Lord Belton died three days afterwards of joy, or gout. I forget which. We had a large party staying here at the time, so we were all very much interested in the whole affair.

Mrs. Allonby : I think to elope is cowardly. It's running away from danger. And danger has become so rare in modern life.

Lady Caroline : As far as I can make out, the young women of the present day seem to make it the sole object of their lives to be always playing with fire.

Mrs. Allonby : The one advantage of playing with fire, Lady Caroline, is that one never gets even singed. It is the people who don't know how to play with it who get burned up.

Lady Stutfield : Yes ; I see that. It is very, very helpful.

Lady Hunstanton : I don't know how the world would get on with such a theory as that, dear Mrs. Allonby.

Lady Stutfield : Ah ! The world was made for men and not for women.

Mrs. Allonby : Oh, don't say that, Lady Stutfield. We have a much better time than they have. There are far more things forbidden to us than are forbidden to them.

Lady Stutfield : Yes ; that is quite, quite true. I had not thought of that.

Enter SIR JOHN *and* MR. KELVIL.

Lady Hunstanton : Well, Mr. Kelvil, have you got through your work ?

Kelvil : I have finished my writing for the day, Lady Hunstanton. It has been an arduous task. The demands on the time of a public man are very heavy nowadays, very heavy indeed. And I don't think they meet with adequate recognition.

Lady Caroline : John, have you got your overshoes on ?

Sir John : Yes, my love.

Lady Caroline : I think you had better come over here, John. It is more sheltered.

Sir John : I am quite comfortable, Caroline.

Lady Caroline : I think not, John. You had better sit beside me.

SIR JOHN *rises and goes across.*

Lady Stutfield : And what have you been writing about this morning, Mr. Kelvil?

Kelvil : On the usual subject, Lady Stutfield.   On Purity.

Lady Stutfield : That must be such a very, very interesting thing to write about.

Kelvil : It is the one subject of really national importance, nowadays, Lady Stutfield. I purpose addressing my constituents on the question before Parliament meets. I find that the poorer classes of this country display a marked desire for a higher ethical standard.

Lady Stutfield : How quite, quite nice of them.

Lady Caroline : Are you in favour of women taking part in politics, Mr. Kettle?

Sir John : Kelvil, my love, Kelvil.

Kelvil : The growing influence of women is the one reassuring thing in our political life, Lady Caroline. Women are always on the side of morality, public and private.

Lady Stutfield : It is so very, very gratifying to hear you say that.

Lady Hunstanton : Ah, yes !—the moral qualities in women—that is the important thing. I am afraid, Caroline, that dear Lord Illingworth doesn't value the moral qualities in women as much as he should.

Enter LORD ILLINGWORTH.

Lady Stutfield : The world says that Lord Illingworth is very, very wicked.

Lord Illingworth : But what world says that, Lady Stutfield ? It must be the next world. This world and I are on excellent terms. (*Sits down beside* MRS. ALLONBY.)

Lady Stutfield : Every one *I* know says you are very, very wicked.

Lord Illingworth : It is perfectly monstrous the way people go about, nowadays, saying things against one behind one's back that are absolutely and entirely true.

Lady Hunstanton : Dear Lord Illingworth is quite hopeless, Lady Stutfield. I have given up trying to reform him. It would take a Public Company with a Board of Directors and a paid Secretary to do that. But you have the secretary already, Lord Illingworth, haven't you ? Gerald Arbuthnot has told us of his good fortune ; it is really most kind of you.

Lord Illingworth : Oh, don't say that, Lady Hunstanton. Kind is a dreadful word. I took a great fancy to young Arbuthnot the moment I met him, and he'll be of considerable use to me in something I am foolish enough to think of doing.

Lady Hunstanton : He is an admirable young man. And his mother is one of my dearest friends. He has just gone for a walk with our pretty American. She is very pretty, is she not ?

Lady Caroline : Far too pretty. These American girls carry off all the good matches. Why can't they stay in their own country ? They are always telling us it is the Paradise of women.

Lord Illingworth : It is, Lady Caroline. That is why, like Eve, they are so extremely anxious to get out of it.

Lady Caroline : Who are Miss Worsley's parents ?

Lord Illingworth : American women are wonderfully clever in concealing their parents.

Lady Hunstanton : My dear Lord Illingworth, what do you mean ? Miss Worsley, Caroline, is an orphan. Her father was a very wealthy millionaire or philanthropist, or both, I believe, who entertained my son quite hospitably, when he visited Boston. I don't know how he made his money, originally.

Kelvil : I fancy in American dry goods.

Lady Hunstanton : What are American dry goods ?

Lord Illingworth : American novels.

Lady Hunstanton : How very singular ! . . . Well, from whatever source her large fortune came, I have a great esteem for Miss Worsley. She dresses exceedingly well. All Americans do dress well. They get their clothes in Paris.

Mrs. Allonby : They say, Lady Hunstanton, that when good Americans die they go to Paris.

Lady Hunstanton : Indeed ? And when bad Americans die, where do they go to ?

Lord Illingworth : Oh, they go to America.

Kelvil : I am afraid you don't appreciate America, Lord Illingworth. It is a very remarkable country, especially considering its youth.

Lord Illingworth : The youth of America is their oldest tradition. It has been going on now for three hundred years. To hear them talk one would imagine they were in their first childhood. As far as civilisation goes they are in their second.

Kelvil : There is undoubtedly a great deal of corruption in American politics. I suppose you allude to that ?

Lord Illingworth : I wonder.

Lady Hunstanton : Politics are in a sad way everywhere, I am told. They certainly are in England. Dear Mr. Cardew is ruining the country. I wonder Mrs. Cardew allows him. I am sure, Lord Illingworth, you don't think that uneducated people should be allowed to have votes ?

Lord Illingworth : I think they are the only people
who should.

Kelvil : Do you take no side then in modern politics,
Lord Illingworth ?

Lord Illingworth : One should never take sides in
anything, Mr. Kelvil. Taking sides is the beginning of
sincerity, and earnestness follows shortly afterwards,
and the human being becomes a bore. However, the
House of Commons really does very little harm. You
can't make people good by Act of Parliament—that
is something.

Kelvil : You cannot deny that the House of Commons
has always shown great sympathy with the sufferings
of the poor.

Lord Illingworth : That is its special vice. That is
the special vice of the age. One should sympathise
with the joy, the beauty, the colour of life. The less
said about life's sores the better, Mr. Kelvil.

Kelvil : Still our East End is a very important
problem.

Lord Illingworth : Quite so. It is the problem of
slavery. And we are trying to solve it by amusing the
slaves.

Lady Hunstanton : Certainly, a great deal may be
done by means of cheap entertainments, as you say,
Lord Illingworth. Dear Dr. Daubeny, our rector here,
provides, with the assistance of his curates, really
admirable recreations for the poor during the winter.
And much good may be done by means of a magic
lantern, or a missionary, or some popular amusement
of that kind.

Lady Caroline : I am not at all in favour of amusements for the poor, Jane. Blankets and coals are
sufficient. There is too much love of pleasure amongst
the upper classes as it is. Health is what we want in
modern life. The tone is not healthy, not healthy at all.

Kelvil : You are quite right, Lady Caroline.

Lady Caroline : I believe I am usually right.

Mrs. Allonby : Horrid word " health."

Lord Illingworth : Silliest word in our language, and one knows so well the popular idea of health. The English country gentleman galloping after a fox—the unspeakable in full pursuit of the uneatable.

Kelvil : May I ask, Lord Illingworth, if you regard the House of Lords as a better institution than the House of Commons ?

Lord Illingworth : A much better institution, of course. We in the House of Lords are never in touch with public opinion. That makes us a civilised body.

Kelvil : Are you serious in putting forward such a view ?

Lord Illingworth : Quite serious, Mr. Kelvil. (*To* MRS. ALLONBY) : Vulgar habit that is people have nowadays of asking one, after one has given them an idea, whether one is serious or not. Nothing is serious except passion. The intellect is not a serious thing, and never has been. It is an instrument on which one plays, that is all. The only serious form of intellect I know is the British intellect. And on the British intellect the illiterates play the drum.

Lady Hunstanton : What are you saying, Lord Illingworth, about the drum ?

Lord Illingworth : I was merely talking to Mrs. Allonby about the leading articles in the London newspapers.

Lady Hunstanton : But do you believe all that is written in the newspapers ?

Lord Illingworth : I do. Nowadays it is only the unreadable that occurs. (*Rises with* MRS. ALLONBY.)

Lady Hunstanton : Are you going, Mrs. Allonby ?

Mrs. Allonby : Just as far as the conservatory. Lord Illingworth told me this morning that there was an orchid there as beautiful as the seven deadly sins.

Lady Hunstanton : My dear, I hope there is nothing of the kind. I will certainly speak to the gardener.

Exit MRS. ALLONBY *and* LORD ILLINGWORTH.

Lady Caroline : Remarkable type, Mrs. Allonby.

Lady Hunstanton : She lets her clever tongue run away with her sometimes.

Lady Caroline : Is that the only thing, Jane, Mrs. Allonby allows to run away with her ?

Lady Hunstanton : I hope so, Caroline, I am sure.

Enter LORD ALFRED.

Dear Lord Alfred, do join us.

LORD ALFRED *sits down beside* LADY STUTFIELD.

Lady Caroline : You believe good of every one, Jane. It is a great fault.

Lady Stutfield : Do you really, really think, Lady Caroline, that one should believe evil of every one ?

Lady Caroline : I think it is much safer to do so, Lady Stutfield. Until, of course, people are found out to be good. But that requires a great deal of investigation nowadays.

Lady Stutfield : But there is so much unkind scandal in modern life.

Lady Caroline : Lord Illingworth remarked to me last night at dinner that the basis of every scandal is an absolutely immoral certainty.

Kelvil : Lord Illingworth is, of course, a very brilliant man, but he seems to me to be lacking in that fine faith in the nobility and purity of life which is so important in this century.

Lady Stutfield : Yes, quite, quite important, is it not ?

Kelvil : He gives me the impression of a man who does not appreciate the beauty of our English home-life. I would say that he was tainted with foreign ideas on the subject.

Lady Stutfield : There is nothing, nothing like the beauty of home-life, is there ?

Kelvil : It is the mainstay of our moral system in England, Lady Stutfield. Without it we would become like our neighbours.

Lady Stutfield : That would be so, so sad, would it not ?

Kelvil : I am afraid, too, that Lord Illingworth regards woman simply as a toy. Now, I have never regarded woman as a toy. Woman is the intellectual helpmeet of man in public as in private life. Without her we should forget the true ideals. (*Sits down beside* LADY STUTFIELD.)

Lady Stutfield : I am so very, very glad to hear you say that.

Lady Caroline : You a married man, Mr. Kettle ?

Sir John : Kelvil, dear, Kelvil.

Kelvil : I am married, Lady Caroline.

Lady Caroline : Family ?

Kelvil : Yes.

Lady Caroline : How many ?

Kelvil : Eight.

LADY STUTFIELD *turns her attention to* LORD ALFRED.

Lady Caroline : Mrs. Kettle and the children are, I suppose, at the seaside ?

SIR JOHN *shrugs his shoulders.*

Kelvil : My wife is at the seaside with the children, Lady Caroline.

Lady Caroline : You will join them later on, no doubt ?

Kelvil : If my public engagements permit me.

Lady Caroline : Your public life must be a great source of gratification to Mrs. Kettle.

Sir John : Kelvil, my love, Kelvil.

Lady Stutfield (to LORD ALFRED) : How very, very charming those gold-tipped cigarettes of yours are, Lord Alfred.

Lord Alfred : They are awfully expensive. I can only afford them when I'm in debt.

Lady Stutfield : It must be terribly, terribly distressing to be in debt.

Lord Alfred : One must have some occupation nowadays. If I hadn't my debts I shouldn't have anything to think about. All the chaps I know are in debt.

Lady Stutfield : But don't the people to whom you owe the money give you a great, great deal of annoyance ?

Enter Footman.

Lord Alfred : Oh, no, they write ; I don't.

Lady Stutfield : How very, very strange.

Lady Hunstanton : Ah, here is a letter, Caroline, from dear Mrs. Arbuthnot. She won't dine. I am so sorry. But she will come in the evening. I am very pleased, indeed. She is one of the sweetest of women. Writes a beautiful hand, too, so large, so firm. *(Hands letter to* LADY CAROLINE.)

Lady Caroline (looking at it) : A little lacking in femininity, Jane. Femininity is the quality I admire most in women.

Lady Hunstanton (taking back letter and leaving it on table) : Oh ! she is very feminine, Caroline, and so good, too. You should hear what the Archdeacon says of her. He regards her as his right hand in the parish. *(Footman speaks to her.)* In the Yellow Drawing-room. Shall we all go in ? Lady Stutfield, shall we go in to tea ?

Lady Stutfield : With pleasure, Lady Hunstanton.

They rise and proceed to go off. SIR JOHN *offers to carry* LADY STUTFIELD'S *cloak.*

Lady Caroline: John ! If you would allow your nephew to look after Lady Stutfield's cloak, you might help me with my work-basket.

Enter LORD ILLINGWORTH *and* MRS. ALLONBY.

Sir John : Certainly, my love.

Exeunt.

Mrs. Allonby: Curious thing, plain women are always jealous of their husbands, beautiful women never are !

Lord Illingworth : Beautiful women never have time. They are always so occupied in being jealous of other people's husbands.

Mrs. Allonby : I should have thought Lady Caroline would have grown tired of conjugal anxiety by this time ! Sir John is her fourth !

Lord Illingworth : So much marriage is certainly not becoming. Twenty years of romance make a woman look like a ruin ; but twenty years of marriage make her something like a public building.

Mrs. Allonby : Twenty years of romance ! Is there such a thing ?

Lord Illingworth : Not in our day. Women have become too brilliant. Nothing spoils a romance so much as a sense of humour in the woman.

Mrs. Allonby : Or the want of it in the man.

Lord Illingworth : You are quite right. In a Temple every one should be serious, except the thing that is worshipped.

Mrs. Allonby : And that should be man ?

Lord Illingworth : Women kneel so gracefully ; men don't.

Mrs. Allonby : You are thinking of Lady Stutfield !

Lord Illingworth : I assure you I have not thought of Lady Stutfield for the last quarter of an hour.

Mrs. Allonby : Is she such a mystery ?

Lord Illingworth : She is more than a mystery—she is a mood.

Mrs. Allonby : Moods don't last.

Lord Illingworth : It is their chief charm.

Enter HESTER *and* GERALD.

Gerald : Lord Illingworth, every one has been congratulating me, Lady Hunstanton and Lady Caroline, and . . . every one. I hope I shall make a good secretary.

Lord Illingworth : You will be the pattern secretary, Gerald. (*Talks to him.*)

Mrs. Allonby : You enjoy country life, Miss Worsley ?

Hester : Very much, indeed.

Mrs. Allonby : Don't find yourself longing for a London dinner-party ?

Hester : I dislike London dinner-parties.

Mrs. Allonby : I adore them. The clever people never listen, and the stupid people never talk.

Hester : I think the stupid people talk a great deal.

Mrs. Allonby : Ah, I never listen !

Lord Illingworth : My dear boy, if I didn't like you I wouldn't have made you the offer. It is because I like you so much that I want to have you with me.

Exit HESTER *with* GERALD.

Charming fellow, Gerald Arbuthnot !

Mrs. Allonby : He is very nice ; very nice indeed. But I can't stand the American young lady.

Lord Illingworth : Why ?

Mrs. Allonby : She told me yesterday, and in quite a loud voice too, that she was only eighteen. It was most annoying.

Lord Illingworth : One should never trust a woman who tells one her real age. A woman who would tell one that, would tell one anything.

Mrs. Allonby : She is a Puritan besides——

Lord Illingworth : Ah, that is inexcusable. I don't mind plain women being Puritans. It is the only excuse they have for being plain. But she is decidedly pretty. I admire her immensely. (*Looks steadfastly at* MRS. ALLONBY.)

Mrs. Allonby : What a thoroughly bad man you must be !

Lord Illingworth : What do you call a bad man ?

Mrs. Allonby : The sort of man who admires innocence.

Lord Illingworth : And a bad woman ?

Mrs. Allonby : Oh ! the sort of woman a man never gets tired of.

Lord Illingworth : You are severe—on yourself.

Mrs. Allonby : Define us as a sex.

Lord Illingworth : Sphinxes without secrets.

Mrs. Allonby : Does that include the Puritan women ?

Lord Illingworth : Do you know, I don't believe in the existence of Puritan women ? I don't think there is a woman in the world who would not be a little flattered if one made love to her. It is that which makes women so irresistibly adorable.

Mrs. Allonby : You think there is no woman in the world who would object to being kissed ?

Lord Illingworth : Very few.

Mrs. Allonby : Miss Worsley would not let you kiss her.

Lord Illingworth : Are you sure ?

Mrs. Allonby : Quite.

Lord Illingworth : What do you think she'd do if I kissed her ?

Mrs. Allonby : Either marry you, or strike you across the face with her glove. What would you do if she struck you across the face with her glove ?

Lord Illingworth : Fall in love with her, probably.

Mrs. Allonby : Then it is lucky you are not going to kiss her !

Lord Illingworth : Is that a challenge ?

Mrs. Allonby : It is an arrow shot into the air.

Lord Illingworth : Don't you know that I always succeed in whatever I try ?

Mrs. Allonby : I am sorry to hear it. We women adore failures. They lean on us.

Lord Illingworth : You worship successes. You cling to them.

Mrs. Allonby : We are the laurels to hide their baldness.

Lord Illingworth : And they need you always, except at the moment of triumph.

Mrs. Allonby : They are uninteresting then.

Lord Illingworth : How tantalising you are ? (*A pause.*)

Mrs. Allonby : Lord Illingworth, there is one thing I shall always like you for.

Lord Illingworth : Only one thing ? And I have so many bad qualities.

Mrs. Allonby : Ah, don't be too conceited about them. You may lose them as you grow old.

Lord Illingworth : I never intend to grow old. The soul is born old but grows young. That is the comedy of life.

Mrs. Allonby : And the body is born young and grows old. That is life's tragedy.

Lord Illingworth : Its comedy also, sometimes. But what is the mysterious reason why you will always like me ?

Mrs. Allonby : It is that you have never made love to me.

Lord Illingworth : I have never done anything else.

Mrs. Allonby : Really ? I have not noticed it.

Lord Illingworth : How unfortunate ! It might have been a tragedy for both of us.

Mrs. Allonby : We should each have survived.

Lord Illingworth : One can survive everything nowadays, except death, and live down anything except a good reputation.

Mrs. Allonby : Have you tried a good reputation ?

Lord Illingworth : It is one of the many annoyances to which I have never been subjected.

Mrs. Allonby : It may come.

Lord Illingworth : Why do you threaten me ?

Mrs. Allonby : I will tell you when you have kissed the Puritan.

> *Enter Footman.*

Francis : Tea is served in the Yellow-Drawing-room, my lord.

Lord Illingworth : Tell her ladyship we are coming in.

Francis : Yes, my lord. (*Exit.*)

Lord Illingworth : Shall we go in to tea ?

Mrs. Allonby : Do you like such simple pleasures ?

Lord Illingworth : I adore simple pleasures. They are the last refuge of the complex. But, if you wish, let us stay here. Yes, let us stay here. The Book of Life begins with a man and a woman in a garden.

Mrs. Allonby : It ends with Revelations.

Lord Illingworth : You fence divinely. But the button has come off your foil.

Mrs. Allonby : I have still the mask.

Lord Illingworth : It makes your eyes lovelier.

Mrs. Allonby : Thank you. Come.

Lord Illingworth (*sees* Mrs. Arbuthnot's *letter on table, and takes it up and looks at envelope*) : What a curious handwriting ! It reminds me of the handwriting of a woman I used to know years ago.

Mrs. Allonby : Who ?

Lord Illingworth : Oh ! no one. No one in particular. A woman of no importance. (*Throws letter down, and passes up the steps of the terrace with* Mrs. Allonby. *They smile at each other.*)

ACT DROP.

SECOND ACT

SCENE

Drawing-room at Hunstanton, after dinner, lamps lit. Door L.C. Door R.C.

Ladies seated on sofa.

Mrs. Allonby : What a comfort it is to have got rid of the men for a little !

Lady Stutfield : Yes ; men persecute us dreadfully, don't they ?

Mrs. Allonby : Persecute us ? I wish they did.

Lady Hunstanton : My dear !

Mrs. Allonby : The annoying thing is that the wretches can be perfectly happy without us. That is why I think it is every woman's duty never to leave them alone for a single moment, except during this short breathing space after dinner ; without which, I believe, we poor women would be absolutely worn to shadows.

Enter Servants with coffee.

Lady Hunstanton : Worn to shadows, dear ?

Mrs. Allonby : Yes, Lady Hunstanton. It is such a strain keeping men up to the mark. They are always trying to escape from us.

Lady Stutfield : It seems to me that it is we who are always trying to escape from them. Men are so very, very heartless. They know their power and use it.

Lady Caroline (takes coffee from Servant) : What stuff and nonsense all this about men is ! The thing to do is to keep men in their proper place.

Mrs. Allonby : But what is their proper place, Lady Caroline ?

Lady Caroline: Looking after their wives, Mrs. Allonby.

Mrs. Allonby (takes coffee from Servant): Really ? And if they're not married ?

Lady Caroline: If they are not married, they would be looking after a wife. It's perfectly scandalous the amount of bachelors who are going about society. There should be a law passed to compel them all to marry within twelve months.

Lady Stutfield (refuses coffee): But if they're in love with some one who, perhaps, is tied to another ?

Lady Caroline: In that case, Lady Stutfield, they would be married off in a week to some plain respectable girl, in order to teach them not to meddle with other people's property.

Mrs. Allonby: I don't think that we should ever be spoken of as other people's property. All men are married women's property. That is the only true definition of what married women's property really is. But we don't belong to any one.

Lady Stutfield: Oh, I am so very, very glad to hear you say so.

Lady Hunstanton: But do you really think, dear Caroline, that legislation would improve matters in any way ? I am told that, nowadays, all the married men live like bachelors, and all the bachelors like married men.

Mrs. Allonby: I certainly never know one from the other.

Lady Stutfield: Oh, I think one can always know at once whether a man has home claims upon his life or not. I have noticed a very, very sad expression in the eyes of so many married men.

Mrs. Allonby: Ah, all that I have noticed is that they are horribly tedious when they are good husbands, and abominably conceited when they are not.

Lady Hunstanton: Well, I suppose the type of husband has completely changed since my young days, but I'm bound to state that poor dear Hunstanton was the most delightful of creatures, and as good as gold.

Mrs. Allonby: Ah, my husband is a sort of promissory note ; I'm tired of meeting him.

Lady Caroline: But you renew him from time to time, don't you ?

Mrs. Allonby: Oh no, Lady Caroline. I have only had one husband as yet. I suppose you look upon me as quite an amateur.

Lady Caroline: With your views on life I wonder you married at all.

Mrs. Allonby: So do I.

Lady Hunstanton: My dear child, I believe you are really very happy in your married life, but that you like to hide your happiness from others.

Mrs. Allonby: I assure you I was horribly deceived in Ernest.

Lady Hunstanton: Oh, I hope not, dear. I knew his mother quite well. She was a Stratton, Caroline, one of Lord Crowland's daughters.

Lady Caroline: Victoria Stratton ? I remember her perfectly. A silly, fair-haired woman with no chin.

Mrs. Allonby: Ah, Ernest has a chin. He has a very strong chin, a square chin. Ernest's chin is far too square.

Lady Stutfield: But do you really think a man's chin can be too square ? I think a man should look very, very strong, and that his chin should be quite, quite square.

Mrs. Allonby: Then you should certainly know Ernest, Lady Stutfield. It is only fair to tell you beforehand he has got no conversation at all.

Lady Stutfield: I adore silent men.

Mrs. Allonby: Oh, Ernest isn't silent. He talks the whole time. But he has got no conversation. What he talks about I don't know. I haven't listened to him for years.

Lady Stutfield: Have you never forgiven him then ?

How sad that seems! But all life is very, very sad,
is it not?

Mrs. Allonby: Life, Lady Stutfield, is simply a
mauvais quart d'heure made up of exquisite moments.

Lady Stutfield: Yes, there are moments, certainly.
But was it something very, very wrong that Mr.
Allonby did? Did he become angry with you, and say
anything that was unkind or true?

Mrs. Allonby: Oh, dear, no. Ernest is invariably
calm. That is one of the reasons he always gets on my
nerves. Nothing is so aggravating as calmness. There
is something positively brutal about the good temper
of most modern men. I wonder we women stand it
as well as we do.

Lady Stutfield: Yes; men's good temper shows
they are not so sensitive as we are, not so finely strung.
It makes a great barrier often between husband and
wife, does it not? But I would so much like to know
what was the wrong thing Mr. Allonby did.

Mrs. Allonby: Well, I will tell you, if you solemnly
promise to tell everybody else.

Lady Stutfield: Thank you, thank you. I will make
a point of repeating it.

Mrs. Allonby: When Ernest and I were engaged,
he swore to me positively on his knees that he had
never loved any one before in the whole course of his
life. I was very young at the time, so I didn't believe
him, I needn't tell you. Unfortunately, however, I
made no inquiries of any kind till after I had been
actually married four or five months. I found out
then that what he had told me was perfectly true.
And that sort of thing makes a man so absolutely
uninteresting.

Lady Hunstanton: My dear!

Mrs. Allonby: Men always want to be a woman's
first love. That is their clumsy vanity. We women
have a more subtle instinct about things. What we
like is to be a man's last romance.

Lady Stutfield: I see what you mean. It's very, very beautiful.

Lady Hunstanton: My dear child, you don't mean to tell me that you won't forgive your husband because he never loved any one else ? Did you ever hear such a thing, Caroline ? I am quite surprised.

Lady Caroline: Oh, women have become so highly educated, Jane, that nothing should surprise us nowadays, except happy marriages. They apparently are getting remarkably rare.

Mrs. Allonby: Oh, they're quite out of date.

Lady Stutfield: Except amongst the middle classes, I have been told.

Mrs. Allonby: How like the middle classes !

Lady Stutfield: Yes—is it not ?—very, very like them.

Lady Caroline: If what you tell us about the middle classes is true, Lady Stutfield, it redounds greatly to their credit. It is much to be regretted that in our rank of life the wife should be so persistently frivolous, under the impression apparently that it is the proper thing to be. It is to that I attribute the unhappiness of so many marriages we all know of in society.

Mrs. Allonby: Do you know, Lady Caroline, I don't think the frivolity of the wife has ever anything to do with it. More marriages are ruined nowadays by the common sense of the husband than by anything else. How can a woman be expected to be happy with a man who insists on treating her as if she was a perfectly rational being ?

Lady Hunstanton: My dear !

Mrs. Allonby: Man, poor, awkward, reliable, necessary man belongs to a sex that has been rational for millions and millions of years. He can't help himself. It is in his race. The History of Woman is very different. We have always been picturesque protests against the mere existence of common sense. We saw its dangers from the first.

Lady Stutfield : Yes, the common sense of husbands is certainly most, most trying. Do tell me your conception of the Ideal Husband. I think it would be so very, very helpful.

Mrs. Allonby : The Ideal Husband ? There couldn't by such a thing. The institution is wrong.

Lady Stutfield : The Ideal Man, then, in his relations to *us.*

Lady Caroline : He would probably be extremely realistic.

Mrs. Allonby : The Ideal Man ! Oh, the Ideal Man should talk to us as if we were goddesses, and treat us as if we were children. He should refuse all our serious requests, and gratify every one of our whims. He should encourage us to have caprices, and forbid us to have missions. He should always say much more than he means, and always mean much more than he says.

Lady Hunstanton : But how could he do both, dear ?

Mrs. Allonby : He should never run down other pretty women. That would show he had no taste, or make one suspect that he had too much. No ; he should be nice about them all, but say that somehow they don't attract him.

Lady Stutfield : Yes, that is always very, very pleasant to hear about other women.

Mrs. Allonby : If we ask him a question about anything, he should give us an answer all about ourselves. He should invariably praise us for whatever qualities he knows we haven't got. But he should be pitiless, quite pitiless, in reproaching us for the virtues that we have never dreamed of possessing. He should never believe that we know the use of useful things. That would be unforgivable. But he should shower on us everything we don't want.

Lady Caroline : As far as I can see, he is to do nothing but pay bills and compliments.

Mrs. Allonby : He should persistently compromise us in public, and treat us with absolute respect when we are alone. And yet he should be always ready to have a perfectly terrible scene, whenever we want one, and to become miserable, absolutely miserable, at a moment's notice, and to overwhelm us with just reproaches in less than twenty minutes, and to be positively violent at the end of half an hour, and to leave us for ever at a quarter to eight, when we have to go and dress for dinner. And when, after that, one has seen him for really the last time, and he has refused to take back the little things he has given one, and promised never to communicate with one again, or to write one any foolish letters, he should be perfectly broken-hearted, and telegraph to one all day long, and send one little notes every half-hour by a private hansom, and dine quite alone at the club, so that every one should know how unhappy he was. And after a whole dreadful week, during which one has gone about everywhere with one's husband, just to show how absolutely lonely one was, he may be given a third last parting, in the evening, and then, if his conduct has been quite irreproachable, and one has behaved really badly to him, he should be allowed to admit that he has been entirely in the wrong, and when he has admitted that, it becomes a woman's duty to forgive, and one can do it all over again from the beginning, with variations.

Lady Hunstanton : How clever you are, my dear ! You never mean a single word you say.

Lady Stutfield : Thank you, thank you. It has been quite, quite entrancing. I must try and remember it all. There are such a number of details that are so very, very important.

Lady Caroline : But you have not told us yet what the reward of the Ideal Man is to be.

Mrs. Allonby : His reward ? Oh, infinite expectation. That is quite enough for him.

Lady Stutfield : But men are so terribly, terribly exacting, are they not ?

Mrs. Allonby : That makes no matter. One should never surrender.

Lady Stutfield : Not even to the Ideal Man ?

Mrs. Allonby : Certainly not to him. Unless, of course, one wants to grow tired of him.

Lady Stutfield : Oh ! . . . Yes. I see that. It is very, very helpful. Do you think, Mrs. Allonby, I shall every meet the Ideal Man ? Or are there more than one ?

Mrs. Allonby : There are just four in London, Lady Stutfield.

Lady Hunstanton : Oh, my dear !

Mrs. Allonby (going over to her) : What has happened ? Do tell me.

Lady Hunstanton (in a low voice) : I had completely forgotten that the American young lady has been in the room all the time. I am afraid some of this clever talk may have shocked her a little.

Mrs. Allonby : Ah, that will do her so much good !

Lady Hunstanton : Let us hope she didn't understand much. I think I had better go over and talk to her. (*Rises and goes across to* HESTER WORSLEY.) Well, dear Miss Worsley. (*Sitting down beside her.*) How quiet you have been in your nice little corner all this time ! I suppose you have been reading a book ? There are so many books here in the library.

Hester : No, I have been listening to the conversation.

Lady Hunstanton : You mustn't believe everything that was said, you know, dear.

Hester : I didn't believe any of it.

Lady Hunstanton : That is quite right, dear.

Hester (continuing) : I couldn't believe that any women could really hold such views of life as I have heard to-night from some of your guests. (*An awkward pause.*)

Lady Hunstanton : I hear you have such pleasant society in America. Quite like our own in places, my son wrote to me.

Hester : There are cliques in America as elsewhere, Lady Hunstanton. But true American society consists simply of all the good women and good men we have in our country.

Lady Hunstanton : What a sensible system, and I dare say quite pleasant, too. I am afraid in England we have too many artificial social barriers. We don't see as much as we should of the middle and lower classes.

Hester : In America we have no lower classes.

Lady Hunstanton : Really? What a very strange arrangement!

Mrs. Allonby : What is that dreadful girl talking about?

Lady Stutfield : She is painfully natural, is she not?

Lady Caroline : There are a great many things you haven't got in America, I am told, Miss Worsley. They say you have no ruins, and no curiosities.

Mrs. Allonby (to LADY STUTFIELD) *:* What nonsense! They have their mothers and their manners.

Hester : The English aristocracy supply us with our curiosities, Lady Caroline. They are sent over to us every summer, regularly, in the steamers, and propose to us the day after they land. As for ruins, we are trying to build up something that will last longer than brick or stone. *(Gets up to take her fan from table.)*

Lady Hunstanton : What is that, dear? Ah, yes, an iron Exhibition, is it not, at that place that has the curious name?

Hester (standing by table) : We are trying to build up life, Lady Hunstanton, on a better, truer, purer basis than life rests on here. This sounds strange to you all, no doubt. How could it sound other than strange? You rich people in England, you don't know how you are living. How could you know? You shut out from your society the gentle and the good. You laugh at the simple and the pure. Living, as you all do, on others and by them, you sneer at self-sacrifice, and if you throw bread to the poor, it is merely to keep them quiet for a season. With all your pomp and wealth and art you don't know how to live—you don't even know that. You love the beauty that you can see and touch and handle, the beauty that you can destroy, and do destroy, but of the unseen beauty of life, of the unseen beauty of a higher life, you know nothing. You have lost life's secret. Oh, your English society seems to me shallow, selfish, foolish. It has blinded its eyes, and stopped its ears. It lies like a leper in purple. It sits like a dead thing smeared with gold. It is all wrong, all wrong.

Lady Stutfield : I don't think one should know of these things. It is not very, very nice, is it?

Lady Hunstanton : My dear Miss Worsley, I thought you liked English society so much. You were such a success in it. And you were so much admired by the best people. I quite forget what Lord Henry Weston said of you—but it was most complimentary, and you know what an authority he is on beauty.

Hester : Lord Henry Weston! I remember him, Lady Hunstanton. A man with a hideous smile and a hideous past. He is asked everywhere. No dinner-party is complete without him. What of those whose ruin is due to him? They are outcasts. They are nameless. If you met them in the street you would turn your head away. I don't complain of their punishment. Let all women who have sinned be punished.

MRS. ARBUTHNOT *enters from terrace behind in a cloak with a lace veil over her head. She hears the last words and starts.*

Lady Hunstanton : My dear young lady!

Hester : It is right that they should be punished, but don't let them be the only ones to suffer. If a man and woman have sinned, let them both go forth into the desert to love or loathe each other there. Let them both be branded. Set a mark, if you wish, on each, but don't punish the one and let the other go free. Don't have one law for men and another for women. You are unjust to women in England. And till you count what is a shame in a woman to be infamy in a man, you will always be unjust, and Right, that pillar of fire, and Wrong, that pillar of cloud, will be made dim to your eyes, or be not seen at all, or if seen, not regarded.

Lady Caroline : Might I, dear Miss Worsley, as you are standing up, ask you for my cotton that is just behind you ? Thank you.

Lady Hunstanton : My dear Mrs. Arbuthnot ! I am so pleased you have come up. But I didn't hear you announced.

Mrs. Arbuthnot : Oh, I came straight in from the terrace, Lady Hunstanton, just as I was. You didn't tell me you had a party.

Lady Hunstanton : Not a party. Only a few guests who are staying in the house, and whom you must know. Allow me. (*Tries to help her. Rings bell.*) Caroline, this is Mrs. Arbuthnot, one of my sweetest friends. Lady Caroline Pontefract, Lady Stutfield, Mrs. Allonby, and my young American friend, Miss Worsley, who has just been telling us all how wicked we are.

Hester : I am afraid you think I spoke too strongly, Lady Hunstanton. But there are some things in England——

Lady Hunstanton : My dear young lady, there was a great deal of truth, I dare say, in what you said, and you looked very pretty while you said it, which is much more important, Lord Illingworth would tell us. The only point where I thought you were a little hard was about Lady Caroline's brother, about poor Lord Henry. He is really such good company.

Enter Footman.

Take Mrs. Arbuthnot's things.

Exit Footman with wraps.

Hester : Lady Caroline, I had no idea it was your brother. I am sorry for the pain I must have caused you—I——

Lady Caroline : My dear Miss Worsley, the only part of your little speech, if I may so term it, with which I thoroughly agreed, was the part about my brother. Nothing that you could possibly say could be too bad for him. I regard Henry as infamous, absolutely infamous. But I am bound to state, as you were remarking, Jane, that he is excellent company, and he has one of the best cooks in London, and after a good dinner one can forgive anybody, even one's own relations.

Lady Hunstanton (to MISS WORSLEY) *:* Now, do come, dear, and make friends with Mrs. Arbuthnot. She is one of the good, sweet, simple people you told us we never admitted into society. I am sorry to say Mrs. Arbuthnot comes very rarely to me. But that is not my fault.

Mrs. Allonby : What a bore it is the men staying so long after dinner ! I expect they are saying the most dreadful things about us.

Lady Stutfield : Do you really think so ?

Mrs. Allonby : I am sure of it.

Lady Stutfield : How very, very horrid of them ! Shall we go on to the terrace ?

Mrs. Allonby : Oh, anything to get away from the dowagers and the dowdies. (*Rises and goes with* LADY STUTFIELD *to door L.C.*) We are only going to look at the stars, Lady Hunstanton.

Lady Hunstanton : You will find a great many, dear, a great many. But don't catch cold. (*To* MRS. ARBUTH-NOT) : We shall all miss Gerald so much, dear Mrs. Arbuthnot.

Mrs. Arbuthnot : But has Lord Illingworth really offered to make Gerald his secretary ?

Lady Hunstanton : Oh, yes ! He has been most charming about it. He has the highest possible opinion of your boy. You don't know Lord Illingworth, I believe, dear.

Mrs. Arbuthnot : I have never met him.

Lady Hunstanton : You know him by name, no doubt ?

Mrs. Arbuthnot : I am afraid I don't. I live so much out of the world, and see so few people. I remember hearing years ago of an old Lord Illingworth who lived in Yorkshire, I think.

Lady Hunstanton : Ah, yes. That would be the last Earl but one. He was a very curious man. He wanted to marry beneath him. Or wouldn't, I believe. There was some scandal about it. The present Lord Illingworth is quite different. He is very distinguished. He does—well, he does nothing, which I am afraid our pretty American visitor here thinks very wrong of anybody, and I don't know that he cares much for the subjects in which you are so interested, dear Mrs. Arbuthnot. Do you think, Caroline, that Lord Illingworth is interested in the Housing of the Poor ?

Lady Caroline : I should fancy not at all, Jane.

Lady Hunstanton : We all have our different tastes, have we not ? But Lord Illingworth has a very high position, and there is nothing he couldn't get if he chose to ask for it. Of course, he is comparatively a young man still, and he has only come to his title within —how long exactly is it, Caroline, since Lord Illingworth succeeded ?

Lady Caroline : About four years, I think, Jane

I know it was the same year in which my brother had his last exposure in the evening newspapers.

Lady Hunstanton : Ah, I remember. That would be about four years ago. Of course, there were a great many people between the present Lord Illingworth and the title, Mrs. Arbuthnot. There was—who was there, Caroline ?

Lady Caroline : There was poor Margaret's baby. You remember how anxious she was to have a boy, and it was a boy, but it died, and her husband died shortly afterwards, and she married almost immediately one of Lord Ascot's sons, who, I am told, beats her.

Lady Hunstanton : Ah, that is in the family, dear, that is in the family. And there was also, I remember, a clergyman who wanted to be a lunatic, or a lunatic who wanted to be a clergyman, I forget which, but I know the Court of Chancery investigated the matter, and decided that he was quite sane. And I saw him afterwards at poor Lord Plumstead's with straws in his hair, or something very odd about him. I can't recall what. I often regret, Lady Caroline, that dear Lady Cecilia never lived to see her son get the title.

Mrs. Arbuthnot : Lady Cecilia ?

Lady Hunstanton : Lord Illingworth's mother, dear Mrs. Arbuthnot, was one of the Duchess of Jerningham's pretty daughters, and she married Sir Thomas Harford, who wasn't considered a very good match for her at the time, though he was said to be the handsomest man in London. I knew them all quite intimately, and both the sons, Arthur and George.

Mrs. Arbuthnot : It was the eldest son who succeeded, of course, Lady Hunstanton ?

Lady Hunstanton : No, dear, he was killed in the hunting field. Or was it fishing, Caroline ? I forget. But George came in for everything. I always tell him that no younger son has ever had such good luck as he has had.

Mrs. Arbuthnot : Lady Hunstanton, I want to speak to Gerald at once. Might I see him ? Can he be sent for ?

Lady Hunstanton : Certainly, dear. I will send one of the servants into the dining-room to fetch him. I don't know what keeps the gentlemen so long. (*Rings bell.*) When I knew Lord Illingworth first as plain George Harford, he was simply a very brilliant young man about town, with not a penny of money except what poor dear Lady Cecilia gave him. She was quite devoted to him. Chiefly, I fancy, because he was on bad terms with his father. Oh, here is the dear Archdeacon. (*To Servant*) : It doesn't matter.

> *Enter* SIR JOHN *and* DOCTOR DAUBENY. SIR JOHN *goes over to* LADY STUTFIELD, DOCTOR DAUBENY *to* LADY HUNSTANTON.

The Archdeacon : Lord Illingworth has been most entertaining. I have never enjoyed myself more. (*Sees* MRS. ARBUTHNOT.) Ah, Mrs. Arbuthnot.

Lady Hunstanton (*to* DOCTOR DAUBENY) : You see I have got Mrs. Arbuthnot to come to me at last.

The Archdeacon : That is a great honour, Lady Hunstanton. Mrs. Daubeny will be quite jealous of you.

Lady Hunstanton : Ah, I am so sorry Mrs. Daubeny could not come with you to-night. Headache as usual, I suppose.

The Archdeacon : Yes, Lady Hunstanton ; a perfect martyr. But she is happiest alone. She is happiest alone.

Lady Caroline (*to her husband*) : John !

> SIR JOHN *goes over to his wife.* DOCTOR DAUBENY *talks to* LADY HUNSTANTON *and* MRS. ARBUTHNOT. MRS. ARBUTHNOT *watches* LORD ILLINGWORTH *the whole time. He has passed across the room without noticing her, and approaches* MRS. ALLONBY,

who with LADY STUTFIELD *is standing by the door looking on to the terrace.*

Lord Illingworth : How is the most charming woman in the world ?

Mrs. Allonby (taking LADY STUTFIELD *by the hand) :* We are both quite well, thank you, Lord Illingworth. But what a short time you have been in the dining-room ! It seems as if we had only just left.

Lord Illingworth : I was bored to death. Never opened my lips the whole time. Absolutely longing to come in to you.

Mrs. Allonby : You should have. The American girl has been giving us a lecture.

Lord Illingworth : Really ? All Americans lecture, I believe. I suppose it is something in their climate. What did she lecture about ?

Mrs. Allonby : Oh, Puritanism, of course.

Lord Illingworth : I am going to convert her, am I not ? How long do you give me ?

Mrs. Allonby : A week.

Lord Illingworth : A week is more than enough.

Enter GERALD *and* LORD ALFRED.

Gerald (going to MRS. ARBUTHNOT) *:* Dear mother !

Mrs. Arbuthnot : Gerald, I don't feel at all well. See me home, Gerald. I shouldn't have come.

Gerald : I am so sorry, mother. Certainly. But you must know Lord Illingworth first. (*Goes across room.*)

Mrs. Arbuthnot : Not to-night, Gerald.

Gerald : Lord Illingworth, I want you so much to know my mother.

Lord Illingworth : With the greatest pleasure. (*To* MRS. ALLONBY) *:* I'll be back in a moment. People's mothers always bore me to death. All women become like their mothers. That is their tragedy.

Mrs. Allonby : No man does. That is his.

Lord Illingworth : What a delightful mood you are in to-night ! (*Turns round and goes across with* GERALD *to* MRS. ARBUTHNOT. *When he sees her, he starts back in wonder. Then slowly his eyes turn towards* GERALD.)

Gerald : Mother, this is Lord Illingworth, who has offered to take me as his private secretary.

MRS. ARBUTHNOT *bows coldly.*

It is a wonderful opening for me, isn't it ? I hope he won't be disappointed in me, that is all. You'll thank Lord Illingworth, mother, won't you ?

Mrs. Arbuthnot : Lord Illingworth is very good, I am sure, to interest himself in you for the moment.

Lord Illingworth (*putting his hand on* GERALD'S *shoulder*) : Oh, Gerald and I are great friends already, Mrs. . . . Arbuthnot.

Mrs. Arbuthnot : There can be nothing in common between you and my son, Lord Illingworth.

Gerald : Dear mother, how can you say so ? Of course, Lord Illingworth is awfully clever and that sort of thing. There is nothing Lord Illingworth doesn't know.

Lord Illingworth : My dear boy !

Gerald : He knows more about life than any one I have ever met. I feel an awful duffer when I am with you, Lord Illingworth. Of course, I have had so few advantages. I have not been to Eton or Oxford like other chaps. But Lord Illingworth doesn't seem to mind that. He had been awfully good to me, mother.

Mrs. Arbuthnot : Lord Illingworth may change his mind. He may not really want you as his secretary.

Gerald : Mother !

Mrs. Arbuthnot : You must remember, as you said yourself, you have had so few advantages.

Mrs. Allonby : Lord Illingworth, I want to speak to you for a moment. Do come over.

Lord Illingworth : Will you excuse me, Mrs. Arbuth-

not ? Now, don't let your charming mother make any
more difficulties, Gerald. The thing is quite settled,
isn't it ?

Gerald : I hope so.

LORD ILLINGWORTH *goes across to* MRS. ALLONBY.

Mrs. Allonby : I thought you were never going to
leave the lady in black velvet.

Lord Illingworth : She is excessively handsome.
(*Looks at* MRS. ARBUTHNOT.)

Lady Hunstanton : Caroline, shall we all make a
move to the music-room ? Miss Worsley is going to
play. You'll come too, dear Mrs. Arbuthnot, won't
you ? You don't know what a treat is in store for
you. (*To* DOCTOR DAUBENY) : I must really take Miss
Worsley down some afternoon to the rectory. I should
so much like dear Mrs. Daubeny to hear her on the
violin. Ah, I forgot. Dear Mrs. Daubeny's hearing is
a little defective, is it not ?

The Archdeacon : Her deafness is a great privation
to her. She can't even hear my sermons now. She
reads them at home. But she has many resources in
herself, many resources.

Lady Hunstanton : She reads a good deal, I suppose ?

The Archdeacon : Just the very largest print. The
eyesight is rapidly going. But she's never morbid,
never morbid.

Gerald (to LORD ILLINGWORTH) : Do speak to my
mother, Lord Illingworth, before you go into the
music-room. She seems to think, somehow, you don't
mean what you said to me.

Mrs. Allonby : Aren't you coming ?

Lord Illingworth : In a few moments. Lady Hunstanton, if Mrs. Arbuthnot would allow me, I would
like to say a few words to her, and we will join you
later on.

Lady Hunstanton : Ah, of course. You will have a

great deal to say to her, and she will have a great deal
to thank you for. It is not every son who gets such an
offer, Mrs. Arbuthnot. But I know you appreciate
that, dear.

Lady Caroline : John !

Lady Hunstanton : Now, don't keep Mrs. Arbuthnot
too long, Lord Illingworth. We can't spare her.

*Exit following the other guests. Sound of violin
heard from music-room.*

Lord Illingworth : So that is our son, Rachel ! Well,
I am very proud of him. He is a Harford, every inch
of him. By the way, why Arbuthnot, Rachel ?

Mrs. Arbuthnot : One name is as good as another,
when one has no right to any name.

Lord Illingworth : I suppose so—but why Gerald ?

Mrs. Arbuthnot : After a man whose heart I broke
—after my father.

Lord Illingworth : Well, Rachel, what is over is over.
All I have got to say now is that I am very, very
much pleased with our boy. The world will know him
merely as my private secretary, but to me he will
be something very near, and very dear. It is a curious
thing, Rachel ; my life seemed to be quite complete. It
was not so. It lacked something, it lacked a son. I
have found my son now, I am glad I have found him.

Mrs. Arbuthnot : You have no right to claim him,
or the smallest part of him. The boy is entirely mine,
and shall remain mine.

Lord Illingworth : My dear Rachel, you have had
him to yourself for over twenty years. Why not let
me have him for a little now ? He is quite as much
mine as yours.

Mrs. Arbuthnot : Are you talking of the child you
abandoned ? Of the child who, as far as you are
concerned, might have died of hunger and of want ?

Lord Illingworth : You forget, Rachel, it was you
who left me. It was not I who left you.

Mrs. Arbuthnot : I left you because you refused to give the child a name. Before my son was born, I implored you to marry me.

Lord Illingworth : I had no expectations then. And besides, Rachel, I wasn't much older than you were. I was only twenty-two. I was twenty-one, I believe, when the whole thing began in your father's garden.

Mrs. Arbuthnot : When a man is old enough to do wrong he should be old enough to do right also.

Lord Illingworth : My dear Rachel, intellectual generalities are always interesting, but generalities in morals mean absolutely nothing. As for saying I left our child to starve, that, of course, is untrue and silly. My mother offered you six hundred a year. But you wouldn't take anything. You simply disappeared, and carried the child away with you.

Mrs. Arbuthnot : I wouldn't have accepted a penny from her. Your father was different. He told you, in my presence, when we were in Paris, that it was your duty to marry me.

Lord Illingworth : Oh, duty is what one expects from others, it is not what one does oneself. Of course, I was influenced by my mother. Every man is when he is young.

Mrs. Arbuthnot : I am glad to hear you say so. Gerald shall certainly not go away with you.

Lord Illingworth : What nonsense, Rachel !

Mrs. Arbuthnot : Do you think I would allow my son——

Lord Illingworth : Our son.

Mrs. Arbuthnot : My son—(LORD ILLINGWORTH *shrugs his shoulders*)—to go away with the man who spoiled my youth, who ruined my life, who has tainted every moment of my days ? You don't realise what my past has been in suffering and in shame.

Lord Illingworth : My dear Rachel, I must candidly say that I think Gerald's future considerably more important than your past.

Mrs. Arbuthnot : Gerald cannot separate his future from my past.

Lord Illingworth : That is exactly what he should do. That is exactly what you should help him to do. What a typical woman you are ! You talk sentimentally, and you are thoroughly selfish the whole time. But don't let us have a scene. Rachel, I want you to look at this matter from the common-sense point of view, from the point of view of what is best for our son, leaving you and me out of the question. What is our son at present ? An underpaid clerk in a small Provincial Bank in a third-rate English town. If you imagine he is quite happy in such a position, you are mistaken. He is thoroughly discontented.

Mrs. Arbuthnot : He was not discontented till he met you. You have made him so.

Lord Illingworth : Of course, I made him so. Discontent is the first step in the progress of a man or a nation. But I did not leave him with a mere longing for things he could not get. No, I made him a charming offer. He jumped at it, I need hardly say. Any young man would. And now, simply because it turns out that I am the boy's own father and he my own son, you propose practically to ruin his career. That is to say, if I were a perfect stranger, you would allow Gerald to go away with me, but as he is my own flesh and blood you won't. How utterly illogical you are !

Mrs. Arbuthnot : I will not allow him to go.

Lord Illingworth : How can you prevent it ? What excuse can you give to him for making him decline such an offer as mine ? I won't tell him in what relations I stand to him, I need hardly say. But you daren't tell him. You know that. Look how you have brought him up.

Mrs. Arbuthnot : I have brought him up to be a good man.

Lord Illingworth : Quite so. And what is the result ? You have educated him to be your judge if he ever finds you out. And a bitter, an unjust judge he will be to you. Don't be deceived, Rachel. Children begin by loving their parents. After a time they judge them. Rarely, if ever, do they forgive them.

Mrs. Arbuthnot : George, don't take my son away from me. I have had twenty years of sorrow, and I have only had one thing to love me, only one thing to love. You have had a life of joy, and pleasure, and success. You have been quite happy, you have never thought of us. There was no reason, according to your views of life, why you should have remembered us at all. Your meeting us was a mere accident, a horrible accident. Forget it. Don't come now, and rob me of— of all I have in the whole world. You are so rich in other things. Leave me the little vineyard of my life ; leave me the walled-in garden and the well of water ; the ewe-lamb God sent me, in pity or in wrath, oh ! leave me that. George, don't take Gerald from me.

Lord Illingworth : Rachel, at the present moment you are not necessary to Gerald's career ; I a·n. There is nothing more to be said on the subject.

Mrs. Arbuthnot : I will not let him go.

Lord Illingworth : Here is Gerald. He has a right to decide for himself.

Enter GERALD.

Gerald : Well, dear mother, I hope you have settled it all with Lord Illingworth ?

Mrs. Arbuthnot : I have not, Gerald.

Lord Illingworth : Your mother seems not to like your coming with me, for some reason.

Gerald : Why, mother ?

Mrs. Arbuthnot : I thought you were quite happy here with me, Gerald. I didn't know you were so anxious to leave me.

Gerald : Mother, how can you talk like that ? Of course I have been quite happy with you. But a man

can't stay always with his mother. No chap does. I
want to make myself a position, to do something. I
thought you would have been proud to see me Lord
Illingworth's secretary.

Mrs. Arbuthnot : I do not think you would be
suitable as a private secretary to Lord Illingworth.
You have no qualifications.

Lord Illingworth : I don't wish to seem to interfere
for a moment, Mrs. Arbuthnot, but as far as your
last objection is concerned, I surely am the best judge.
And I can only tell you that your son has all the
qualifications I had hoped for. He has more, in fact,
than I had even thought of. Far more. (MRS.
ARBUTHNOT *remains silent.*) Have you any other
reason, Mrs. Arbuthnot, why you don't wish your son
to accept this post ?

Gerald : Have you, mother ? Do answer.

Lord Illingworth : If you have, Mrs. Arbuthnot,
pray, pray say it. We are quite by ourselves here.
Whatever it is, I need not say I will not repeat it.

Gerald : Mother ?

Lord Illingworth : If you would like to be alone
with your son, I will leave you. You may have some
other reason you don't wish me to hear.

Mrs. Arbuthnot : I have no other reason.

Lord Illingworth : Then, my dear boy, we may look
on the thing as settled. Come, you and I will smoke a
cigarette on the terrace together. And Mrs. Arbuthnot,
pray let me tell you, that I think you have acted very,
very wisely.

Exit with GERALD. MRS. ARBUTHNOT *is left
alone. She stands immobile with a look of un-
utterable sorrow on her face.*

ACT DROP.

THIRD ACT

SCENE

The Picture Gallery at Hunstanton. Door at back leading on to terrace.

LORD ILLINGWORTH *and* GERALD, *R.C.* LORD ILLINGWORTH *lolling on a sofa.* GERALD *in a chair.*

Lord Illingworth : Thoroughly sensible woman, your mother, Gerald. I knew she would come round in the end.

Gerald : My mother is awfully conscientious, Lord Illingworth, and I know she doesn't think I am educated enough to be your secretary. She is perfectly right, too. I was fearfully idle when I was at school, and I couldn't pass an examination now to save my life.

Lord Illingworth : My dear Gerald, examinations are of no value whatsoever. If a man is a gentleman, he knows quite enough, and if he is not a gentleman, whatever he knows is bad for him.

Gerald : But I am so ignorant of the world, Lord Illingworth.

Lord Illingworth : Don't be afraid, Gerald. Remember that you've got on your side the most wonderful thing in the world—youth! There is nothing like youth. The middle-aged are mortgaged to Life. The old are in life's lumber-room. But youth is the Lord of Life. Youth has a kingdom waiting for it. Every one is born a king, and most people die in exile, like most kings. To win back my youth, Gerald, there is nothing I wouldn't do—except take exercise, get up early, or be a useful member of the community.

441

Gerald: But you don't call yourself old, Lord Illingworth?

Lord Illingworth: I am old enough to be your father, Gerald.

Gerald: I don't remember my father; he died years ago.

Lord Illingworth: So Lady Hunstanton told me.

Gerald: It is very curious, my mother never talks to me about my father. I sometimes think she must have married beneath her.

Lord Illingworth (winces slightly): Really? (*Goes over and puts his hand on* GERALD's *shoulder.*) You have missed not having a father, I suppose, Gerald?

Gerald: Oh, no; my mother has been so good to me. No one ever had such a mother as I have had.

Lord Illingworth: I am quite sure of that. Still I should imagine that most mothers don't quite understand their sons. Don't realise, I mean, that a son has ambitions, a desire to see life, to make himself a name. After all, Gerald, you couldn't be expected to pass all your life in such a hole as Wrockley, could you?

Gerald: Oh, no! It would be dreadful!

Lord Illingworth: A mother's love is very touching, of course, but it is often curiously selfish. I mean, there is a good deal of selfishness in it.

Gerald (slowly): I suppose there is.

Lord Illingworth: Your mother is a thoroughly good woman. But good women have such limited views of life, their horizon is so small, their interests are so petty, aren't they?

Gerald: They are awfully interested, certainly, in things we don't care much about.

Lord Illingworth: I suppose your mother is very religious, and that sort of thing.

Gerald: Oh, yes, she's always going to church.

Lord Illingworth: Ah! she is not modern, and to be modern is the only thing worth being nowadays. You want to be modern, don't you, Gerald? You want to know life as it really is. Not to be put off with any old-fashioned theories about life. Well, what you have to do at present is simply to fit yourself for the best society. A man who can dominate a London dinner-table can dominate the world. The future belongs to the dandy. It is the exquisites who are going to rule.

Gerald : I should like to wear nice things awfully, but I have always been told that a man should not think so much about his clothes.

Lord Illingworth : People nowadays are so absolutely superficial that they don't understand the philosophy of the superficial. By the way, Gerald, you should learn how to tie your tie better. Sentiment is all very well for the button-hole. But the essential thing for a necktie is style. A well-tied tie is the first serious step in life.

Gerald (laughing) : I might be able to learn how to tie a tie, Lord Illingworth, but I should never be able to talk as you do. I don't know how to talk.

Lord Illingworth : Oh! talk to every woman as if you loved her, and to every man as if he bored you, and at the end of your first season you will have the reputation of possessing the most perfect social tact.

Gerald : But it is very difficult to get into society, isn't it?

Lord Illingworth : To get into the best society, nowadays, one has either to feed people, amuse people, or shock people—that is all!

Gerald : I suppose society is wonderfully delightful!

Lord Illingworth : To be in it is merely a bore. But to be out of it simply a tragedy. Society is a necessary thing. No man has any real success in this world unless he has got women to back him, and women rule society. If you have not got women on your side you are quite over. You might just as well be a barrister or a stockbroker, or a journalist at once.

Gerald : It is very difficult to understand women. is it not ?

Lord Illingworth : You should never try to understand them. Women are pictures. Men are problems. If you want to know what a woman really means—which, by the way, is always a dangerous thing to do —look at her, don't listen to her.

Gerald : But women are awfully clever, aren't they ?

Lord Illingworth : One should always tell them so. But, to the philosopher, my dear Gerald, women represent the triumph of matter over mind—just as men represent the triumph of mind over morals.

Gerald : How then can women have so much power as you say they have ?

Lord Illingworth : The history of women is the history of the worst form of tyranny the world has ever known. The tyranny of the weak over the strong. It is the only tyranny that lasts.

Gerald : But haven't women got a refining influence ?

Lord Illingworth : Nothing refines but the intellect.

Gerald : Still, there are many different kinds of women, aren't there ?

Lord Illingworth : Only two kinds in society : the plain and the coloured.

Gerald : But there are good women in society, aren't there ?

Lord Illingworth : Far too many.

Gerald : But do you think women shouldn't be good ?

Lord Illingworth : One should never tell them so, they'd all become good at once. Women are a fascinatingly wilful sex. Every woman is a rebel, and usually in wild revolt against herself.

Gerald : You have never been married, Lord Illingworth, have you ?

Lord Illingworth : Men marry because they are tired ; women because they are curious. Both are disappointed.

Gerald : But don't you think one can be happy when one is married ?

Lord Illingworth : Perfectly happy. But the happiness of a married man, my dear Gerald, depends on the people he has not married.

Gerald : But if one is in love ?

Lord Illingworth : One should always be in love. That is the reason one should never marry.

Gerald : Love is a very wonderful thing, isn't it ?

Lord Illingworth : When one is in love one begins by deceiving oneself. And one ends by deceiving others. That is what the world calls a romance. But a really *grande passion* is comparatively rare nowadays. It is the privilege of people who have nothing to do. That is the one use of the idle classes in a country, and the only possible explanation of us Harfords.

Gerald : Harfords, Lord Illingworth ?

Lord Illingworth : That is my family name. You should study the Peerage, Gerald. It is the one book a young man about town should know thoroughly, and it is the best thing in fiction the English have ever done. And now, Gerald, you are going into a perfectly new life with me, and I want you to know how to live.

MRS. ARBUTHNOT *appears on terrace behind.*

For the world has been made by fools that wise men should live in it !

Enter L.C. LADY HUNSTANTON *and* DR. DAUBENY.

Lady Hunstanton : Ah ! here you are, dear Lord Illingworth. Well, I suppose you have been telling our young friend, Gerald, what his new duties are to be, and giving him a great deal of good advice over a pleasant cigarette.

Lord Illingworth : I have been giving him the best of advice, Lady Hunstanton, and the best of cigarettes.

Lady Hunstanton : I am so sorry I was not here to listen to you, but I suppose I am too old now to learn. Except from you, dear Archdeacon, when you are in your nice pulpit. But then I always know what you are going to say, so I don't feel alarmed. (*Sees* MRS. ARBUTHNOT.) Ah! dear Mrs. Arbuthnot, do come and join us. Come, dear.

Enter MRS. ARBUTHNOT.

Gerald has been having such a long talk with Lord Illingworth ; I am sure you must feel very much flattered at the pleasant way in which everything has turned out for him. Let us sit down. (*They sit down.*) And how is your beautiful embroidery going on ?

Mrs. Arbuthnot : I am always at work, Lady Hunstanton.

Lady Hunstanton : Mrs. Daubeny embroiders a little, too, doesn't she ?

The Archdeacon : She was very deft with her needle once, quite a Dorcas. But the gout has crippled her fingers a good deal. She has not touched the tambour frame for nine or ten years. But she has many other amusements. She is very much interested in her own health.

Lady Hunstanton : Ah! that is always a nice distraction, is it not ? Now, what are you talking about, Lord Illingworth ? Do tell us.

Lord Illingworth : I was on the point of explaining to Gerald that the world has always laughed at its own tragedies, that being the only way in which it has been able to bear them. And that, consequently, whatever the world has treated seriously belongs to the comedy side of things.

Lady Hunstanton : Now I am quite out of my depth. I usually am when Lord Illingworth says anything.

And the Humane Society is most careless. **They never** rescue me. I am left to sink. I have a dim idea, **dear** Lord Illingworth, that you are always on the side of the sinners, and I know I always try to be on the side of the saints, but that is as far as I get. And after all, it may be merely the fancy of a drowning person.

Lord Illingworth : The only difference between the saint and the sinner is that every saint has a past, and every sinner has a future.

Lady Hunstanton : Ah ! that quite does for me. I haven't a word to say. You and I, dear Mrs. Arbuthnot, are behind the age. We can't follow Lord Illingworth. Too much care was taken with our education, I am afraid. To have been well brought up is a great drawback nowadays. It shuts one out from so much.

Mrs. Arbuthnot : I should be sorry to follow Lord Illingworth in any of his opinions.

Lady Hunstanton : You are quite right, dear.

GERALD *shrugs his shoulders and looks irritably over at his mother. Enter* LADY CAROLINE.

Lady Caroline : Jane, have you seen John anywhere ?

Lady Hunstanton : You needn't be anxious about him, dear. He is with Lady Stutfield ; I saw them some time ago, in the Yellow Drawing-room. They seem quite happy together. You are not going, Caroline ? Pray sit down.

Lady Caroline : I think I had better look after John.

Exit LADY CAROLINE.

Lady Hunstanton : It doesn't do to pay men so much attention. And Caroline has really nothing to be anxious about. Lady Stutfield is very sympathetic. She is just as sympathetic about one thing as she is about another. A beautiful nature.

Enter Sir John *and* Mrs. Allonby.

Ah ! here is Sir John ! And with Mrs. Allonby too !
I suppose it was Mrs. Allonby I saw him with. Sir
John, Caroline has been looking everywhere for you.

Mrs. Allonby : We have been waiting for her in
the Music-room, dear Lady Hunstanton.

Lady Hunstanton : Ah ! the Music-room, of course.
I thought it was the Yellow Drawing-room, my
memory is getting so defective. (*To the* Archdeacon)
Mrs. Daubeny has a wonderful memory, hasn't she ?

The Archdeacon : She used to be quite remarkable
for her memory, but since her last attack she recalls
chiefly the events of her early childhood. But she
finds great pleasure in such retrospections, great
pleasure.

Enter Lady Stutfield *and* Mr. Kelvil.

Lady Hunstanton : Ah ! dear Lady Stutfield ! and
what has Mr. Kelvil been talking to you about ?

Lady Stutfield : About Bimetallism, as well as I
remember.

Lady Hunstanton : Bimetallism ! Is that quite a
nice subject ? However, I know people discuss everything very freely nowadays. What did Sir John talk
to you about, dear Mrs. Allonby ?

Mrs. Allonby : About Patagonia.

Lady Hunstanton : Really ? What a remote topic !
But very improving, I have no doubt.

Mrs. Allonby : He has been most interesting on the
subject of Patagonia. Savages seem to have quite the
same views as cultured people on almost all subjcets.
They are excessively advanced.

Lady Hunstanton : What do they do ?

Mrs. Allonby : Apparently everything.

Lady Hunstanton : Well, it is very gratifying, dear
Archdeacon, is it not, to find that Human Nature is

permanently one.—On the whole, the world is the same world, is it not?

Lord Illingworth : The world is simply divided into two classes—those who believe the incredible, like the public—and those who do the improbable——

Mrs. Allonby : Like yourself?

Lord Illingworth : Yes; I am always astonishing myself. It is the only thing that makes life worth living.

Lady Stutfield : And what have you been doing lately that astonishes you?

Lord Illingworth : I have been discovering all kinds of beautiful qualities in my own nature.

Mrs. Allonby : Ah! don't become quite perfect all at once. Do it gradually!

Lord Illingworth : I don't intend to grow perfect at all. At least, I hope I shan't. It would be most inconvenient. Women love us for our defects. If we have enough of them, they will forgive us everything, even our gigantic intellects.

Mrs. Allonby : It is premature to ask us to forgive analysis. We forgive adoration ; that is quite as much as should be expected from us.

Enter LORD ALFRED. *He joins* LADY STUTFIELD.

Lady Hunstanton : Ah! we women should forgive everything, shouldn't we, dear Mrs. Arbuthnot? I am sure you agree with me in that.

Mrs. Arbuthnot : I do not, Lady Hunstanton. I think there are many things women should never forgive.

Lady Hunstanton : What sort of things?

Mrs. Arbuthnot : The ruin of another woman's life. (*Moves slowly away to back of stage.*)

Lady Hunstanton : Ah! those things are very sad, no doubt, but I believe there are admirable homes where people of that kind are looked after and reformed, and I think on the whole that the secret of life is to take things very, very easily.

Mrs. Allonby: The secret of life is never to have an emotion that is unbecoming.

Lady Stutfield: The secret of life is to appreciate the pleasure of being terribly, terribly deceived.

Kelvil: The secret of life is to resist temptation, Lady Stutfield.

Lord Illingworth: There is no secret of life. Life's aim, if it has one, is simply to be always looking for temptations. There are not nearly enough. I sometimes pass a whole day without coming across a single one. It is quite dreadful. It makes one so nervous about the future.

Lady Hunstanton (shakes her fan at him): I don't know how it is, dear Lord Illingworth, but everything you have said to-day seems to me excessively immoral. It has been most interesting, listening to you.

Lord Illingworth: All thought is immoral. Its very essence is destruction. If you think of anything, you kill it. Nothing survives being thought of.

Lady Hunstanton: I don't understand a word, Lord Illingworth. But I have no doubt it is all quite true. Personally, I have very little to reproach myself with, on the score of thinking. I don't believe in women thinking too much. Women should think in moderation, as they should do all things in moderation.

Lord Illingworth: Moderation is a fatal thing, Lady Hunstanton. Nothing succeeds like excess.

Lady Hunstanton: I hope I shall remember that. It sounds an admirable maxim. But I'm beginning to forget everything. It's a great misfortune.

Lord Illingworth: It is one of your most fascinating qualities, Lady Hunstanton. No woman should have a memory. Memory in a woman is the beginning of dowdiness. One can always tell from a woman's bonnet whether she has got a memory or not.

Lady Hunstanton: How charming you are, dear

Lord Illingworth. You always find out that one's most glaring fault is one's most important virtue. You have the most comforting view of life.

Enter FARQUHAR.

Farquhar: Doctor Daubeny's carriage!

Lady Hunstanton: My dear Archdeacon! It is only half-past ten.

The Archdeacon (rising): I am afraid I must go, Lady Hunstanton. Tuesday is always one of Mrs. Daubeny's bad nights.

Lady Hunstanton (rising): Well, I won't keep you from her. (*Goes with him towards door.*) I have told Farquhar to put a brace of partridge into the carriage. Mrs. Daubeny may fancy them.

The Archdeacon: It is very kind of you, but Mrs. Daubeny never touches solids now. Lives entirely on jellies. But she is wonderfully cheerful, wonderfully cheerful. She has nothing to complain of.

Exit with LADY HUNSTANTON.

Mrs. Allonby (goes over to LORD ILLINGWORTH*):* There is a beautiful moon to-night.

Lord Illingworth: Let us go and look at it. To look at anything that is inconstant is charming nowadays.

Mrs. Allonby: You have your looking-glass.

Lord Illingworth: It is unkind. It merely shows me my wrinkles.

Mrs. Allonby: Mine is better behaved. It never tells me the truth.

Lord Illingworth: Then it is in love with you.

Exeunt SIR JOHN, LADY STUTFIELD, MR. KELVIL, *and* LORD ALFRED.

Gerald (to LORD ILLINGWORTH*):* May I come too?

Lord Illingworth : Do, my dear boy. (*Moves towards door with* MRS. ALLONBY *and* GERALD.)

LADY CAROLINE *enters, looks rapidly round and goes out in opposite direction to that taken by* SIR JOHN *and* LADY STUTFIELD.

Mrs. Arbuthnot : Gerald !
Gerald : What, mother !

Exit LORD ILLINGWORTH *with* MRS. ALLONBY.

Mrs. Arbuthnot : It is getting late. Let us go home.
Gerald : My dear mother. Do let us wait a little longer. Lord Illingworth is so delightful, and, by the way, mother, I have a great surprise for you. We are starting for India at the end of this month.
Mrs. Arbuthnot : Let us go home.
Gerald : If you really want to, of course, mother, but I must bid good-bye to Lord Illingworth first. I'll be back in five minutes. (*Exit.*)
Mrs. Arbuthnot : Let him leave me if he chooses, but not with him—not with him ! I couldn't bear it. (*Walks up and down.*)

Enter HESTER.

Hester : What a lovely night it is, Mrs. Arbuthnot.
Mrs. Arbuthnot : Is it ?
Hester : Mrs. Arbuthnot, I wish you would let us be friends. You are so different from the other women here. When you came into the Drawing-room this evening, somehow you brought with you a sense of what is good and pure in life. I had been foolish. There are things that are right to say, but that may be said at the wrong time and to the wrong people.
Mrs. Arbuthnot : I heard what you said. I agree with it, Miss Worsley.

Hester : I didn't know you had heard it. But I knew you would agree with me. A woman who has sinned should be punished, shouldn't she ?

Mrs. Arbuthnot : Yes.

Hester : She shouldn't be allowed to come into the society of good men and women ?

Mrs. Arbuthnot : She should not.

Hester : And the man should be punished in the same way ?

Mrs. Arbuthnot : In the same way. And the children, if there are children, in the same way also ?

Hester : Yes, it is right that the sins of the parents should be visited on the children. It is a just law. It is God's law.

Mrs. Arbuthnot : It is one of God's terrible laws. (*Moves away to fireplace.*)

Hester : You are distressed about your son leaving you, Mrs. Arbuthnot ?

Mrs. Arbuthnot : Yes.

Hester : Do you like him going away with Lord Illingworth ? Of course there is position, no doubt, and money, but position and money are not everything, are they ?

Mrs. Arbuthnot : They are nothing ; they bring misery.

Hester : Then why do you let your son go with him ?

Mrs. Arbuthnot : He wishes it himself.

Hester : But if you asked him he would stay, would he not ?

Mrs. Arbuthnot : He has set his heart on going.

Hester : He couldn't refuse you anything. He loves you too much. Ask him to stay. Let me send him to you. He is on the terrace at this moment with Lord Illingworth. I heard them laughing together as I passed through the Music-room.

Mrs. Arbuthnot : Don't trouble, Miss Worsley, I can wait. It is of no consequence.

Hester : No, I'll tell him you want him. Do—do ask him to stay.

Exit HESTER.

Mrs. Arbuthnot : He won't come—I know he won't come.

Enter LADY CAROLINE. *She looks round anxiously.*
Enter GERALD.

Lady Caroline : Mr. Arbuthnot, may I ask you is Sir John anywhere on the terrace ?
Gerald : No, Lady Caroline, he is not on the terrace.
Lady Caroline : It is very curious. It is time for him to retire.

Exit LADY CAROLINE.

Gerald : Dear mother, I am afraid I kept you waiting. I forgot all about it. I am so happy to-night, mother ; I have never been so happy.
Mrs. Arbuthnot : At the prospect of going away ?
Gerald : Don't put it like that, mother. Of course I am sorry to leave you. Why, you are the best mother in the whole world. But after all, as Lord Illingworth says, it is impossible to live in such a place as Wrockley. You don't mind it. But I'm ambitious ; I want something more than that. I want to have a career. I want to do something that will make you proud of me, and Lord Illingworth is going to help me. He is going to do everything for me.
Mrs. Arbuthnot : Gerald, don't go away with Lord Illingworth. I implore you not to. Gerald, I beg you !
Gerald : Mother, how changeable you are ! You don't seem to know your own mind for a single moment. An hour and a half ago in the Drawing-room you agreed to the whole thing ; now you turn round and make objections, and try to force me to give up my one chance in life. Yes, my one chance. You don't suppose

that men like Lord Il ingworth are to be found every
day, do you, mother? It is very strange that when
I have had such a wonderful piece of good luck, the
one person to put difficulties in my way should be my
own mother. Besides, you know, mother, I love
Hester Worsley. Who could help loving her? I love
her more than I have ever told you, far more. And
if I had a position, if I had prospects, I could—I could
ask her to. . . . Don't you understand now, mother,
what it means to me to be Lord Illingworth's secretary?
To start like that is to find a career ready for one—
before one—waiting for one. If I were Lord Illingworth's secretary I could ask Hester to be my wife.
As a wretched bank clerk with a hundred a year it
would be an impertinence.

Mrs. Arbuthnot : I fear you need have no hopes of
Miss Worsley. I know her views on life. She has just
told them to me. (*A pause.*)

Gerald : Then I have my ambition left, at any rate.
That is something—I am glad I have that! You have
always tried to crush my ambition, mother—haven't
you? You have told me that the world is a wicked
place, that success is not worth having, that society
is shallow, and all that sort of thing—well, I don't
believe it, mother. I think the world must be delightful.
I think society must be exquisite. I think success is
a thing worth having. You have been wrong in all
that you taught me, mother, quite wrong. Lord
Illingworth is a successful man. He is a fashionable
man. He is a man who lives in the world and for it. Well,
I would give anything to be just like Lord Illingworth.

Mrs. Arbuthnot : I would sooner see you dead.

Gerald : Mother, what is your objection to Lord
Illingworth? Tell me—tell me right out. What is it?

Mrs. Arbuthnot : He is a bad man.

Gerald : In what way bad? I don't understand
what you mean.

Mrs. Arbuthnot : I will tell you.

Gerald : I suppose you think him bad, because he doesn't believe the same things as you do. Well, men are different from women, mother. It is natural that they should have different views.

Mrs. Arbuthnot : It is not what Lord Illingworth believes, or what he does not believe, that makes him bad. It is what he is.

Gerald : Mother, is it something you know of him ? Something you actually know ?

Mrs. Arbuthnot : It is something I know.

Gerald : Something you are quite sure of ?

Mrs. Arbuthnot : Quite sure of.

Gerald : How long have you known it ?

Mrs. Arbuthnot : For twenty years.

Gerald : Is it fair to go back twenty years in any man's career ? And what have you or I to do with Lord Illingworth's early life ? What business is it of ours ?

Mrs. Arbuthnot : What this man has been, he is now, and will be always.

Gerald : Mother, tell me what Lord Illingworth did ? If he did anything shameful, I will not go away with him. Surely you know me well enough for that ?

Mrs. Arbuthnot : Gerald, come near to me. Quite close to me, as you used to do when you were a little boy, when you were mother's own boy.

> GERALD *sits down beside his mother. She runs her fingers through his hair, and strokes his hands.*

Gerald, there was a girl once, she was very young, she was little over eighteen at the time. George Harford —that was Lord Illingworth's name then—George Harford met her. She knew nothing about life. He —knew everything. He made this girl love him. He made her love so much that she left her father's house with him one morning. She loved him so much, and he had promised to marry her ! He had solemnly

promised to marry her, and she had believed him. She
was very young, and—and ignorant of what life really
is. But he put the marriage off from week to week, and
month to month.—She trusted in him all the while.
She loved him.—Before her child was born—for she
had a child—she implored him for the child's sake to
marry her, that the child might have a name, that
her sin might not be visited on the child, who was
innocent. He refused. After the child was born she
left him, taking the child away, and her life was
ruined, and her soul ruined, and all that was sweet,
and good, and pure in her ruined also. She suffered
terribly—she suffers now. She will always suffer.
For her there is no joy, no peace, no atonement. She
is a woman who drags a chain like a guilty thing.
She is a woman who wears a mask, like a thing that
is a leper. The fire cannot purify her. The waters
cannot quench her anguish. Nothing can heal her !
no anodyne can give her sleep ! no poppies forgetfulness ! She is lost ! She is a lost soul !—That is why I
call Lord Illingworth a bad man. That is why I
don't want my boy to be with him.

Gerald : My dear mother, it all sounds very tragic,
of course. But I dare say the girl was just as much
to blame as Lord Illingworth was.—After all, would a
really nice girl, a girl with any nice feelings at all, go
away from her home with a man to whom she was not
married, and live with him as his wife ? No nice girl
would.

Mrs. Arbuthnot (after a pause) : Gerald, I withdraw
all my objections. You are at liberty to go away with
Lord Illingworth, when and where you choose.

Gerald : Dear mother, I knew you wouldn't stand
in my way. You are the best woman God ever made.
And, as for Lord Illingworth, I don't believe he is
capable of anything infamous or base. I can't believe
it of him—I can't.

Hester (outside) : Let me go ? Let me go !

Enter HESTER *in terror, and rushes over to* GERALD *and flings herself in his arms.*

Hester : Oh ! save me—save me from him !
Gerald : From whom ?
Hester : He has insulted me ! Horribly insulted me ! Save me !
Gerald : Who ? Who has dared——?

LORD ILLINGWORTH *enters at back of stage.* HESTER *breaks from* GERALD'S *arms and points to him.*

Gerald (he is quite beside himself with rage and indignation) : Lord Illingworth, you have insulted the purest thing on God's earth, a thing as pure as my own mother. You have insulted the woman I love most in the world with my own mother. As there is a God in Heaven, I will kill you !
Mrs. Arbuthnot (rushing across and catching hold of him) : No ! no !
Gerald (thrusting her back) : Don't hold me, mother. Don't hold me—I'll kill him !
Mrs. Arbuthnot : Gerald !
Gerald : Let me go, I say !
Mrs. Arbuthnot : Stop, Gerald, stop ! He is your own father !

GERALD *clutches his mother's hands and looks into her face. She sinks slowly on the ground in shame.* HESTER *steals towards the door.* LORD ILLINGWORTH *frowns and bites his lip. After a time* GERALD *raises his mother up, puts his arm round her, and leads her from the room.*

ACT DROP.

FOURTH ACT

SCENE

Sitting-room at Mrs. Arbuthnot's. Large open French window at back, looking on to garden. Doors R.C. and L.C.

GERALD ARBUTHNOT *writing at table.*
Enter ALICE R.C. *followed by* LADY HUNSTANTON *and* MRS. ALLONBY.

Alice : Lady Hunstanton and Mrs. Allonby. (*Exit L.C.*)

Lady Hunstanton : Good-morning, Gerald.

Gerald (*rising*) : Good-morning, Lady Hunstanton. Good-morning, Mrs. Allonby.

Lady Hunstanton (*sitting down*) : We came to inquire for your dear mother, Gerald. I hope she is better ?

Gerald : My mother has not come down yet, Lady Hunstanton.

Lady Hunstanton : Ah, I am afraid the heat was too much for her last night. I think there must have been thunder in the air. Or perhaps it was the music. Music makes one feel so romantic—at least it always gets on one's nerves.

Mrs. Allonby : It's the same thing, nowadays.

Lady Hunstanton : I am so glad I don't know what you mean, dear. I am afraid you mean something wrong. Ah, I see you're examining Mrs. Arbuthnot's pretty room. Isn't it nice and old-fashioned ?

Mrs. Allonby (*surveying the room through her lorgnette*) : It looks quite the happy English home.

Lady Hunstanton : That's just the word, dear ; that just describes it. One feels your mother's good influence in everything she has about her, Gerald.

459

Mrs. Allonby : Lord Illingworth says that all influence is bad, but that a good influence is the worst in the world.

Lady Hunstanton : When Lord Illingworth knows Mrs. Arbuthnot better he will change his mind. I must certainly bring him here.

Mrs. Allonby : I should like to see Lord Illingworth in a happy English home.

Lady Hunstanton : It would do him a great deal of good, dear. Most women in London, nowadays, seem to furnish their rooms with nothing but orchids, foreigners, and French novels. But here we have the room of a sweet saint. Fresh natural flowers, books that don't shock one, pictures that one can look at without blushing.

Mrs. Allonby : But I like blushing.

Lady Hunstanton : Well, there *is* a good deal to be said for blushing, if one can do it at the proper moment. Poor dear Hunstanton used to tell me I didn't blush nearly often enough. But then he was so very particular. He wouldn't let me know any of his men friends, except those who were over seventy, like poor Lord Ashton ; who afterwards, by the way, was brought into the Divorce Court. A most unfortunate case.

Mrs. Allonby : I delight in men over seventy. They always offer one the devotion of a lifetime. I think seventy an ideal age for a man.

Lady Hunstanton : She is quite incorrigible, Gerald, isn't she ? By-the-by, Gerald, I hope your dear mother will come and see me more often now. You and Lord Illingworth start almost immediately, don't you ?

Gerald : I have given up my intention of being Lord Illingworth's secretary.

Lady Hunstanton : Surely not, Gerald ! It would be most unwise of you. What reason can you have ?

Gerald : I don't think I should be suitable for the post.

Mrs. Allonby : I wish Lord Illingworth would ask

me to be his secretary. But he says I am not serious enough.

Lady Hunstanton : My dear, you really mustn't talk like that in this house. Mrs. Arbuthnot doesn't know anything about the wicked society in which we all live. She won't go into it. She is far too good. I consider it was a great honour her coming to me last night. It gave quite an atmosphere of respectability to the party.

Mrs. Allonby : Ah, that must have been what you thought was thunder in the air.

Lady Hunstanton : My dear, how can you say that ? There is no resemblance between the two things at all. But really, Gerald, what do you mean by not being suitable ?

Gerald : Lord Illingworth's views of life and mine are too different.

Lady Hunstanton : But, my dear Gerald, at your age you shouldn't have any views of life. They are quite out of place. You must be guided by others in this matter. Lord Illingworth has made you the most flattering offer, and travelling with him you would see the world—as much of it, at least, as one should look at—under the best auspices possible, and stay with all the right people, which is so important at this solemn moment in your career.

Gerald : I don't want to see the world ; I've seen enough of it.

Mrs. Allonby : I hope you don't think you have exhausted life, Mr. Arbuthnot. When a man says that, one knows that life has exhausted him.

Gerald : I don't wish to leave my mother.

Lady Hunstanton : Now, Gerald, that is pure laziness on your part. Not leave your mother ! If I were your mother I would insist on your going.

Enter ALICE *L.C.*

Alice : Mrs. Arbuthnot's compliments, my lady, but she has a bad headache, and cannot see any one this morning. *(Exit R.C.)*

Lady Hunstanton (rising) : A bad headache ! I am so sorry ! Perhaps you'll bring her up to Hunstanton this afternoon, if she is better, Gerald.

Gerald : I am afraid not this afternoon, Lady Hunstanton.

Lady Hunstanton : Well, to-morrow, then. Ah, if you had a father, Gerald, he wouldn't let you waste your life here. He would send you off with Lord Illingworth at once. But mothers are so weak. They give up to their sons in everything. We are all heart, all heart. Come, dear, I must call at the rectory and inquire for Mrs. Daubeny, who, I am afraid, is far from well. It is wonderful how the Archdeacon bears up, quite wonderful. He is the most sympathetic of husbands. Quite a model. Good-bye, Gerald, give my fondest love to your mother.

Mrs. Allonby : Good-bye, Mr. Arbuthnot.

Gerald : Good-bye.

    Exit LADY HUNSTANTON *and* MRS. ALLONBY. GERALD *sits down and reads over his letter.*

Gerald : What name can I sign? I, who have no right to any name. *(Signs name, puts letter into envelope, addresses it, and is about to seal it, when door L.C. opens and* MRS. ARBUTHNOT *enters.* GERALD *lays down sealing-wax. Mother and son look at each other.)*

Lady Hunstanton (through French window at the back) : Good-bye again, Gerald. We are taking the short cut across your pretty garden. Now, remember my advice to you—start at once with Lord Illingworth.

Mrs. Allonby : Au revoir, Mr. Arbuthnot. Mind you bring me back something nice from your travels—not an Indian shawl—on no account an Indian shawl. *(Exeunt.)*

Gerald : Mother, I have just written to him.

Mrs. Arbuthnot : To whom ?

Gerald : To my father. I have written to tell him to come here at four o'clock this afternoon.

Mrs. Arbuthnot : He shall not come here. He shall not cross the threshold of my house.

Gerald : He must come.

Mrs. Arbuthnot : Gerald, if you are going away with Lord Illingworth, go at once. Go before it kills me ; but don't ask me to meet him.

Gerald : Mother, you don't understand. Nothing in the world would induce me to go away with Lord Illingworth, or to leave you. Surely you know me well enough for that. No ; I have written to him to say——

Mrs. Arbuthnot : What can you have to say to him ?

Gerald : Can't you guess, mother, what I have written in this letter ?

Mrs. Arbuthnot : No.

Gerald : Mother, surely you can. Think, think what must be done, now, at once, within the next few days.

Mrs. Arbuthnot : There is nothing to be done.

Gerald : I have written to Lord Illingworth to tell him that he must marry you.

Mrs. Arbuthnot : Marry me ?

Gerald : Mother, I will force him to do it. The wrong that has been done you must be repaired. Atonement must be made. Justice may be slow, mother, but it comes in the end. In a few days you shall be Lord Illingworth's lawful wife.

Mrs. Arbuthnot : But, Gerald——

Gerald : I will insist upon his doing it. I will make him do it ; he will not dare to refuse.

Mrs. Arbuthnot : But, Gerald, it is I who refuse. I will not marry Lord Illingworth.

Gerald : Not marry him ? Mother !

Mrs. Arbuthnot : I will not marry him.

Gerald : But you don't understand : it is for your sake I am talking, not for mine. This marriage, this necessary marriage, this marriage which for obvious reasons must inevitably take place, will not help me, will not give me a name that will be really, rightly mine to bear. But surely it will be something for you, that you, my mother, should, however late, become the wife of the man who is my father. Will not that be something ?

Mrs. Arbuthnot : I will not marry him.

Gerald : Mother, you must.

Mrs. Arbuthnot : I will not. You talk of atonement for a wrong done. What atonement can be made to me ? There is no atonement possible. I am disgraced ; he is not. That is all. It is the usual history of a man and a woman as it usually happens, as it always happens. And the ending is the ordinary ending. The woman suffers. The man goes free.

Gerald : I don't know if that is the ordinary ending, mother ; I hope it is not. But your life, at any rate, shall not end like that. The man shall make whatever reparation is possible. It is not enough. It does not wipe out the past, I know that. But at least it makes the future better, better for you, mother.

Mrs. Arbuthnot : I refuse to marry Lord Illingworth.

Gerald : If he came to you himself and asked you to be his wife you would give him a different answer. Remember, he is my father.

Mrs. Arbuthnot : If he came himself, which he will not do, my answer would be the same. Remember I am your mother.

Gerald : Mother, you make it terribly difficult for me by talking like that ; and I can't understand why you won't look at this matter from the right, from the only proper standpoint. It is to take away the bitterness out of your life, to take away the shadow that lies on your name, that this marriage must take place. There is no alternative ; and after the marriage you and I can go away together. But the marriage must take place first. It is a duty that you owe, not merely to yourself, but to all other women—yes ; to all the other women in the world, lest he betray more.

Mrs. Arbuthnot : I owe nothing to other women. There is not one of them to help me. There is not one woman in the world to whom I could go for pity, if I would take it, or for sympathy, if I could win it. Women are hard on each other. That girl, last night, good though she is, fled from the room as though I were a tainted thing. She was right. I am a tainted thing. But my wrongs are my own, and I will bear them alone. I must bear them alone. What have women who have not sinned to do with me, or I with them ? We do not understand each other.

Enter HESTER *behind.*

Gerald : I implore you to do what I ask you.

Mrs. Arbuthnot : What son has ever asked of his mother to make so hideous a sacrifice ? None.

Gerald : What mother has ever refused to marry the father of her own child ? None.

Mrs. Arbuthnot : Let me be the first, then. I will not do it.

Gerald : Mother, you believe in religion, and you brought me up to believe in it also. Well, surely your religion, the religion that you taught me when I was a boy, mother, must tell you that I am right. You know it, you feel it.

Mrs. Arbuthnot : I do not know it. I do not feel it, nor will I ever stand before God's altar and ask God's blessing on so hideous a mockery as a marriage between me and George Harford. I will not say the words the Church bids us to say. I will not say them. I dare not. How could I swear to love the man I loathe, to honour him who wrought you dishonour, to obey him who, in his mastery, made me to sin ? No ; marriage is a sacrament for those who love each other. It is not for such as him, or such as me. Gerald, to save you from the world's sneers and taunts I have lied to the world. For twenty years I have lied to the world. I could not tell the world the truth. Who can, ever ? But not for my own sake will I lie to God, and in God's presence. No, Gerald, no ceremony, Church-hallowed or State-made, shall ever bind me to George Harford. It may be that I am too bound to him already, who, robbing me, yet left me richer, so that in the mire of my life I found the pearl of price, or what I thought would be so.

Gerald : I don't understand you now.

Mrs. Arbuthnot : Men don't understand what mothers are. I am no different from other women except in the wrong done me and the wrong I did, and my very heavy punishments and great disgrace. And yet, to bear you I had to look on death. To nurture you I had to wrestle with it. Death fought with me for you. All women have to fight with death to keep their children. Death, being childless, wants our children from us. Gerald, when you were naked I clothed you, when you were hungry I gave you food. Night and day all that long winter I tended you. No office is too mean, no care too lowly for the thing we women love—and oh ! how *I* loved *you*. Not Hannah, Samuel more. And you needed love, for you were weakly, and only love could have kept you alive. Only love can keep any one alive. And boys are careless often, and without thinking give pain, and we always fancy that when they come to man's estate and know us better they will repay us. But it is not so. The world draws them from our side, and they make friends with whom they are happier than they are with us, and have amusements from which we are barred, and interests that are not ours ; and they are unjust to us often, for when they find life bitter they blame us for it, and when they find it sweet we do not taste its sweetness with them. . . . You made many friends and went into their houses and were glad with them, and I, knowing my secret, did not dare to follow, but stayed at home and closed the door, shut out the sun and sat in darkness. What should I have done in honest households? My past was ever with me. . . . And you thought I didn't care for the pleasant things of life. I tell you I longed for them, but did not dare to touch them, feeling I had no right. You thought I was happier working amongst the poor. That was my mission, you imagined. It was not, but where else was I to go? The sick do not ask if the hand that smooths their pillow is pure, nor the dying care if the lips that touch their brow have known the kiss of sin. It was you I thought of all the time; I gave to them the love you did not need; lavished on them a love that was not theirs. . . . And you thought I spent too much of my time in going to Church, and in Church duties. But where else could I turn? God's house is the only house where sinners are made welcome, and you were always in my heart, Gerald, too much in my heart. For, though day after day, at morn or evensong, I have knelt in God's house, I have never repented of my sin. How could I repent of my sin when you, my love, were its fruit. Even now that you are bitter to me I cannot repent. I do not. You are more to me than innocence. I would rather be your mother—oh! much rather!—than have been always pure. . . . Oh, don't you see? don't you understand? It is my dishonour that has made you so dear to me. It is my disgrace that has bound you so closely to me. It is the price I paid for you —the price of soul and body—that makes me love you as I do. Oh, don't ask me to do this horrible thing. Child of my shame, be still the child of my shame!

Gerald: Mother, I didn't know you loved me so much as that. And I will be a better son to you than I have been. And you and I must never leave each other . . . but, mother . . . I can't help it . . . you

must become my father's wife. You must marry him.
It is your duty.

Hester (running forward and embracing MRS. ARBUTH-
NOT) : No, no ; you shall not. That would be real
dishonour, the first you have ever known. That
would be real disgrace : the first to touch you. Leave
him and come with me. There are other countries
than England. . . . Oh ! other countries over sea,
better, wiser, and less unjust lands. The world is very
wide and very big.

Mrs. Arbuthnot : No, not for me. For me the world
is shrivelled to a palm's breadth, and where I walk
there are thorns.

Hester : It shall not be so. We shall somewhere
find green valleys and fresh waters, and if we weep,
well, we shall weep together. Have we not both
loved him ?

Gerald : Hester !

Hester (waving him back) : Don't, don't ! You cannot
love me at all unless you love her also. You cannot
honour me, unless she's holier to you. In her all woman-
hood is martyred. Not she alone, but all of us are
stricken in her house.

Gerald : Hester, Hester, what shall I do ?

Hester : Do you respect the man who is your
father ?

Gerald : Respect him ? I despise him ! He is
infamous.

Hester : I thank you for saving me from him last
night.

Gerald : Ah, that is nothing. I would die to save
you. But you don't tell me what to do now !

Hester : Have I not thanked you for saving *me* ?

Gerald : But what should I do ?

Hester : Ask your own heart, not mine. I never
had a mother to save, or shame.

Mrs. Arbuthnot : He is hard—he is hard. Let me
go away.

Gerald (rushes over and kneels down beside his mother) :
Mother, forgive me ; I have been to blame.

Mrs. Arbuthnot : Don't kiss my hands ; they are
cold. My heart is cold ; something has broken it.

Hester : Ah, don't say that. Hearts live by being
wounded. Pleasure may turn a heart to stone, riches
may make it callous, but sorrow—oh, sorrow cannot
break it. Besides, what sorrows have you now ? Why,
at this moment you are more dear to him than ever,
dear though you have *been*, and oh ! how dear you
have been always. Ah ! be kind to him.

Gerald : You are my mother and my father all in
one. I need no second parent. It was for you I spoke,
for you alone. Oh, say something, mother. Have I
but found one love to lose another ? Don't tell me that.
O mother, you are cruel. *(Gets up and flings himself
sobbing on a sofa.)*

Mrs. Arbuthnot (to HESTER*)* : But has he found
indeed another love ?

Hester : You know I have loved him always.

Mrs. Arbuthnot : But we are very poor.

Hester : Who, being loved, is poor ? Oh, no one. I
hate my riches. They are a burden. Let him share it
with me.

Mrs. Arbuthnot : But we are disgraced. We rank
among the outcasts. Gerald is nameless. The sins of
the parents should be visited on the children. It is
God's law.

Hester : I was wrong. God's law is only Love.

Mrs. Arbuthnot (rises, and taking HESTER *by the hand,
goes slowly over to where* GERALD *is lying on the sofa
with his head buried in his hands. She touches him and
he looks up)* : Gerald, I cannot give you a father, but
I have brought you a wife.

Gerald : Mother, I am not worthy either of her
or you.

Mrs. Arbuthnot : So she comes first, you are worthy.
And when you are away, Gerald . . . with . . . her

—oh, think of me sometimes. Don't forget me. And when you pray, pray for me. We should pray when we are happiest, and you will be happy, Gerald.

Hester : Oh, you don't think of leaving us ?

Gerald : Mother, you won't leave us ?

Mrs. Arbuthnot : I might bring shame upon you !

Gerald : Mother !

Mrs. Arbuthnot : For a little then ; and if you let me, near you always.

Hester (to MRS. ARBUTHNOT*) :* Come out with us to the garden.

Mrs. Arbuthnot : Later on, later on.

> *Exeunt* HESTER *and* GERALD.
> MRS. ARBUTHNOT *goes towards door L.C. Stops at looking-glass over mantelpiece and looks into it. Enter* ALICE *R.C.*

Alice : A gentleman to see you, ma'am.

Mrs. Arbuthnot : Say I am not at home. Show me the card. (*Takes card from salver and looks at it.*) Say I will not see him.

> LORD ILLINGWORTH *enters.* MRS. ARBUTHNOT *sees him in the glass and starts, but does not turn round. Exit* ALICE.

What can you have to say to me to-day, George Harford ? You can have nothing to say to me. You must leave this house.

Lord Illingworth : Rachel, Gerald knows everything about you and me now, so some arrangement must be come to that will suit us all three. I assure you, he will find in me the most charming and generous of fathers.

Mrs. Arbuthnot : My son may come in at any moment. I saved you last night. I may not be able to save you again. My son feels my dishonour strongly, terribly strongly. I beg you to go.

Lord Illingworth (sitting down) : Last night was excessively unfortunate. That silly Puritan girl making a scene merely because I wanted to kiss her. What harm is there in a kiss ?

Mrs. Arbuthnot (turning round) : A kiss may ruin a human life, George Harford. *I* know that. *I* know that too well.

Lord Illingworth : We won't discuss that at present. What is of importance to-day, as yesterday, is still our son. I am extremely fond of him, as you know, and odd though it may seem to you, I admired his conduct last night immensely. He took up the cudgels for that pretty prude with wonderful promptitude. He is just what I should have liked a son of mine to be. Except that no son of mine should ever take the side of the Puritans ; that is always an error. Now, what I propose is this.

Mrs. Arbuthnot : Lord Illingworth, no proposition of yours interests me.

Lord Illingworth : According to our ridiculous English laws, I can't legitimise Gerald. But I can leave him my property. Illingworth is entailed, of course, but it is a tedious barrack of a place. He can have Ashby, which is much prettier, Harborough, which has the best shooting in the north of England, and the house in St. James's Square. What more can a gentleman desire in this world ?

Mrs. Arbuthnot : Nothing more, I am quite sure.

Lord Illingworth : As for a title, a title is really rather a nuisance in these democratic days. As George Harford I had everything I wanted. Now I have merely everything that other people want, which isn't nearly so pleasant. Well, my proposal is this.

Mrs. Arbuthnot : I told you I was not interested, and I beg you to go.

Lord Illingworth : The boy is to be with you for six months in the year, and with me for the other six. That is perfectly fair, is it not ? You can have whatever

allowance you like, and live where you choose. As
for your past, no one knows anything about it except
myself and Gerald. There is the Puritan, of course,
the Puritan in white muslin, but she doesn't count.
She couldn't tell the story without explaining that she
objected to being kissed, could she ? And all the
women would think her a fool and the men think her
a bore. And you need not be afraid that Gerald won't
be my heir. I needn't tell you I have not the slightest
intention of marrying.

Mrs. Arbuthnot : You come too late. My son has no
need of you. You are not necessary.

Lord Illingworth : What do you mean, Rachel ?

Mrs. Arbuthnot : That you are not necessary to
Gerald's career. He does not require you.

Lord Illingworth : I do not understand you.

Mrs. Arbuthnot : Look into the garden. LORD
ILLINGWORTH *rises and goes towards window.*) You had
better not let them see you ; you bring unpleasant
memories. (LORD ILLINGWORTH *looks out and starts.*)
She loves him. They love each other. We are safe
from you, and we are going away.

Lord Illingworth : Where ?

Mrs. Arbuthnot : We will not tell you, and if you
find us we will not know you. You seem surprised.
What welcome would you get from the girl whose lips
you tried to soil, from the boy whose life you have
shamed, from the mother whose dishonour comes
from you ?

Lord Illingworth : You have grown hard, Rachel.

Mrs. Arbuthnot : I was too weak once. It is well for
me that I have changed.

Lord Illingworth : I was very young at the time. We
men know life too early.

Mrs. Arbuthnot : And we women know life too late.
That is the difference between men and women.
(*A pause.*)

Lord Illingworth : Rachel, I want my son. My money

may be of no use to him now. I may be of no use to
him, but I want my son. Bring us together, Rachel.
You can do it if you choose. (*Sees letter on table.*)

Mrs. Arbuthnot : There is no room in my boy's life
for *you*. He is not interested in *you*.

Lord Illingworth : Then why does he write to me ?

Mrs. Arbuthnot : What do you mean ?

Lord Illingworth : What letter is this ? (*Takes up
letter.*)

Mrs. Arbuthnot : That—is nothing. Give it to me.

Lord Illingworth : It is addressed to *me*.

Mrs. Arbuthnot : You are not to open it. I forbid
you to open it.

Lord Illingworth : And in Gerald's handwriting.

Mrs. Arbuthnot : It was not to have been sent. It
is a letter he wrote to you this morning, before he
saw me. But he is sorry now he wrote it, very sorry.
You are not to open it. Give it to me.

Lord Illingworth : It belongs to me. (*Opens it, sits
down and reads it slowly.* MRS. ARBUTHNOT *watches him
all the time.*) You have read this letter, I suppose,
Rachel ?

Mrs. Arbuthnot : No.

Lord Illingworth : You know what is in it ?

Mrs. Arbuthnot : Yes !

Lord Illingworth : I don't admit for a moment that
the boy is right in what he says. I don't admit that it
is any duty of mine to marry you. I deny it entirely.
But to get my son back I am ready—yes, I am ready
to marry you, Rachel—and to treat you always with
the deference and respect due to my wife. I will
marry you as soon as you choose. I give you my word
of honour.

Mrs. Arbuthnot : You made that promise to me once
before and broke it.

Lord Illingworth . I will keep it now. And that will
show you that I love my son, at least as much as you
love him. For when I marry you, Rachel, there are

some ambitions I shall have to surrender. High ambitions, too, if any ambition is high.

Mrs. Arbuthnot : I decline to marry you, Lord Illingworth.

Lord Illingworth : Are you serious ?

Mrs. Arbuthnot : Yes.

Lord Illingworth : Do tell me your reasons. They would interest me enormously.

Mrs. Arbuthnot : I have already explained them to my son.

Lord Illingworth : I suppose they were intensely sentimental, weren't they ? You women live by your emotions and for them. You have no philosophy of life.

Mrs. Arbuthnot : You are right. We women live by our emotions and for them. By our passions, and for them, if you will. I have two passions, Lord Illingworth : my love of him, my hate of you. You cannot kill those. They feed each other.

Lord Illingworth : What sort of love is that which needs to have hate as its brother ?

Mrs. Arbuthnot : It is the sort of love I have for Gerald. Do you think that terrible ? Well, it is terrible. All love is terrible. All love is a tragedy. I loved you once, Lord Illingworth. Oh, what a tragedy for a woman to have loved you !

Lord Illingworth : So you really refuse to marry me ?

Mrs. Arbuthnot : Yes.

Lord Illingworth : Because you hate me ?

Mrs. Arbuthnot : Yes.

Lord Illingworth : And does my son hate me as you do ?

Mrs. Arbuthnot : No.

Lord Illingworth : I am glad of that, Rachel.

Mrs. Arbuthnot : He merely despises you.

Lord Illingworth : What a pity l What a pity for him, I mean.

Mrs. Arbuthnot : Don't be deceived, George.

Children begin by loving their parents. After a time they judge them. Rarely if ever do they forgive them.

Lord Illingworth (*reads letter over again, very slowly*): May I ask by what arguments you made the boy who wrote this letter, this beautiful, passionate letter, believe that you should not marry his father, the father of your own child ?

Mrs. Arbuthnot : It was not I who made him see it. It was another.

Lord Illingworth : What *fin-de-siècle* person ?

Mrs. Arbuthnot : The Puritan, Lord Illingworth. (*A pause*)

Lord Illingworth (*winces, then rises slowly and goes over to table where his hat and gloves are.* MRS. ARBUTH- NOT *is standing close to the table. He picks up one of the gloves, and begins putting it on*) *:* There is not much then for me to do here, Rachel ?

Mrs. Arbuthnot : Nothing.

Lord Illingworth : It is good-bye, is it ?

Mrs. Arbuthnot : For ever, I hope, this time, Lord Illingworth.

Lord Illingworth : How curious ! At this moment you look exactly as you looked the night you left me twenty years ago. You have just the same expression in your mouth. Upon my word, Rachel, no woman ever loved me as you did. Why, you gave yourself to me like a flower, to do anything I liked with. You were the prettiest of playthings, the most fascinating of small romances. . . . (*Pulls out watch.*) Quarter to two ! Must be strolling back to Hunstanton. Don't suppose I shall see you there again. I'm sorry, I am, really. It's been an amusing experience to have met amongst people of one's own rank, and treated quite seriously too, one's mistress and one's——

MRS. ARBUTHNOT *snatches up glove and strikes* LORD ILLINGWORTH *across the face with it.* LORD ILLINGWORTH *starts. He is dazed by the insult of his punishmeut. Then he controls himself and goes to window and looks out at his son. Sighs and leaves the room.*

Mrs. Arbuthnot (falls sobbing on the sofa) : He would have said it. He would have said it.

Enter GERALD *and* HESTER *from the garden.*

Gerald : Well, dear mother. You never came out after all. So we have come in to fetch you. Mother, you have not been crying ? *(Kneels down beside her.)*
Mrs. Arbuthnot : My boy ! My boy ! My boy ! *(Running her fingers through his hair.)*
Hester (coming over) : But you have two children now. You'll let me be your daughter ?
Mrs. Arbuthnot (looking up) : Would you choose me for a mother ?
Hester : You of all women I have ever known.

They move towards the door leading into garden with their arms round each other's waists. GERALD *goes to table L.C. for his hat. On turning round he sees* LORD ILLINGWORTH'S *glove lying on the floor, and picks it up.*

Gerald : Hallo, mother, whose glove is this ? You have had a visitor. Who was it ?
Mrs. Arbuthnot (turning round) : Oh ! no one. No one in particular. A man of no importance.

CURTAIN.

AN IDEAL HUSBAND

TO
FRANK HARRIS
A SLIGHT TRIBUTE TO
HIS POWER AND DISTINCTION
AS AN ARTIST
HIS CHIVALRY AND NOBILITY
AS A FRIEND

THE PERSONS OF THE PLAY

THE EARL OF CAVERSHAM, K.G.
VISCOUNT GORING, his son
SIR ROBERT CHILTERN, Bart., Under-Secretary for
    Foreign Affairs
VICOMTE DE NANJAC, Attaché at the French Embassy
    in London
MR. MONTFORD
MASON, Butler to Sir Robert Chiltern
PHIPPS, Lord Goring's servant
JAMES   }Footmen
HAROLD

LADY CHILTERN
LADY MARKBY
THE COUNTESS OF BASILDON
MRS. MARCHMONT
MISS MABEL CHILTERN, Sir Robert Chiltern's sister
MRS. CHEVELEY

THE SCENES OF THE PLAY

ACT   I.   *The Octagon Room in Sir Robert Chiltern's*
           House in Grosvenor Square.
ACT II.   *Morning-room in Sir Robert Chiltern's*
           House.
ACT III.   *The Library of Lord Goring's House in*
           Curzon Street.
ACT IV. *Same as Act II.*

TIME: *The Present.*
PLACE: *London.*

    The action of the Play is completed within
           twenty four hours.

THEATRE ROYAL, HAYMARKET

Sole Lessee : Mr. Herbert Beerbohm Tree
Managers : Mr. Lewis Waller and Mr. H. H. Morell
January 3rd, 1895

THE EARL OF CAVERSHAM	*Mr. Alfred Bishop*
VISCOUNT GORING	*Mr. Charles H. Hawtrey*
SIR ROBERT CHILTERN	*Mr. Lewis Waller*
VICOMTE DE NANJAC	*Mr. Cosmo Stuart*
MR. MONTFORD	*Mr. Harry Stanford*
PHIPPS	*Mr. C. H. Brookfield*
MASON	*Mr. H. Deane*
JAMES (Footman)	*Mr. Charles Meyrick*
HAROLD (Footman)	*Mr. Goodhart*
LADY CHILTERN	*Miss Julia Neilson*
LADY MARKBY	*Miss Fanny Brough*
COUNTESS OF BASILDON	*Miss Vane Featherston*
MRS. MARCHMONT	*Miss Helen Forsyth*
MISS MABEL CHILTERN	*Miss Maud Millett*
MRS. CHEVELEY	*Miss Florence West*

FIRST ACT

SCENE

The octagon room at Sir Robert Chiltern's house in Grosvenor Square.

The room is brilliantly lighted and full of guests.

At the top of the staircase stands LADY CHILTERN, *a woman of grave Greek beauty, about twenty-seven years of age. She receives the guests as they come up. Over the well of the staircase hangs a great chandelier with wax lights, which illumine a large eighteenth-century French tapestry—representing the Triumph of Love, from a design by Boucher—that is stretched on the staircase wall. On the right is the entrance to the music-room. The sound of a string quartette is faintly heard. The entrance on the left leads to other reception-rooms.* MRS. MARCHMONT *and* LADY BASILDON, *two very pretty women, are seated together on a Louis Seize sofa. They are types of exquisite fragility. Their affectation of manner has a delicate charm. Watteau would have loved to paint them.*

Mrs. Marchmont: Going on to the Hartlocks' to-night, Margaret?

Lady Basildon: I suppose so. Are you?

Mrs. Marchmont: Yes. Horribly tedious parties they give, don't they?

Lady Basildon: Horribly tedious! Never know why I go. Never know why I go anywhere.

Mrs. Marchmont: I come here to be educated.

Lady Basildon: Ah! I hate being educated!

Mrs. Marchmont: So do I. It puts one almost on a level with the commercial classes, doesn't it? But

481

dear Gertrude Chiltern is always telling me that I should have some serious purpose in life. So I come here to try to find one.

Lady Basildon (looking round through her lorgnette) : I don't see anybody here to-night whom one could possibly call a serious purpose. The man who took me in to dinner talked to me about his wife the whole time.

Mrs. Marchmont : How very trivial of him!

Lady Basildon : Terribly trivial! What did your man talk about?

Mrs. Marchmont : About myself.

Lady Basildon (languidly) : And were you interested?

Mrs. Marchmont (shaking her head) : Not in the smallest degree.

Lady Basildon : What martyrs we are, dear Margaret!

Mrs. Marchmont (rising) : And how well it becomes us, Olivia!

> *They rise and go towards the music-room. The* VICOMTE DE NANJAC, *a young attaché known for his neckties and his Anglomania, approaches with a low bow, and enters into conversation.*

Mason (announcing guests from the top of the staircase) : Mr. and Lady Jane Barford. Lord Caversham.

> *Enter* LORD CAVERSHAM, *an old gentleman of seventy, wearing the riband and star of the Garter. A fine Whig type. Rather like a portrait by Lawrence.*

Lord Caversham : Good-evening, Lady Chiltern! Has my good-for-nothing young son been here?

Lady Chiltern (smiling) : I don't think Lord Goring has arrived yet.

Mabel Chiltern (coming up to LORD CAVERSHAM) *:* Why do you call Lord Goring good-for-nothing?

> MABEL CHILTERN *is a perfect example of the English type of prettiness, the apple-blossom type. She has all the fragrance and freedom of a flower.*

There is ripple after ripple of sunlight in her hair, and the little mouth, with its parted lips, is expectant, like the mouth of a child. She has the fascinating tyranny of youth, and the astonishing courage of innocence. To sane people she is not reminiscent of any work of art. But she is really like a Tanagra statuette, and would be rather annoyed if she were told so.

Lord Caversham : Because he leads such an idle life.

Mabel Chiltern : How can you say such a thing? Why, he rides in the Row at ten o'clock in the morning. goes to the Opera three times a week, changes his clothes at least five times a day, and dines out every night of the season. You don't call that leading an idle life, do you?

Lord Caversham (looking at her with a kindly twinkle in his eyes) : You are a very charming young lady!

Mabel Chiltern : How sweet of you to say that, Lord Caversham! Do come to us more often. You know we are always at home on Wednesdays, and you look so well with your star!

Lord Caversham : Never go anywhere now. Sick of London Society. Shouldn't mind being introduced to my own tailor; he always votes on the right side. But object strongly to being sent down to dinner with my wife's milliner. Never could stand Lady Caversham's bonnets.

Mabel Chiltern : Oh, I love London Society! I think it has immensely improved. It is entirely composed now of beautiful idiots and brilliant lunatics. Just what Society should be.

Lord Caversham : Hum! Which is Goring? Beautiful idiot, or the other thing?

Mabel Chiltern (gravely) : I have been obliged for the present to put Lord Goring into a class quite by himself. But he is developing charmingly!

Lord Caversham : Into what?

Mabel Chiltern (with a little curtsey) : I hope to let you know very soon, Lord Caversham !

Mason (announcing guests) : Lady Markby. Mrs. Cheveley.

Enter LADY MARKBY *and* MRS. CHEVELEY. LADY MARKBY *is a pleasant, kindly, popular woman, with gray hair à la marquise and good lace.* MRS. CHEVELEY, *who accompanies her, is tall and rather slight. Lips very thin and highly-coloured, a line of scarlet on a pallid face. Venetian red hair, aquiline nose, and long throat. Rouge accentuates the natural paleness of her complexion. Gray-green eyes that move restlessly. She is in heliotrope, with diamonds. She looks rather like an orchid, and makes great demands on one's curiosity. In all her movements she is extremely graceful. A work of art, on the whole, but showing the influence of too many schools.*

Lady Markby : Good-evening, dear Gertrude ! So kind of you to let me bring my friend, Mrs. Cheveley. Two such charming women should know each other !

Lady Chiltern (advances towards MRS. CHEVELEY *with a sweet smile. Then suddenly stops, and bows rather distantly)* : I think Mrs. Cheveley and I have met before. I did not know she had married a second time.

Lady Markby (genially) : Ah, nowadays people marry as often as they can, don't they ? It is most fashionable. (*To* DUCHESS OF MARYBOROUGH) : Dear Duchess, and how is the Duke ? Brain still weak, I suppose ? Well, that is only to be expected, is it not ? His good father was just the same. There is nothing like race, is there ?

Mrs. Cheveley (playing with her fan) : But have we really met before, Lady Chiltern ? I can't remember where. I have been out of England for so long.

Lady Chiltern : We were at school together, Mrs. Cheveley.

Mrs. Cheveley (superciliously): Indeed? I have forgotten all about my schooldays. I have a vague impression that they were detestable.

Lady Chiltern (coldly): I am not surprised!

Mrs. Cheveley (in her sweetest manner): Do you know, I am quite looking forward to meeting your clever husband, Lady Chiltern. Since he has been at the Foreign Office, he has been so much talked of in Vienna. They actually succeed in spelling his name right in the newspapers. That in itself is fame, on the continent.

Lady Chiltern: I hardly think there will be much in common between you and my husband, Mrs. Cheveley! (*Moves away.*)

Vicomte de Nanjac: Ah, chère Madame, quelle surprise! I have not seen you since Berlin!

Mrs. Cheveley: Not since Berlin, Vicomte. Five years ago!

Vicomte de Nanjac: And you are younger and more beautiful than ever. How do you manage it?

Mrs. Cheveley: By making it a rule only to talk to perfectly charming people like yourself.

Vicomte de Nanjac: Ah! you flatter me. You butter me, as they say here.

Mrs. Cheveley: Do they say that here? How dreadful of them!

Vicomte de Nanjac: Yes, they have a wonderful language. It should be more widely known.

SIR ROBERT CHILTERN *enters. A man of forty, but looking somewhat younger. Clean-shaven, with finely-cut features, dark-haired and dark-eyed. A personality of mark. Not popular—few personalities are. But intensely admired by the few, and deeply respected by the many. The note of his manner is that of perfect distinction, with a slight touch of pride. One feels that he is conscious of the success he has made in life. A nervous temperament, with a tired look. The firmly-chiselled mouth and chin contrast strikingly with the romantic expression in the deep-set eyes. The variance is suggestive of an almost complete separation of passion and intellect, as though thought and emotion were each isolated in its own sphere through some violence of will-power. There is nervousness in the nostrils, and in the pale thin, pointed hands. It would be inaccurate to call him picturesque. Picturesqueness cannot survive the House of Commons. But Vandyck would have liked to have painted his head.*

Sir Robert Chiltern : Good-evening, Lady Markby. I hope you have brought Sir John with you?

Lady Markby : Oh! I have brought a much more charming person than Sir John. Sir John's temper since he has taken seriously to politics has become quite unbearable. Really, now that the House of Commons is trying to become useful, it does a great deal of harm.

Sir Robert Chiltern : I hope not, Lady Markby. At any rate we do our best to waste the public time, don't we? But who is this charming person you have been kind enough to bring to us?

Lady Markby : Her name is Mrs. Cheveley! One of the Dorsetshire Cheveleys, I suppose. But I really don't know. Families are so mixed nowadays. Indeed, as a rule, everybody turns out to be somebody else.

Sir Robert Chiltern : Mrs. Cheveley? I seem to know the name.

Lady Markby : She has just arrived from Vienna.

Sir Robert Chiltern : Ah! yes. I think I know whom you mean.

Lady Markby : Oh! she goes everywhere there, and has such pleasant scandals about all her friends. I really must go to Vienna next winter. I hope there is a good chef at the Embassy.

Sir Robert Chiltern : If there is not, the Ambassador

will certainly have to be recalled. Pray point out Mrs. Cheveley to me. I should like to see her.

Lady Markby : Let me introduce you. (*To* Mrs. Cheveley) *:* My dear, Sir Robert Chiltern is dying to know you !

Sir Robert Chiltern (bowing) : Every one is dying to know the brilliant Mrs. Cheveley. Our attachés at Vienna write to us about nothing else.

Mrs. Cheveley : Thank you, Sir Robert. An acquaintance that begins with a compliment is sure to develop into a real friendship. It starts in the right manner. And I find that I know Lady Chiltern already.

Sir Robert Chiltern : Really ?

Mrs. Cheveley : Yes. She has just reminded me that we were at school together. I remember it perfectly now. She always got the good conduct prize. I have a distinct recollection of Lady Chiltern always getting the good conduct prize !

Sir Robert Chiltern (smiling) : And what prizes did you get, Mrs. Cheveley ?

Mrs. Cheveley : My prizes came a little later on in life. I don't think any of them were for good conduct. I forget !

Sir Robert Chiltern : I am sure they were for something charming !

Mrs. Cheveley : I don't know that women are always rewarded for being charming. I think they are usually punished for it ! Certainly, more women grow old nowadays through the faithfulness of their admirers than through anything else ! At least that is the only way I can account for the terribly haggard look of most of your pretty women in London !

Sir Robert Chiltern : What an appalling philosophy that sounds ! To attempt to classify you, Mrs. Cheveley, would be an impertinence. But may I ask, at heart, are you an optimist or a pessimist ? Those seem to be the only two fashionable religions left to us nowadays.

Mrs. Cheveley : Oh, I'm neither. Optimism begins in a broad grin, and Pessimism ends with blue spectacles. Besides, they are both of them merely poses.

Sir Robert Chiltern : You prefer to be natural ?

Mrs. Cheveley : Sometimes. But it is such a very difficult pose to keep up.

Sir Robert Chiltern : What would those modern psychological novelists, of whom we hear so much, say to such a theory as that ?

Mrs. Cheveley : Ah ! the strength of women comes from the fact that psychology cannot explain us. Men can be analysed, women . . . merely adored.

Sir Robert Chiltern : You think science cannot grapple with the problem of women ?

Mrs. Cheveley : Science can never grapple with the irrational. That is why it has no future before it, in this world.

Sir Robert Chiltern : And women represent the irrational.

Mrs. Cheveley : Well-dressed women do.

Sir Robert Chiltern (with a polite bow) : I fear I could hardly agree with you there. But do sit down. And now tell me, what makes you leave your brilliant Vienna for our gloomy London—or perhaps the question is indiscreet ?

Mrs. Cheveley : Questions are never indiscreet. Answers sometimes are.

Sir Robert Chiltern : Well, at any rate, may I know if it is politics or pleasure ?

Mrs. Cheveley : Politics are my only pleasure. You see nowadays it is not fashionable to flirt till one is forty, or to be romantic till one is forty-five, so we poor women who are under thirty, or say we are, have nothing open to us but politics or philanthropy. And philanthropy seems to me to have become simply the refuge of people who wish to annoy their fellow-creatures. I prefer politics. I think they are more . . . becoming !

Sir Robert Chiltern: A political life is a noble career!

Mrs. Cheveley: Sometimes. And sometimes it is a clever game, Sir Robert. And sometimes it is a great nuisance.

Sir Robert Chiltern: Which do you find it?

Mrs. Cheveley: A combination of all three. (*Drops her fan.*)

Sir Robert Chiltern (picks up fan): Allow me!

Mrs. Cheveley: Thanks.

Sir Robert Chiltern: But you have not told me yet what makes you honour London so suddenly. Our season is almost over.

Mrs. Cheveley: Oh! I don't care about the London season! It is too matrimonial. People are either hunting for husbands, or hiding from them. I wanted to meet you. It is quite true. You know what a woman's curiosity is. Almost as great as a man's! I wanted immensely to meet you, and . . . to ask you to do something for me.

Sir Robert Chiltern: I hope it is not a little thing, Mrs. Cheveley. I find that little things are so very difficult to do.

Mrs. Cheveley (after a moment's reflection): No, I don't think it is quite a little thing.

Sir Robert Chiltern: I am so glad. Do tell me what it is.

Mrs. Cheveley: Later on. (*Rises.*) And now may I walk through your beautiful house? I hear your pictures are charming. Poor Baron Arnheim—you remember the Baron?—used to tell me you had some wonderful Corots.

Sir Robert Chiltern (with an almost imperceptible start): Did you know Baron Arnheim well?

Mrs. Cheveley (smiling): Intimately. Did you?

Sir Robert Chiltern: At one time.

Mrs. Cheveley: Wonderful man, wasn't he?

Sir Robert Chiltern (after a pause): He was very remarkable, in many ways.

Mrs. Cheveley : I often think it such a pity he never wrote his memoirs. They would have been most interesting.

Sir Robert Chiltern : Yes: he knew men and cities well, like the old Greek.

Mrs. Cheveley : Without the dreadful disadvantage of having a Penelope waiting at home for him.

Mason : Lord Goring.

> *Enter* LORD GORING. *Thirty-four, but always says he is younger. A well-bred, expressionless face. He is clever, but would not like to be thought so. A flawless dandy, he would be annoyed if he were considered romantic. He plays with life, and is on perfectly good terms with the world. He is fond of being misunderstood. It gives him a post of vantage.*

Sir Robert Chiltern : Good-evening, my dear Arthur ! Mrs. Cheveley, allow me to introduce to you Lord Goring, the idlest man in London.

Mrs. Cheveley : I have met Lord Goring before.

Lord Goring (bowing) : I did not think you would remember me, Mrs. Cheveley.

Mrs. Cheveley : My memory is under admirable control. And are you still a bachelor ?

Lord Goring : I . . . believe so.

Mrs. Cheveley : How very romantic !

Lord Goring : Oh ! I am not at all romantic. I am not old enough. I leave romance to my seniors.

Sir Robert Chiltern : Lord Goring is the result of Boodle's Club, Mrs. Cheveley.

Mrs. Cheveley : He reflects every credit on the institution.

Lord Goring : May I ask are you staying in London long ?

Mrs. Cheveley : That depends partly on the weather, partly on the cooking, and partly on Sir Robert.

Sir Robert Chiltern : You are not going to plunge us into a European war, I hope ?

Mrs. Cheveley : There is no danger, at present !

She nods to LORD GORING, *with a look of amuse-
ment in her eyes, and goes out with* SIR ROBERT
CHILTERN. LORD GORING *saunters over to* MABEL
CHILTERN.

Mabel Chiltern : You are very late !
Lord Goring : Have you missed me ?
Mabel Chiltern : Awfully !
Lord Goring : Then I am sorry I did not stay
away longer. I like being missed.
Mabel Chiltern : How very selfish of you !
Lord Goring : I am very selfish.
Mabel Chiltern : You are always telling me of your
bad qualities, Lord Goring.
Lord Goring : I have only told you half of them as
yet, Miss Mabel !
Mabel Chiltern : Are the others very bad ?
Lord Goring : Quite dreadful ! When I think of
them at night I go to sleep at once.
Mabel Chiltern : Well, I delight in your bad qualities.
I wouldn't have you part with one of them.
Lord Goring : How very nice of you ! But then you
are always nice. By the way, I want to ask you a
question, Miss Mabel. Who brought Mrs. Cheveley
here ? That woman in heliotrope, who has just gone
out of the room with your brother ?
Mabel Chiltern : Oh, I think Lady Markby brought
her. Why do you ask ?
Lord Goring : I haven't seen her for years, that is all.
Mabel Chiltern : What an absurd reason !
Lord Goring : All reasons are absurd.
Mabel Chiltern : What sort of a woman is she ?
Lord Goring : Oh ! a genius in the daytime and a
beauty at night !
Mabel Chiltern : I dislike her already.

Lord Goring : That shows your admirable good taste.

Vicomte de Nanjac (approaching) : Ah, the English young lady is the dragon of good taste, is she not ? Quite the dragon of good taste.

Lord Goring : So the newspapers are always telling us.

Vicomte de Nanjac : I read all your English news-papers. I find them so amusing.

Lord Goring : Then, my dear Nanjac, you must certainly read between the lines.

Vicomte de Nanjac : I should like to, but my professor objects. (*To* MABEL CHILTERN) : May I have the pleasure of escorting you to the music-room, Made-moiselle ?

Mabel Chiltern (looking very disappointed) : Delighted, Vicomte, quite delighted ! (*Turning to* LORD GORING) : Aren't you coming to the music-room ?

Lord Goring : Not if there is any music going on, Miss Mabel.

Mabel Chiltern (severely) : The music is in German. You would not understand it.

> *Goes out with the* VICOMTE DE NANJAC. LORD CAVERSHAM *comes up to his son.*

Lord Caversham : Well, sir ! what are you doing here ? Wasting your life as usual ! You should be in bed, sir. You keep too late hours ! I heard of you the other night at Lady Rufford's dancing till four o'clock in the morning !

Lord Goring : Only a quarter to four, father.

Lord Caversham : Can't make out how you stand London Society. The thing has gone to the dogs, a lot of damned nobodies talking about nothing.

Lord Goring : I love talking about nothing, father. It is the only thing I know anything about.

Lord Caversham : You seem to me to be living entirely for pleasure.

Lord Goring : What else is there to live for, father ? Nothing ages like happiness.

Lord Caversham : You are heartless, sir, very heartless.

Lord Goring : I hope not, father. Good-evening, Lady Basildon !

Lady Basildon (arching two pretty eyebrows) : Are you here ? I had no idea you ever came to political parties.

Lord Goring : I adore political parties. They are the only place left to us where people don't talk politics.

Lady Basildon : I delight in talking politics. I talk them all day long. But I can't bear listening to them. I don't know how the unfortunate men in the House stand these long debates.

Lord Goring : By never listening.

Lady Basildon : Really ?

Lord Goring (in his most serious manner) : Of course. You see, it is a very dangerous thing to listen. If one listens one may be convinced ; and a man who allows himself to be convinced by an argument is a thoroughy unreasonable person.

Lady Basildon : Ah ! that accounts for so much in men that I have never understood, and so much in women that their husbands never appreciate in them !

Mrs. Marchmont (with a sigh) : Our husbands never appreciate anything in us. We have to go to others for that !

Lady Basildon (emphatically) : Yes, always to others, have we not ?

Lord Goring (smiling) : And those are the views of the two ladies who are known to have the most admirable husbands in London.

Mrs. Marchmont : That is exactly what we can't stand. My Reginald is quite hopelessly faultless. He is really unendurably so, at times ! There is not the smallest element of excitement in knowing him.

Lord Goring : How terrible ! Really, the thing should be more widely known !

Lady Basildon : Basildon is quite as bad ; he is as domestic as if he was a bachelor.

Mrs. Marchmont (pressing LADY BASILDON's *hand) :* My poor Olivia ! We have married perfect husbands, and we are well punished for it.

Lord Goring : I should have thought it was the husbands who were punished.

Mrs. Marchmont (drawing herself up) : Oh, dear no ! They are as happy as possible ! And as for trusting us, it is tragic how much they trust us.

Lady Basildon : Perfectly tragic !

Lord Goring : Or comic, Lady Basildon ?

Lady Basildon : Certainly not comic, Lord Goring. How unkind of you to suggest such a thing !

Mrs. Marchmont : I am afraid Lord Goring is in the camp of the enemy, as usual. I saw him talking to that Mrs. Cheveley when he came in.

Lord Goring : Handsome woman, Mrs. Cheveley !

Lady Basildon (stiffly) : Please don't praise other women in our presence. You might wait for us to do that !

Lord Goring : I did wait.

Mrs. Marchmont : Well, we are not going to praise her. I hear she went to the Opera on Monday night, and told Tommy Rufford at supper that, as far as she could see, London Society was entirely made up of dowdies and dandies.

Lord Goring : She is quite right, too. The men are all dowdies and the women are all dandies, aren't they ?

Mrs. Marchmont (after a pause) : Oh ! do you really think that is what Mrs. Cheveley meant ?

Lord Goring : Of course. And a very sensible remark for Mrs. Cheveley to make, too.

Enter MABEL CHILTERN. *She joins the group.*

Mabel Chiltern : Why are you talking about Mrs. Cheveley ? Everybody is talking about Mrs. Cheveley !

Lord Goring says—what did you say, Lord Goring, about Mrs. Cheveley? Oh! I remember, that she was a genius in the daytime and a beauty at night.

Lady Basildon: What a horrid combination! So very unnatural!

Mrs. Marchmont (in her most dreamy manner): I like looking at geniuses, and listening to beautiful people!

Lord Goring: Ah! that is morbid of you, Mrs. Marchmont!

Mrs. Marchmont (brightening to a look of real pleasure): I am so glad to hear you say that. Marchmont and I have been married for seven years, and he has never once told me that I was morbid. Men are so painfully unobservant.

Lady Basildon (turning to her): I have always said, dear Margaret, that you were the most morbid person in London.

Mrs. Marchmont: Ah! but you are always sympathetic, Olivia!

Mabel Chiltern: Is it morbid to have a desire for food? I have a great desire for food. Lord Goring, will you give me some supper?

Lord Goring: With pleasure, Miss Mabel. (*Moves away with her.*)

Mabel Chiltern: How horrid you have been! You have never talked to me the whole evening!

Lord Goring: How could I? You went away with the child-diplomatist.

Mabel Chiltern: You might have followed us. Pursuit would have been only polite. I don't think I like you at all this evening!

Lord Goring: I like you immensely.

Mabel Chiltern: Well, I wish you'd show it in a more marked way!

They go downstairs.

Mrs. Marchmont: Olivia, I have a curious feeling

of absolute faintness. I think I should like some supper
very much. I know I should like some supper.

Lady Basildon : I am positively dying for supper,
Margaret !

Mrs. Marchmont : Men are so horribly selfish, they
never think of these things.

Lady Basildon : Men are grossly material, grossly
material !

The VICOMTE DE NANJAC *enters from the music-
room with some other guests. After having carefully
examined all the people present, he approaches* LADY
BASILDON.

Vicomte de Nanjac : May I have the honour of taking
you down to supper, Comtesse ?

Lady Basildon (coldly) : I never take supper, thank
you, Vicomte. (*The* VICOMTE *is about to retire.* LADY
BASILDON, *seeing this, rises at once and takes his arm.*)
But I will come down with you with pleasure.

Vicomte de Nanjac : I am so fond of eating ! I am
very English in all my tastes.

Lady Basildon : You look quite English, Vicomte,
quite English.

They pass out. MR. MONTFORD, *a perfectly
groomed young dandy, approaches* MRS. MARCHMONT.

Mr. Montford : Like some supper, Mrs. Marchmont ?

Mrs. Marchmont (languidly) : Thank you, Mr. Montford, I never touch supper. (*Rises hastily and takes his
arm.*) But I will sit beside you, and watch you.

Mr. Montford : I don't know that I like being
watched when I am eating !

Mrs. Marchmont : Then I will watch some one else.

Mr. Montford : I don't know that I should like
that either.

Mrs. Marchmont (severely) : Pray, Mr. Montford, do not make these painful scenes of jealousy in public !

They go downstairs with the other guests, passing SIR ROBERT CHILTERN *and* MRS. CHEVELEY, *who now enter.*

Sir Robert Chiltern : And are you going to any of our country houses before you leave England, Mrs. Cheveley ?

Mrs. Cheveley : Oh, no ! I can't stand your English house-parties. In England people actually try to be brilliant at breakfast. That is so dreadful of them ! Only dull people are brilliant at breakfast. And then the family skeleton is always reading family prayers. My stay in England really depends on you, Sir Robert. (*Sits down on the sofa.*)

Sir Robert Chiltern (taking a seat beside her) : Seriously ?

Mrs. Cheveley : Quite seriously. I want to talk to you about a great political and financial scheme, about this Argentine Canal Company, in fact.

Sir Robert Chiltern : What a tedious, practical subject for you to talk about, Mrs. Cheveley !

Mrs. Cheveley : Oh, I like tedious, practical subjects. What I don't like are tedious, practical people. There is a wide difference. Besides, you are interested, I know, in International Canal schemes. You were Lord Radley's secretary, weren't you, when the Government bought the Suez Canal shares ?

Sir Robert Chiltern : Yes. But the Suez Canal was a very great and splendid undertaking. It gave us our direct route to India. It had imperial value. It was necessary that we should have control. This Argentine scheme is a commonplace Stock Exchange swindle.

Mrs. Cheveley : A speculation, Sir Robert ! A brilliant, daring speculation.

Sir Robert Chiltern : Believe me, Mrs. Cheveley, it is a swindle. Let us call things by their proper names. It makes matters simpler. We have all the information about it at the Foreign Office. In fact, I sent out a special Commission to inquire into the matter privately, and they report that the works are hardly begun, and as for the money already subscribed, no one seems to know what has become of it. The whole thing is a second Panama, and with not a quarter of the chance of success that miserable affair ever had. I hope you have not invested in it. I am sure you are far too clever to have done that.

Mrs. Cheveley : I have invested very largely in it.

Sir Robert Chiltern : Who could have advised you to do such a foolish thing ?

Mrs. Cheveley : Your old friend—and mine.

Sir Robert Chiltern : Who ?

Mrs. Cheveley : Baron Arnheim.

Sir Robert Chiltern (frowning) : Ah ! yes. I remember hearing, at the time of his death, that he had been mixed up in the whole affair.

Mrs. Cheveley : It was his last romance. His last but one, to do him justice.

Sir Robert Chiltern (rising) : But you have not seen my Corots yet. They are in the music-room. Corots seem to go with music, don't they ? May I show them to you ?

Mrs. Cheveley (shaking her head) : I am not in a mood to-night for silver twilights, or rose-pink dawns. I want to talk business. (*Motions to him with her fan to sit down again beside her.*)

Sir Robert Chiltern : I fear I have no advice to give you, Mrs. Cheveley, except to interest yourself in something less dangerous. The success of the Canal depends, of course, on the attitude of England, and I am going to lay the report of the Commissioners before the House to-morrow night.

Mrs. Cheveley : That you must not do. In your

own interests, Sir Robert, to say nothing of mine, you must not do that.

Sir Robert Chiltern (looking at her in wonder) : In my own interests ? My dear Mrs. Cheveley, what do you mean ? *(Sits down beside her.)*

Mrs. Cheveley : Sir Robert, I will be quite frank with you. I want you to withdraw the report that you had intended to lay before the House, on the ground that you have reasons to believe that the Commissioners have been prejudiced or misinformed, or something. Then I want you to say a few words to the effect that the Government is going to reconsider the question, and that you have reason to believe that the Canal, if completed, will be of great international value. You know the sort of things ministers say in cases of this kind. A few ordinary platitudes will do. In modern life nothing produces such an effect as a good platitude. It makes the whole world kin. Will you do that for me ?

Sir Robert Chiltern : Mrs. Cheveley, you cannot be serious in making me such a proposition !

Mrs. Cheveley : I am quite serious.

Sir Robert Chiltern (coldly) : Pray allow me to believe that you are not.

Mrs. Cheveley (speaking with great deliberation and emphasis) : Ah ! but I am. And if you do what I ask you, I . . . will pay you very handsomely !

Sir Robert Chiltern : Pay me !

Mrs. Cheveley : Yes.

Sir Robert Chiltern : I am afraid I don't quite understand what you mean.

Mrs. Cheveley (leaning back on the sofa and looking at him) : How very disappointing ! And I have come all the way from Vienna in order that you should thoroughly understand me.

Sir Robert Chiltern : I fear I don't.

Mrs. Cheveley (in her most nonchalant manner) : My dear Sir Robert, you are a man of the world, and you have your price, I suppose. Everybody has nowadays. The drawback is that most people are so dreadfully expensive. I know I am. I hope you will be more reasonable in your terms.

Sir Robert Chiltern (rises indignantly): If you will allow me, I will call your carriage for you. You have lived so long abroad, Mrs. Cheveley, that you seem to be unable to realise that you are talking to an English gentleman.

Mrs. Cheveley (detains him by touching his arm with her fan, and keeping it there while she is talking): I realise that I am talking to a man who laid the foundation of his fortune by selling to a Stock Exchange speculator a Cabinet secret.

Sir Robert Chiltern (biting his lip): What do you mean?

Mrs. Cheveley (rising and facing him): I mean that I know the real origin of your wealth and your career, and I have got your letter, too.

Sir Robert Chiltern: What letter?

Mrs. Cheveley (contemptuously): The letter you wrote to Baron Arnheim, when you were Lord Radley's secretary, telling the Baron to buy Suez Canal shares— a letter written three days before the Government announced its own purchase.

Sir Robert Chiltern (hoarsely): It is not true.

Mrs. Cheveley: You thought that letter had been destroyed. How foolish of you! It is in my possession.

Sir Robert Chiltren: The affair to which you allude was no more than a speculation. The House of Commons had not yet passed the bill; it might have been rejected.

Mrs. Cheveley: It was a swindle, Sir Robert. Let us call things by their proper names. It makes everything simpler. And now I am going to sell you that letter, and the price I ask for it is your public support of the Argentine scheme. You made your own fortune out of one canal. You must help me and my friends to make our fortunes out of another !

Sir Robert Chiltern : It is infamous, what you propose —infamous !

Mrs. Cheveley : Oh, no ! This is the game of life as we all have to play it, Sir Robert, sooner or later !

Sir Robert Chiltern : I cannot do what you ask me.

Mrs. Cheveley : You mean you cannot help doing it. You know you are standing on the edge of a precipice. And it is not for you to make terms. It is for you to accept them. Supposing you refuse——

Sir Robert Chiltern : What then ?

Mrs. Cheveley : My dear Sir Robert, what then ? You are ruined, that is all ! Remember to what a point your Puritanism in England has brought you. In old days nobody pretended to be a bit better than his neighbours. In fact, to be a bit better than one's neighbour was considered excessively vulgar and middle-class. Nowadays, with our modern mania for morality, every one has to pose as a paragon of purity, incorruptibility, and all the other seven deadly virtues —and what is the result ? You all go over like ninepins —one after the other. Not a year passes in England without somebody disappearing. Scandals used to lend charm, or at least interest, to a man—now they crush him. And yours is a very nasty scandal. You couldn't survive it. If it were known that as a young man, secretary to a great and important minister, you sold a Cabinet secret for a large sum of money, and that was the origin of your wealth and career, you would be hounded out of public life, you would disappear completely. And after all, Sir Robert, why should you sacrifice your entire future rather than deal diplomatically with your enemy ? For the moment I am your enemy. I admit it ! And I am much stronger than you are. The big battalions are on my side. You have a splendid position, but it is your splendid position that makes you so vulnerable. You can't defend it !

And I am in attack. Of course I have not talked morality to you. You must admit in fairness that I have spared you that. Years ago you did a clever, unscrupulous thing ; it turned out a great success. You owe to it your fortune and position. And now you have got to pay for it. Sooner or later we have all to pay for what we do. You have to pay now. Before I leave you to-night, you have got to promise me to suppress your report, and to speak in the House in favour of this scheme.

Sir Robert Chiltern : What you ask is impossible.

Mrs. Cheveley : You must make it possible. You are going to make it possible. Sir Robert, you know what your English newspapers are like. Suppose that when I leave this house I drive down to some newspaper office, and give them this scandal and the proofs of it ! Think of their loathsome joy, of the delight they would have in dragging you down, of the mud and mire they would plunge you in. Think of the hypocrite with his greasy smile penning his leading article, and arranging the foulness of the public placard.

Sir Rovert Chiltern : Stop ! You want me to withdraw the report and to make a short speech stating that I believe there are possibilities in the scheme ?

Mrs. Cheveley (sitting down on the sofa) : Those are my terms.

Sir Robert Chiltern (in a low voice) : I will give you any sum of money you want.

Mrs. Cheveley : Even you are not rich enough, Sir Robert, to buy back your past. No man is.

Sir Robert Chiltern : I will not do what you ask me. I will not.

Mrs. Cheveley : You have to. If you don't. . . . (*Rises from the sofa.*)

Sir Robert Chiltern (bewildered and unnerved) : Wait a moment ! What did you propose ? You said that you would give me back my letter, didn't you ?

Mrs. Cheveley : Yes. That is agreed. I will be in the Ladies' Gallery to-morrow night at half-past eleven. If by that time—and you will have had heaps of opportunity—you have made an announcement to the House in the terms I wish, I shall hand you back your letter with the prettiest thanks, and the best, or at any rate the most suitable, compliment I can think of. I intend to play quite fairly with you. One should always play fairly . . . when one has the winning cards. The Baron taught me that . . . amongst other things.

Sir Robert Chiltern : You must let me have time to consider your proposal.

Mrs. Cheveley : No ; you must settle now !

Sir Robert Chiltern : Give me a week—three days !

Mrs. Cheveley : Impossible ! I have got to telegraph to Vienna to-night.

Sir Robert Chiltern : My God ! what brought you into my life ?

Mrs. Cheveley : Circumstances. (*Moves towards the door.*)

Sir Robert Chiltern : Don't go. I consent. The report shall be withdrawn. I will arrange for a question to be put to me on the subject.

Mrs. Cheveley : Thank you. I knew we should come to an amicable agreement. I understood your nature from the first. I analysed you, though you did not adore me. And now you can get my carriage for me, Sir Robert. I see the people coming up from supper, and Englishmen always get romantic after a meal, and that bores me dreadfully. (*Exit* SIR ROBERT CHILTERN.)

Enter Guests, LADY CHILTERN, LADY MARKBY, LORD CAVERSHAM, LADY BASILDON, MRS. MARCH-MONT, VICOMTE DE NANJAC, MR. MONTFORD.

Lady Markby : Well, dear Mrs. Cheveley, I hope

you have enjoyed yourself. Sir Robert is very entertaining, is he not?

Mrs. Cheveley: Most entertaining! I have enjoyed my talk with him immensely.

Lady Markby: He has had a very interesting and brilliant career. And he has married a most admirable wife. Lady Chiltern is a woman of the very highest principles, I am glad to say. I am a little too old now, myself, to trouble about setting a good example, but I always admire people who do. And Lady Chiltern has a very ennobling effect on life, though her dinner-parties are rather dull sometimes. But one can't have everything, can one? And now I must go, dear. Shall I call for you to-morrow?

Mrs. Cheveley: Thanks.

Lady Markby: We might drive in the Park at five. Everything looks so fresh in the Park now!

Mrs. Cheveley: Except the people!

Lady Markby: Perhaps the people are a little jaded. I have often observed that the Season as it goes on produces a kind of softening of the brain. However, I think anything is better than high intellectual pressure. That is the most unbecoming thing there is. It makes the noses of the young girls so particularly large. And there is nothing so difficult to marry as a large nose; men don't like them. Good-night, dear! (*To* LADY CHILTERN): Good-night, Gertrude! (*Goes out on* LORD CAVERSHAM'S *arm.*)

Mrs. Cheveley: What a charming house you have, Lady Chiltern! I have spent a delightful evening. It has been so interesting getting to know your husband.

Lady Chiltern: Why did you wish to meet my husband, Mrs. Cheveley?

Mrs. Cheveley: Oh, I will tell you. I wanted to interest him in this Argentine Canal scheme, of which I dare say you have heard. And I found him most susceptible—susceptible to reason, I mean. A rare thing in a man. I converted him in ten minutes. He is going to make a speech in the House to-morrow night in favour of the idea. We must go to the Ladies' Gallery and hear him ! It will be a great occasion !

Lady Chiltern : There must be some mistake. That scheme could never have my husband's support.

Mrs. Cheveley : Oh, I assure you it's all settled. I don't regret my tedious journey from Vienna now. It has been a great success. But, of course, for the next twenty-four hours the whole thing is a dead secret.

Lady Chiltern (gently) : A secret ? Between whom ?

Mrs. Cheveley (with a flash of amusement in her eyes) Between your husband and myself.

Sir Robert Chiltern (entering) : Your carriage is here, Mrs. Cheveley !

Mrs. Cheveley : Thanks ! Good-evening, Lady Chiltern ! Good-night, Lord Goring ! I am at Claridge's. Don't you think you might leave a card ?

Lord Goring : If you wish it, Mrs. Cheveley !

Mrs. Cheveley : Oh, don't be so solemn about it, or I shall be obliged to leave a card on you. In England I suppose that would hardly be considered *en règle.* Abroad, we are more civilised. Will you see me down, Sir Robert ? Now that we have both the same interests at heart we shall be great friends, I hope !

Sails out on Sir Robert Chiltern's *arm.* Lady Chiltern *goes to the top of the staircase and looks down at them as they descend. Her expression is troubled. After a little time she is joined by some of the guests, and passes with them into another reception-room.*

Mabel Chiltern : What a horrid woman !

Lord Goring : You should go to bed, Miss Mabel.

Mabel Chiltern : Lord Goring !

Lord Goring : My father told me to go to bed an hour ago. I don't see why I shouldn't give you the same advice. I always pass on good advice. It is the only thing to do with it. It is never of any use to oneself.

Mabel Chiltern : Lord Goring, you are always ordering me out of the room. I think it most courageous of you. Especially as I am not going to bed for hours. (*Goes over to the sofa.*) You can come and sit down if you like, and talk about anything in the world, except the Royal Academy, Mrs. Cheveley, or novels in Scotch dialect. They are not improving subjects. (*Catches sight of something that is lying on the sofa half-hidden by the cushion.*) What is this? Some one has dropped a diamond brooch! Quite beautiful, isn't it? (*Shows it to him.*) I wish it was mine, but Gertrude won't let me wear anything but pearls, and I am thoroughly sick of pearls. They make one look so plain, so good and so intellectual. I wonder whom the brooch belongs to.

Lord Goring : I wonder who dropped it.

Mabel Chiltern : It is a beautiful brooch.

Lord Goring : It is a handsome bracelet.

Mabel Chiltern : It isn't a bracelet. It's a brooch.

Lord Goring : It can be used as a bracelet. (*Takes it from her, and, pulling out a green letter-case, puts the ornament carefully in it, and replaces the whole thing in his breast-pocket with the most perfect sang froid.*)

Mabel Chiltern : What are you doing?

Lord Goring : Miss Mabel, I am going to make a rather strange request to you.

Mabel Chiltern (eagerly) : Oh, pray do! I have been waiting for it all the evening.

Lord Goring (is a little taken aback, but recovers himself): Don't mention to anybody that I have taken charge of this brooch. Should any one write and claim it, let me know at once.

Mabel Chiltern : That is a strange request.

Lord Goring : Well, you see I gave this brooch to somebody once, years ago.

Mabel Chiltern : You did ?
Lord Goring : Yes.

LADY CHILTERN *enters alone. The other guests have gone.*

Mabel Chiltern : Then I shall certainly bid you good-night. Good-night, Gertrude ! (*Exit.*)
Lady Chiltern : Good-night, dear ! (*To* LORD GORING) : You saw whom Lady Markby brought here to-night ?
Lord Goring : Yes. It was an unpleasant surprise. What did she come here for ?
Lady Chiltern : Apparently to try and lure Robert to uphold some fraudulent scheme in which she is interested. The Argentine Canal, in fact.
Lord Goring : She has mistaken her man, hasn't she ?
Lady Chiltern : She is incapable of understanding an upright nature like my husband's !
Lord Goring : Yes. I should fancy she came to grief if she tried to get Robert into her toils. It is extraordinary what astounding mistakes clever women make.
Lady Chiltern : I don't call women of that kind clever. I call them stupid !
Lord Goring : Same thing often. Good-night, Lady Chiltern !
Lady Chiltern : Good-night !

Enter SIR ROBERT CHILTERN.

Sir Robert Chiltern : My dear Arthur, you are not going ? Do stop a little !
Lord Goring : Afraid I can't, thanks. I have promised to look in at the Hartlocks'. I believe they have got a mauve Hungarian band that plays mauve Hungarian music. See you soon. Good-bye ! (*Exit.*)

Sir Robert Chiltern: How beautiful you look to-night, Gertrude!

Lady Chiltern: Robert, it is not true, is it? You are not going to lend your support to this Argentine speculation? You couldn't!

Sir Robert Chiltern (starting): Who told you I intended to do so?

Lady Chiltern: That woman who has just gone out, Mrs. Cheveley, as she calls herself now. She seemed to taunt me with it. Robert, I know this woman. You don't. We were at school together. She was untruthful, dishonest, an evil influence on every one whose trust or friendship she could win. I hated, I despised her. She stole things, she was a thief. She was sent away for being a thief. Why do you let her influence you?

Sir Robert Chiltern: Gertrude, what you tell me may be true, but it happened many years ago. It is best forgotten! Mrs. Cheveley may have changed since then. No one should be entirely judged by their past.

Lady Chiltern (sadly): One's past is what one is. It is the only way by which people should be judged.

Sir Robert Chiltern: That is hard saying, Gertrude!

Lady Chiltern: It is a true saying, Robert. And what did she mean by boasting that she had got you to lend your support, your name, to a thing I have heard you describe as the most dishonest and fraudulent scheme there has ever been in political life?

Sir Robert Chiltern (biting his lip): I was mistaken in the view I took. We all may make mistakes.

Lady Chiltern: But you told me yesterday that you had received the report from the Commission, and that it entirely condemned the whole thing.

Sir Robert Chiltern (walking up and down): I have reasons now to believe that the Commission was prejudiced, or, at any rate, misinformed. Besides, Gertrude, public and private life are different things. They have different laws, and move on different lines.

Lady Chiltern : They should both represent man at his highest. I see no difference between them.

Sir Robert Chiltern (stopping) : In the present case, on a matter of practical politics, I have changed my mind. That is all.

Lady Chiltern : All !

Sir Robert Chiltern (sternly) : Yes !

Lady Chiltern : Robert ! Oh ! it is horrible that I should have to ask you such a question—Robert, are you telling me the whole truth ?

Sir Robert Chiltern : Why do you ask me such a question ?

Lady Chiltern (after a pause) : Why do you not answer it ?

Sir Robert Chiltern (sitting down) : Gertrude, truth is a very complex thing, and politics is a very complex business. There are wheels within wheels. One may be under certain obligations to people that one must pay. Sooner or later in political life one has to compromise. Every one does.

Lady Chiltern : Compromise ? Robert, why do you talk so differently to-night from the way I have always heard you talk ? Why are you changed ?

Sir Robert Chiltern : I am not changed. But circumstances alter things.

Lady Chiltern : Circumstances should never alter principles.

Sir Robert Chiltern : But if I told you——

Lady Chiltern : What ?

Sir Robert Chiltern : That it was necessary, vitally necessary ?

Lady Chiltern : It can never be necessary to do what is not honourable. Or if it be necessary, then what is it that I have loved ! But it is not, Robert ; tell me it is not. Why should it be ? What gain would you get ? Money ? We have no need of that ! And money that comes from a tainted source is a degradation. Power ? But power is nothing in itself. It is power to do good that is fine—that, and that only. What is it, then ? Robert, tell me why you are going to do this dishonourable thing !

Sir Robert Chiltern : Gertrude, you have no right to use that word. I told you it was a question of rational compromise. It is no more than that.

Lady Chiltern : Robert, that is all very well for other men, for men who treat life simply as a sordid speculation ; but not for you, Robert, not for you. You are different. All your life you have stood apart from others. You have never let the world soil you. To the world, as to myself, you have been an ideal always. Oh ! be that ideal still. That great inheritance throw not away—that tower of ivory do not destroy. Robert, men can love what is beneath them—things unworthy, stained, dishonoured. We women worship when we love ; and when we lose our worship, we lose everything. Oh ! don't kill my love for you, don't kill that !

Sir Robert Chiltern : Gertrude !

Lady Chiltern : I know that there are men with horrible secrets in their lives—men who have done some shameful thing, and who in some critical moment have to pay for it, by doing some other act of shame— oh ! don't tell me you are such as they are ! Robert, is there in your life any secret dishonour or disgrace ? Tell me, tell me at once, that——

Sir Robert Chiltern : That what ?

Lady Chiltern (speaking very slowly) : That our lives may drift apart.

Sir Robert Chiltern : Drift apart ?

Lady Chiltern : That they may entirely separate. It would be better for us both.

Sir Robert Chiltern : Gertrude, there is nothing in my past life that you might not know.

Lady Chiltern : I was sure of it, Robert, I was sure of it. But why did you say those dreadful things, things so unlike your real self ? Don't let us ever talk about the subject again. You will write, won't you, to

Mrs Cheveley, and tell her that you cannot support this scandalous scheme of hers ? If you have given her any promise you must take it back, that is all !

Sir Robert Chiltern : Must I write and tell her that ?

Lady Chiltern : Surely, Robert ! What else is there to do ?

Sir Robert Chiltern : I might see her personally. It would be better.

Lady Chiltern : You must never see her again, Robert. She is not a woman you should ever speak to. She is not worthy to talk to a man like you. No ; you must write to her at once, now, this moment, and let your letter show her that your decision is quite irrevocable !

Sir Robert Chiltern : Write this moment !

Lady Chiltern : Yes.

Sir Robert Chiltern : But it is so late. It is close on twelve.

Lady Chiltern : That makes no matter. She must know at once that she has been mistaken in you—and that you are not a man to do anything base or underhand or dishonourable. Write here, Robert. Write that you decline to support this scheme of hers, as you hold it to be a dishonest scheme. Yes—write the word dishonest. She knows what that word means. (SIR ROBERT CHILTERN *sits down and writes a letter. His wife takes it up and reads it.*). Yes ; that will do. (*Rings bell.*) And now the envelope. (*He writes the envelope slowly. Enter* MASON.) Have this letter sent at once to Claridge's Hotel. There is no answer. (*Exit* MASON. LADY CHILTERN *kneels down beside her husband and puts her arms around him.*) Robert, love gives one an instinct to things. I feel to-night that I have saved you from something that might have been a danger to you, from something that might have made men honour you less than they do. I don't think you realise sufficiently, Robert, that you have brought into the political life of our time a nobler atmosphere, a finer

attitude towards life, a freer air of purer aims and
higher ideals—I know it, and for that I love you,
Robert.

Sir Robert Chiltern : Oh, love me always, Gertrude,
love me always !

Lady Chiltern : I will love you always, because you
will always be worthy of love. We needs must love
the highest when we see it ! (*Kisses him and rises and
goes out.*)

SIR ROBERT CHILTERN *walks up and down for a
moment ; then sits down and buries his face in his
hands. The Servant enters and begins putting out
the lights.* SIR ROBERT CHILTERN *looks up.*

Sir Robert Chiltern : Put out the lights, Mason, put
out the lights !

*The Servant puts out the lights. The room becomes
almost dark. The only light there is comes from the
great chandelier that hangs over the staircase and
illumines the tapestry of the Triumph of Love.*

ACT DROP.

SECOND ACT

SCENE

Morning-room at Sir Robert Chiltern's house.

LORD GORING, *dressed in the height of fashion, is lounging in an arm-chair.* SIR ROBERT CHILTERN *is standing in front of the fireplace. He is evidently in a state of great mental excitement and distress. As the scene progresses he paces nervously up and down the room.*

Lord Goring : My dear Robert, it's a very awkward business, very awkward indeed. You should have told your wife the whole thing. Secrets from other people's wives are a necessary luxury in modern life. So, at least, I am always told at the club by people who are bald enough to know better. But no man should have a secret from his own wife. She invariably finds it out. Women have a wonderful instinct about things. They can discover everything except the obvious.

Sir Robert Chiltern : Arthur, I couldn't tell my wife. When could I have told her ? Not last night. It would have made a life-long separation between us, and I would have lost the love of the one woman in the world I worship, of the only woman who had ever stirred love within me. Last night it would have been quite impossible. She would have turned from me in horror . . . in horror and in contempt.

Lord Goring : Is Lady Chiltern as perfect as all that ?

Sir Robert Chiltern : Yes ; my wife is as perfect as all that.

Lord Goring (taking off his left-hand glove) : What a pity ! I beg your pardon, my dear fellow, I didn't

513

quite mean that. But if what you tell me is true, I should like to have a serious talk about life with Lady Chiltern.

Sir Robert Chiltern : It would be quite useless.

Lord Goring : May I try?

Sir Robert Chiltern : Yes; but nothing could make her alter her views.

Lord Goring : Well, at the worst it would simply be a psychological experiment.

Sir Robert Chiltern : All such experiments are terribly dangerous.

Lord Goring : Everything is dangerous, my dear fellow. If it wasn't so, life wouldn't be worth living. . . . Well, I am bound to say that I think you should have told her years ago.

Sir Robert Chiltern : When? When we were engaged? Do you think she would have married me if she had known that the origin of my fortune is such as it is, the basis of my career such as it is, and that I had done a thing that I suppose most men would call shameful and dishonourable?

Lord Goring (slowly) : Yes; most men would call it ugly names. There is no doubt of that.

Sir Robert Chiltern (bitterly) : Men who every day do something of the same kind themselves. Men who, each one of them, have worse secrets in their own lives.

Lord Goring : That is the reason they are so pleased to find out other people's secrets. It distracts public attention from their own.

Sir Robert Chiltern : And, after all, whom did I wrong by what I did? No one.

Lord Goring (looking at him steadily) : Except yourself, Robert.

Sir Robert Chiltern (after a pause) : Of course I had private information about a certain transaction contemplated by the Government of the day, and I acted on it. Private information is practically the source of every large modern fortune.

Lord Goring (tapping his boot with his cane) : And public scandal invariably the result.

Sir Robert Chiltern (pacing up and down the room) : Arthur, do you think that what I did nearly eighteen years ago should be brought up against me now ? Do you think it fair that a man's whole career should be ruined for a fault done in one's boyhood almost ? I was twenty-two at the time, and I had the double misfortune of being well-born and poor, two unforgivable things nowadays. Is it fair that the folly, the sin of one's youth, if men choose to call it a sin, should wreck a life like mine, should place me in the pillory, should shatter all that I have worked for, all that I have built up ? Is it fair, Arthur ?

Lord Goring : Life is never fair, Robert. And perhaps it is a good thing for most of us that it is not.

Sir Robert Chiltern : Every man of ambition has to fight his century with its own weapons. What this century worships is wealth. The God of this century is wealth. To succeed one must have wealth. At all costs one must have wealth.

Lord Goring : You underrate yourself, Robert. Believe me, without wealth you could have succeeded just as well.

Sir Robert Chiltern : When I was old, perhaps. When I had lost my passion for power, or could not use it. When I was tired, worn out, disappointed. I wanted my success when I was young. Youth is the time for success. I couldn't wait.

Lord Goring : Well, you certainly have had your success while you are still young. No one in our day has had such a brilliant success. Under-Secretary for Foreign Affairs at the age of forty—that's good enough for any one, I should think.

Sir Robert Chiltern : And if it is all taken away from me now ? If I lose everything over a horrible scandal ? If I am hounded from public life ?

Lord Goring : Robert, how could you have sold yourself for money ?

Sir Robert Chiltern (excitedly) : I did not sell myself for money. I bought success at a great price. That is all.

Lord Goring (gravely) : Yes ; you certainly paid a great price for it. But what first made you think of doing such a thing ?

Sir Robert Chiltern : Baron Arnheim.

Lord Goring : Damned scoundrel !

Sir Robert Chiltern : No ; he was a man of a most subtle and refined intellect. A man of culture, charm, and distinction. One of the most intellectual men I ever met.

Lord Goring : Ah ! I prefer a gentlemanly fool any day. There is more to be said for stupidity than people imagine. Personally I have a great admiration for stupidity. It is a sort of fellow-feeling, I suppose. But how did he do it ? Tell me the whole thing.

Sir Robert Chiltern (throws himself into an arm-chair by the writing-table) : One night after dinner at Lord Radley's the Baron began talking about success in modern life as something that one could reduce to an absolutely definite science. With that wonderfully fascinating quiet voice of his he expounded to us the most terrible of all philosophies, the philosophy of power, preached to us the most marvellous of all gospels, the gospel of gold. I think he saw the effect he had produced on me, for some days afterwards he wrote and asked me to come and see him. He was living then in Park Lane, in the house Lord Woolcomb has now. I remember so well how, with a strange smile on his pale, curved lips, he led me through his wonderful picture gallery, showed me his tapestries, his enamels, his jewels, his carved ivories, made me wonder at the strange loveliness of the luxury in which he lived ; and then told me that luxury was nothing but a background, a painted scene in a play, and that power, power over other men, power over the world, was the one thing worth having, the one supreme pleasure worth knowing, the one joy one never tired of, and that in our century only the rich possessed it.

Lord Goring (with great deliberation) : A thoroughly shallow creed.

Sir Robert Chiltern (rising) : I didn't think so then. I don't think so now. Wealth has given me enormous power. It gave me at the very outset of my life freedom, and freedom is everything. You have never been poor, and never known what ambition is. You cannot understand what a wonderful chance the Baron gave me. Such a chance as few men get.

Lord Goring : Fortunately for them, if one is to judge by results. But tell me definitely, how did the Baron finally persuade you to—well, to do what you did ?

Sir Robert Chiltern : When I was going away he said to me that if I ever could give him any private information of real value he would make me a very rich man. I was dazed at the prospect he held out to me, and my ambition and my desire for power were at that time boundless. Six weeks later certain private documents passed through my hands.

Lord Goring (keeping his eyes steadily fixed on the carpet) : State documents ?

Sir Robert Chiltern : Yes.

LORD GORING *sighs, then passes his hand across his forehead and looks up.*

Lord Goring : I had no idea that you, of all men in the world, could have been so weak, Robert, as to yield to such a temptation as Baron Arnheim held out to you.

Sir Robert Chiltern : Weak ? Oh, I am sick of hearing that phrase. Sick of using it about others. Weak ! Do you really think, Arthur, that it is weakness that yields to temptation ? I tell you that there are terrible temptations that it requires strength, strength and courage, to yield to. To stake all one's life on a single moment, to risk everything on one throw, whether the stake be power or pleasure, I care not—there is no weakness in that. There is a horrible, a terrible courage. I had that courage. I sat down the same afternoon and wrote Baron Arnheim the letter this woman now holds. He made three-quarters of a million over the transaction.

Lord Goring : And you ?

Sir Robert Chiltern : I received from the Baron £110,000.

Lord Goring : You were worth more, Robert.

Sir Robert Chiltern : No ; that money gave me exactly what I wanted, power over others. I went into the House immediately. The Baron advised me in finance from time to time. Before five years I had almost trebled my fortune. Since then everything that I have touched has turned out a success. In all things connected with money I have had a luck so extraordinary that sometimes it has made me almost afraid. I remember having read somewhere, in some strange book, that when the gods wish to punish us they answer our prayers.

Lord Goring : But tell me, Robert, did you never suffer any regret for what you had done ?

Sir Robert Chiltern : No. I felt that I had fought the century with its own weapons, and won.

Lord Goring (sadly) : You thought you had won.

Sir Robert Chiltern : I thought so. (*After a long pause*) : Arthur, do you despise me for what I have told you ?

Lord Goring (with deep feeling in his voice) : I am very sorry for you, Robert, very sorry indeed.

Sir Robert Chiltern : I don't say that I suffered any remorse. I didn't. Not remorse in the ordinary, rather silly sense of the word. But I have paid conscience money many times. I had a wild hope that I might

disarm destiny. The sum Baron Arnheim gave me I
have distributed twice over in public charities since
then.

Lord Goring (looking up): In public charities?
Dear me! what a lot of harm you must have done,
Robert!

Sir Robert Chiltern: Oh, don't say that, Arthur;
don't talk like that!

Lord Goring: Never mind what I say, Robert! I
am always saying what I shouldn't say. In fact, I
usually say what I really think. A great mistake
nowadays. It makes one so liable to be understood.
As regards this dreadful business, I will help you in
whatever way I can. Of course you know that.

Sir Robert Chiltern: Thank you, Arthur, thank you.
But what is to be done? What can be done?

*Lord Goring (leaning back with his hands in his
pockets):* Well, the English can't stand a man who is
always saying he is in the right, but they are very
fond of a man who admits that he has been in the
wrong. It is one of the best things in them. However,
in your case, Robert, a confession would not do. The
money, if you will allow me to say so, is . . . awkward.
Besides, if you did make a clean breast of the whole
affair, you would never be able to talk morality again.
And in England a man who can't talk morality twice
a week to a large, popular, immoral audience is quite
over as a serious politician. There would be nothing left
for him as a profession except Botany or the Church.
A confession would be of no use. It would ruin you.

Sir Robert Chiltern: It would ruin me. Arthur, the
only thing for me to do now is to fight the thing out.

Lord Goring (rising from his chair): I was waiting
for you to say that, Robert. It is the only thing to do
now. And you must begin by telling your wife the
whole story.

Sir Robert Chiltern: That I will not do.

Lord Goring: Robert, believe me, you are wrong.

Sir Robert Chiltern : I couldn't do it. It would kill her love for me. And now about this woman, this Mrs. Cheveley. How can I defend myself against her ? You knew her before, Arthur, apparently.

Lord Goring : Yes.

Sir Robert Chiltern : Did you know her well ?

Lord Goring (arranging his necktie) : So little that I got engaged to be married to her once, when I was staying at the Tenbys'. The affair lasted for three days . . . nearly.

Sir Robert Chiltern : Why was it broken off ?

Lord Goring (airily) : Oh, I forget. At least, it makes no matter. By the way, have you tried her with money ? She used to be confoundedly fond of money.

Sir Robert Chiltern : I offered her any sum she wanted. She refused.

Lord Goring : Then the marvellous gospel of gold breaks down sometimes. The rich can't do everything, after all.

Sir Robert Chiltern : Not everything. I suppose you are right. Arthur, I feel that public disgrace is in store for me. I feel certain of it. I never knew what terror was before. I know it now. It is as if a hand of ice were laid upon one's heart. It is as if one's heart were beating itself to death in some empty hollow.

Lord Goring (striking the table) : Robert, you must fight her. You must fight her.

Sir Robert Chiltern : But how ?

Lord Goring : I can't tell you how at present. I have not the smallest idea. But every one has some weak point. There is some flaw in each one of us. *(Strolls over to the fireplace and looks at himself in the glass.)* My father tells me that even I have faults. Perhaps I have. I don't know.

Sir Robert Chiltern : In defending myself against Mrs. Cheveley, I have a right to use any weapon I can find, have I not ?

Lord Goring (still looking in the glass): In your place I don't think I should have the smallest scruple in doing so. She is thoroughly well able to take care of herself.

Sir Robert Chiltern (sits down at the table and takes a pen in his hand): Well, I shall send a cipher telegram to the Embassy at Vienna, to inquire if there is anything known against her. There may be some secret scandal she might be afraid of.

Lord Goring (settling his buttonhole): Oh, I should fancy Mrs. Cheveley is one of those very modern women of our time who find a new scandal as becoming as a new bonnet, and air them both in the Park every afternoon at five-thirty. I am sure she adores scandals, and that the sorrow of her life at present is that she can't manage to have enough of them.

Sir Robert Chiltern (writing): Why do you say that?

Lord Goring (turning round): Well, she wore far too much rouge last night, and not quite enough clothes. That is always a sign of despair in a woman.

Sir Robert Chiltern (striking a bell): But it is worth while my wiring to Vienna, is it not?

Lord Goring: It is always worth while asking a question, though it is not always worth while answering one.

Enter MASON.

Sir Robert Chiltern: Is Mr. Trafford in his room?

Mason: Yes, Sir Robert.

Sir Robert Chiltern (puts what he has written into an envelope, which he then carefully closes): Tell him to have this sent off in cipher at once. There must not be a moment's delay.

Mason: Yes, Sir Robert.

Sir Robert Chiltern: Oh! just give that back to me again.

Writes something on the envelope. MASON *then goes out with the letter.*

Sir Robert Chiltern : She must have had some curious hoid over Baron Arnheim. I wonder what it was.

Lord Goring (smiling) : I wonder.

Sir Robert Chiltern : I will fight her to the death, as long as my wife knows nothing.

Lord Goring (strongly) : Oh, fight in any case—in any case.

Sir Robert Chiltern (with a gesture of despair) : If my wife found out, there would be little left to fight for. Well, as soon as I hear from Vienna, I shall let you know the result. It is a chance, just a chance, but I believe in it. And as I fought the age with its own weapons, I will fight her with her weapons. It is only fair, and she looks like a woman with a past, doesn't she ?

Lord Goring : Most pretty women do. But there is a fashion in pasts just as there is a fashion in frocks. Perhaps Mrs. Cheveley's past is merely a slightly *décolleté* one, and they are excessively popular nowadays. Besides, my dear Robert, I should not build too high hopes on frightening Mrs. Cheveley. I should not fancy Mrs. Cheveley is a woman who would be easily frightened. She has survived all her creditors, and she shows wonderful presence of mind.

Sir Robert Chiltern : Oh ! I live on hopes now. I clutch at every chance. I feel like a man on a ship that is sinking. The water is round my feet, and the very air is bitter with storm. Hush ! I hear my wife's voice.

Enter LADY CHILTERN *in walking dress.*

Lady Chiltern : Good-afternoon, Lord Goring.

Lord Goring : Good-afternoon, Lady Chiltern ! Have you been in the Park ?

Lady Chiltern : No ; I have just come from the Woman's Liberal Association, where, by the way, Robert, your name was received with loud applause, and now I have come in to have my tea. (*To* Lord Goring) : You will wait and have some tea, won't you ?

Lord Goring : I'll wait for a short time, thanks.

Lady Chiltern : I will be back in a moment. I am only going to take my hat off.

Lord Goring (in his most earnest manner) : Oh ! please don't. It is so pretty. One of the prettiest hats I ever saw. I hope the Woman's Liberal Association received it with loud applause.

Lady Chiltern (with a smile) : We have much more important work to do than look at each other's bonnets, Lord Goring.

Lord Goring : Really ? What sort of work ?

Lady Chiltern : Oh ! dull, useful, delightful things, Factory Acts, Female Inspectors, the Eight Hours' Bill, the Parliamentary Franchise. . . . Everything, in fact, that you would find thoroughly uninteresting.

Lord Goring : And never bonnets ?

Lady Chiltern (with mock indignation) : Never bonnets, never !

> Lady Chiltern *goes out through the door leading to her boudoir.*

Sir Robert Chiltern (takes Lord Goring's *hand) :* You have been a good friend to me, Arthur, a thoroughly good friend.

Lord Goring : I don't know that I have been able to do much for you, Robert, as yet. In fact, I have not been able to do anything for you, as far as I can see. I am thoroughly disappointed with myself.

Sir Robert Chiltern : You have enabled me to tell you the truth. That is something. The truth has always stifled me.

Lord Goring : Ah ! the truth is a thing I get rid of as soon as possible ! Bad habit, by the way. Makes one very unpopular at the club . . . with the older members. They call it being conceited. Perhaps it is.

Sir Robert Chiltern : I would to God that I had been able to tell the truth . . . to live the truth. Ah ! that is the great thing in life, to live the truth. (*Sighs, and goes towards the door.*) I'll see you soon again, Arthur, shan't I ?

Lord Goring : Certainly. Whenever you like. I'm going to look in at the Bachelors' Ball to-night, unless I find something better to do. But I'll come round to-morrow morning. If you should want me to-night by any chance, send round a note to Curzon Street.

Sir Robert Chiltern : Thank you.

       As he reaches the door, LADY CHILTERN *enters from her boudoir.*

Lady Chiltern : You are not going, Robert ?

Sir Robert Chiltern : I have some letters to write, dear.

Lady Chiltern (going to him) : You work too hard, Robert. You seem never to think of yourself, and you are looking so tired.

Sir Robert Chiltern : It is nothing, dear, nothing. (*He kisses her and goes out.*)

Lady Chiltern (to LORD GORING*) :* Do sit down. I am so glad you have called. I want to talk to you about . . . well, not about bonnets, or the Woman's Liberal Association. You take far too much interest in the first subject, and not nearly enough in the second.

Lord Goring : You want to talk to me about Mrs. Cheveley ?

Lady Chiltern : Yes. You have guessed it. After you left last night I found out that what she had said was really true. Of course I made Robert write her a letter at once, withdrawing his promise.

Lord Goring : So he gave me to understand.

Lady Chiltern : To have kept it would have been the first stain on a career that has been stainless always. Robert must be above reproach. He is not like other men. He cannot afford to do what other men do. (*She looks at* LORD GORING, *who remains silent.*) Don't you agree with me ? You are Robert's greatest friend. You are our greatest friend, Lord Goring. No one, except myself, knows Robert better than you do. He has no secrets from me, and I don't think he has any from you.

Lord Goring : He certainly has no secrets from me. At least I don't think so.

Lady Chiltern : Then am I not right in my estimate of him ? I know I am right. But speak to me frankly.

Lord Goring (looking straight at her) : Quite frankly ?

Lady Chiltern : Surely. You have nothing to conceal, have you ?

Lord Goring : Nothing. But, my dear Lady Chiltern, I think, if you will allow me to say so, that in practical life——

Lady Chiltern (smiling) : Of which you know so little, Lord Goring——

Lord Goring : Of which I know nothing by experience, though I know something by observation. I think that in practical life there is something about success, actual success, that is a little unscrupulous, something about ambition that is unscrupulous always. Once a man has set his heart and soul on getting to a certain point, if he has to climb the crag, he climbs the crag ; if he has to walk in the mire——

Lady Chiltern : Well ?

Lord Goring : He walks in the mire. Of course I am only talking generally about life.

Lady Chiltern (gravely) : I hope so. Why do you look at me so strangely, Lord Goring ?

Lord Goring : Lady Chiltern, I have sometimes thought that . . . perhaps you are a little hard in some of your views on life. I think that . . . often you don't make sufficient allowances. In every nature there are elements of weakness, or worse than weakness.

Supposing, for instance, that—that any public man, my father, or Lord Merton, or Robert, say, had, years ago, written some foolish letter to some one. . . .

Lady Chiltern : What do you mean by a foolish letter ?

Lord Goring : A letter gravely compromising one's position. I am only putting an imaginary case.

Lady Chiltern : Robert is as incapable of doing a foolish thing as he is of doing a wrong thing.

Lord Goring (after a long pause) : Nobody is incapable of doing a foolish thing. Nobody is incapable of doing a wrong thing.

Lady Chiltern : Are you a Pessimist ? What will the other dandies say ? They will all have to go into mourning.

Lord Goring (rising) : No, Lady Chiltern, I am not a Pessimist. Indeed I am not sure that I quite know what pessimism really means. All I do know is that life cannot be understood without much charity, cannot be lived without much charity. It is love, and not German philosophy, that is the true explanation of this world, whatever may be the explanation of the next. And if you are ever in trouble, Lady Chiltern, trust me absolutely, and I will help you in every way I can. If you ever want me, come to me for my assistance, and you shall have it. Come at once to me.

Lady Chiltern (looking at him in surprise) : Lord Goring, you are talking quite seriously. I don't think I ever heard you talk seriously before.

Lord Goring (laughing) : You must excuse me, Lady Chiltern. It won't occur again, if I can help it.

Lady Chiltern : But I like you to be serious.

Enter MABEL CHILTERN, *in the most ravishing frock.*

Mabel Chiltern : Dear Gertrude, don't say such a dreadful thing to Lord Goring. Seriousness would be very unbecoming to him. Good-afternoon, Lord Goring! Pray be as trivial as you can.

Lord Goring : I should like to, Miss Mabel, but I am afraid I am . . . a little out of practice this morning ; and besides, I have to be going now.

Mabel Chiltern : Just when I have come in! What dreadful manners you have! I am sure you were very badly brought up.

Lord Goring : I was.

Mabel Chiltern : I wish I had brought you up!

Lord Goring : I am so sorry you didn't.

Mabel Chiltern : It is too late now, I suppose?

Lord Goring (smiling) : I am not so sure.

Mabel Chiltern : Will you ride to-morrow morning?

Lord Goring : Yes, at ten.

Mabel Chiltern : Don't forget.

Lord Goring : Of course I shan't. By the way, Lady Chiltern, there is no list of your guests in *The Morning Post* of to-day. It has apparently been crowded out by the County Council, or the Lambeth Conference, or something equally boring. Could you let me have a list? I have a particular reason for asking you.

Lady Chiltern : I am sure Mr. Trafford will be able to give you one.

Lord Goring : Thanks, so much.

Mabel Chiltern : Tommy is the most useful person in London.

Lord Goring (turning to her) : And who is the most ornamental?

Mabel Chiltern (triumphantly) : I am.

Lord Goring : How clever of you to guess it! *(Takes up his hat and cane.)* Good-bye, Lady Chiltern! You will remember what I said to you, won't you?

Lady Chiltern : Yes ; but I don't know why you said it to me.

Lord Goring : I hardly know myself. Good-bye, Miss Mabel!

Mabel Chiltern (with a little moue of disappointment) :

I wish you were not going. I have had four wonderful adventures this morning ; four and a half, in fact. You might stop and listen to some of them.

Lord Goring : How very selfish of you to have four and a half ! There won't be any left for me.

Mabel Chiltern : I don't want you to have any. They would not be good for you.

Lord Goring : That is the first unkind thing you have ever said to me. How charmingly you said it ! Ten to-morrow.

Mabel Chiltern : Sharp.

Lord Goring : Quite sharp. But don't bring Mr. Trafford.

Mabel Chiltern (with a little toss of the head) : Of course I shan't bring Tommy Trafford. Tommy Trafford is in great disgrace.

Lord Goring : I am delighted to hear it. (*Bows and goes out.*)

Mabel Chiltern : Gertrude, I wish you would speak to Tommy Trafford.

Lady Chiltern : What has poor Mr. Trafford done this time ? Robert says he is the best secretary he has ever had.

Mabel Chiltern : Well, Tommy has proposed to me again. Tommy really does nothing but propose to me. He proposed to me last night in the music-room, when I was quite unprotected, as there was an elaborate trio going on. I didn't dare to make the smallest repartee, I need hardly tell you. If I had, it would have stopped the music at once. Musical people are so absurdly unreasonable. They always want one to be perfectly dumb at the very moment when one is longing to be absolutely deaf. Then he proposed to me in broad daylight this morning, in front of that dreadful statue of Achilles. Really, the things that go on in front of that work of art are quite appalling. The police should interfere. At luncheon I saw by the glare in his eye that he was going to propose again, and I just managed to check him in time by assuring him that I was a bimetallist. Fortunately I don't know what bimetallism means. And I don't believe anybody else does either. But the observation crushed Tommy for ten minutes. He looked quite shocked. And then Tommy is so annoying in the way he proposes. If he proposed at the top of his voice, I should not mind so much. That might produce some effect on the public. But he does it in a horrid confidential way. When Tommy wants to be romantic he talks to one just like a doctor. I am very fond of Tommy, but his methods of proposing are quite out of date. I wish, Gertrude, you would speak to him, and tell him that once a week is quite often enough to propose to any one, and that it should always be done in a manner that attracts some attention.

Lady Chiltern: Dear Mabel, don't talk like that. Besides, Robert thinks very highly of Mr. Trafford. He believes he has a brilliant future before him.

Mabel Chiltern: Oh! I wouldn't marry a man with a future before him for anything under the sun.

Lady Chiltern: Mabel!

Mabel Chiltern: I know, dear. You married a man with a future, didn't you? But then Robert was a genius, and you have a noble, self-sacrificing character. You can stand geniuses. I have no character at all, and Robert is the only genius I could ever bear. As a rule, I think they are quite impossible. Geniuses talk so much, don't they? Such a bad habit! And they are always thinking about themselves, when I want them to be thinking about me. I must go round now and rehearse at Lady Basildon's. You remember, we are having tableaux, don't you? The Triumph of something, I don't know what! I hope it will be triumph of me. Only triumph I am really interested in at present. (*Kisses* LADY CHILTERN *and goes out; then comes running back.*) Oh, Gertrude, do you know who is coming to see you ? That dreadful Mrs. Cheveley, in a most lovely gown. Did you ask her ?

Lady Chiltern (rising) : Mrs. Cheveley ! Coming to see me ? Impossible !

Mabel Chiltern : I assure you she is coming upstairs, as large as life and not nearly so natural.

Lady Chiltern : You need not wait, Mabel. Remember, Lady Basildon is expecting you.

Mabel Chiltern : Oh ! I must shake hands with Lady Markby. She is delightful. I love being scolded by her.

Enter MASON.

Mason : Lady Markby. Mrs. Cheveley.

Enter LADY MARKBY *and* MRS. CHEVELEY.

Lady Chiltern (advancing to meet them) : Dear Lady Markby, how nice of you to come and see me ! (*Shakes hands with her, and bows somewhat distantly to* MRS. CHEVELEY.) Won't you sit down, Mrs. Cheveley ?

Mrs. Cheveley : Thanks. Isn't that Miss Chiltern ? I should like so much to know her.

Lady Chiltern : Mabel, Mrs. Cheveley wishes to know you. (MABEL CHILTERN *gives a little nod.*)

Mrs. Cheveley (sitting down) : I thought your frock so charming last night, Miss Chiltern. So simple and . . . suitable.

Mabel Chiltern : Really ? I must tell my dressmaker. It will be such a surprise to her. Good-bye, Lady Markby !

Lady Markby : Going already ?

Mabel Chiltern : I am so sorry but I am obliged to. I am just off to rehearsal. I have got to stand on my head in some tableaux.

Lady Markby : On your head, child ? Oh ! I hope not. I believe it is most unhealthy. (*Takes a seat on the sofa next* LADY CHILTERN.)

Mabel Chiltern : But it is for an excellent charity ; in aid of the Undeserving, the only people I am really

interested in. I am the secretary, and Tommy Trafford
is treasurer.

Mrs. Cheveley : And what is Lord Goring ?

Mabel Chiltern : Oh ! Lord Goring is president.

Mrs. Cheveley : The post should suit him admirably,
unless he has deteriorated since I knew him first.

Lady Markby (reflecting) : You are remarkably
modern, Mabel. A little too modern, perhaps. Nothing
is so dangerous as being too modern. One is apt to
grow old-fashioned quite suddenly. I have known
many instances of it.

Mabel Chiltern : What a dreadful prospect !

Lady Markby : Ah ! my dear, you need not be
nervous. You will always be as pretty as possible.
That is the best fashion there is, and the only fashion
that England succeeds in setting.

Mabel Chiltern (with a curtsey) : Thank you so much,
Lady Markby, for England . . . and myself. (*Goes
out.*)

Lady Markby (turning to LADY CHILTERN) *:* Dear
Gertrude, we just called to know if Mrs. Cheveley's
diamond brooch has been found.

Lady Chiltern : Here ?

Mrs. Cheveley : Yes. I missed it when I got back to
Claridge's, and I thought I might possibly have dropped
it here.

Lady Chiltern : I have heard nothing about it. But
I will send for the butler and ask. (*Touches the bell.*)

Mrs. Cheveley : Oh, pray don't trouble, Lady
Chiltern. I dare say I lost it at the Opera, before we
came on here.

Lady Markby : Ah yes, I suppose it must have been
at the Opera. The fact is, we all scramble and jostle
so much nowadays that I wonder we have anything
at all left on us at the end of an evening. I know
myself that, when I am coming back from the Drawing
Room, I always feel as if I hadn't a shred on me,
except a small shred of decent reputation, just enough

to prevent the lower classes making painful observations through the windows of the carriage. The fact is that our Society is terribly over-populated. Really, some one should arrange a proper scheme of assisted emigration. It would do a great deal of good.

Mrs. Cheveley : I quite agree with you, Lady Markby. It is nearly six years since I have been in London for the Season, and I must say Society has become dreadfully mixed. One sees the oddest people everywhere.

Lady Markby : That is quite true, dear. But one needn't know them. I'm sure I don't know half the people who come to my house. Indeed, from all I hear, I shouldn't like to.

Enter MASON.

Lady Chiltern : What sort of a brooch was it that you lost, Mrs. Cheveley ?

Mrs. Cheveley : A diamond snake-brooch with a ruby, a rather large ruby.

Lady Markby : I thought you said there was a sapphire on the head, dear ?

Mrs. Cheveley (smiling) : No, Lady Markby—a ruby.

Lady Markby (nodding her head) : And very becoming, I am quite sure.

Lady Chiltern : Has a ruby and diamond brooch been found in any of the rooms this morning, Mason ?

Mason : No, my lady.

Mrs. Cheveley : It really is of no consequence, Lady Chiltern. I am so sorry to have put you to any inconvenience.

Lady Chiltern (coldly) : Oh, it has been no inconvenience. That will do, Mason. You can bring tea. (*Exit* MASON.)

Lady Markby : Well, I must say it is most annoying to lose anything. I remember once at Bath, years ago, losing in the Pump Room an exceedingly handsome cameo bracelet that Sir John had given me. I don't think he has ever given me anything since, I am sorry to say. He has sadly degenerated. Really, this horrid House of Commons quite ruins our husbands for us. I think the Lower House by far the greatest blow to a happy married life that there has been since that terrible thing called the Higher Education of Women was invented.

Lady Chiltern : Ah ! it is heresy to say that in this house, Lady Markby. Robert is a great champion of the Higher Education of Woman, and so, I am afraid, am I.

Mrs. Cheveley : The higher education of men is what I should like to see. Men need it so sadly.

Lady Markby : They do, dear. But I am afraid such a scheme would be quite unpractical. I don't think man has much capacity for development. He has got as far as he can, and that is not far, is it ? With regard to women, well, dear Gertrude, you belong to the younger generation, and I am sure it is all right if you approve of it. In my time, of course, we were taught not to understand anything. That was the old system, and wonderfully interesting it was. I assure you that the amount of things I and my poor dear sister were taught not to understand was quite extra-ordinary. But modern women understand everything, I am told.

Mrs. Cheveley : Except their husbands. That is the one thing the modern woman never understands.

Lady Markby : And a very good thing too, dear, I dare say. It might break up many a happy home if they did. Not yours, I need hardly say, Gertrude. You have married a pattern husband. I wish I could say as much for myself. But since Sir John has taken to attending the debates regularly, which he never used to do in the good old days, his language has become quite impossible. He always seems to think that he is addressing the House, and consequently whenever he discusses the state of the agricultural labourer, or the Welsh Church, or something quite improper of that kind, I am obliged to send all the servants out of the room. It is not pleasant to see one's own butler, who has been with one for twenty-three years, actually blushing at the sideboard, and the footmen making contortions in corners like persons in circuses. I assure you my life will be quite ruined unless they send John at once to the Upper House. He won't take any interest in politics then, will he ? The House of Lords is so sensible. An assembly of gentlemen. But in his present state, Sir John is really a great trial. Why, this morning before breakfast was half over, he stood up on the hearth-rug, put his hands in his pockets, and appealed to the country at the top of his voice. I left the table as soon as I had my second cup of tea, I need hardly say. But his violent language could be heard all over the house ! I trust, Gertrude, that Sir Robert is not like that ?

Lady Chiltern : But I am very much interested in politics, Lady Markby. I love to hear Robert talk about them.

Lady Markby : Well, I hope he is not as devoted to Blue Books as Sir John is. I don't think they can be quite improving reading for any one.

Mrs. Cheveley (languidly) : I have never read a Blue Book. I prefer books . . . in yellow covers.

Lady Markby (genially unconscious) : Yellow is a gayer colour, is it not ? I used to wear yellow a good deal in my early days, and would do so now if Sir John was not so painfully personal in his observations, and a man on the question of dress is always ridiculous, is he not ?

Mrs. Cheveley : Oh, no ! I think men are the only authorities on dress.

Lady Markby : Really ? One wouldn't say so from the sort of hats they wear ? would one ?

The butler enters, followed by the footman. Tea is set on a small table close to LADY CHILTERN.

Lady Chiltern: May I give you some tea, Mrs. Cheveley.

Mrs. Cheveley: Thanks. (*The butler hands* MRS. CHEVELEY *a cup of tea on a salver.*)

Lady Chiltern: Some tea, Lady Markby?

Lady Markby: No thanks, dear. (*The servants go out.*) The fact is, I have promised to go round for ten minutes to see poor Lady Brancaster, who is in very great trouble. Her daughter, quite a well-brought-up girl, too, has actually become engaged to be married to a curate in Shropshire. It is very sad, very sad indeed. I can't understand this modern mania for curates. In my time we girls saw them, of course, running about the place like rabbits. But we never took any notice of them, I need hardly say. But I am told that nowadays country society is quite honeycombed with them. I think it most irreligious. And then the eldest son has quarrelled with his father, and it is said that when they meet at the club Lord Brancaster always hides himself behind the money article in *The Times.* However, I believe that is quite a common occurrence nowadays and that they have to take in extra copies of *The Times* at all the clubs in St. James's Street; there are so many sons who won't have anything to do with their fathers, and so many fathers who won't speak to their sons. I think myself, it is very much to be regretted.

Mrs. Cheveley: So do I. Fathers have so much to learn from their sons nowadays.

Lady Markby: Really, dear? What?

Mrs. Cheveley: The art of living. The only really Fine Art we have produced in modern times.

Lady Markby (shaking her head): Ah! I am afraid Lord Brancaster knew a good deal about that. More than his poor wife ever did. (*Turning to* LADY CHILTERN): You know Lady Brancaster, don't you, dear?

Lady Chiltern: Just slightly. She was staying at Langton last autumn, when we were there.

Lady Markby : Well, like all stout women, she looks the very picture of happiness, as no doubt you noticed. But there are many tragedies in her family, besides this affair of the curate. Her own sister, Mrs. Jekyll, had a most unhappy life ; through no fault of her own, I am sorry to say. She ultimately was so broken-hearted that she went into a convent, or on to the operatic stage, I forget which. No ; I think it was decorative art-needlework she took up. I know she had lost all sense of pleasure in life. (*Rising*) : And now, Gertrude, if you will allow me, I shall leave Mrs. Cheveley in your charge and call back for her in a quarter of an hour. Or perhaps, dear Mrs. Cheveley, you wouldn't mind waiting in the carriage while I am with Lady Brancaster. As I intend it to be a visit of condolence, I shan't stay long.

Mrs. Cheveley (*rising*) : I don't mind waiting in the carriage at all, provided there is somebody to look at one.

Lady Markby : Well, I hear the curate is always prowling about the house.

Mrs. Cheveley : I am afraid I am not fond of girl friends.

Lady Chiltern (*rising*) : Oh, I hope Mrs. Cheveley will stay here a little. I should like to have a few minutes' conversation with her.

Mrs. Cheveley : How very kind of you, Lady Chiltern ! Believe me, nothing would give me greater pleasure.

Lady Markby : Ah ! no doubt you both have many pleasant reminiscences of your schooldays to talk over together. Good-bye, dear Gertrude ! Shall I see you at Lady Bonar's to-night ? She has discovered a wonderful new genius. He does . . . nothing at all, I believe. That is a great comfort, is it not ?

Lady Chiltern : Robert and I are dining at home by ourselves to-night, and I don't think I shall go anywhere afterwards. Robert, of course, will have to be in the House. But there is nothing interesting on.

Lady Markby : Dining at home by yourselves ? Is that quite prudent ? Ah, I forgot, your husband is an exception. Mine is the general rule, and nothing ages a woman so rapidly as having married the general rule.

Exit LADY MARKBY.

Mrs. Cheveley : Wonderful woman, Lady Markby, isn't she ? Talks more and says less than anybody I ever met. She is made to be a public speaker. Much more so than her husband, though he is a typical Englishman, always dull and usually violent.

Lady Chiltern (makes no answer, but remains standing. There is a pause. Then the eyes of the two women meet. LADY CHILTERN *looks stern and pale.* MRS. CHEVELEY *seems rather amused) :* Mrs. Cheveley, I think it is right to tell you quite frankly that, had I known who you really were, I should not have invited you to my house last night.

Mrs. Cheveley (with an impertinent smile) : Really ?

Lady Chiltern : I could not have done so.

Mrs. Cheveley : I see that after all these years you have not changed a bit, Gertrude.

Lady Chiltern : I never change.

Mrs. Cheveley (elevating her eyebrows) : Then life has taught you nothing ?

Lady Chiltern : It has taught me that a person who has once been guilty of a dishonest and dishonourable action may be guilty of it a second time, and should be shunned.

Mrs. Cheveley : Would you apply that rule to every one ?

Lady Chiltern : Yes, to every one, without exception.

Mrs. Cheveley : Then I am sorry for you, Gertrude, very sorry for you.

Lady Chiltern : You see now, I am sure, that for many reasons any further acquaintance between us during your stay in London is quite impossible ?

Mrs. Cheveley (leaning back in her chair) : Do you know, Gertrude, I don't mind your talking morality a bit. Morality is simply the attitude we adopt towards people whom we personally dislike. You dislike me. I am quite aware of that. And I have always detested you. And yet I have come here to do you a service.

Lady Chiltern (contemptuously) : Like the service you wished to render my husband last night, I suppose. Thank heaven, I saved him from that.

Mrs. Cheveley (starting to her feet) : It was you who made him write that insolent letter to me ? It was you who made him break his promise ?

Lady Chiltern : Yes.

Mrs. Cheveley : Then you must make him keep it. I give you till to-morrow morning—no more. If by that time your husband does not solemnly bind himself to help me in this great scheme in which I am interested——

Lady Chiltern : This fraudulent speculation——

Mrs. Cheveley : Call it what you choose. I hold your husband in the hollow of my hand, and if you are wise you will make him do what I tell him.

Lady Chiltern (rising and going towards her) : You are impertinent. What has my husband to do with you ? With a woman like you ?

Mrs. Cheveley (with a bitter laugh) : In this world like meets with like. It is because your husband is himself fraudulent and dishonest that we pair so well together. Between you and him there are chasms. He and I are closer than friends. We are enemies linked together. The same sin binds us.

Lady Chiltern : How dare you class my husband with yourself ? How dare you threaten him or me ? Leave my house. You are unfit to enter it.

SIR ROBERT CHILTERN *enters from behind. He hears his wife's last words, and sees to whom they are addressed. He grows deadly pale.*

Mrs. Cheveley : Your house ! A house bought with the price of dishonour. A house, everything in which has been paid for by fraud. (*Turns round and sees* SIR ROBERT CHILTERN.) Ask him what the origin of his fortune is ! Get him to tell you how he sold to a stockbroker a Cabinet secret. Learn from him to what you owe your position.

Lady Chiltern : It is not true ! Robert ! It is not true !

Mrs. Cheveley (*pointing at him with outstretched finger*) : Look at him ! Can he deny it ? Does he dare to ?

Sir Robert Chiltern : Go ! Go at once. You have done your worst now.

Mrs. Cheveley : My worst ? I have not yet finished with you, with either of you. I give you both till to-morrow at noon. If by then you don't do what I bid you to do, the whole world shall know the origin of Robert Chiltern.

SIR ROBERT CHILTERN *strikes the bell. Enter* MASON.

Sir Robert Chiltern : Show Mrs. Cheveley out.

MRS. CHEVELEY *starts ; then bows with somewhat exaggerated politeness to* LADY CHILTERN, *who makes no sign of response. As she passes by* SIR ROBERT CHILTERN, *who is standing close to the door, she pauses for a moment and looks him straight in the face. She then goes out, followed by the servant, who closes the door after him. The husband and wife are left alone.* LADY CHILTERN *stands like some one in a dreadful dream. Then she turns round and looks at her husband. She looks at him with strange eyes, as though she was seeing him for the first time.*

Lady Chiltern : You sold a Cabinet secret for money ! You began your life with fraud ! You built up your career on dishonour ! Oh, tell me it is not true ! Lie to me ! Lie to me ! Tell me it is not true.

Sir Robert Chiltern : What this woman said is quite true. But, Gertrude, listen to me. You don't realise how I was tempted. Let me tell you the whole thing. (*Goes towards her.*)

Lady Chiltern : Don't come near me. Don't touch me. I feel as if you had soiled me for ever. Oh ! what a mask you have been wearing all these years ! A horrible painted mask ! You sold yourself for money. Oh ! a common thief were better. You put yourself up to sale to the highest bidder ! You were bought in the market. You lied to the whole world. And yet you will not lie to me.

Sir Robert Chiltern (*rushing towards her*) *:* Gertrude ! Gertrude !

Lady Chiltern (*thrusting him back with outstretched hands*) *:* No, don't speak ! Say nothing ! Your voice wakes terrible memories—memories of things that made me love you—memories of words that made me love you—memories that now are horrible to me And how I worshipped you ! You were to me something apart from common life, a thing pure, noble, honest, without stain. The world seemed to me finer because you were in it, and goodness more real because you lived. And now—oh, when I think that I made of a man like you my ideal ! the ideal of my life !

Sir Robert Chiltern : There was your mistake. There was your error. The error all women commit. Why can't you women love us, faults and all ? Why do you place us on monstrous pedestals ? We have all feet of clay, women as well as men ; but when we men love women, we love them knowing their weaknesses, their follies, their imperfections, love them all the more, it may be, for that reason. It is not the perfect, but the imperfect, who have need of love. It is when we are wounded by our own hands, or by the hands of others, that love should come to cure us—else what use is love at all ? All sins, except a sin against itself, Love should forgive. All lives, save loveless lives, true Love should pardon. A man's love is like that. It is wider, larger, more human than a woman's. Women think that they are making ideals of men. What they are making of us are false idols merely. You made your false idol of me, and I had not the courage to come down, show you my wounds, tell you my weaknesses. I was afraid that I might lose your love, as I have lost it now. And so, last night you ruined my life for me— yes, ruined it! What this woman asked of me was nothing compared to what she offered to me. She offered security, peace, stability. The sin of my youth, that I had thought was buried, rose up in front of me, hideous, horrible, with its hands at my throat. I could have killed it for ever, sent it back into its tomb, destroyed its record, burned the one witness against me. You prevented me. No one but you, you know it. And now what is there before me but public disgrace, ruin, terrible shame, the mockery of the world, a lonely dishonoured life, a lonely dishonoured death, it may be, some day? Let women make no more ideals of men! let them not put them on altars and bow before them or they may ruin other lives as completely as you— you whom I have so wildly loved—have ruined mine!

He passes from the room. LADY CHILTERN *rushes towards him, but the door is closed when she reaches it. Pale with anguish, bewildered, helpless, she sways like a plant in the water. Her hands, outstretched, seem to tremble in the air like blossoms in the wind. Then she flings herself down beside a sofa and buries her face. Her sobs are like the sobs of a child.*

ACT DROP.

THIRD ACT

SCENE

The Library in Lord Goring's house. An Adam room. On the right is the door leading into the hall. On the left, the door of the smoking-room. A pair of folding doors at the back open into the drawing-room. The fire is lit. Phipps, the butler, is arranging some newspapers on the writing-table. The distinction of Phipps is his impassivity. He has been termed by enthusiasts the Ideal Butler. The Sphinx is not so incommunicable. He is a mask with a manner. Of his intellectual or emotional life, history knows nothing. He represents the dominance of form.

Enter LORD GORING *in evening dress with a buttonhole. He is wearing a silk hat and Inverness cape. White-gloved, he carries a Louis Seize cane. His are all the delicate fopperies of Fashion. One sees that he stands in immediate relation to modern life, makes it indeed, and so masters it. He is the first well-dressed philosopher in the history of thought.*

Lord Goring : Got my second buttonhole for me, Phipps ?

Phipps : Yes, my lord. (*Takes his hat, cane, and cape, and presents new buttonhole on salver.*)

Lord Goring : Rather distinguished thing, Phipps. I am the only person of the smallest importance in London at present who wears a buttonhole.

Phipps : Yes, my lord. I have observed that.

Lord Goring (*taking out old buttonhole*) : You see, Phipps, Fashion is what one wears oneself. What is unfashionable is what other people wear.

Phipps : Yes, my lord.

Lord Goring : Just as vulgarity is simply the conduct of other people.

Phipps : Yes, my lord.

Lord Goring (putting in new buttonhole) : And false-hoods the truths of other people.

Phipps : Yes, my lord.

Lord Goring : Other people are quite dreadful. The only possible society is oneself.

Phipps : Yes, my lord.

Lord Goring : To love oneself is the beginning of a lifelong romance, Phipps.

Phipps : Yes, my lord.

Lord Goring (looking at himself in the glass) : Don't think I quite like this buttonhole, Phipps. Makes me look a little too old. Makes me almost in the prime of life, eh, Phipps ?

Phipps : I don't observe any alteration in your lordship's appearance.

Lord Goring : You don't, Phipps ?

Phipps : No, my lord.

Lord Goring : I am not quite sure. For the future a more trivial buttonhole, Phipps, on Thursday evenings.

Phipps : I will speak to the florist, my lord. She has had a loss in her family lately, which perhaps accounts for the lack of triviality your lordship complains of in the buttonhole.

Lord Goring : Extraordinary thing about the lower classes in England—they are always losing their relations.

Phipps : Yes, my lord ! They are extremely fortunate in that respect.

Lord Goring (turns round and looks at him. PHIPPS *remains impassive)* : Hum ! Any letters, Phipps ?

Phipps : Three, my lord. (*Hands letters on a salver.*)

Lord Goring (takes letters) : Want my cab round in twenty minutes.

Phipps : Yes, my lord. (*Goes towards door.*)

Lord Goring (*holds up letter in pink envelope*) : Ahem Phipps, when did this letter arrive ?

Phipps : It was brought by hand just after your lordship went to the club.

Lord Goring : That will do. (*Exit* PHIPPS.) Lady Chiltern's handwriting on Lady Chiltern's pink note-paper. That is rather curious. I thought Robert was to write. Wonder what Lady Chiltern has got to say to me ? (*Sits at bureau and opens letter, and reads it.*) ' I want you. I trust you. I am coming to you. Gertrude.' (*Puts down the letter with a puzzled look. Then takes it up, and reads it again slowly.*) ' I want you. I trust you. I am coming to you.' So she has found out everything ! Poor woman ! Poor woman ! (*Pulls out watch and looks at it.*) But what an hour to call ! Ten o'clock ! I shall have to give up going to the Berkshires. However, it is always nice to be expected, and not to arrive. I am not expected at the Bachelors', so I shall certainly go there. Well, I will make her stand by her husband. That is the only thing for any woman to do. It is the growth of the moral sense in women that makes marriage such a hopeless, one-sided institution. Ten o'clock. She should be here soon. I must tell Phipps I am not in to any one else. (*Goes towards bell.*)

Enter PHIPPS.

Phipps : Lord Caversham.

Lord Goring : Oh, why will parents always appear at the wrong time ? Some extraordinary mistake in nature, I suppose. (*Enter* LORD CAVERSHAM.) Delighted to see you, my dear father. (*Goes to meet him.*)

Lord Caversham : Take my cloak off.

Lord Goring : Is it worth while, father ?

Lord Caversham : Of course it is worth while, sir. Which is the most comfortable chair ?

Lord Goring : This one, father. It is the chair I use myself, when I have visitors.

Lord Caversham : Thank ye. No draught, I hope, in this room ?

Lord Goring : No, father.

Lord Caversham (sitting down) : Glad to hear it. Can't stand draughts. No draughts at home.

Lord Goring : Good many breezes, father.

Lord Caversham : Eh ? Eh ? Don't understand what you mean. Want to have a serious conversation with you, sir.

Lord Goring : My dear father ! At this hour ?

Lord Caversham : Well, sir, it is only ten o'clock. What is your objection to the hour ? I think the hour is an admirable hour !

Lord Goring : Well, the fact is, father, this is not my day for talking seriously. I am very sorry, but it is not my day.

Lord Caversham : What do you mean, sir ?

Lord Goring : During the Season, father, I only talk seriously on the first Tuesday in every month, from four to seven.

Lord Caversham : Well, make it Tuesday, sir, make it Tuesday.

Lord Goring : But it is after seven, father, and my doctor says I must not have any serious conversation after seven. It makes me talk in my sleep.

Lord Caversham : Talk in your sleep, sir ? What does that matter ? You are not married.

Lord Goring : No, father, I am not married.

Lord Caversham : Hum ! That is what I have come to talk to you about, sir. You have got to get married, and at once. Why, when I was your age, sir, I had been an inconsolable widower for three months, and was already paying my addresses to your admirable mother. Damme, sir, it is your duty to get married. You can't be always living for pleasure. Every man of position is married nowadays. Bachelors are not fashionable any more. They are a damaged lot. Too much is known about them. You must get a wife, sir.

Look where your friend Robert Chiltern has got to by probity, hard work, and a sensible marriage with a good woman. Why don't you imitate him, sir? Why don't you take him for your model?

Lord Goring : I think I shall, father.

Lord Caversham : I wish you would, sir. Then I should be happy. At present I make your mother's life miserable on your account. You are heartless, sir, quite heartless.

Lord Goring : I hope not, father.

Lord Caversham : And it is high time for you to get married. You are thirty-four years of age, sir.

Lord Goring : Yes, father, but I only admit to thirty-two—thirty-one and a half when I have a really good buttonhole. This buttonhole is not . . . trivial enough.

Lord Caversham : I tell you you are thirty-four, sir. And there is a draught in your room, besides, which makes your conduct worse. Why did you tell me there was no draught, sir? I feel a draught, sir, I feel it distinctly.

Lord Goring : So do I, father. It is a dreadful draught. I will come and see you to-morrow, father. We can talk over anything you like. Let me help you on with your cloak, father.

Lord Caversham : No, sir; I have called this evening for a definite purpose, and I am going to see it through at all costs to my health or yours. Put down my cloak, sir.

Lord Goring : Certainly, father. But let us go into another room. (*Rings bell.*) There is a dreadful draught here. (*Enter* PHIPPS.) Phipps, is there a good fire in the smoking-room?

Phipps : Yes, my lord.

Lord Goring : Come in there, father. Your sneezes are quite heartrending.

Lord Caversham : Well, sir, I suppose I have a right to sneeze when I choose?

Lord Goring (apologetically) : Quite so, father. I was merely expressing sympathy.

Lord Caversham : Oh, damn sympathy. There is a great deal too much of that sort of thing going on nowadays.

Lord Goring : I quite agree with you, father. If there was less sympathy in the world there would be less trouble in the world.

Lord Caversham (going towards the smoking-room) : That is a paradox, sir. I hate paradoxes.

Lord Goring : So do I, father. Everybody one meets is a paradox nowadays. It is a great bore. It makes society so obvious.

Lord Caversham (turning round, and looking at his son beneath his bushy eyebrows) : Do you always really understand what you say, sir ?

Lord Goring (after some hesitation) : Yes, father, if I listen attentively.

Lord Caversham (indignantly) : If you listen attentively ! . . . Conceited young puppy !

Goes off grumbling into the smoking-room. PHIPPS *enters.*

Lord Goring : Phipps, there is a lady coming to see me this evening on particular business. Show her into the drawing-room when she arrives. You understand ?

Phipps : Yes, my lord.

Lord Goring : It is a matter of the gravest importance, Phipps.

Phipps : I understand, my lord.

Lord Goring : No one else is to be admitted, under any circumstances.

Phipps : I understand, my lord. *(Bell rings.)*

Lord Goring : Ah ! that is probably the lady. I shall see her myself.

Just as he is going towards the door LORD
CAVERSHAM *enters from the smoking-room.*

Lord Caversham : Well, sir ? am I to wait attendance
on you ?
Lord Goring (considerably perplexed) : In a moment,
father. Do excuse me. (LORD CAVERSHAM *goes back.*)
Well, remember my instructions, Phipps—into that
room.
Phipps : Yes, my lord.

LORD GORING *goes into the smoking-room.*
HAROLD, *the footman, shows* MRS. CHEVELEY *in.*
*Lamia-like, she is in green and silver. She has a
cloak of black satin, lined with dead rose-leaf silk.*

Harold : What name, madam ?
Mrs. Cheveley (to PHIPPS, *who advances towards her) :*
Is Lord Goring not here ? I was told he was at home ?
Phipps : His lordship is engaged at present with
Lord Caversham, madam.

Turns a cold, glassy eye on HAROLD, *who at once
retires.*

Mrs. Cheveley (to herself) : How very filial !
Phipps : His lordship told me to ask you, madam,
to be kind enough to wait in the drawing-room for him.
His lordship will come to you there.
Mrs. Cheveley (with a look of surprise) : Lord Goring
expects me ?
Phipps : Yes, madam.
Mrs. Cheveley : Are you quite sure ?
Phipps : His lordship told me that if a lady called
I was to ask her to wait in the drawing-room. (*Goes to
the door of the drawing-room and opens it.*) His lordship's
directions on the subject were very precise.
Mrs. Cheveley (to herself) : How thoughtful of him !
To expect the unexpected shows a thoroughly modern
intellect. (*Goes towards the drawing-room and looks in.*)

Ugh! How dreary a bachelor's drawing-room always looks. I shall have to alter all this. (PHIPPS *brings the lamp from the writing-table*.) No, I don't care for that lamp. It is far too glaring. Light some candles.

Phipps (*replaces lamp*) : Certainly, madam.

Mrs. Cheveley : I hope the candles have very becoming shades.

Phipps : We have had no complaints about them, madam, as yet.

Passes into the drawing-room and begins to light the candles.

Mrs. Cheveley (*to herself*) : I wonder what woman he is waiting for to-night. It will be delightful to catch him. Men always look so silly when they are caught. And they are always being caught. (*Looks about room and approaches the writing-table*.) What a very interesting room! What a very interesting picture! Wonder what his correspondence is like. (*Takes up letters*.) Oh, what a very uninteresting correspondence! Bills and cards, debts and dowagers! Who on earth writes to him on pink paper? How silly to write on pink paper! It looks like the beginning of a middle-class romance. Romance should never begin with sentiment. It should begin with science and end with a settlement. (*Puts letter down, then takes it up again*.) I know that handwriting. That is Gertrude Chiltern's. I remember it perfectly. The ten commandments in every stroke of the pen, and the moral law all over the page. Wonder what Gertrude is writing to him about? Something horrid about me, I suppose. How I detest that woman! (*Reads it*.) " I trust you. I want you. I am coming to you. Gertrude." " I trust you. I want you. I am coming to you."

A look of triumph comes over her face. She is just about to steal the letter, when PHIPPS comes in.

Phipps : The candles in the drawing-room are lit, madam, as you directed.

Mrs. Cheveley : Thank you. (*Rises hastily and slips the letter under a large silver-cased blotting-book that is lying on the table.*)

Phipps : I trust the shades will be to your liking, madam. They are the most becoming we have. They are the same as his lordship uses himself when he is dressing for dinner.

Mrs. Cheveley (with a smile) : Then I am sure they will be perfectly right.

Phipps (gravely) : Thank you, madam.

MRS. CHEVELEY *goes into the drawing-room.* PHIPPS *closes the door and retires. The door is then slowly opened, and* MRS. CHEVELEY *comes out and creeps stealthily towards the writing-table. Suddenly voices are heard from the smoking-room.* MRS. CHEVELEY *grows pale, and stops. The voices grow louder, and she goes back into the drawing-room, biting her lip.*

Enter LORD GORING *and* LORD CAVERSHAM.

Lord Goring (expostulating) : My dear father, if I am to get married, surely you will allow me to choose the time, place, and person ? Particularly the person.

Lord Caversham (testily) : That is a matter for me, sir. You would probably make a very poor choice, It is I who should be consulted, not you. There is property at stake. It is not a matter for affection. Affection comes later on in married life.

Lord Goring : Yes. In married life affection comes when people thoroughly dislike each other, father, doesn't it ? (*Puts on* LORD CAVERSHAM'S *cloak for him.*)

Lord Caversham : Certainly, sir. I mean certainly not, sir. You are talking very foolishly to-night. What I say is that marriage is a matter for common sense.

Lord Goring : But women who have common sense

are so curiously plain, father, aren't they? Of course
I only speak from hearsay.

Lord Caversham : No woman, plain or pretty, has
any common sense at all, sir. Common sense is the
privilege of our sex.

Lord Goring : Quite so. And we men are so self-
sacrificing that we never use it, do we, father?

Lord Caversham : I use it, sir. I use nothing else.

Lord Goring : So my mother tells me.

Lord Caversham : It is the secret of your mother's
happiness. You are very heartless, sir, very heartless.

Lord Goring : I hope not, father.

> *Goes out for a moment. Then returns, looking
> rather put out, with* SIR ROBERT CHILTERN.

Sir Robert Chiltern : My dear Arthur, what a piece of
good luck meeting you on the doorstep! Your servant
had just told me you were not at home. How extraordinary!

Lord Goring : The fact is, I am horribly busy to-
night, Robert, and I gave orders I was not at home to
any one. Even my father had a comparatively cold
reception. He complained of a draught the whole time.

Sir Robert Chiltern : Ah! you must be at home to
me, Arthur. You are my best friend. Perhaps by
to-morrow you will be my only friend. My wife has
discovered everything.

Lord Goring : Ah! I guessed as much!

Sir Robert Chiltern (looking at him) : Really! How!

Lord Goring (after some hesitation) : Oh, merely by
something in the expression of your face as you came
in. Who told her?

Sir Robert Chiltern : Mrs. Cheveley herself. And the
woman I love knows that I began my career with an
act of low dishonesty, that I built up my life upon sands
of shame—that I sold, like a common huckster, the
secret that had been intrusted to me as a man of
honour. I thank heaven poor Lord Radley died without

knowing that I betrayed him. I would to God I had died before I had been so horribly tempted, or had fallen so low. (*Burying his face in his hands.*)

Lord Goring (*after a pause*) : You have heard nothing from Vienna yet, in answer to your wire ?

Sir Robert Chiltern (*looking up*) : Yes ; I got a telegram from the first secretary at eight o'clock tonight.

Lord Goring : Well ?

Sir Robert Chiltern : Nothing is absolutely known against her. On the contrary, she occupies a rather high position in society. It is a sort of open secret that Baron Arnheim left her the greater portion of his immense fortune. Beyond that I can learn nothing.

Lord Goring : She doesn't turn out to be a spy, then ?

Sir Robert Chiltern : Oh ! spies are of no use nowadays. Their profession is over. The newspapers do 'their work instead.

Lord Goring : And thunderingly well they do it.

Sir Robert Chiltern : Arthur, I am parched with thirst. May I ring for something ? Some hock and seltzer ?

Lord Goring : Certainly. Let me. (*Rings the bell.*)

Sir Robert Chiltern : Thanks ! I don't know what to do, Arthur, I don't know what to do, and you are my only friend. But what a friend you are—the one friend I can trust. I can trust you absolutely, can't I ?

Enter PHIPPS.

Lord Goring : My dear Robert, of course. (*To* PHIPPS) : Bring some hock and seltzer.

Phipps : Yes, my lord.

Lord Goring : And Phipps !

Phipps : Yes, my lord.

Lord Goring : Will you excuse me for a moment, Robert ? I want to give some directions to my servant.

Sir Robert Chiltern : Certainly.

Lord Goring : When that lady calls, tell her that I am not expected home this evening. Tell her that I have been suddenly called out of town. You understand ?

Phipps : The lady is in that room, my lord. You told me to show her into that room, my lord.

Lord Goring : You did perfectly right. (*Exit* PHIPPS.) What a mess I am in. No ; I think I shall get through it. I'll give her a lecture through the door. Awkward thing to manage, though.

Sir Robert Chiltern : Arthur, tell me what I should do. My life seems to have crumbled about me. I am a ship without a rudder in a night without a star.

Lord Goring : Robert, you love your wife, don't you ?

Sir Robert Chiltern : I love her more than anything in the world. I used to think ambition the great thing. It is not. Love is the great thing in the world. There is nothing but love, and I love her. But I am defamed in her eyes. I am ignoble in her eyes. There is a wide gulf between us now. She had found me out, Arthur, she has found me out.

Lord Goring : Has she never in her life done some folly—some indiscretion—that she should not forgive your sin ?

Sir Robert Chiltern : My wife ! Never ! She does not know what weakness or temptation is. I am of clay like other men. She stands apart as good women do— pitiless in her perfection—cold and stern and without mercy. But I love her, Arthur. We are childless, and I have no one else to love, no one else to love me. Perhaps if God had sent us children she might have been kinder to me. But God has given us a lonely house. And she has cut my heart in two. Don't let us talk of it. I was brutal to her this evening. But I suppose when sinners talk to saints they are brutal always. I said to her things that were hideously true, on my side, from my standpoint, from the standpoint of men. But don't let us talk of that.

Lord Goring : Your wife will forgive you. Perhaps at this moment she is forgiving you. She loves you, Robert. Why should she not forgive ?

Sir Robert Chiltern : God grant it ! God grant it ! (*Buries his face in his hands.*) But there is something more I have to tell you, Arthur.

Enter PHIPPS *with drinks.*

Phipps (*hands hock and seltzer to* SIR ROBERT CHILTERN) : Hock and seltzer, sir.
Sir Robert Chiltern : Thank you.
Lord Goring : Is your carriage here, Robert ?
Sir Robert Chiltern : No ; I walked from the club.
Lord Goring : Sir Robert will take my cab, Phipps.
Phipps : Yes, my lord.

Exit.

Lord Goring : Robert, you don't mind my sending you away ?
Sir Robert Chiltern : Arthur, you must let me stay for five minutes. I have made up my mind what I am going to do to-night in the House. The debate on the Argentine Canal is to begin at eleven. (*A chair falls in the drawing-room.*) What is that ?
Lord Goring : Nothing.
Sir Robert Chiltern : I heard a chair fall in the next room. Some one has been listening.
Lord Goring : No, no ; there is no one there.
Sir Robert Chiltern : There is some one. There are lights in the room, and the door is ajar. Some one has been listening to every secret of my life. Arthur, what does this mean ?
Lord Goring : Robert, you are excited, unnerved. I tell you there is no one in that room. Sit down, Robert.
Sir Robert Chiltern : Do you give me your word that there is no one there ?

Lord Goring : Yes.

Sir Robert Chiltern : Your word of honour ? (*Sits down.*)

Lord Goring : Yes.

Sir Robert Chiltern (*rises*) : Arthur, let me see for myself.

Lord Goring : No, no.

Sir Robert Chiltern : If there is no one there why should I not look in that room ? Arthur, you must let me go into that room and satisfy myself. Let me know that no eavesdropper has heard my life's secret. Arthur, you don't realise what I am going through.

Lord Goring : Robert, this must stop. I have told you that there is no one in that room—that is enough.

Sir Robert Chiltern (*rushes to the door of the room*) : It is not enough. I insist on going into this room. You have told me there is no one there, so what reason can you have for refusing me ?

Lord Goring : For God's sake, don't ! There is some one there. Some one whom you must not see.

Sir Robert Chiltern : Ah, I thought so !

Lord Goring : I forbid you to enter that room.

Sir Robert Chiltern : Stand back. My life is at stake. And I don't care who is there. I will know who it is to whom I have told my secret and my shame. (*Enters room.*)

Lord Goring : Great heavens ! his own wife !

SIR ROBERT CHILTERN *comes back, with a look of scorn and anger on his face.*

Sir Robert Chiltern : What explanation have you to give for the presence of that woman here ?

Lord Goring : Robert, I swear to you on my honour that that lady is stainless and guiltless of all offence towards you.

Sir Robert Chiltern : She is a vile, an infamous thing !

Lord Goring : Don't say that, Robert ! It was for your sake she came here. It was to try and save you she came here. She loves you and no one else.

Sir Robert Chiltern : You are mad. What have I to do with her intrigues with you ? Let her remain your mistress ! You are well suited to each other. She, corrupt and shameful—you, false as a friend, treacherous as an enemy even——

Lord Goring : It is not true, Robert. Before heaven, it is not true. In her presence and in yours I will explain all.

Sir Robert Chiltern : Let me pass, sir. You have lied enough upon your word of honour.

SIR ROBERT CHILTERN *goes out.* LORD GORING *rushes to the door of the drawing-room, when* MRS. CHEVELEY *comes out, looking radiant and much amused.*

Mrs. Cheveley (with a mock curtsey) : Good-evening, Lord Goring !

Lord Goring : Mrs. Cheveley ! Great heavens ! . . . May I ask what you were doing in my drawing-room ?

Mrs. Cheveley : Merely listening. I have a perfect passion for listening through keyholes. One always hears such wonderful things through them.

Lord Goring : Doesn't that sound rather like tempting Providence ?

Mrs. Cheveley : Oh ! surely Providence can resist temptation by this time. (*Makes a sign to him to take her cloak off, which he does.*)

Lord Goring : I am glad you have called. I am going to give you some good advice.

Mrs. Cheveley : Oh ! pray don't. One should never give a woman anything that she can't wear in the evening.

Lord Goring : I see you are quite as wilful as you used to be.

Mrs. Cheveley : Far more ! I have greatly improved. I have had more experience.

Lord Goring : Too much experience is a dangerous thing. Pray have a cigarette. Half the pretty women in London smoke cigarettes. Personally I prefer the other half.

Mrs. Cheveley : Thanks. I never smoke. My dressmaker wouldn't like it, and a woman's first duty in life is to her dressmaker, isn't it ? What the second duty is, no one has as yet discovered.

Lord Goring : You have come here to sell me Robert Chiltern's letter, haven't you ?

Mrs. Cheveley : To offer it to you on conditions ! How did you guess that ?

Lord Goring : Because you haven't mentioned the subject. Have you got it with you ?

Mrs. Cheveley (sitting down) : Oh, no ! A well-made dress has no pockets.

Lord Goring : What is your price for it ?

Mrs. Cheveley : How absurdly English you are ! The English think that a cheque-book can solve every problem in life. Why, my dear Arthur, I have very much more money than you have, and quite as much as Robert Chiltern has got hold of. Money is not what I want.

Lord Goring : What do you want then, Mrs. Cheveley ?

Mrs. Cheveley : Why don't you call me Laura ?

Lord Goring : I don't like the name.

Mrs. Cheveley : You used to adore it.

Lord Goring : Yes ; that's why. (MRS. CHEVELEY *motions to him to sit down beside her. He smiles, and does so.)*

Mrs. Cheveley : Arthur, you loved me once.

Lord Goring : Yes.

Mrs. Cheveley : And you asked me to be your wife.

Lord Goring : That was the natural result of my loving you.

Mrs. Cheveley : And you threw me over because you saw, or said you saw, poor old Lord Mortlake trying to have a violent flirtation with me in the conservatory at Tenby.

Lord Goring : I am under the impression that my lawyer settled that matter with you on certain terms . . . dictated by yourself.

Mrs. Cheveley : At that time I was poor ; you were rich.

Lord Goring : Quite so. That is why you pretended to love me.

Mrs. Cheveley (shrugging her shoulders) : Poor old Lord Mortlake, who had only two topics of conversation, his gout and his wife ! I never could quite make out which of the two he was talking about. He used the most horrible language about them both. Well, you were silly, Arthur. Why, Lord Mortlake was never anything more to me than an amusement. One of those utterly tedious amusements one only finds at an English country house on an English country Sunday I don't think any one at all morally responsible for what he or she does at an English country house.

Lord Goring : Yes. I know lots of people think that.

Mrs. Cheveley : I loved you, Arthur.

Lord Goring : My dear Mrs. Cheveley, you have always been far too clever to know anything about love.

Mrs. Cheveley : I did love you. And you loved me. You know you loved me ; and love is a very wonderful thing. I suppose that when a man has once loved a woman, he will do anything for her, except continue to love her ? (*Puts her hand on his.*)

Lord Goring (taking his hand away quietly) : Yes ; except that.

Mrs. Cheveley (after a pause) : I am tired of living abroad. I want to come back to London. I want to have a charming house here. I want to have a salon. If one could only teach the English how to talk, and the Irish how to listen, society here would be quite

civilised. Besides, I have arrived at the romantic stage.
When I saw you last night at the Chilterns', I knew you
were the only person I had ever cared for, if I ever have
cared for anybody, Arthur. And so, on the morning
of the day you marry me, I will give you Robert
Chiltern's letter. That is my offer. I will give it to
you now, if you promise to marry me.

Lord Goring : Now ?

Mrs. Cheveley (smiling) : To-morrow.

Lord Goring : Are you really serious ?

Mrs. Cheveley : Yes, quite serious.

Lord Goring : I should make you a very bad husband.

Mrs. Cheveley : I don't mind bad husbands. I have
had two. They amused me immensely.

Lord Goring : You mean that you amused yourself
immensely, don't you ?

Mrs. Cheveley : What do you know about my
married life ?

Lord Goring : Nothing ; but I can read it like a book.

Mrs. Cheveley : What book ?

Lord Goring (rising) : The Book of Numbers.

Mrs. Cheveley : Do you think it is quite charming of
you to be so rude to a woman in your own house ?

Lord Goring : In the case of very fascinating women,
sex is a challenge, not a defence.

Mrs. Cheveley : I suppose that is meant for a
compliment. My dear Arthur, women are never disarmed by compliments. Men always are. That is the
difference between the two sexes.

Lord Goring : Women are never disarmed by anything, as far as I know them.

Mrs. Cheveley (after a pause) : Then you are going
to allow your greatest friend, Robert Chiltern, to be
ruined, rather than marry some one who really has
considerable attractions left. I thought you would
have risen to some great height of self-sacrifice, Arthur.
I think you should. And the rest of your life you could
spend in contemplating your own perfections.

Lord Goring: Oh! I do that as it is. And self-sacrifice is a thing that should be put down by law. It is so demoralising to the people for whom one sacrifices oneself. They always go to the bad.

Mrs. Cheveley: As if anything could demoralise Robert Chiltern! You seem to forget that I know his real character.

Lord Goring: What you know about him is not his real character. It was an act of folly done in his youth, dishonourable, I admit, shameful, I admit, unworthy of him, I admit, and therefore . . . not his true character.

Mrs. Cheveley: How you men stand up for each other!

Lord Goring: How you women war against each other!

Mrs. Cheveley (bitterly): I only war against one woman, against Gertrude Chiltern. I hate her. I hate her now more than ever.

Lord Goring: Because you have brought a real tragedy into her life, I suppose.

Mrs. Cheveley (with a sneer): Oh, there is only one real tragedy in a woman's life. The fact that her past is always her lover, and her future invariably her husband.

Lord Goring: Lady Chiltern knows nothing of the kind of life to which you are alluding.

Mrs. Cheveley: A woman whose size in gloves is seven and three-quarters never knows much about anything. You know Gertrude has always worn seven and three-quarters? That is one of the reasons why there was never any moral sympathy between us. . . . Well, Arthur, I suppose this romantic interview may be regarded as at an end. You admit it was romantic, don't you? For the privilege of being your wife I was ready to surrender a great prize, the climax of my diplomatic career. You decline. Very well. If Sir Robert doesn't uphold my Argentine scheme, I expose him. *Voila tout.*

Lord Goring : You mustn't do that. It would be vile, horrible, infamous.

Mrs. Cheveley (shrugging her shoulders) : Oh ! don't use big words. They mean so little. It is a commercial transaction. That is all. There is no good mixing up sentimentality in it. I offered to sell Robert Chiltern a certain thing. If he won't pay me my price, he will have to pay the world a greater price. There is no more to be said. I must go. Good-bye. Won't you shake hands ?

Lord Goring : With you ? No. Your transaction with Robert Chiltern may pass as a loathsome commercial transaction of a loathsome commercial age ; but you seem to have forgotten that you came here to-night to talk of love, you whose lips desecrated the word love, you to whom the thing is a book closely sealed, went this afternoon to the house of one of the most noble and gentle women in the world to degrade her husband in her eyes, to try and kill her love for him, to put poison in her heart, and bitterness in her life, to break her idol, and, it may be, spoil her soul. That I cannot forgive you. That was horrible. For that there can be no forgiveness.

Mrs. Cheveley : Arthur, you are unjust to me. Believe me, you are quite unjust to me. I didn't go to taunt Gertrude at all. I had no idea of doing anything of the kind when I entered. I called with Lady Markby simply to ask whether an ornament, a jewel, that I lost somewhere last night, had been found at the Chilterns'. If you don't believe me, you can ask Lady Markby. She will tell you it is true. The scene that occurred happened after Lady Markby had left, and was really forced on me by Gertrude's rudeness and sneers. I called, oh !—a little out of malice if you like —but really to ask if a diamond brooch of mine had been found. That was the origin of the whole thing.

Lord Goring : A diamond snake-brooch with a ruby ?

Mrs. Cheveley : Yes. How do you know ?

Lord Goring : Because it is found. In point of fact, I found it myself, and stupidly forgot to tell the butler anything about it as I was leaving. (*Goes over to the writing-table and pulls out the drawers.*) It is in this drawer. No, that one. This is the brooch, isn't it ? (*Holds up the brooch.*)

Mrs. Cheveley : Yes. I am so glad to get it back. It was . . . a present.

Lord Goring : Won't you wear it ?

Mrs. Cheveley : Certainly, if you pin it in. (LORD GORING *suddenly clasps it on her arm.*) Why do you put it on as a bracelet ? I never knew it could be worn as a bracelet.

Lord Goring : Really ?

Mrs. Cheveley (*holding out her handsome arm*) *:* No ; but it looks very well on me as a bracelet, doesn't it ?

Lord Goring : Yes ; much better than when I saw it last.

Mrs. Cheveley : When did you see it last ?

Lord Goring (*calmly*) *:* Oh, ten years ago, on Lady Berkshire, from whom you stole it.

Mrs. Cheveley (*starting*) *:* What do you mean ?

Lord Goring : I mean that you stole that ornament from my cousin, Mary Berkshire, to whom I gave it when she was married. Suspicion fell on a wretched servant, who was sent away in disgrace. I recognised it last night. I determined to say nothing about it till I had found the thief. I have found the thief now, and I have heard her own confession.

Mrs. Cheveley (*tossing her head*) *:* It is not true.

Lord Goring : You know it is true. Why, thief is written across your face at this moment.

Mrs. Cheveley : I will deny the whole affair from beginning to end. I will say that I have never seen this wretched thing, that it was never in my possession.

MRS. CHEVELEY *tries to get the bracelet off her arm, but fails.* LORD GORING *looks on amused. Her*

*thin fingers tear at the jewel to no purpose. A curse
breaks from her.*

Lord Goring : The drawback of stealing a thing,
Mrs. Cheveley, is that one never knows how wonderful
the thing that one steals is. You can't get that bracelet
off, unless you know where the spring is. And I see you
don't know where the spring is. It is rather difficult
to find.

Mrs. Cheveley : You brute ! You coward ! (*She tries
again to unclasp the bracelet, but fails.*)

Lord Goring : Oh ! don't use big words. They mean
so little.

Mrs. Cheveley (*again tears at the bracelet in a paroxysm
of rage, with inarticulate sounds. Then stops, and looks
at* LORD GORING) *:* What are you going to do ?

Lord Goring : I am going to ring for my servant. He
is an admirable servant. Always comes in the moment
one rings for him. When he comes I will tell him to
fetch the police.

Mrs. Cheveley (*trembling*) *:* The police ? What for ?

Lord Goring : To-morrow the Berkshires will
prosecute you. That is what the police are for.

Mrs. Cheveley (*is now in an agony of physical terror.
Her face is distorted. Her mouth awry. A mask has
fallen from her. She is, for the moment, dreadful to look
at*) *:* Don't do that. I will do anything you want.
Anything in the world you want.

Lord Goring : Give me Robert Chiltern's letter.

Mrs. Cheveley : Stop ! Stop ! Let me have time to
think.

Lord Goring : Give me Robert Chiltern's letter.

Mrs. Cheveley : I have not got it with me. I will
give it to you to-morrow.

Lord Goring : You know you are lying. Give it to
me at once. (MRS. CHEVELEY *pulls the letter out, and
hands it to him. She is horribly pale.*) This is it ?

Mrs. Cheveley (*in a hoarse voice*) *:* Yes.

Lord Goring (takes the letter, examines it, sighs, and burns it over the lamp) : For so well-dressed a woman, Mrs. Cheveley, you have moments of admirable common sense. I congratulate you.

Mrs. Cheveley (catches sight of LADY CHILTERN'S *letter, the cover of which is just showing from under the blotting-book)* : Please get me a glass of water.

Lord Goring : Certainly. *(Goes to the corner of the room and pours out a glass of water. While his back is turned* MRS. CHEVELEY *steals* LADY CHILTERN'S *letter. When* LORD GORING *returns with the glass she refuses it with a gesture.)*

Mrs. Cheveley : Thank you. Will you help me on with my cloak ?

Lord Goring : With pleasure. *(Puts her cloak on.)*

Mrs. Cheveley : Thanks. I am never going to try to harm Robert Chiltern again.

Lord Goring : Fortunately you have not the chance, Mrs. Cheveley.

Mrs. Cheveley : Well, if even I had the chance, I wouldn't. On the contrary, I am going to render him a great service.

Lord Goring : I am charmed to hear it. It is a reformation.

Mrs. Cheveley : Yes. I can't bear so upright a gentleman, so honourable an English gentleman, being so shamefully deceived and so——

Lord Goring : Well ?

Mrs. Cheveley : I find that somehow Gertrude Chiltern's dying speech and confession has strayed into my pocket.

Lord Goring : What do you mean ?

Mrs. Cheveley (with a bitter note of triumph in her voice) : I mean that I am going to send Robert Chiltern the love-letter his wife wrote to you to-night.

Lord Goring : Love-letter ?

Mrs. Cheveley (laughing) : " I want you. I trust you. I am coming to you. Gertrude."

LORD GORING *rushes to the bureau and takes up the envelope, finds it empty, and turns round.*

Lord Goring : You wretched woman, must you always be thieving ? Give me back that letter. I'll take it from you by force. You shall not leave my room till I have got it.

He rushes rowards her, but MRS. CHEVELEY *at once puts her hand on the electric bell that is on the table. The bell sounds with shrill reverberations, and* PHIPPS *enters.*

Mrs. Cheveley (after a pause) : Lord Goring merely rang that you should show me out. Good-night, Lord Goring !

Goes out followed by PHIPPS. *Her face is illumined with evil triumph. There is joy in her eyes. Youth seems to come back to her. Her last glance is like a swift arrow.* LORD GORING *bites his lip, and lights a cigarette.*

ACT DROP.

FOURTH ACT

Same as Act II.

LORD GORING *is standing by the fireplace with his hands in his pockets. He is looking rather bored.*

Lord Goring (*pulls out his watch, inspects it, and rings the bell*) : It is a great nuisance. I can't find any one in this house to talk to. And I am full of interesting information. I feel like the latest edition of something or other.

Enter servant.

James : Sir Robert is still at the Foreign Office, my lord.

Lord Goring : Lady Chiltern not down yet ?

James : Her ladyship has not yet left her room. Miss Chiltern has just come in from riding.

Lord Goring (*to himself*) : Ah ! that is something.

James : Lord Caversham has been waiting some time in the library for Sir Robert. I told him your lordship was here.

Lord Goring : Thank you. Would you kindly tell him I've gone ?

James (*bowing*) : I shall do so, my lord.

Exit servant.

Lord Goring : Really, I don't want to meet my father three days running. It is a great deal too much excitement for any son. I hope to goodness he won't

566

come up. Fathers should be neither seen nor heard. That is the only proper basis for family life. Mothers are different. Mothers are darlings. (*Throws himself down into a chair, picks up a paper and begins to read it.*)

Enter LORD CAVERSHAM.

Lord Caversham : Well, sir, what are you doing here ? Wasting your time as usual, I suppose ?

Lord Goring (*throws down paper and rises*) : My dear father, when one pays a visit it is for the purpose of wasting other people's time, not one's own.

Lord Caversham : Have you been thinking over what I spoke to you about last night ?

Lord Goring : I have been thinking about nothing else.

Lord Caversham : Engaged to be married yet ?

Lord Goring (*genially*) : Not yet ; but I hope to be before lunch-time.

Lord Caversham (*caustically*) : You can have till dinner-time if it would be of any convenience to you.

Lord Goring : Thanks awfully, but I think I'd sooner be engaged before lunch.

Lord Caversham : Humph ! Never know when you are serious or not.

Lord Goring : Neither do I, father.

A pause.

Lord Caversham : I suppose you have read *The Times* this morning ?

Lord Goring (*airily*) : *The Times* ? Certainly not. I only read *The Morning Post.* All that one should know about modern life is where the Duchesses are ; anything else is quite demoralising.

Lord Caversham : Do you mean to say you have not read *The Times* leading article on Robert Chiltern's career ?

Lord Goring : Good heavens ! No. What does it say ?

Lord Caversham : What should it say, sir ? Everything complimentary, of course. Chiltern's speech last night on this Argentine Canal scheme was one of the finest pieces of oratory ever delivered in the House since Canning.

Lord Goring : Ah ! Never heard of Canning. Never wanted to. And did . . . did Chiltern uphold the scheme ?

Lord Caversham : Uphold it, sir ? How little you know him ! Why, he denounced it roundly, and the whole system of modern political finance. This speech is the turning-point in his career, as *The Times* points out. You should read this article, sir. (*Opens* The Times.) " Sir Robert Chiltern . . . most rising of our young statesmen. . . . Brilliant orator. . . . Unblemished career. . . . Well-known integrity of character. . . . Represents what is best in English public life. . . . Noble contrast to the lax morality so common among foreign politicians." They will never say that of you, sir.

Lord Goring : I sincerely hope not, father. However, I am delighted at what you tell me about Robert, thoroughly delighted. It shows he has got pluck.

Lord Caversham : He has got more than pluck, sir, he has got genius.

Lord Goring : Ah ! I prefer pluck. It is not so common, nowadays, as genius is.

Lord Caversham : I wish you would go into Parliament.

Lord Goring : My dear father, only people who look dull ever get into the House of Commons, and only people who are dull ever succeed there.

Lord Caversham : Why don't you try to do something useful in life ?

Lord Goring : I am far too young.

Lord Caversham (testily) : I hate this affectation of

youth, sir. It is a great deal too prevalent nowadays.

Lord Goring: Youth isn't an affectation. Youth is an art.

Lord Caversham: Why don't you propose to that pretty Miss Chiltern?

Lord Goring: I am of a very nervous disposition, especially in the morning.

Lord Caversham: I don't suppose there is the smallest chance of her accepting you.

Lord Goring: I don't know how the betting stands to-day.

Lord Caversham: If she did accept you she would be the prettiest fool in England.

Lord Goring: That is just what I should like to marry. A thoroughly sensible wife would reduce me to a condition of absolute idiocy in less than six months.

Lord Caversham: You don't deserve her, sir.

Lord Goring: My dear father, if we men married the women we deserved, we should have a very bad time of it.

Enter MABEL CHILTERN.

Mabel Chiltern: Oh!... How do you do, Lord Caversham? I hope Lady Caversham is quite well?

Lord Caversham: Lady Caversham is as usual, as usual.

Lord Goring: Good-morning, Miss Mabel!

Mabel Chiltern (taking no notice at all of LORD GORING, *and addressing herself exclusively to* LORD CAVERSHAM): And Lady Caversham's bonnets... are they at all better?

Lord Caversham: They have had a serious relapse, I am sorry to say.

Lord Goring: Good-morning, Miss Mabel.

Mabel Chiltern (to LORD CAVERSHAM): I hope an operation will not be necessary.

Lord Caversham (*smiling at her pertness*) : If it is, we shall have to give Lady Caversham a narcotic. Otherwise she would never consent to have a feather touched.

Lord Goring (*with increased emphasis*) : Good-morning, Miss Mabel !

Mabel Chiltern (*turning round with feigned surprise*) : Oh, are you here ? Of course you understand that after your breaking your appointment I am never going to speak to you again.

Lord Goring : Oh, please don't say such a thing. You are the one person in London I really like to have to listen to me.

Mabel Chiltern : Lord Goring, I never believe a single word that either you or I say to each other.

Lord Caversham : You are quite right, my dear, quite right as far as he is concerned, I mean.

Mabel Chiltern : Do you think you could possibly make your son behave a little better occasionally ? Just as a change.

Lord Caversham : I regret to say, Miss Chiltern, that I have no influence at all over my son. I wish I had. If I had, I know what I would make him do.

Mabel Chiltern : I am afraid that he has one of those terribly weak natures that are not susceptible to influence.

Lord Caversham : He is very heartless, very heartless.

Lord Goring : It seems to me that I am a little in the way here.

Mabel Chiltern : It is very good for you to be in the way, and to know what people say of you behind your back.

Lord Goring : I don't at all like knowing what people say of me behind my back. It makes me far too conceited.

Lord Caversham : After that, my dear, I really must bid you good-morning.

Mabel Chiltern : Oh ! I hope you are not going to

leave me all alone with Lord Goring ? Especially at such an early hour in the day.

Lord Caversham : I am afraid I can't take him with me to Downing Street. It is not the Prime Minister's day for seeing the unemployed.

> *Shakes hands with* MABEL CHILTERN, *takes up his hat and stick, and goes out, with a parting glare of indignation at* LORD GORING.

Mabel Chiltern (takes up roses and begins to arrange them in a bowl on the table) : People who don't keep their appointments in the Park are horrid.

Lord Goring : Detestable.

Mabel Chiltern : I am glad you admit it. But I wish you wouldn't look so pleased about it.

Lord Goring : I can't help it. I always look pleased when I am with you.

Mabel Chiltern (sadly) : Then I suppose it is my duty to remain with you ?

Lord Goring : Of course it is.

Mabel Chiltern : Well, my duty is a thing I never do, on principle. It always depresses me. So I am afraid I must leave you.

Lord Goring : Please don't, Miss Mabel. I have something very particular to say to you.

Mabel Chiltern (rapturously) : Oh ! is it a proposal ?

Lord Goring (somewhat taken aback) : Well, yes, it is —I am bound to say it is.

Mabel Chiltern (with a sigh of pleasure) : I am so glad. That makes the second to-day.

Lord Goring (indignantly) : The second to-day ? What conceited ass has been impertinent enough to dare to propose to you before I had proposed to you ?

Mabel Chiltern : Tommy Trafford, of course. It is one of Tommy's days for proposing. He always proposes on Tuesdays and Thursdays, during the Season.

Lord Goring : You didn't accept him, I hope ?

Mabel Chiltern : I make it a rule never to accept

Tommy. That is why he goes on proposing. Of course, as you didn't turn up this morning, I very nearly said yes. It would have been an excellent lesson both for him and for you if I had. It would have taught you both better manners.

Lord Goring : Oh ! bother Tommy Trafford. Tommy is a silly little ass. I love you.

Mabel Chiltern : I know. And I think you might have mentioned it before. I am sure I have given you heaps of opportunities.

Lord Goring : Mabel, do be serious. Please be serious.

Mabel Chiltern : Ah ! that is the sort of thing a man always says to a girl before he has been married to her. He never says it afterwards.

Lord Goring (taking hold of her hand) : Mabel, I have told you that I love you. Can't you love me a little in return ?

Mabel Chiltern : You silly Arthur ! If you knew anything about . . anything, which you don't, you would know that I adore you. Every one in London knows it except you. It is a public scandal the way I adore you. I have been going about for the last six months telling the whole of society that I adore you. I wonder you consent to have anything to say to me. I have no character left at all. At least, I feel so happy that I am quite sure I have no character left at all.

Lord Goring (catches her in his arms and kisses her. Then there is a pause of bliss) : Dear ! Do you know I was awfully afraid of being refused !

Mabel Chiltern (looking up at him) : But you never have been refused yet by anybody, have you, Arthur ? I can't imagine any one refusing you.

Lord Goring (after kissing her again) : Of course I'm not nearly good enough for you, Mabel.

Mabel Chiltern (nestling close to him) : I am so glad, darling. I was afraid you were.

Lord Goring (after some hesitation) : And I'm . . . I'm a little over thirty.

Mabel Chiltern : Dear, you look weeks younger than that.

Lord Goring (enthusiastically) : How sweet of you to say so ! . . . And it is only fair to tell you frankly that I am fearfully extravagant.

Mabel Chiltern : But so am I, Arthur. So we're sure to agree. And now I must go and see Gertrude.

Lord Goring : Must you really ? *(Kisses her.)*

Mabel Chiltern : Yes.

Lord Goring : Then do tell her I want to talk to her particularly. I have been waiting here all the morning to see either her or Robert.

Mabel Chiltern : Do you mean to say you didn't come here expressly to propose to me ?

Lord Goring (triumphantly) : No ; that was a flash of genius.

Mabel Chiltern : Your first.

Lord Goring (with determination) : My last.

Mabel Chiltern : I am delighted to hear it. Now don't stir. I'll be back in five minutes. And don't fall into any temptations while I am away.

Lord Goring : Dear Mabel, while you are away, there are none. It makes me horribly dependent on you.

Enter LADY CHILTERN.

Lady Chiltern : Good-morning, dear ! How pretty you are looking !

Mabel Chiltern : How pale you are looking, Gertrude ! It is most becoming !

Lady Chiltern : Good-morning, Lord Goring !

Lord Goring (bowing) : Good-morning, Lady Chiltern!

Mabel Chiltern (aside to LORD GORING) : I shall be in the conservatory, under the second palm tree on the left.

Lord Goring : Second on the left ?

Mabel Chiltern (with a look of mock surprise) : Yes ; the usual palm tree.

Blows a kiss to him, unobserved by LADY CHIL-
TERN, *and goes out.*

Lord Goring : Lady Chiltern, I have a certain amount
of very good news to tell you. Mrs. Cheveley gave me
up Robert's letter last night, and I burned it. Robert
is safe.

Lady Chiltern (sinking on the sofa) : Safe ! Oh ! I
am so glad of that. What a good friend you are to
him—to us !

Lord Goring : There is only one person now that
could be said to be in any danger.

Lady Chiltern : Who is that ?

Lord Goring (sitting down beside her) : Yourself.

Lady Chiltern : I ! In danger ? What do you mean ?

Lord Goring : Danger is too great a word. It is a
word I should not have used. But I admit I have
something to tell you that may distress you, that
terribly distresses me. Yesterday evening you wrote
me a very beautiful, womanly letter, asking me for
my help. You wrote to me as one of your oldest
friends, one of your husband's oldest friends. Mrs.
Cheveley stole that letter from my rooms.

Lady Chiltern : Well, what use is it to her ? Why
should she not have it ?

Lord Goring (rising) : Lady Chiltern, I will be quite
frank with you. Mrs. Cheveley puts a certain construction on that letter and proposes to send it to
your husband.

Lady Chiltern : But what construction could she put
on it ? . . . Oh ! not that ! not that ! If I in—in
trouble, and wanting your help, trusting you, propose
to come to you . . . that you may advise me . . .
assist me. . . . Oh ! are there women so horrible as
that . . . ? And she proposes to send it to my
husband ? Tell me what happened. Tell me all that
happened.

Lord Goring : Mrs. Cheveley was concealed in a

room adjoining my library, without my knowledge. I thought that the person who was waiting in that room to see me was yourself. Robert came in unexpectedly. A chair or something fell in the room. He forced his way in, and he discovered her. We had a terrible scene. I still thought it was you. He left me in anger. At the end of everything Mrs. Cheveley got possession of your letter—she stole it, when or how, I don't know.

Lady Chiltern : At what hour did this happen ?

Lord Goring : At half-past ten. And now I propose that we tell Robert the whole thing at once.

Lady Chiltern (looking at him with amazement that is almost terror) : You want me to tell Robert that the woman you expected was not Mrs. Cheveley, but myself ? That it was I whom you thought was concealed in a room in your house, at half-past ten o'clock at night ? You want me to tell him that ?

Lord Goring : I think it is better that he should know the exact truth.

Lady Chiltern (rising) : Oh, I couldn't, I couldn't !

Lord Goring : May I do it ?

Lady Chiltern : No.

Lord Goring (gravely) : You are wrong, Lady Chiltern.

Lady Chiltern : No. The letter must be intercepted. That is all. But how can I do it ? Letters arrive for him every moment of the day. His secretaries open them and hand them to him. I dare not ask the servants to bring me his letters. It would be impossible. Oh ! why don't you tell me what to do ?

Lord Goring : Pray be calm, Lady Chiltern, and answer the questions I am going to put to you. You said his secretaries open his letters.

Lady Chiltern : Yes.

Lord Goring : Who is with him to-day ? Mr. Trafford, isn't it ?

Lady Chiltern : No. Mr. Montford, I think.

Lord Goring : You can trust him ?

Lady Chiltern (with a gesture of despair) : Oh ! how do I know ?

Lord Goring : He would do what you asked him, wouldn't he ?

Lady Chiltern : I think so.

Lord Goring : Your letter was on pink paper. He could recognise it without reading it, couldn't he ? By the colour ?

Lady Chiltern : I suppose so.

Lord Goring : Is he in the house now ?

Lady Chiltern : Yes.

Lord Goring : Then I will go and see him myself, and tell him that a certain letter, written on pink paper, is to be forwarded to Robert to-day, and that at all costs it must not reach him. (*Goes to the door, and opens it.*) Oh ! Robert is coming upstairs with the letter in his hand. It has reached him already.

Lady Chiltern (with a cry of pain) : Oh ! you have saved his life ; what have you done with mine ?

> *Enter* SIR ROBERT CHILTERN. *He has the letter in his hand, and is reading it. He comes towards his wife, not noticing* LORD GORING'S *presence.*

Sir Robert Chiltern : " I want you. I trust you. I am coming to you. Gertrude." Oh, my love ! Is this true ? Do you indeed trust me, and want me ? If so, it was for me to come to you, not for you to write of coming to me. This letter of yours, Gertrude, makes me feel that nothing that the world may do can hurt me now. You want me, Gertrude.

> LORD GORING, *unseen by* SIR ROBERT CHILTERN, *makes an imploring sign to* LADY CHILTERN *to accept the situation and* SIR ROBERT'S *error.*

Lady Chiltern : Yes.

Sir Robert Chiltern : You trust me, Gertrude ?

Lady Chiltern : Yes.

Sir Robert Chiltern : Ah ! why did you not add you loved me ?

Lady Chiltern (taking his hand) : Because I loved you.

LORD GORING *passes into the conservatory.*

Sir Robert Chiltern (kisses her) : Gertrude, you don't know what I feel. When Montford passed me your letter across the table—he had opened it by mistake, I suppose, without looking at the handwriting on the envelope—and I read it—oh ! I did not care what disgrace or punishment was in store for me, I only thought you loved me still.

Lady Chiltern : There is no disgrace in store for you, nor any public shame. Mrs. Cheveley has handed over to Lord Goring the document that was in her possession, and he has destroyed it.

Sir Robert Chiltern : Are you sure of this, Gertrude ?

Lady Chiltern : Yes ; Lord Goring has just told me.

Sir Robert Chiltern : Then I am safe ! Oh ! what a wonderful thing to be safe ! For two days I have been in terror. I am safe now. How did Arthur destroy my letter ? Tell me.

Lady Chiltern : He burned it.

Sir Robert Chiltern : I wish I had seen that one sin of my youth burning to ashes. How many men there are in modern life who would like to see their past burning to white ashes before them ! Is Arthur still here ?

Lady Chiltern : Yes ; he is in the conservatory.

Sir Robert Chiltern : I am so glad now I made that speech last night in the House, so glad. I made it thinking that public disgrace might be the result. But it has not been so.

Lady Chiltern : Public honour has been the result.

Sir Robert Chiltern : I think so. I fear so, almost. For although I am safe from detection, although every proof against me is destroyed, I suppose, Gertrude . . . I suppose I should retire from public life ? (*He looks anxiously at his wife.*)

Lady Chiltern (eagerly) : Oh yes, Robert, you should do that. It is your duty to do that.

Sir Robert Chiltern : It is much to surrender.

Lady Chiltern : No ; it will be much to gain.

SIR ROBERT CHILTERN *walks up and down the room with a troubled expression. Then comes over to his wife, and puts his hand on her shoulder.*

Sir Robert Chiltern : And you would be happy living somewhere alone with me, abroad perhaps, or in the country away from London, away from public life ? You would have no regrets ?

Lady Chiltern : Oh ! none, Robert.

Sir Robert Chiltern (sadly) : And your ambition for me ? You used to be ambitious for me.

Lady Chiltern : Oh, my ambition ! I have none now, but that we two may love each other. It was your ambition that led you astray. Let us not talk about ambition.

LORD GORING *returns from the conservatory, looking very pleased with himself, and with an entirely new buttonhole that some one has made for him.*

Sir Robert Chiltern (going towards him) : Arthur, I have to thank you for what you have done for me. I don't know how I can repay you. (*Shakes hands with him.*)

Lord Goring : My dear fellow, I'll tell you at once. At the present moment, under the usual palm tree . . . I mean in the conservatory . . .

Enter MASON.

Mason : Lord Caversham.

Lord Goring : That admirable father of mine really makes a habit of turning up at the wrong moment. It is very heartless of him, very heartless indeed.

Enter LORD CAVERSHAM. MASON *goes out.*

Lord Caversham : Good-morning, Lady Chiltern ! Warmest congratulations to you, Chiltern, on your brilliant speech last night. I have just left the Prime Minister, and you are to have the vacant seat in the Cabinet.

Sir Robert Chiltern (with a look of joy and triumph) : A seat in the Cabinet ?

Lord Caversham : Yes ; here is the Prime Minister's letter. *(Hands letter.)*

Sir Robert Chiltern (takes letter and reads it) : A seat in the Cabinet !

Lord Caversham : Certainly, and you well deserve it too. You have got what we want so much in political life nowadays—high character, high moral tone, high principles. *(To* LORD GORING*) :* Everything that you have not got, sir, and never will have.

Lord Goring : I don't like principles, father. I prefer prejudices.

> SIR ROBERT CHILTERN *is on the brink of accepting the Prime Minister's offer, when he sees his wife looking at him with her clear, candid eyes. He then realises that it is impossible.*

Sir Robert Chiltern : I cannot accept this offer, Lord Caversham. I have made up my mind to decline it.

Lord Caversham : Decline it, sir !

Sir Robert Chiltern : My intention is to retire at once from public life.

Lord Caversham (angrily) : Decline a seat in the Cabinet, and retire from public life ? Never heard such damned nonsense in the whole course of my existence. I beg your pardon, Lady Chiltern. Chiltern, I beg your pardon. (*To* LORD GORING) *:* Don't grin like that, sir.

Lord Goring : No, father.

Lord Caversham : Lady Chiltern, you are a sensible woman, the most sensible woman in London, the most sensible woman I know. Will you kindly prevent your husband from making such a . . . from talking such. . . . Will you kindly do that, Lady Chiltern ?

Lady Chiltern : I think my husband is right in his determination, Lord Caversham. I approve of it.

Lord Caversham : You approve of it ? Good heavens !

Lady Chiltern (taking her husband's hand) : I admire him for it. I admire him immensely for it. I have never admired him so much before. He is finer than even I thought him. (*To* SIR ROBERT CHILTERN) *:* You will go and write your letter to the Prime Minister now, won't you ? Don't hesitate about it, Robert.

Sir Robert Chiltern (with a touch of bitterness) : I suppose I had better write it at once. Such offers are not repeated. I will ask you to excuse me for a moment, Lord Caversham.

Lady Chiltern : I may come with you, Robert, may I not ?

Sir Robert Chiltern : Yes, Gertrude.

LADY CHILTERN *goes with him.*

Lord Caversham : What is the matter with this family ? Something wrong here, eh ? (*Tapping his forehead.*) Idiocy ? Hereditary, I suppose. Both of them, too. Wife as well as husband. Very sad. Very sad indeed ! And they are not an old family. Can't understand it.

Lord Goring : It is not idiocy, father, I assure you.

Lord Caversham : What is it then, sir ?

Lord Goring (after some hesitation) : Well, it is what

is called nowadays a high moral tone, father. That is all.

Lord Caversham : Hate these new-fangled names. Same thing as we used to call idiocy fifty years ago. Shan't stay in this house any longer.

Lord Goring (taking his arm) : Oh ! just go in here for a moment, father. Third palm tree to the left, the usual palm tree.

Lord Caversham : What, sir ?

Lord Goring : I beg your pardon, father, I forgot. The conservatory, father, the conservatory—there is some one there I want you to talk to.

Lord Caversham : What about, sir ?

Lord Goring : About me, father.

Lord Caversham (grimly) : Not a subject on which much eloquence is possible.

Lord Goring : No, father ; but the lady is like me. She doesn't care much for eloquence in others. She thinks it a little loud.

LORD CAVERSHAM *goes into the conservatory.* LADY CHILTERN *enters.*

Lord Goring : Lady Chiltern, why are you playing Mrs. Cheveley's cards ?

Lady Chiltern (startled) : I don't understand you.

Lord Goring : Mrs. Cheveley made an attempt to ruin your husband. Either to drive him from public life, or to make him adopt a dishonourable position. From the latter tragedy you saved him. The former you are now thrusting on him. Why should you do him the wrong Mrs. Cheveley tried to do and failed ?

Lady Chiltern : Lord Goring ?

Lord Goring (pulling himself together for a great effort, and showing the philosopher that underlies the dandy) : Lady Chiltern, allow me. You wrote me a letter last night in which you said you trusted me and wanted my help. Now is the moment when you really want my help, now is the time when you have got to trust me, to trust in my counsel and judgment. You love Robert. Do you want to kill his love for you? What sort of existence will he have if you rob him of the fruits of his ambition, if you take him from the splendour of a great political career, if you close the doors of public life against him, if you condemn him to sterile failure, he who was made for triumph and success? Women are not meant to judge us, but to forgive us when we need forgiveness. Pardon, not punishment, is their mission. Why should you scourge him with rods for a sin done in his youth, before he knew you, before he knew himself? A man's life is of more value than a woman's. It has larger issues, wider scope, greater ambitions. A woman's life revolves in curves of emotions. It is upon lines of intellect that a man's life progresses. Don't make any terrible mistake, Lady Chiltern. A woman who can keep a man's love, and love him in return, has done all the world wants of women, or should want of them.

Lady Chiltern (troubled and hesitating): But it is my husband himself who wishes to retire from public life. He feels it is his duty. It was he who first said so.

Lord Goring: Rather than lose your love, Robert would do anything, wreck his whole career, as he is on the brink of doing now. He is making for you a terrible sacrifice. Take my advice, Lady Chiltern, and do not accept a sacrifice so great. If you do, you will live to repent it bitterly. We men and women are not made to accept such sacrifices from each other. We are not worthy of them. Besides, Robert has been punished enough.

Lady Chiltern: We have both been punished. I set him up too high.

Lord Goring (with deep feeling in his voice): Do not for that reason set him down now too low. If he has fallen from his altar, do not thrust him into the mire. Failure to Robert would be the very mire of shame. Power is his passion. He would lose everything, even his power to feel love. Your husband's life is at this moment in your hands, your husband's love is in your hands. Don't mar both for him.

Enter SIR ROBERT CHILTERN.

Sir Robert Chiltern : Gertrude, here is the draft of my letter. Shall I read it to you ?
Lady Chiltern : Let me see it.

SIR ROBERT *hands her the letter. She reads it, and then, with a gesture of passion, tears it up.*

Sir Robert Chiltern : What are you doing ?
Lady Chiltern : A man's life is of more value than a woman's. It has larger issues, wider scope, greater ambitions. Our lives revolve in curves of emotions. It is upon lines of intellect that a man's life progresses. I have just learnt this, and much else with it, from Lord Goring. And I will not spoil your life for you, nor see you spoil it as a sacrifice to me, a useless sacrifice !
Sir Robert Chiltern : Gertrude ! Gertrude !
Lady Chiltern : You can forget. Men easily forget. And I forgive. That is how women help the world. I see that now.
Sir Robert Chiltern (deeply overcome by emotion, embraces her) : My wife ! my wife ! (*To* LORD GORING) : Arthur, it seems that I am always to be in your debt.
Lord Goring : Oh dear no, Robert. Your debt is to Lady Chiltern, not to me !
Sir Robert Chiltern : I owe you much. And now tell me what you were going to ask me just now as Lord Caversham came in.
Lord Goring : Robert, you are your sister's guardian, and I want your consent to my marriage with her. That is all.
Lady Chiltern : Oh, I am so glad ! I am so glad ! (*Shakes hands with* LORD GORING.)

Lord Goring : Thank you, Lady Chiltern.

Sir Robert Chiltern (with a troubled look) : My sister to be your wife ?

Lord Goring : Yes.

Sir Robert Chiltern (speaking with great firmness) : Arthur, I am very sorry, but the thing is quite out of the question. I have to think of Mabel's future happiness. And I don't think her happiness would be safe in your hands. And I cannot have her sacrificed !

Lord Goring : Sacrificed !

Sir Robert Chiltern : Yes, utterly sacrificed. Loveless marriages are horrible. But there is one thing worse than an absolutely loveless marriage. A marriage in which there is love, but on one side only ; faith, but on one side only ; devotion, but on one side only, and in which of the two hearts one is sure to be broken.

Lord Goring : But I love Mabel. No other woman has any place in my life.

Lady Chiltern : Robert, if they love each other, why should they not be married ?

Sir Robert Chiltern : Arthur cannot bring Mabel the love that she deserves.

Lord Goring : What reason have you for saying that ?

Sir Robert Chiltern (after a pause) : Do you really require me to tell you ?

Lord Goring : Certainly I do.

Sir Robert Chiltern : As you choose. When I called on you yesterday evening I found Mrs. Cheveley concealed in your rooms. It was between ten and eleven o'clock at night. I do not wish to say anything more. Your relations with Mrs. Cheveley have, as I said to you last night, nothing whatsoever to do with me. I know you were engaged to be married to her once. The fascination she exercised over you then seems to have returned. You spoke to me last night of her as of a woman pure and stainless, a woman whom you respected and honoured. That may be so. But I cannot give my sister's life into your hands. It would be wrong of me. It would be unjust, infamously unjust to her.

Lord Goring : I have nothing more to say.

Lady Chiltern : Robert, it was not Mrs. Cheveley whom Lord Goring expected last night.

Sir Robert Chiltern : Not Mrs. Cheveley ! Who was it then ?

Lord Goring : Lady Chiltern.

Lady Chiltern : It was your own wife. Robert, yesterday afternoon Lord Goring told me that if ever I was in trouble I could come to him for help, as he was our oldest and best friend. Later on, after that terrible scene in this room, I wrote to him telling him that I trusted him, that I had need of him, that I was coming to him for help and advice. (SIR ROBERT CHILTERN *takes the letter out of his pocket.*) Yes, that letter. I didn't go to Lord Goring's, after all. I felt that it is from ourselves alone that help can come. Pride made me think that. Mrs. Cheveley went. She stole my letter and sent it anonymously to you this morning, that you should think. . . . Oh ! Robert, I cannot tell you what she wished you to think. . . .

Sir Robert Chiltern : What ! Had I fallen so low in your eyes that you thought that even for a moment I could have doubted your goodness ? Gertrude, Gertrude, you are to me the white image of all good things, and sin can never touch you. Arthur, you can go to Mabel, and you have my best wishes ! Oh ! stop a moment. There is no name at the beginning of this letter. The brilliant Mrs. Cheveley does not seem to have noticed that. There should be a name.

Lady Chiltern : Let me write yours. It is you I trust and need. You and none else.

Lord Goring : Well, really, Lady Chiltern, I think I should have back my own letter.

Lady Chiltern (*smiling*) *:* No ; you shall have Mabel. (*Takes the letter and writes her husband's name on it.*)

Lord Goring : Well, I hope she hasn't changed her mind. It's nearly twenty minutes since I saw her last.

Enter MABEL CHILTERN *and* LORD CAVERSHAM.

Mabel Chiltern : Lord Goring, I think your father's conversation much more improving than yours. I am only going to talk to Lord Caversham in the future, and always under the usual palm tree.

Lord Goring : Darling ! (*Kisses her.*)

Lord Caversham (*Considerably taken aback*) *:* What does this mean, sir ? You don't mean to say that this charming, clever young lady has been so foolish as to accept you ?

Lord Goring : Certainly, father ! And Chiltern's been wise enough to accept the seat in the Cabinet.

Lord Caversham : I am very glad to hear that, Chiltern . . . I congratulate you, sir. If the country doesn't go to the dogs or the Radicals, we shall have you Prime Minister, some day.

Enter MASON.

Mason : Luncheon is on the table, my Lady ! (MASON *goes out.*)

Mabel Chiltern : You'll stop to luncheon, Lord Caversham, won't you ?

Lord Caversham : With pleasure, and I'll drive you down to Downing Street afterwards, Chiltern. You have a great future before you, a great future. Wish I could say the same for you, sir. (*To* LORD GORING) *:* But your career will have to be entirely domestic.

Lord Goring : Yes, father, I prefer it domestic.

Lord Caversham : And if you don't make this young lady an ideal husband, I'll cut you off with a shilling.

Mabel Chiltern : An ideal husband ! Oh, I don't think I should like that. It sounds like something in the next world.

Lord Caversham: What do you want him to be then, dear?

Mabel Chiltern: He can be what he chooses. All I want is to be . . . to be . . . oh! a real wife to him.

Lord Caversham: Upon my word, there is a good deal of common sense in that, Lady Chiltern.

They all go out except SIR ROBERT CHILTERN. *He sinks into a chair, wrapt in thought. After a little time* LADY CHILTERN *returns to look for him.*

Lady Chiltern (leaning over the back of the chair): Aren't you coming in, Robert?

Sir Robert Chiltern (taking her hand): Gertrude, is it love you feel for me, or is it pity merely?

Lady Chiltern (kisses him): It is love, Robert. Love, and only love. For both of us a new life is beginning.

CURTAIN.

THE IMPORTANCE OF BEING EARNEST

TO
ROBERT BALDWIN ROSS
IN APPRECIATION
IN
AFFECTION

THE PERSONS OF THE PLAY

John Worthing, J.P.
Algernon Moncrieff
Rev. Canon Chasuble, D.D.
Merriman, Butler
Lane, Manservant

Lady Bracknell
Hon. Gwendolen Fairfax
Cecily Cardew
Miss Prism, Governess

THE SCENES OF THE PLAY

Act I. *Algernon Moncrieff's Flat in Half-Moon Street, W.*
Act II. *The Garden at the Manor House, Woolton.*
Act III. *Drawing-room at the Manor House, Woolton.*
Time: *The Present.*

LONDON : ST. JAMES'S THEATRE

Lessee and Manager : Mr. George Alexander
February, 14th, 1895

JOHN WORTHING, J.P.	*Mr. George Alexander.*
ALGERNON MONCRIEFF	*Mr. Allen Aynesworth*
REV. CANON CHASUBLE, D.D.	*Mr. H. H. Vincent.*
MERRIMAN (*Butler*)	*Mr. Frank Dyall.*
LANE (*Manservant*)	*Mr. F. Kinsey Peile.*
LADY BRACKNELL	*Miss Rose Leclercq.*
HON. GWENDOLEN FAIRFAX	*Miss Irene Vanburgh.*
CECILY CARDEW	*Miss Evelyn Millard.*
MISS PRISM (*Governess*)	*Mrs. George Canninge*

FIRST ACT

*Morning-room in Algernon's flat in Half-Moon
Street. The room is luxuriously and artistically
furnished. The sound of a piano is heard in the
adjoining room.*

LANE *is arranging afternoon tea on the table, and
after the music has ceased,* ALGERNON *enters.*

Algernon : Did you hear what I was playing, Lane ?

Lane : I didn't think it polite to listen, sir.

Algernon : I'm sorry for that, for your sake. I
don't play accurately—any one can play accurately—
but I play with wonderful expression. As far as the
piano is concerned, sentiment is my forte. I keep
science for Life.

Lane : Yes, sir.

Algernon : And, speaking of the science of Life, have
you got the cucumber sandwiches cut for Lady
Bracknell ?

Lane : Yes, sir. (*Hands them on a salver.*)

Algernon (*inspects them, takes two, and sits down on
the sofa*) *:* Oh ! . . . by the way, Lane, I see from
your book that on Thursday night, when Lord Shore-
man and Mr. Worthing were dining with me, eight
bottles of champagne are entered as having been
consumed.

Lane : Yes, sir ; eight bottles and a pint.

Algernon : Why is it that at a bachelor's establish-
ment the servants invariably drink the champagne ?
I ask merely for information.

Lane : I attribute it to the superior quality of the

wine, sir. I have often observed that in married households the champagne is rarely of a first-rate brand.

Algernon : Good heavens! Is marriage so demoralising as that ?

Lane : I believe it *is* a very pleasant state, sir. I
have had very little experience of it myself up to the
present. I have only been married once. That was in
consequence of a misunderstanding between myself
and a young person.

Algernon (languidly) : I don't know that I am
much interested in your family life, Lane.

Lane : No, sir ; it is not a very interesting subject.
I never think of it myself.

Algernon : Very natural, I am sure. That will do,
Lane, thank you.

Lane : Thank you, sir.

LANE *goes out.*

Algernon : Lane's views on marriage seem somewhat
lax. Really, if the lower orders don't set us a good
example, what on earth is the use of them? They
seem, as a class, to have absolutely no sense of moral
responsibility.

Enter LANE.

Lane : Mr. Ernest Worthing.

Enter JACK. LANE *goes out.*

Algernon : How are you, my dear Ernest ? What
brings you up to town ?

Jack : Oh, pleasure, pleasure ! What else should
bring one anywhere ? Eating as usual, I see, Algy !

Algernon (stiffly) : I believe it is customary in good
society to take some slight refreshment at five o'clock.
Where have you been since last Thursday ?

Jack (smiling down on the sofa) : In the country.

Algernon : What on earth do you do there ?

Jack (pulling off his gloves) : When one is in town one amuses oneself. When one is in the country one amuses other people. It is excessively boring.

Algernon : And who are the people you amuse ?

Jack (airily) : Oh, neighbours, neighbours.

Algernon : Got nice neighbours in your part of Shropshire ?

Jack : Perfectly horrid ! Never speak to one of them.

Algernon : How immensely you must amuse them ! *(Goes over and takes sandwich.)* By the way, Shropshire is your county, is it not ?

Jack : Eh ? Shropshire ? Yes, of course. Hallo ! Why all these cups ? Why cucumber sandwiches ? Why such reckless extravagance in one so young ? Who is coming to tea ?

Algernon : Oh ! merely Aunt Augusta and Gwendolen.

Jack : How perfectly delightful !

Algernon : Yes, that is all very well ; but I am afraid Aunt Augusta won't quite approve of your being here.

Jack : May I ask why ?

Algernon : My dear fellow, the way you flirt with Gwendolen is perfectly disgraceful. It is almost as bad as the way Gwendolen flirts with you.

Jack : I am in love with Gwendolen. I have come up to town expressly to propose to her.

Algernon : I thought you had come up for pleasure ? . . I call that business.

Jack : How utterly unromantic you are !

Algernon : I really don't see anything romantic in proposing. It is very romantic to be in love. But there is nothing romantic about a definite proposal. Why, one may be accepted. One usually is, I believe. Then the excitement is all over. The very essence of romance is uncertainty. If ever I get married, I'll certainly try to forget the fact.

Jack : I have no doubt about that, dear Algy. The Divorce Court was specially invented for people whose memories are so curiously constituted.

Algernon : Oh ! there is no use speculating on that subject. Divorces are made in Heaven—— (JACK *puts out his hand to take a sandwich.* ALGERNON *at once interferes.*) Please don't touch the cucumber sandwiches. They are ordered specially for Aunt Augusta. (*Takes one and eats it.*)

Jack : Well, you have been eating them all the time.

Algernon : That is quite a different matter. She is my aunt. (*Takes plate from below.*) Have some bread and butter. The bread and butter is for Gwendolen. Gwendolen is devoted to bread and butter.

Jack (*advancing to table and helping himself*) *:* And very good bread and butter it is too.

Algernon : Well, my dear fellow, you need not eat as if you were going to eat it all. You behave as if you were married to her already. You are not married to her already, and I don't think you ever will be.

Jack : Why on earth do you say that ?

Algernon : Well, in the first place girls never marry the men they flirt with. Girls don't think it right.

Jack : Oh, that is nonsense !

Algernon : It isn't. It is a great truth. It accounts for the extraordinary number of bachelors that one sees all over the place. In the second place, I don't give my consent.

Jack : Your consent !

Algernon : My dear fellow, Gwendolen is my first cousin. And before I allow you to marry her, you will have to clear up the whole question of Cecily. (*Rings bell.*)

Jack : Cecily ! What on earth do you mean ? What do you mean, Algy, by Cecily ! I don't know any one of the name of Cecily.

Enter LANE.

Algernon : Bring me that cigarette case Mr. Worthing left in the smoking-room the last time he dined here.
Lane : Yes, sir.

LANE *goes out.*

Jack : Do you mean to say you have had my cigarette case all this time ? I wish to goodness you had let me know. I have been writing frantic letters to Scotland Yard about it. I was very nearly offering a large reward.
Algernon : Well, I wish you would offer one. I happen to be more than usually hard up.
Jack : There is no good offering a large reward now that the thing is found.

Enter LANE *with the cigarette case on a salver.*
ALGERNON *takes it at once.* LANE *goes out.*

Algernon : I think that is rather mean of you, Ernest, I must say. (*Opens case and examines it.*) However, it makes no matter, for, now that I look at the inscription inside, I find that the thing isn't yours after all.
Jack : Of course it's mine. (*Moving to him.*) You have seen me with it a hundred times, and you have no right whatsoever to read what is written inside. It is a very ungentlemanly thing to read a private cigarette case.
Algernon : Oh ! it is absurd to have a hard and fast rule about what one should read and what one shouldn't. More than half of modern culture depends on what one shouldn't read.
Jack : I am quite aware of the fact, and I don't propose to discuss modern culture. It isn't the sort of thing one should talk of in private. I simply want my cigarette case back.

Algernon : Yes ; but this isn't your cigarette case. This cigarette case is a present from some one of the name of Cecily, and you said you didn't know any one of that name.

Jack : Well, if you want to know, Cecily happens to be my aunt.

Algernon : Your aunt !

Jack : Yes. Charming old lady she is, too. Lives at Tunbridge Wells. Just give it back to me, Algy.

Algernon (retreating to back of sofa) : But why does she call herself little Cecily if she is your aunt and lives at Tunbridge Wells ? *(Reading.)* " From little Cecily with her fondest love."

Jack (moving to sofa and kneeling upon it) : My dear fellow, what on earth is there in that ? Some aunts are tall, some aunts are not tall. That is a matter that surely an aunt may be allowed to decide for herself. You seem to think that every aunt should be exactly like your aunt ! That is absurd ! For Heaven's sake give me back my cigarette case. *(Follows* ERNEST *round the room.)*

Algernon : Yes. But why does your aunt call you her uncle ? " From little Cecily, with her fondest love to her dear Uncle Jack." There is no objection, I admit, to an aunt being a small aunt, but why an aunt, no matter what her size may be, should call her own nephew her uncle, I can't quite make out. Besides, your name isn't Jack at all ; it is Ernest.

Jack : It isn't Ernest ; it's Jack.

Algernon : You have always told me it was Ernest; I have introduced you to every one as Ernest. You answer to the name of Ernest. You look as if your name was Ernest. You are the most earnest-looking person I ever saw in my life. It is perfectly absurd your saying that your name isn't Ernest. It's on your cards. Here is one of them. *(Taking it from case.)* " Mr. Ernest Worthing, B. 4, The Albany." I'll keep this as a proof that your name is Ernest if ever you attempt to deny it to me, or to Gwendolen, or to any one else. (*Puts the card in his pocket.*)

Jack : Well, my name is Ernest in town and Jack in the country, and the cigarette case was given to me in the country.

Algernon : Yes, but that does not account for the fact that your small Aunt Cecily, who lives at Tunbridge Wells, calls you her dear uncle. Come, old boy, you had much better have the thing out at once.

Jack : My dear Algy, you talk exactly as if you were a dentist. It is very vulgar to talk like a dentist when one isn't a dentist. It produces a false impression.

Algernon : Well, that is exactly what dentists always do. Now, go on ! Tell me the whole thing. I may mention that I have always suspected you of being a confirmed and secret Bunburyist ; and I am quite sure of it now.

Jack : Bunburyist ? What on earth do you mean by a Bunburyist ?

Algernon : I'll reveal to you the meaning of that incomparable expression as soon as you are kind enough to inform me why you are Ernest in town and Jack in the country.

Jack : Well, produce my cigarette case first.

Algernon : Here it is. (*Hands cigarette case.*) Now produce your explanation, and pray make it improbable. (*Sits on sofa.*)

Jack : My dear fellow, there is nothing improbable about my explanation at all. In fact, it's perfectly ordinary. Old Mr. Thomas Cardew, who adopted me when I was a little boy, made me in his will guardian to his grand-daughter, Miss Cecily Cardew. Cecily, who addresses me as her uncle from motives of respect that you could not possibly appreciate, lives at my place in the country under the charge of her admirable governess, Miss Prism.

Algernon : Where is that place in the country, by the way ?

Jack : That is nothing to you, dear boy. You are not going to be invited. . . . I may tell you candidly that the place is not in Shropshire.

Algernon : I suspected that, my dear fellow ! I have Bunburyed all over Shropshire on two separate occasions. Now, go on. Why are you Ernest in town and Jack in the country ?

Jack : My dear Algy, I don't know whether you will be able to understand my real motives. You are hardly serious enough. When one is placed in the position of guardian, one has to adopt a very high moral tone on all subjects. It's one's duty to do so. And as a high moral tone can hardly be said to conduce very much to either one's health or one's happiness, in order to get up to town I have always pretended to have a younger brother of the name of Ernest, who lives in the Albany, and gets into the most dreadful scrapes. That, my dear Algy, is the whole truth pure and simple.

Algernon : The truth is rarely pure and never simple. Modern life would be very tedious if it were either, and modern literature a complete impossibility !

Jack : That wouldn't be at all a bad thing.

Algernon : Literary criticism is not your forte, my dear fellow. Don't try it. You should leave that to people who haven't been at a University. They do it so well in the daily papers. What you really are is a Bunburyist. I was quite right in saying you were a Bunburyist. You are one of the most advanced Bunburyists I know.

Jack : What an earth do you mean ?

Algernon : You have invented a very useful younger brother called Ernest, in order that you may be able to come up to town as often as you like. I have invented an invaluable permanent invalid called Bunbury, in order that I may be able to go down into the country whenever I choose. Bunbury is perfectly invaluable. If it wasn't for Bunbury's extraordinary bad health, for instance, I wouldn't be able to dine with you at

Willis's to-night, for I have been really engaged to Aunt Augusta for more than a week.

Jack : I haven't asked you to dine with me any‧where to-night.

Algernon : I know. You are absurdly careless about sending out invitations. It is very foolish of you. Nothing annoys people so much as not receiving invitations.

Jack : You had much better dine with your Aunt Augusta.

Algernon : I haven't the smallest intention of doing anything of the kind. To begin with, I dined there on Monday, and once a week is quite enough to dine with one's own relations. In the second place, whenever I do dine there I am always treated as a member of the family, and sent down with either no woman at all, or two. In the third place, I know perfectly well whom she will place me next to, to-night. She will place me next Mary Farquhar, who always flirts with her own husband across the dinner-table. That is not very pleasant. Indeed, it is not even decent . . . and that sort of thing is enormously on the increase. The amount of women in London who flirt with their own husbands is perfectly scandalous. It looks so bad. It is simply washing one's clean linen in public. Besides, now that I know you to be a confirmed Bunburyist I naturally want to talk to you about Bunburying. I want to tell you the rules.

Jack : I'm not a Bunburyist at all. If Gwendolen accepts me, I am going to kill my brother, indeed I think I'll kill him in any case. Cecily is a little too much interested in him. It is rather a bore. So I am going to get rid of Ernest. And I strongly advise you to do the same with Mr. . . . with your invalid friend who has the absurd name.

Algernon : Nothing will induce me to part with Bunbury, and if you ever get married, which seems to me extremely problematic, you will be very glad to know Bunbury. A man who marries without knowing Bunbury has a very tedious time of it.

Jack : That is nonsense. If I marry a charming girl like Gwendolen, and she is the only girl I ever saw in my life that I would marry, I certainly won't want to know Bunbury.

Algernon : Then your wife will. You don't seem to realise, that in married life three is company and two is none.

Jack (sententiously) : That, my dear young friend, is the theory that the corrupt French Drama has been propounding for the last fifty years.

Algernon : Yes ; and that the happy English home has proved in half the time.

Jack : For heaven's sake, don't try to be cynical. It's perfectly easy to be cynical.

Algernon : My dear fellow, it isn't easy to be anything nowadays. There's such a lot of beastly competition about. (*The sound of an electric bell is heard.*) Ah ! that must be Aunt Augusta. Only relatives, or creditors, ever ring in that Wagnerian manner. Now, if I get her out of the way for ten minutes, so that you can have an opportunity for proposing to Gwendolen, may I dine with you to-night at Willis's ?

Jack : I suppose so, if you want to.

Algernon : Yes, but you must be serious about it. I hate people who are not serious about meals. It is so shallow of them.

Enter LANE.

Lane : Lady Bracknell and Miss Fairfax.

ALGERNON *goes forward to meet them. Enter* LADY BRACKNELL *and* GWENDOLEN.

Lady Bracknell : Good-afternoon, dear Algernon, I hope you are behaving very well.

Algernon : I'm feeling very well, Aunt Augusta.

Lady Bracknell : That's not quite the same thing. In fact the two things rarely go together. (*Sees* JACK *and bows to him with icy coldness.*)

Algernon (*to* GWENDOLEN) *:* Dear me, you are smart !

Gwendolen : I am always smart ! Am I not, Mr. Worthing ?

Jack : You're quite perfect, Miss Fairfax.

Gwendolen : Oh ! I hope I am not that. It would leave no room for developments, and I intend to develop in many directions. (GWENDOLEN *and* JACK *sit down together in the corner.*)

Lady Bracknell : I'm sorry if we are a little late, Algernon, but I was obliged to call on dear Lady Harbury. I hadn't been there since her poor husband's death. I never saw a woman so altered ; she looks quite twenty years younger. And now I'll have a cup of tea, and one of those nice cucumber sandwiches you promised me.

Algernon : Certainly, Aunt Augusta. (*Goes over to tea-table.*)

Lady Bracknell : Won't you come and sit here, Gwendolen ?

Gwendolen : Thanks, mamma, I'm quite comfortable where I am.

Algernon (*picking up empty plate in horror*) *:* Good heavens ! Lane ! Why are there no cucumber sandwiches ? I ordered them specially.

Lane (*gravely*) *:* There were no cucumbers in the market this morning, sir. I went down twice.

Algernon : No cucumbers !

Lane : No, sir. Not even for ready money.

Algernon : That will do, Lane, thank you.

Lane : Thank you, sir. (*Goes out.*)

Algernon : I am greatly distressed, Aunt Augusta, about there being no cucumbers. not even for ready money.

Lady Bracknell : It really makes no matter, Algernon. I had some crumpets with Lady Harbury, who seems to me to be living entirely for pleasure now.

Algernon : I hear her hair has turned quite gold from grief.

Lady Bracknell : It certainly has changed its colour. From what cause I, of course, cannot say. (ALGERNON *crosses and hands tea.*) Thank you. I've quite a treat for you to-night, Algernon. I am going to send you down with Mary Farquhar. She is such a nice woman, and so attentive to her husband. It's delightful to watch them.

Algernon : I am afraid, Aunt Augusta, I shall have to give up the pleasure of dining with you to-night after all.

Lady Bracknell (frowning) : I hope not, Algernon. It would put my table completely out. Your uncle would have to dine upstairs. Fortunately he is accustomed to that.

Algernon : It is a great bore, and, I need hardly say, a terrible disappointment to me, but the fact is I have just had a telegram to say that my poor friend Bunbury is very ill again. (*Exchanges glances with* JACK.) They seem to think I should be with him.

Lady Bracknell : It is very strange. This Mr. Bunbury seems to suffer from curiously bad health.

Algernon : Yes ; poor Bunbury is a dreadful invalid.

Lady Bracknell : Well, I must say, Algernon, that I think it is high time that Mr. Bunbury made up his mind whether he was going to live or to die. This shilly-shallying with the question is absurd. Nor do I in any way approve of the modern sympathy with invalids. I consider it morbid. Illness of any kind is hardly a thing to be encouraged in others. Health is the primary duty of life. I am always telling that to your poor uncle, but he never seems to take much notice . . . as far as any improvement in his ailment goes. I should be much obliged if you would ask Mr.

Bunbury, from me, to be kind enough not to have a relapse on Saturday, for I rely on you to arrange my music for me. It is my last reception, and one wants something that will encourage conversation, particularly at the end of the season when every one has practically said whatever they had to say, which, in most cases, was probably not much.

Algernon : I'll speak to Bunbury, Aunt Augusta, if he is still conscious, and I think I can promise you he'll be all right by Saturday. Of course the music is a great difficulty. You see, if one plays good music, people don't listen, and if one plays bad music people don't talk. But I'll run over the programme I've drawn out, if you will kindly come into the next room for a moment.

Lady Bracknell : Thank you, Algernon. It is very thoughtful of you. (*Rising, and following* ALGERNON.) I'm sure the programme will be delightful, after a few expurgations. French songs I cannot possibly allow. People always seem to think that they are improper, and either look shocked, which is vulgar, or laugh, which is worse. But German sounds a thoroughly respectable language, and indeed, I believe is so. Gwendolen, you will accompany me.

Gwendolen : Certainly, mamma.

LADY BRACKNELL *and* ALGERNON *go into the music-room,* GWENDOLEN *remains behind.*

Jack : Charming day it has been, Miss Fairfax.

Gwendolen : Pray don't talk to me about the weather, Mr. Worthing. Whenever people talk to me about the weather, I always feel quite certain that they mean something else. And that makes me so nervous.

Jack : I do mean something else.

Gwendolen : I thought so. In fact, I am never wrong.

Jack : And I would like to be allowed to take advantage of Lady Bracknell's temporary absence . . .

Gwendolen: I would certainly advise you to do so. Mamma has a way of coming back suddenly into a room that I have often had to speak to her about.

Jack (nervously): Miss Fairfax, ever since I met you I have admired you more than any girl . . . I have ever met since . . . I met you.

Gwendolen: Yes, I am quite well aware of the fact. And I often wish that in public, at any rate, you had been more demonstrative. For me you have always had an irresistible fascination. Even before I met you I was far from indifferent to you. (JACK *looks at her in amazement.*) We live, as I hope you know, Mr. Worthing, in an age of ideals. The fact is constantly mentioned in the more expensive monthly magazines, and has reached the provincial pulpits, I am told ; and my ideal has always been to love some one of the name of Ernest. There is something in that name that inspires absolute confidence. The moment Algernon first mentioned to me that he had a friend called Ernest, I knew I was destined to love you.

Jack: You really love me, Gwendolen ?

Gwendolen: Passionately !

Jack: Darling ! You don't know how happy you've made me.

Gwendolen: My own Ernest !

Jack: But you don't really mean to say that you couldn't love me if my name wasn't Ernest ?

Gwendolen: But your name is Ernest.

Jack: Yes, I know it is. But supposing it was something else ? Do you mean to say you couldn't love me then ?

Gwendolen (glibly): Ah ! that is clearly a metaphysical speculation, and like most metaphysical speculations has very little reference at all to the actual facts of real life, as we know them.

Jack: Personally, darling, to speak quite candidly, I don't much care about the name of Ernest. . . . I don't think the name suits me at all.

Gwendolen: It suits you perfectly. It is a divine name. It has a music of its own. It produces vibrations.

Jack: Well, really, Gwendolen, I must say that I think there are lots of other much nicer names. I think Jack, for instance, a charming name.

Gwendolen: Jack? . . . No, there is very little music in the name Jack, if any at all, indeed. It does not thrill. It produces absolutely no vibrations. . . . I have known several Jacks, and they all, without exception, were more than usually plain. Besides, Jack is a notorious domesticity for John ! And I pity any woman who is married to a man called John. She would probably never be allowed to know the entrancing pleasure of a single moment's solitude. The only really safe name is Ernest.

Jack: Gwendolen, I must get christened at once— I mean we must get married at once. There is no time to be lost.

Gwendolen: Married, Mr. Worthing ?

Jack (astounded): Well . . . surely. You know that I love you, and you led me to believe, Miss Fairfax, that you were not absolutely indifferent to me.

Gwendolen: I adore you. But you haven't proposed to me yet. Nothing has been said at all about marriage. The subject has not even been touched on.

Jack: Well . . . may I propose to you now ?

Gwendolen: I think it would be an admirable opportunity. And to spare you any possible disappointment, Mr. Worthing, I think it only fair to tell you quite frankly beforehand that I am fully determined to accept you.

Jack: Gwendolen !

Gwendolen: Yes, Mr. Worthing, what have you got to say to me ?

Jack: You know what I have got to say to you.

Gwendolen: Yes, but you don't say it.

Jack: Gwendolen, will you marry me ? (*Goes on his knees.*)

Gwendolen : Of course I will, darling. How long you have been about it ! I am afraid you have had very little experience in how to propose.

Jack : My own one, I have never loved any one in the world but you.

Gwendolen : Yes, but men often propose for practice. I know my brother Gerald does. All my girl-friends tell me so. What wonderfully blue eyes you have, Ernest ! They are quite, quite, blue. I hope you will always look at me just like that, especially when there are other people present.

Enter LADY BRACKNELL.

Lady Bracknell : Mr. Worthing ! Rise, sir, from this semi-recumbent posture. It is most indecorous.

Gwendolen : Mamma ! (*He tries to rise ; she restrains him.*) I must beg you to retire. This is no place for you. Besides, Mr. Worthing has not quite finished yet.

Lady Bracknell : Finished what, may I ask ?

Gwendolen : I am engaged to Mr. Worthing, mamma. (*They rise together.*)

Lady Bracknell : Pardon me, you are not engaged to any one. When you do become engaged to some one, I, or your father, should his health permit him, will inform you of the fact. An engagement should come on a young girl as a surprise, pleasant or unpleasant, as the case may be. It is hardly a matter that she could be allowed to arrange for herself. . . . And now I have a few questions to put to you, Mr. Worthing. While I am making these inquiries, you, Gwendolen, will wait for me below in the carriage.

Gwendolen (reproachfully) : Mamma !

Lady Bracknell : In the carriage, Gwendolen !

GWENDOLEN *goes to the door. She and* JACK *blow kisses to each other behind* LADY BRACKNELL'S *back.* LADY BRACKNELL *looks vaguely about as if she could not understand what the noise was. Finally turns round.*

Gwendolen, the carriage !

Gwendolen : Yes, mamma. (*Goes out, looking back at* JACK.)

Lady Bracknell (sitting down) : You can take a seat, Mr. Worthing.

Looks in her pocket for note-book and pencil.

Jack : Thank you, Lady Bracknell, I prefer standing.

Lady Bracknell (pencil and note-book in hand) : I feel bound to tell you that you are not down on my list of eligible young men, although I have the same list as the dear Duchess of Bolton has. We work together, in fact. However, I am quite ready to enter your name, should your answers be what a really affectionate mother requires. Do you smoke ?

Jack : Well, yes, I must admit I smoke.

Lady Bracknell : I am glad to hear it. A man should always have an occupation of some kind. There are far too many idle men in London as it is. How old are you ?

Jack : Twenty-nine.

Lady Bracknell : A very good age to be married at. I have always been of opinion that a man who desires to get married should know either everything or nothing. Which do you know ?

Jack (after some hesitation) : I know nothing, Lady Bracknell.

Lady Bracknell : I am pleased to hear it. I do not approve of anything that tampers with natural ignorance. Ignorance is like a delicate exotic fruit ; touch it and the bloom is gone. The whole theory of modern education is radically unsound. Fortunately in England, at any rate, education produces no effect whatsoever. If it did, it would prove a serious danger to the upper classes, and probably lead to acts of violence in Grosvenor Square. What is your income?

Jack: Between seven and eight thousand a year.

Lady Bracknell (makes a note in her book): In land, or in investments?

Jack: In investments, chiefly.

Lady Bracknell: That is satisfactory. What between the duties expected of one during one's lifetime, and the duties exacted from one after one's death, land has ceased to be either a profit or a pleasure. It gives one position, and prevents one from keeping it up. That's all that can be said about land.

Jack: I have a country house with some land, of course, attached to it, about fifteen hundred acres, I believe; but I don't depend on that for my real income. In fact, as far as I can make out, the poachers are the only people who make anything out of it.

Lady Bracknell: A country house! How many bedrooms? Well, that point can be cleared up afterwards. You have a town house, I hope? A girl with a simple, unspoiled nature, like Gwendolen, could hardly be expected to reside in the country.

Jack: Well, I own a house in Belgrave Square, but it is let by the year to Lady Bloxham. Of course, I can get it back whenever I like, at six months' notice.

Lady Bracknell: Lady Bloxham? I don't know her.

Jack: Oh, she goes about very little. She is a lady considerably advanced in years.

Lady Bracknell: Ah, nowadays that is no guarantee of respectability of character. What number in Belgrave Square?

Jack: 149.

Lady Bracknell (shaking her head): The unfashionable side. I thought there was something. However, that could easily be altered.

Jack: Do you mean the fashion, or the side?

Lady Bracknell (sternly): Both, if necessary, I presume. What are your politics?

Jack : Well, I am afraid I really have none. I am a Liberal Unionist.

Lady Bracknell : Oh, they count as Tories. They dine with us. Or come in the evening, at any rate. Now to minor matters. Are your parents living ?

Jack : I have lost both my parents.

Lady Bracknell : Both ? . . . That seems like carelessness. Who was your father ? He was evidently a man of some wealth. Was he born in what the Radical papers call the purple of commerce, or did he rise from the ranks of the aristocracy ?

Jack : I am afraid I really don't know. The fact is, Lady Bracknell, I said I had lost my parents. It would be nearer the truth to say that my parents seem to have lost me. . . . I don't actually know who I am by birth. I was . . . well, I was found.

Lady Bracknell : Found !

Jack : The late Mr. Thomas Cardew, an old gentleman of a very charitable and kindly disposition, found me, and gave me the name of Worthing, because he happened to have a first-class ticket for Worthing in his pocket at the time. Worthing is a place in Sussex. It is a seaside resort.

Lady Bracknell : Where did the charitable gentleman who had a first-class ticket for this seaside resort find you ?

Jack (gravely) : In a hand-bag.

Lady Bracknell : A hand-bag ?

Jack (very seriously) : Yes, Lady Bracknell. I was in a hand-bag—a somewhat large, black leather hand-bag, with handles to it—an ordinary hand-bag in fact.

Lady Bracknell : In what locality did this Mr. James, or Thomas, Cardew come across this ordinary hand-bag ?

Jack : In the cloak-room at Victoria Station. It was given to him in mistake for his own.

Lady Bracknell : The cloak-room at Victoria Station ?

Jack : Yes. The Brighton line.

Lady Bracknell: The line is immaterial. Mr. Worthing, I confess I feel somewhat bewildered by what you have just told me. To be born, or at any rate bred, in a hand-bag, whether it had handles or not, seems to me to display a contempt for the ordinary decencies of family life that reminds one of the worst excesses of the French Revolution. And I presume you know what that unfortunate movement led to ? As for the particular locality in which the hand-bag was found, a cloak-room at a railway station might serve to conceal a social indiscretion—has probably, indeed, been used for that purpose before now—but it could hardly be regarded as an assured basis for a recognised position in good society.

Jack: May I ask you then what you would advise me to do ? I need hardly say I would do anything in the world to ensure Gwendolen's happiness.

Lady Bracknell: I would strongly advise you, Mr. Worthing, to try and acquire some relations as soon as possible, and to make a definite effort to produce at any rate one parent, of either sex, before the season is quite over.

Jack: Well, I don't see how I could possibly manage to do that. I can produce the hand-bag at any moment. It is in my dressing-room at home. I really think that should satisfy you, Lady Bracknell.

Lady Bracknell: Me, sir ! What has it to do with me ? You can hardly imagine that I and Lord Bracknell would dream of allowing our only daughter—a girl brought up with the utmost care—to marry into a cloak-room, and form an alliance with a parcel. Good-morning, Mr. Worthing !

LADY BRACKNELL *sweeps out in majestic indignation.*

Jack: Good-morning ! (ALGERNON, *from the other room, strikes up the Wedding March.* JACK *looks*

perfectly furious, and goes to the door.) For goodness'
sake don't play that ghastly tune, Algy ! How idiotic
you are !

The music stops and ALGERNON *enters cheerily.*

Algernon : Didn't it go off all right, old boy ? You
don't mean to say Gwendolen refused you ? I know
it is a way she has. She is always refusing people.
I think it is most ill-natured of her.

Jack : Oh, Gwendolen is as right as a trivet. As
far as she is concerned, we are engaged. Her mother
is perfectly unbearable. Never met such a Gorgon.
. . . I don't really know what a Gorgon is like, but I
am quite sure that Lady Bracknell is one. In any case,
she is a monster, without being a myth, which is rather
unfair. . . . I beg your pardon, Algy, I suppose I
shouldn't talk about your own aunt in that way
before you.

Algernon : My dear boy, I love hearing my relations
abused. It is the only thing that makes me put up
with them at all. Relations are simply a tedious pack
of people, who haven't got the remotest knowledge
of how to live, nor the smallest instinct about when
to die.

Jack : Oh, that is nonsense !

Algernon : It isn't !

Jack : Well, I won't argue about the matter. You
always want to argue about things.

Algernon : That is exactly what things were originally
made for.

Jack : Upon my word, if I thought that, I'd shoot
myself. . . . (*A Pause.*) You don't think there is any
chance of Gwendolen becoming like her mother in
about a hundred and fifty years, do you, Algy ?

Algernon : All women become like their mothers.
That is their tragedy. No man does. That's his.

Jack : Is that clever ?

Algernon : It is perfectly phrased ! And quite as true as any observation in civilised life should be.

Jack : I am sick to death of cleverness. Everybody is clever nowadays. You can't go anywhere without meeting clever people. The thing has become an absolute public nuisance. I wish to goodness we had a few fools left.

Algernon : We have.

Jack : I should extremely like to meet them. What do they talk about ?

Algernon : The fools ? Oh ! about the clever people of course.

Jack : What fools.

Algernon : By the way, did you tell Gwendolen the truth about your being Ernest in town, and Jack in the country ?

Jack (in a very patronising manner) : My dear fellow, the truth isn't quite the sort of thing one tells to a nice, sweet, refined girl. What extraordinary ideas you have about the way to behave to a woman !

Algernon : The only way to behave to a woman is to make love to her, if she is pretty, and to some one else, if she is plain.

Jack : Oh, that is nonsense.

Algernon : What about your brother ? What about the profligate Ernest ?

Jack : Oh, before the end of the week I shall have got rid of him. I'll say he died in Paris of apoplexy. Lots of people die of apoplexy, quite suddenly, don't they ?

Algernon : Yes, but it's hereditary, my dear fellow. It's a sort of thing that runs in families. You had much better say a severe chill.

Jack : You are sure a severe chill isn't hereditary, or anything of that kind ?

Algernon : Of course it isn't !

Jack : Very well, then. My poor brother Ernest

is carried off suddenly, in Paris, by a severe chill. That gets rid of him.

Algernon : But I thought you said that . . . Miss Cardew was a little too much interested in your poor brother Ernest ? Won't she feel his loss a good deal ?

Jack : Oh, that is all right. Cecily is not a silly romantic girl, I am glad to say. She has got a capital appetite, goes long walks, and pays no attention at all to her lessons.

Algernon : I would rather like to see Cecily.

Jack : I will take very good care you never do. She is excessively pretty, and she is only just eighteen.

Algernon : Have you told Gwendolen yet that you have an excessively pretty ward who is only just eighteen ?

Jack : Oh ! one doesn't blurt these things out to people. Cecily and Gwendolen are perfectly certain to be extremely great friends. I'll bet you anything you like that half an hour after they have met, they will be calling each other sister.

Algernon : Women only do that when they have called each other a lot of other things first. Now, my dear boy, if we want to get a good table at Willis's, we really must go and dress. Do you know it is nearly seven ?

Jack (irritably) : Oh ! it always is nearly seven.

Algernon : Well, I'm hungry.

Jack : I never knew you when you weren't. . . .

Algernon : What shall we do after dinner ? Go to a theatre ?

Jack : Oh no ! I loathe listening.

Algernon : Well, let us go to the Club ?

Jack : Oh, no ! I hate talking.

Algernon : Well, we might trot round to the Empire at ten ?

Jack : Oh, no ! I can't bear looking at things. It is so silly.

Algernon : Well, what shall we do ?

Jack : Nothing !

Algernon : It is awfully hard work doing nothing. However, I don't mind hard work where there is no definite object of any kind.

Enter LANE.

Lane : Miss Fairfax.

Enter GWENDOLEN. LANE *goes out.*

Algernon : Gwendolen, upon my word !

Gwendolen : Algy, kindly turn your back. I have something very particular to say to Mr. Worthing.

Algernon : Really, Gwendolen, I don't think I can allow this at all.

Gwendolen : Algy, you always adopt a strictly immoral attitude towards life. You are not quite old enough to do that. (ALGERNON *retires to the fireplace.*)

Jack : My own darling !

Gwendolen : Ernest, we may never be married. From the expression on mamma's face I fear we never shall. Few parents nowadays pay any regard to what their children say to them. The old-fashioned respect for the young is fast dying out. Whatever influence I ever had over mamma, I lost at the age of three. But although she may prevent us from becoming man and wife, and I may marry some one else, and marry often, nothing that she can possibly do can alter my eternal devotion to you.

Jack : Dear Gwendolen !

Gwendolen : The story of your romantic origin, as related to me by mamma, with unpleasing comments, has naturally stirred the deeper fibres of my nature. Your Christian name has an irresistible fascination. The simplicity of your character makes you exquisitely incomprehensible to me. Your town address at the Albany I have. What is your address in the country ?

Jack : The Manor House, Woolton, Hertfordshire.

ALGERNON, *who has been carefully listening, smiles to himself, and writes the address on his shirt-cuff. Then picks up the Railway Guide.*

Gwendolen : There is a good postal service, I suppose ? It may be necessary to do something desperate. That, of course, will require serious consideration. I will communicate with you daily.

Jack : My own one !

Gwendolen : How long do you remain in town ?

Jack : Till Monday.

Gwendolen : Good ! Algy, you may turn round now.

Algernon : Thanks, I've turned round already.

Gwendolen : You may also ring the bell.

Jack : You will let me see you to your carriage, my own darling ?

Gwendolen : Certainly.

Jack (To LANE, *who now enters) :* I will see Miss Fairfax out.

Lane : Yes, sir.

JACK *and* GWENDOLEN *go off.*

LANE *presents several letters on a salver to* ALGERNON. *It is to be surmised that they are bills, as* ALGERNON, *after looking at the envelopes, tears them up.*

Algernon : A glass of sherry, Lane.

Lane : Yes, sir.

Algernon : To-morrow, Lane, I'm going Bunburying.

Lane : Yes, sir.

Algernon : I shall probably not be back till Monday. You can put up my dress clothes, my smoking jacket, and all the Bunbury suits . . .

Lane : Yes, sir. (*Handing sherry.*)

Algernon : I hope to-morrow will be a fine day, Lane.
Lane : It never is, sir.
Algernon : Lane, you're a perfect pessimist.
Lane : I do my best to give satisfaction, sir.

Enter JACK. LANE *goes off.*

Jack : There's a sensible, intellectual girl ! the only girl I ever cared for in my life. (ALGERNON *is laughing immoderately*.) What on earth are you so amused at ?
Algernon : Oh, I'm a little anxious about poor Bunbury, that is all.
Jack : If you don't take care, your friend Bunbury will get you into a serious scrape some day.
Algernon : I love scrapes. They are the only things that are never serious.
Jack : Oh, that's nonsense, Algy. You never talk anything but nonsense.
Algernon : Nobody ever does.

JACK *looks indignantly at him, and leaves the room.* ALGERNON *lights a cigarette, reads his shirt-cuff, and smiles.*

ACT DROP.

SECOND ACT

SCENE

Garden at the Manor House. A flight of grey stone steps leads up to the house. The garden, an old-fashioned one, full of roses. Time of year, July. Basket chairs, and a table covered with books, are set under a large yew-tree.

MISS PRISM *discovered seated at the table.* CECILY *is at the back watering flowers.*

Miss Prism (calling) : Cecily, Cecily ! Surely such a utilitarian occupation as the watering of flowers is rather Moulton's duty than yours ? Especially at a moment when intellectual pleasures await you. Your German grammar is on the table. Pray open it at page fifteen. We will repeat yesterday's lesson.

Cecily (coming over very slowly) : But I don't like German. It isn't at all a becoming language. I know perfectly well that I look quite plain after my German lesson.

Miss Prism : Child, you know how anxious your guardian is that you should improve yourself in every way. He laid particular stress on your German, as he was leaving for town yesterday. Indeed, he always lays stress on your German when he is leaving for town.

Cecily : Dear Uncle Jack is so very serious ! Sometimes he is so serious that I think he cannot be quite well.

Miss Prism (drawing herself up) : Your guardian enjoys the best of health, and his gravity of demeanour is especially to be commended in one so comparatively

619

young as he is. I know no one who has a higher sense
of duty and responsibility.

Cecily : I suppose that is why he often looks a little
bored when we three are together.

Miss Prism : Cecily! I am surprised at you. Mr.
Worthing has many troubles in his life. Idle merriment
and triviality would be out of place in his conversation.
You must remember his constant anxiety about that
unfortunate young man his brother.

Cecily : I wish Uncle Jack would allow that unfortunate young man, his brother, to come down here
sometimes. We might have a good influence over him,
Miss Prism. I am sure you certainly would. You know
German, and geology, and things of that kind influence
a man very much.

CECILY *begins to write in her diary.*

Miss Prism (shaking her head) : I do not think that
even I could produce any effect on a character that
according to his own brother's admission is irretrievably
weak and vacillating. Indeed I am not sure that I
would desire to reclaim him. I am not in favour of this
modern mania for turning bad people into good people
at a moment's notice. As a man sows so let him reap.
You must put away your diary, Cecily. I really don't
see why you should keep a diary at all.

Cecily : I keep a diary in order to enter the wonderful
secrets of my life. If I didn't write them down, I
should probably forget all about them.

Miss Prism : Memory, my dear Cecily, is the diary
that we all carry about with us.

Cecily : Yes, but it usually chronicles the things
that have never happened, and couldn't possibly have
happened. I believe that Memory is responsible for
nearly all the three-volume novels that Mudie sends us.

Miss Prism : Do not speak slightingly of the three-
volume novel, Cecily. I wrote one myself in earlier
days.

Cecily : Did you really, Miss Prism ? How wonderfully clever you are ! I hope it did not end happily ? I don't like novels that end happily. They depress me so much.

Miss Prism : The good ended happily, and the bad unhappily. That is what Fiction means.

Cecily : I suppose so. But it seems very unfair. And was your novel ever published ?

Miss Prism : Alas ! no. The manuscript unfortunately was abandoned. (CECILY *starts*.) I use the word in the sense of lost or mislaid. To your work, child, these speculations are profitless.

Cecily (smiling) : But I see dear Dr. Chasuble coming up through the garden.

Miss Prism (rising and advancing) : Dr. Chasuble ! This is indeed a pleasure.

Enter CANON CHASUBLE.

Chasuble : And how are we this morning ? Miss Prism, you are, I trust, well ?

Cecily : Miss Prism has just been complaining of a slight headache. I think it would do her so much good to have a short stroll with you in the Park, Dr. Chasuble.

Miss Prism : Cecily, I have not mentioned anything about a headache.

Cecily : No, dear Miss Prism, I know that, but I felt instinctively that you had a headache. Indeed I was thinking about that, and not about my German lesson, when the Rector came in.

Chasuble : I hope, Cecily, you are not inattentive.

Cecily : Oh, I am afraid I am.

Chasuble : That is strange. Were I fortunate enough to be Miss Prism's pupil, I would hang upon her lips. (MISS PRISM *glares*.) I spoke metaphorically.—My metaphor was drawn from bees. Ahem ! Mr. Worthing, I suppose, has not returned from town yet ?

Miss Prism : We do not expect him till Monday afternoon.

Chasuble : Ah yes, he usually likes to spend his Sunday in London. He is not one of those whose sole aim is enjoyment, as, by all accounts, that unfortunate young man his brother seems to be. But I must not disturb Egeria and her pupil any longer.

Miss Prism : Egeria ? My name is Lætitia, Doctor.

Chasuble (bowing) : A classical allusion merely, drawn from the Pagan authors. I shall see you both no doubt at Evensong ?

Miss Prism : I think, dear Doctor, I will have a stroll with you. I find I have a headache after all, and a walk might do it good.

Chasuble : With pleasure, Miss Prism, with pleasure. We might go as far as the schools and back.

Miss Prism : That would be delightful. Cecily, you will read your Political Economy in my absence. The chapter on the Fall of the Rupee you may omit. It is somewhat too sensational. Even these metallic problems have their melodramatic side.

Goes down the garden with DR. CHASUBLE.

Cecily (picks up books and throws them back on table) : Horrid Political Economy ! Horrid Geography ! Horrid, horrid German !

Enter MERRIMAN *with a card on a salver.*

Merriman : Mr. Ernest Worthing has just driven over from the station. He has brought his luggage with him.

Cecily (takes the card and reads it) : " Mr. Ernest Worthing, B.4, The Albany, W." Uncle Jack's brother ! Did you tell him Mr. Worthing was in town ?

Merriman : Yes, Miss. He seemed very much disappointed. I mentioned that you and Miss Prism were in the garden. He said he was anxious to speak to you privately for a moment.

Cecily : Ask Mr. Ernest Worthing to come here. I suppose you had better talk to the housekeeper about a room for him.

Merriman : Yes, Miss.

MERRIMAN *goes off.*

Cecily : I have never met any really wicked person before. I feel rather frightened. I am so afraid he will look just like every one else.

Enter ALGERNON, *very gay and debonair.*

He does !

Algernon (raising his hat) : You are my little cousin Cecily, I'm sure.

Cecily : You are under some strange mistake. I am not little. In fact, I believe I am more than usually tall for my age. (ALGERNON *is rather taken aback.*) But I am your cousin Cecily. You, I see from your card, are Uncle Jack's brother, my cousin Ernest, my wicked cousin Ernest.

Algernon : Oh ! I am not really wicked at all, cousin Cecily. You mustn't think that I am wicked.

Cecily : If you are not, then you have certainly been deceiving us all in a very inexcusable manner. I hope you have not been leading a double life, pretending to be wicked and being really good all the time. That would be hyprocrisy.

Algernon (looks at her in amazement) : Oh ! Of course I have been rather reckless.

Cecily : I am glad to hear it.

Algernon : In fact, now you mention the subject, I have been very bad in my own small way.

Cecily : I don't think you should be so proud of that, though I am sure it must have been very pleasant.

Algernon : It is much pleasanter being here with you.

Cecily : I can't understand how you are here at all. Uncle Jack won't be back till Monday afternoon.

Algernon : That is a great disappointment. I am obliged to go up by the first train on Monday morning. I have a business appointment that I am anxious . . . to miss !

Cecily : Couldn't you miss it anywhere but in London ?

Algernon : No ; the appointment is in London.

Cecily : Well, I know, of course, how important it is not to keep a business engagement, if one wants to retain any sense of the beauty of life, but still I think you had better wait till Uncle Jack arrives. I know he wants to speak to you about your emigrating.

Algernon : About my what ?

Cecily : Your emigrating. He has gone up to buy your outfit.

Algernon : I certainly wouldn't let Jack buy my outfit. He has no taste in neckties at all.

Cecily : I don't think you will require neckties. Uncle Jack is sending you to Australia.

Algernon : Australia ! I'd sooner die.

Cecily : Well, he said at dinner on Wednesday night, that you would have to choose between this world, the next world, and Australia.

Algernon : Oh, well ! The accounts I have received of Australia and the next world, are not particularly encouraging. This world is good enough for me, cousin Cecily.

Cecily : Yes, but are you good enough for it ?

Algernon : I'm afraid I'm not that. That is why I want you to reform me. You might make that your mission, if you don't mind, cousin Cecily.

Cecily : I'm afraid I've no time, this afternoon.

Algernon : Well, would you mind my reforming myself this afternoon ?

Cecily : It is rather Quixotic of you. But I think you should try.

Algernon : I will. I feel better already.

Cecily : You are looking a little worse.

Algernon : That is because I am hungry.

Cecily : How thoughtless of me. I should have remembered that when one is going to lead an entirely new life, one requires regular and wholesome meals. Won't you come in ?

Algernon : Thank you. Might I have a buttonhole first ? I never have any appetite unless I have a buttonhole first.

Cecily : A Maréchal Niel ? (*Picks up scissors.*)

Algernon : No, I'd sooner have a pink rose.

Cecily : Why ? (*Cuts a flower.*)

Algernon : Because you are like a pink rose, cousin Cecily.

Cecily : I don't think it can be right for you to talk to me like that. Miss Prism never says such things to me.

Algernon : Then Miss Prism is a short-sighted old lady. (CECILY *puts the rose in his buttonhole.*) You are the prettiest girl I ever saw.

Cecily : Miss Prism says that all good looks are a snare.

Algernon : They are a snare that every sensible man would like to be caught in.

Cecily : Oh, I don't think I would care to catch a sensible man. I shouldn't know what to talk to him about.

    They pass into the house. MISS PRISM *and* DR. CHASUBLE *return.*

Miss Prism : You are too much alone, dear Dr. Chasuble. You should get married. A misanthrope I can understand—a womanthrope, never !

Chasuble (*with a scholar's shudder*) *:* Believe me, I do not deserve so neologistic a phrase. The precept as well as the practice of the Primitive Church was distinctly against matrimony.

Miss Prism (sententiously) : That is obviously the reason why the Primitive Church has not lasted up to the present day. And you do not seem to realise, dear Doctor, that by persistently remaining single, a man converts himself into a permanent public temptation. Men should be more careful ; this very celibacy leads weaker vessels astray.

Chasuble : But is a man not equally attractive when married ?

Miss Prism : No married man is ever attractive except to his wife.

Chasuble : And often, I've been told, not even to her.

Miss Prism : That depends on the intellectual sympathies of the woman. Maturity can always be depended on. Ripeness can be trusted. Young women are green. (DR. CHASUBLE *starts.*) I spoke horti-culturally. My metaphor was drawn from fruits. But where is Cecily ?

Chasuble : Perhaps she followed us to the schools.

> *Enter* JACK *slowly from the back of the garden. He is dressed in the deepest mourning, with crepe hatband and black gloves.*

Miss Prism : Mr. Worthing !

Chasuble : Mr. Worthing ?

Miss Prism : This is indeed a surprise. We did not look for you till Monday afternoon.

Jack (shakes MISS PRISM'S *hand in a tragic manner) :* I have returned sooner than I expected. Dr. Chasuble, I hope you are well ?

Chasuble : Dear Mr. Worthing, I trust this garb of woe does not betoken some terrible calamity ?

Jack : My brother.

Miss Prism : More shameful debts and extra-vagance ?

Chasuble : Still leading his life of pleasure ?

Jack (shaking his head) : Dead !

Chasuble : Your brother Ernest dead ?

Jack : Quite dead.

Miss Prism : What a lesson for him ! I trust he will profit by it.

Chasuble : Mr. Worthing, I offer you my sincere condolence. You have at least the consolation of knowing that you were always the most generous and forgiving of brothers.

Jack : Poor Ernest ! He had many faults, but it is a sad, sad blow.

Chasuble : Very sad indeed. Were you with him at the end ?

Jack : No. He died abroad ; in Paris, in fact. I had a telegram last night from the manager of the Grand Hotel.

Chasuble : Was the cause of death mentioned ?

Jack : A severe chill, it seems.

Miss Prism : As a man sows, so shall he reap.

Chasuble (raising his hand) : Charity, dear Miss Prism, charity ! None of us are perfect. I myself am peculiarly susceptible to draughts. Will the interment take place here ?

Jack : No. He seems to have expressed a desire to be buried in Paris.

Chasuble : In Paris ! (*Shakes his head.*) I fear that hardly points to any very serious state of mind at the last. You would no doubt wish me to make some slight allusion to this tragic domestic affliction next Sunday. (JACK *presses his hand convulsively.*) My sermon on the meaning of the manna in the wilderness can be adapted to almost any occasion, joyful, or, as in the present case, distressing. (*All sigh.*) I have preached it at harvest celebrations, christenings, confirmations, on days of humiliation and festal days. The last time I delivered it was in the Cathedral, as a charity sermon on behalf of the Society for the Prevention of Discontent among the Upper Orders. The Bishop, who was present, was much struck by some of the analogies I drew.

Jack : Ah! that reminds me, you mentioned christenings, I think, Dr. Chasuble? I suppose you know how to christen all right? (DR. CHASUBLE *looks astounded.*) I mean, of course, you are continually christening, aren't you?

Miss Prism : It is, I regret to say, one of the Rector's most constant duties in this parish. I have often spoken to the poorer classes on the subject. But they don't seem to know what thrift is.

Chasuble : But is there any particular infant in whom you are interested, Mr. Worthing? Your brother was, I believe, unmarried, was he not?

Jack : Oh yes.

Miss Prism (bitterly) : People who live entirely for pleasure usually are.

Jack : But it is not for any child, dear Doctor. I am very fond of children. No! the fact is, I would like to be christened myself, this afternoon, if you have nothing better to do.

Chasuble : But surely, Mr. Worthing, you have been christened already?

Jack : I don't remember anything about it.

Chasuble : But have you any grave doubts on the subject?

Jack : I certainly intend to have. Of course I don't know if the thing would bother you in any way, or if you think I am a little too old now.

Chasuble : Not at all. The sprinkling, and, indeed, the immersion of adults is a perfectly canonical practice.

Jack : Immersion!

Chasuble : You need have no apprehensions. Sprinkling is all that is necessary, or indeed I think advisable. Our weather is so changeable. At what hour would you wish the ceremony performed?

Jack : Oh, I might trot round about five if that would suit you.

Chasuble : Perfectly, perfectly! In fact, I have two

similar ceremonies to perform at that time. A case of twins that occurred recently in one of the outlying cottages on your own estate. Poor Jenkins the carter, a most hard-working man.

Jack : Oh ! I don't see much fun in being christened along with other babies. It would be childish. Would half-past five do ?

Chasuble : Admirably ! Admirably ! (*Takes out watch.*) And now, dear Mr. Worthing, I will not intrude any longer into a house of sorrow. I would merely beg you not to be too much bowed down by grief. What seem to us bitter trials are often blessings in disguise.

Miss Prism : This seems to me a blessing of an extremely obvious kind.

Enter CECILY *from the house.*

Cecily : Uncle Jack ! Oh, I am pleased to see you back. But what horrid clothes you have got on ! Do go and change them.

Miss Prism : Cecily !

Chasuble : My child ! my child !

CECILY *goes towards* JACK ; *he kisses her brow in a melancholy manner.*

Cecily : What is the matter, Uncle Jack ? Do look happy ! You look as if you had toothache, and I have got such a surprise for you. Who do you think is in the dining-room ? Your brother !

Jack : Who ?

Cecily : Your brother Ernest. He arrived about half an hour ago.

Jack : What nonsense ! I haven't got a brother.

Cecily : Oh, don't say that. However badly he may have behaved to you in the past he is still your brother. You couldn't be so heartless as to disown him. I'll tell him to come out. And you will shake hands with him, won't you, Uncle Jack? (*Runs back into the house.*)

Chasuble : These are very joyful tidings.

Miss Prism : After we had all been resigned to his loss, his sudden return seems to me peculiarly distressing.

Jack : My brother is in the dining-room? I don't know what it all means. I think it is perfectly absurd.

Enter ALGERNON *and* CECILY *hand in hand. They come slowly up to* JACK.

Jack : Good heavens! (*Motions* ALGERNON *away.*)

Algernon : Brother John, I have come down from town to tell you that I am very sorry for all the trouble I have given you, and that I intend to lead a better life in the future. (JACK *glares at him and does not take his hand.*)

Cecily : Uncle Jack, you are not going to refuse your own brother's hand?

Jack : Nothing will induce me to take his hand. I think his coming down here disgraceful. He knows perfectly well why.

Cecily : Uncle Jack, do be nice. There is some good in every one. Ernest has just been telling me about his poor invalid friend Mr. Bunbury whom he goes to visit so often. And surely there must be much good in one who is kind to an invalid, and leaves the pleasures of London to sit by a bed of pain.

Jack : Oh! he has been talking about Bunbury, has he?

Cecily : Yes, he has told me all about poor Mr. Bunbury, and his terrible state of health.

Jack : Bunbury! Well, I won't have him talk to you about Bunbury or about anything else. It is enough to drive one perfectly frantic.

Algernon : Of course I admit that the faults were all on my side. But I must say that I think that

Brother John's coldness to me is peculiarly painful, I expected a more enthusiastic welcome, especially considering it is the first time I have come here.

Cecily : Uncle Jack, if you don't shake hands with Ernest I will never forgive you.

Jack : Never forgive me ?

Cecily : Never, never, never !

Jack : Well, this is the last time I shall ever do it. (*Shakes hands with* ALGERNON *and glares.*)

Chasuble : It's pleasant, is it not, to see so perfect a reconciliation ? I think we might leave the two brothers together.

Miss Prism : Cecily, you will come with us.

Cecily : Certainly, Miss Prism. My little task of re-conciliation is over.

Chasuble : You have done a beautiful action to-day, dear child.

Miss Prism : We must not be premature in our judgments.

Cecily : I feel very happy.

They all go off except JACK *and* ALGERNON.

Jack : You young scoundrel, Algy, you must get out of this place as soon as possible. I don't allow any Bunburying here.

Enter MERRIMAN.

Merriman : I have put Mr. Ernest's things in the room next to yours, sir. I suppose that is all right ?

Jack : What ?

Merriman : Mr. Ernest's luggage, sir. I have un-packed it and put it in the room next to your own.

Jack : His luggage ?

Merriman : Yes, sir. Three portmanteaus, a dressing case, two hat-boxes, and a large luncheon-basket.

Algernon : I am afraid I can't stay more than a week this time.

Jack : Merriman, order the dog-cart at once. Mr. Ernest has been suddenly called back to town.

Merriman : Yes, sir. (*Goes back into the house.*)

Algernon : What a fearful liar you are, Jack. I have not been called back to town at all.

Jack : Yes, you have.

Algernon : I haven't heard any one call me.

Jack : Your duty as a gentleman calls you back.

Algernon : My duty as a gentleman has never interfered with my pleasures in the smallest degree.

Jack : I can quite understand that.

Algernon : Well, Cecily is a darling.

Jack : You are not to talk of Miss Cardew like that. I don't like it.

Algernon : Well, I don't like your clothes. You look perfectly ridiculous in them. Why on earth don't you go up and change ? It is perfectly childish to be in deep mourning for a man who is actually staying for a whole week with you in your house as a guest. I call it grotesque.

Jack : You are certainly not staying with me for a whole week as a guest or anything else. You have got to leave . . . by the four-five train.

Algernon : I certainly won't leave you so long as you are in mourning. It would be most unfriendly. If I were in mourning you would stay with me, I suppose. I should think it very unkind if you didn't.

Jack : Well, will you go if I change my clothes ?

Algernon : Yes, if you are not too long. I never saw anybody take so long to dress, and with such little result.

Jack : Well, at any rate, that is better than being always over-dressed as you are.

Algernon : If I am occasionally a little over-dressed, I make up for it by being always immensely over-educated.

Jack : Your vanity is ridiculous, your conduct an outrage, and your presence in my garden utterly absurd. However, you have got to catch the four-five, and I hope you will have a pleasant journey back to town. This Bunburying, as you call it, has not been a great success for you. (*Goes into the house.*)

Algernon : I think it has been a great success. I'm in love with Cecily, and that is everything.

> *Enter* CECILY *at the back of the garden. She picks up the can and begins to water the flowers.*

But I must see her before I go, and make arrangements for another Bunbury. Ah, there she is.

Cecily : Oh, I merely came back to water the roses. I thought you were with Uncle Jack.

Algernon : He's gone to order the dog-cart for me.

Cecily : Oh, is he going to take you for a nice drive ?

Algernon : He's going to send me away.

Cecily : Then have we got to part ?

Algernon : I am afraid so. It's a very painful parting.

Cecily : It is always painful to part from people whom one has known for a very brief space of time. The absence of old friends one can endure with equanimity. But even a momentary separation from any one to whom one has just been introduced is almost unbearable.

Algernon : Thank you.

> *Enter* MERRIMAN.

Merriman : The dog-cart is at the door, sir.

> ALGERNON *looks appealing at* CECILY.

Cecily : It can wait, Merriman, for five minutes.

Merriman : Yes, Miss.

> *Exit* MERRIMAN.

Algernon : I hope, Cecily, I shall not offend you if I state quite frankly and openly that you seem to me to be in every way the visible personification of absolute perfection.

Cecily : I think your frankness does you great credit, Ernest. If you will allow me, I will copy your remarks into my diary. (*Goes over to table and begins writing in diary.*)

Algernon : Do you really keep a diary ? I'd give anything to look at it. May I ?

Cecily : Oh no. (*Puts her hand over it.*) You see, it is simply a very young girl's record of her own thoughts and impressions, and consequently meant for publication. When it appears in volume form I hope you will order a copy. But pray, Ernest, don't stop. I delight in taking down from dictation. I have reached "absolute perfection." You can go on. I am quite ready for more.

Algernon (somewhat taken aback) : Ahem ! Ahem !

Cecily : Oh, don't cough, Ernest. When one is dictating one should speak fluently and not cough. Besides, I don't know how to spell a cough. (*Writes as* ALGERNON *speaks.*)

Algernon (speaking very rapidly) : Cecily, ever since I first looked upon your wonderful and incomparable beauty, I have dared to love you wildly, passionately, devotedly, hopelessly.

Cecily : I don't think that you should tell me that you love me wildly, passionately, devotedly, hopelessly. Hopelessly doesn't seem to make much sense, does it ?

Algernon : Cecily !

Enter MERRIMAN.

Merriman : The dog-cart is waiting, sir.

Algernon : Tell it to come round next week, at the same hour.

Merriman (looks at CECILY, *who makes no sign) :* Yes, sir.

MERRIMAN *retires.*

Cecily : Uncle Jack would be very much annoyed if he knew you were staying on till next week, at the same hour.

Algernon : Oh, I don't care about Jack. I don't care for anybody in the whole world but you. I love you, Cecily. You will marry me, won't you ?

Cecily : You silly boy ! Of course. Why, we have been engaged for the last three months.

Algernon : For the last three months ?

Cecily : Yes, it will be exactly three months on Thursday.

Algernon : But how did we become engaged ?

Cecily : Well, ever since dear Uncle Jack first confessed to us that he had a younger brother who was very wicked and bad, you, of course, have formed the chief topic of conversation between myself and Miss Prism. And, of course, a man who is much talked about is always very attractive. One feels there must be something in him, after all. I dare say it was foolish of me, but I fell in love with you, Ernest.

Algernon : Darling. And when was the engagement actually settled ?

Cecily : On the 14th of February last. Worn out by your entire ignorance of my existence, I determined to end the matter one way or the other, and after a long struggle with myself I accepted you under this dear old tree here. The next day I bought this little ring in your name, and this is the little bangle with the true lover's knot I promised you always to wear.

Algernon : Did I give you this ? It's very pretty, isn't it ?

Cecily : Yes, you've wonderfully good taste, Ernest. It's the excuse I've always given for your leading such a bad life. And this is the box in which I keep all your dear letters. (*Kneels at table, opens box, and produces letters tied up with blue ribbon.*)

Algernon : My letters ! But, my own sweet Cecily, I have never written you any letters.

Cecily : You need hardly remind me of that, Ernest. I remember only too well that I was forced to write your letters for you. I wrote always three times a week, and sometimes oftener.

Algernon : Oh, do let me read them, Cecily ?

Cecily : Oh, I couldn't possibly. They would make you far too conceited. (*Replaces box.*) The three you wrote me after I had broken off the engagement are so beautiful, and so badly spelled, that even now I can hardly read them without crying a little.

Algernon : But was our engagement ever broken off ?

Cecily : Of course it was. On the 22nd of last March. You can see the entry if you like. (*Shows diary.*) " To-day I broke off my engagement with Ernest. I feel it is better to do so. The weather still continues charming."

Algernon : But why on earth did you break it off ? What had I done ? I had done nothing at all. Cecily, I am very much hurt indeed to hear you broke it off. Particularly when the weather was so charming

Cecily : It would hardly have been a really serious engagement if it hadn't been broken off at least once. But I forgave you before the week was out.

Algernon (*crossing to her, and kneeling*) *:* What a perfect angel you are, Cecily.

Cecily : You dear romantic boy. (*He kisses her, she puts her fingers through his hair.*) I hope your hair curls naturally, does it ?

Algernon : Yes, darling, with a little help from others.

Cecily : I am so glad.

Algernon : You'll never break off our engagement again, Cecily ?

Cecily : I don't think I could break it off now that I have actually met you. Besides, of course, there is the question of your name.

Algernon : Yes, of course. (*Nervously.*)

Cecily : You must not laugh at me, darling, but it had always been a girlish dream of mine to love some one whose name was Ernest.

ALGERNON *rises,* CECILY *also.*

There is something in that name that seems to inspire absolute confidence. I pity any poor married woman whose husband is not called Ernest.

Algernon : But, my dear child, do you mean to say you could not love me if I had some other name ?

Cecily : But what name ?

Algernon : Oh, any name you like—Algernon—for instance . . .

Cecily : But I don't like the name of Algernon.

Algernon : Well, my own dear, sweet, loving little darling, I really can't see why you should object to the name of Algernon. It is not at all a bad name. In fact, it is rather an aristocratic name. Half of the chaps who get into the Bankruptcy Court are called Algernon. But seriously, Cecily—(*moving to her*)—if my name was Algy, couldn't you love me ?

Cecily (rising) : I might respect you, Ernest, I might admire your character, but I fear that I should not be able to give you my undivided attention.

Algernon : Ahem ! Cecily ! (*Picking up hat.*) Your Rector here is, I suppose, thoroughly experienced in the practice of all the rites and ceremonials of the Church ?

Cecily : Oh, yes. Dr. Chasuble is a most learned man. He has never written a single book, so you can imagine how much he knows.

Algernon : I must see him at once on a most important christening—I mean on most important business.

Cecily : Oh !

Algernon : I shan't be away more than half an hour.

Cecily : Considering that we have been engaged since February the 14th, and that I only met you to-day for the first time, I think it is rather hard that you should leave me for so long a period as half an hour. Couldn't you make it twenty minutes ?

Algernon : I'll be back in no time. (*Kisses her and rushes down the garden.*)

Cecily : What an impetuous boy he is ! I like his hair so much. I must enter his proposal in my diary.

Enter MERRIMAN.

Merriman : A Miss Fairfax has just called to see Mr. Worthing. On very important business, Miss Fairfax states.

Cecily : Isn't Mr. Worthing in his library ?

Merriman : Mr. Worthing went over in the direction of the Rectory some time ago.

Cecily : Pray ask the lady to come out here ; Mr. Worthing is sure to be back soon. And you can bring tea.

Merriman : Yes, Miss. (*Goes out.*)

Cecily : Miss Fairfax ! I suppose one of the many good elderly women who are associated with Uncle Jack in some of his philanthropic work in London. I don't quite like women who are interested in Philanthropic work. I think it is so forward of them.

Enter MERRIMAN.

Merriman : Miss Fairfax.

Enter GWENDOLEN. *Exit* MERRIMAN.

Cecily (*advancing to meet her*) : Pray let me introduce myself to you. My name is Cecily Cardew.

Gwendolen : Cecily Cardew ? (*Moving to her and shaking hands.*) What a very sweet name ! Something tells me that we are going to be great friends. I like you already more than I can say. My first impressions of people are never wrong.

Cecily : How nice of you to like me so much after we have known each other such a comparatively short time. Pray sit down.

Gwendolen (still standing up) : I may call you Cecily, may I not ?

Cecily : With pleasure !

Gwendolen : And you will always call me Gwendolen, won't you ?

Cecily : If you wish.

Gwendolen : Then that is all quite settled, is it not ?

Cecily : I hope so.

A pause. They both sit down together.

Gwendolen : Perhaps this might be a favourable opportunity for my mentioning who I am. My father is Lord Bracknell. You have never heard of papa, I suppose ?

Cecily : I don't think so.

Gwendolen : Outside the family circle, papa, I am glad to say, is entirely unknown. I think that is quite as it should be. The home seems to me to be the proper sphere for the man. And certainly once a man begins to neglect his domestic duties he becomes painfully effeminate, does he not ? And I don't like that. It makes men so very attractive. Cecily, mamma, whose views on education are remarkably strict, has brought me up to be extremely short-sighted ; it is part of her system ; so do you mind my looking at you through my glasses ?

Cecily : Oh ! not at all, Gwendolen. I am very fond of being looked at.

Gwendolen (after examining CECILY *carefully through a lorgnette)* : You are here on a short visit, I suppose.

Cecily : Oh no ! I live here.

Gwendolen (*severely*) : Really ? Your mother, no doubt, or some female relative of advanced years, resides here also ?

Cecily : Oh no ! I have no mother, nor, in fact, any relations.

Gwendolen : Indeed ?

Cecily : My dear guardian, with the assistance of Miss Prism, has the arduous task of looking after me.

Gwendolen : Your guardian ?

Cecily : Yes, I am Mr. Worthing's ward.

Gwendolen : Oh ! It is strange he never mentioned to me that he had a ward. How secretive of him ! He grows more interesting hourly. I am not sure, however, that the news inspires me with feelings of unmixed delight. (*Rising and going to her*.) I am very fond of you, Cecily ; I have liked you ever since I met you ! But I am bound to state that now that I know that you are Mr. Worthing's ward, I cannot help expressing a wish you were—well, just a little older than you seem to be—and not quite so very alluring in appearance. In fact, if I may speak candidly——

Cecily : Pray do ! I think that whenever one has anything unpleasant to say, one should always be quite candid.

Gwendolen : Well, to speak with perfect candour, Cecily, I wish that you were fully forty-two, and more than usually plain for your age. Ernest has a strong upright nature. He is the very soul of truth and honour. Disloyalty would be as impossible to him as deception. But even men of the noblest possible moral character are extremely susceptible to the influence of the physical charms of others. Modern, no less than Ancient History, supplies us with many most painful examples of what I refer to. If it were not so, indeed, History would be quite unreadable.

Cecily : I beg your pardon, Gwendolen, did you say Ernest ?

Gwendolen : Yes.

Cecily : Oh, but it is not Mr. Ernest Worthing who is my guardian. It is his brother—his elder brother.

Gwendolen (sitting down again) : Ernest never mentioned to me that he had a brother.

Cecily : I am sorry to say they have not been on good terms for a long time.

Gwendolen : Ah ! that accounts for it. And now that I think of it I have never heard any man mention his brother. The subject seems distasteful to most men. Cecily, you have lifted a load from my mind. I was growing almost anxious. It would have been terrible if any cloud had come across a friendship like ours, would it not ? Of course you are quite, quite sure that it is not Mr. Ernest Worthing who is your guardian ?

Cecily : Quite sure. (*A pause.*) In fact, I am going to be his.

Gwendolen (inquiringly) : I beg your pardon ?

Cecily (rather shy and confidingly) : Dearest Gwendolen, there is no reason why I should make a secret of it to you. Our little county newspaper is sure to chronicle the fact next week. Mr. Ernest Worthing and I are engaged to be married.

Gwendolen (quite politely, rising) : My darling Cecily, I think there must be some slight error. Mr. Ernest Worthing is engaged to me. The announcement will appear in the *Morning Post* on Saturday at the latest.

Cecily (very politely, rising) : I am afraid you must be under some misconception. Ernest proposed to me exactly ten minutes ago. (*Shows diary.*)

Gwendolen (examines diary through her lorgnette carefully) : It is certainly very curious, for he asked me to be his wife yesterday afternoon at 5.30. If you would care to verify the incident, pray do so. (*Produces diary of her own.*) I never travel without my diary. One should always have something sensational to read in the train. I am so sorry, dear Cecily, if it is any disappointment to you, but I am afraid I have the prior claim.

Cecily : It would distress me more than I can tell you, dear Gwendolen, if it caused you any mental or physical anguish, but I feel bound to point out that since Ernest proposed to you he clearly has changed his mind.

Gwendolen (meditatively) : If the poor fellow has been entrapped into any foolish promise I shall consider it my duty to rescue him at once, and with a firm hand.

Cecily (thoughtfully and sadly) : Whatever unfortunate entanglement my dear boy may have got into, I will never reproach him with it after we are married.

Gwendolen : Do you allude to me, Miss Cardew, as an entanglement ? You are presumptuous. On an occasion of this kind it becomes more than a moral duty to speak one's mind. It becomes a pleasure.

Cecily : Do you suggest, Miss Fairfax, that I entrapped Ernest into an engagement ? How dare you ? This is no time for wearing the shallow mask of manners. When I see a spade I call it a spade.

Gwendolen (satirically) : I am glad to say that I have never seen a spade. It is obvious that our social spheres have been widely different.

Enter MERRIMAN, *followed by the footman. He carries a salver, table cloth, and plate stand.* CECILY *is about to retort. The presence of the servants exercises a restraining influence, under which both girls chafe.*

Merriman : Shall I lay tea here as usual, Miss ?
Cecily (sternly, in a calm voice) : Yes, as usual.

MERRIMAN *begins to clear table and lay cloth. A long pause.* CECILY *and* GWENDOLEN *glare at each other*

Gwendolen : Are there many interesting walks in the vicinity, Miss Cardew ?

Cecily : Oh ! yes ! a great many. From the top of one of the hills quite close one can see five counties.

Gwendolen : Five counties ! I don't think I should like that ; I hate crowds.

Cecily (sweetly) : I suppose that is why you live in town ?

GWENDOLEN *bites her lip, and beats her foot nervously with her parasol.*

Gwendolen (looking round) : Quite a well-kept garden this is, Miss Cardew.

Cecily : So glad you like it, Miss Fairfax.

Gwendolen : I had no idea there were any flowers in the country.

Cecily : Oh, flowers are as common here, Miss Fairfax, as people are in London.

Gwendolen : Personally I cannot understand how anybody manages to exist in the country, if anybody who is anybody does. The country always bores me to death.

Cecily : Ah ! This is what the newspapers call agricultural depression, is it not ? I believe the aristocracy are suffering very much from it just at present. It is almost an epidemic amongst them, I have been told. May I offer you some tea, Miss Fairfax ?

Gwendolen (with elaborate politeness) : Thank you. (*Aside) :* Detestable girl ! But I require tea !

Cecily (sweetly) : Sugar ?

Gwendolen (superciliously) : No, thank you. Sugar is not fashionable any more.

CECILY *looks angrily at her, takes up the tongs and puts four lumps of sugar into the cup.*

Cecily (severely) : Cake or bread and butter ?

Gwendolen (in a bored manner) : Bread and butter, please. Cake is rarely seen at the best houses nowadays.

Cecily (cuts a very large slice of cake and puts it on the tray) : Hand that to Miss Fairfax.

> MERRIMAN *does so, and goes out with footman.*
> GWENDOLEN *drinks the tea and makes a grimace.*
> *Puts down cup at once, reaches out her hand to the*
> *bread and butter, looks at it, and finds it is cake.*
> *Rises in indignation.*

Gwendolen : You have filled my tea with lumps of sugar, and though I asked most distinctly for bread and butter, you have given me cake. I am known for the gentleness of my disposition, and the extraordinary sweetness of my nature, but I warn you, Miss Cardew, you may go too far.

Cecily (rising) : To save my poor, innocent, trusting boy from the machinations of any other girl there are no lengths to which I would not go.

Gwendolen : From the moment I saw you I distrusted you. I felt that you were false and deceitful. I am never deceived in such matters. My first impressions of people are invariably right.

Cecily : It seems to me, Miss Fairfax, that I am trespassing on your valuable time. No doubt you have many other calls of a similar character to make in the neighbourhood.

> *Enter* JACK.

Gwendolen (catching sight of him) : Ernest ! My own Ernest !

Jack : Gwendolen ! Darling ! (*Offers to kiss her.*)

Gwendolen (drawing back) : A moment ! May I ask if you are engaged to be married to this young lady ? (*Points to* CECILY.)

Jack (laughing) : To dear little Cecily ! Of course

not! What could have put such an idea into your pretty little head?

Gwendolen: Thank you. You may! (*Offers her cheek.*)

Cecily (very sweetly): I knew there must be some misunderstanding, Miss Fairfax. The gentleman whose arm is at present round your waist is my guardian, Mr. John Worthing.

Gwendolen: I beg your pardon?

Cecily: This is Uncle Jack.

Gwendolen (receding): Jack! Oh!

Enter ALGERNON.

Cecily: Here is Ernest.

Algernon (goes straight over to CECILY without noticing any one else): My own love! (*Offers to kiss her.*)

Cecily (drawing back): A moment, Ernest! May I ask you—are you engaged to be married to this young lady?

Algernon (looking round): To what young lady? Good heavens! Gwendolen!

Cecily: Yes! to good heavens, Gwendolen, I mean to Gwendolen.

Algernon (laughing): Of course not! What could have put such an idea into your pretty little head?

Cecily: Thank you. (*Presenting her cheek to be kissed.*) You may. (ALGERNON *kisses her.*)

Gwendolen: I felt there was some slight error, Miss Cardew. The gentleman who is now embracing you is my cousin, Mr. Algernon Moncrieff.

Cecily (breaking away from ALGERNON): Algernon Moncrieff! Oh!

The two girls move towards each other and put their arms round each other's waists as if for protection.

Cecily : Are you called Algernon ?

Algernon : I cannot deny it.

Cecily : Oh !

Gwendolen : Is your name really John ?

Jack (standing rather proudly) : I could deny it if I liked. I could deny anything if I liked. But my name certainly is John. It has been John for years.

Cecily (To GWENDOLEN) *:* A gross deception has been practised on both of us.

Gwendolen : My poor wounded Cecily !

Cecily : My sweet wronged Gwendolen !

Gwendolen (slowly and seriously) : You will call me sister, will you not ?

They embrace. JACK *and* ALGERNON *groan and walk up and down.*

Cecily (rather brightly) : There is just one question I would like to be allowed to ask my guardian.

Gwendolen : An admirable idea ! Mr. Worthing, there is just one question I would like to be permitted to put to you. Where is your brother Ernest ? We are both engaged to be married to your brother Ernest, so it is a matter of some importance to us to know where your brother Ernest is at present.

Jack (slowly and hesitatingly) : Gwendolen—Cecily —it is very painful for me to be forced to speak the truth. It is the first time in my life that I have ever been reduced to such a painful position, and I am really quite inexperienced in doing anything of the kind. However, I will tell you quite frankly that I have no brother Ernest. I have no brother at all. I never had a brother in my life, and I certainly have not the smallest intention of ever having one in the future.

Cecily (surprised) : No brother at all ?

Jack (cheerily) : None !

Gwendolen (severely) : Had you never a brother of any kind ?

Jack (*pleasantly*) : Never. Not even of any kind.

Gwendolen : I am afraid it is quite clear, Cecily, that neither of us is engaged to be married to any one.

Cecily : It is not a very pleasant position for a young girl suddenly to find herself in. Is it ?

Gwendolen : Let us go into the house. They will hardly venture to come after us there.

Cecily : No, men are so cowardly, aren't they ?

They retire into the house with scornful looks.

Jack : This ghastly state of things is what you call Bunburying, I suppose ?

Algernon : Yes, and a perfectly wonderful Bunbury it is. The most wonderful Bunbury I have ever had in my life.

Jack : Well, you've no right whatsoever to Bunbury here.

Algernon : That is absurd. One has a right to Bunbury anywhere one chooses. Every serious Bunburyist knows that.

Jack : Serious Bunburyist ! Good heavens !

Algernon : Well, one must be serious about something, if one wants to have any amusement in life. I happen to be serious about Bunburying. What on earth you are serious about I haven't got the remotest idea. About everything, I should fancy. You have such an absolutely trivial nature.

Jack : Well, the only small satisfaction I have in the whole of this wretched business is that your friend Bunbury is quite exploded. You won't be able to run down to the country quite so often as you used to do, dear Algy. And a very good thing too.

Algernon : Your brother is a little off colour, isn't he, dear Jack ? You won't be able to disappear to London quite so frequently as your wicked custom was. And not a bad thing either.

Jack : As for your conduct towards Miss Cardew, I must say that your taking in a sweet, simple, innocent girl like that is quite inexcusable. To say nothing of the fact that she is my ward.

Algernon : I can see no possible defence at all for your deceiving a brilliant, clever, thoroughly experienced young lady like Miss Fairfax. To say nothing of the fact that she is my cousin.

Jack : I wanted to be engaged to Gwendolen, that is all. I love her.

Algernon : Well, I simply wanted to be engaged to Cecily. I adore her.

Jack : There is certainly no chance of your marrying Miss Cardew.

Algernon : I don't think there is much likelihood, Jack, of you and Miss Fairfax being united.

Jack : Well, that is no business of yours.

Algernon : If it was my business, I wouldn't talk about it. (*Begins to eat muffins.*) It is very vulgar to talk about one's business. Only people like stockbrokers do that, and then merely at dinner parties.

Jack : How can you sit there, calmly eating muffins when we are in this horrible trouble, I can't make out. You seem to me to be perfectly heartless.

Algernon : Well, I can't eat muffins in an agitated manner. The butter would probably get on my cuffs. One should always eat muffins quite calmly. It is the only way to eat them.

Jack : I say it's perfectly heartless your eating muffins at all, under the circumstances.

Algernon : When I am in trouble, eating is the only thing that consoles me. Indeed, when I am in really great trouble, as any one who knows me intimately will tell you, I refuse everything except food and drink. At the present moment I am eating muffins because I am unhappy. Besides, I am particularly fond of muffins. (*Rising.*)

Jack (*rising*) *:* Well, that is no reason why you should eat them all in that greedy way. (*Takes muffins from* ALGERNON.)

Algernon (offering tea-cake) : I wish you would have tea-cake instead. I don't like tea-cake.

Jack : Good heavens ! I suppose a man may eat his own muffins in his own garden.

Algernon : But you have just said it was perfectly heartless to eat muffins.

Jack : I said it was perfectly heartless of you, under the circumstances. That is a very different thing.

Algernon : That may be. But the muffins are the same. (*He seizes the muffin-dish from* JACK.)

Jack : Algy, I wish to goodness you would go.

Algernon : You can't possibly ask me to go without having some dinner. It's absurd. I never go without my dinner. No one ever does, except vegetarians and people like that. Besides I have just made arrangements with Dr. Chasuble to be christened at a quarter to six under the name of Ernest.

Jack : My dear fellow, the sooner you give up that nonsense the better. I made arrangements this morning with Dr. Chasuble to be christened myself at 5.30, and I naturally will take the name of Ernest. Gwendolen would wish it. We can't both be christened Ernest. It's absurd. Besides, I have a perfect right to be christened if I like. There is no evidence at all that I have ever been christened by anybody. I should think it extremely probable I never was, and so does Dr. Chasuble. It is entirely different in your case. You have been christened already.

Algernon : Yes, but I have not been christened for years.

Jack : Yes, but you have been christened. That is the important thing.

Algernon : Quite so. So I know my constitution can stand it. If you are not quite sure about your ever having been christened, I must say I think it rather dangerous your venturing on it now. It might make you very unwell. You can hardly have forgotten that some one very closely connected with you was very nearly carried off this week in Paris by a severe chill.

Jack : Yes, but you said yourself that a severe chill was not hereditary.

Algernon : It usen't to be, I know—but I dare say it is now. Science is always making wonderful improvements in things.

Jack (picking up the muffin-dish) : Oh, that is nonsense ; you are always talking nonsense.

Algernon : Jack, you are at the muffins again ! I wish you wouldn't. There are only two left. (*Takes them.*) I told you I was particularly fond of muffins.

Jack : But I hate tea-cake.

Algernon : Why on earth then do you allow tea-cake to be served up for your guests ? What ideas you have of hospitality !

Jack : Algernon ! I have already told you to go. I don't want you here. Why don't you go !

Algernon : I haven't quite finished my tea yet ! and there is still one muffin left.

JACK *groans, and sinks into a chair.* ALGERNON *still continues eating.*

ACT DROP.

THIRD ACT

SCENE

Morning-room at the Manor House.
GWENDOLEN *and* CECILY *are at the window,
looking out into the garden.*

Gwendolen : The fact that they did not follow us
at once into the house, as any one else would have done,
seems to me to show that they have some sense of
shame left.

Cecily : They have been eating muffins. That looks
like repentance.

Gwendolen (after a pause) : They don't seem to
notice us at all. Couldn't you cough?

Cecily : But I haven't got a cough.

Gwendolen : They're looking at us. What effrontery!

Cecily : They're approaching. That's very forward
of them.

Gwendolen : Let us preserve a dignified silence.

Cecily : Certainly. It's the only thing to do now.

Enter JACK *followed by* ALGERNON. *They whistle
some dreadful popular air from a British Opera.*

Gwendolen : This dignified silence seems to produce
an unpleasant effect.

Cecily : A most distasteful one.

Gwendolen : But we will not be the first to speak.

Cecily : Certainly not.

Gwendolen : Mr. Worthing, I have something very
particular to ask you. Much depends on your reply.

Cecily : Gwendolen, your common sense is invaluable.
Mr. Moncrieff, kindly answer me the following question.

651

Why did you pretend to be my guardian's brother ?

Algernon : In order that I might have an opportunity of meeting you.

Cecily (to GWENDOLEN) *:* That certainly seems a satisfactory explanation, does it not ?

Gwendolen : Yes, dear, if you can believe him.

Cecily : I don't. But that does not affect the wonderful beauty of his answer.

Gwendolen : True. In matters of grave importance, style, not sincerity is the vital thing. Mr. Worthing, what explanation can you offer to me for pretending to have a brother ? Was it in order that you might have an opportunity of coming up to town to see me as often as possible ?

Jack : Can you doubt it, Miss Fairfax ?

Gwendolen : I have the gravest doubts upon the subject. But I intend to crush them. This is not the moment for German scepticism. (*Moving to* CECILY.) Their explanations appear to be quite satisfactory, especially Mr. Worthing's. That seems to me to have the stamp of truth upon it.

Cecily : I am more than content with what Mr. Moncrieff said. His voice alone inspires one with absolute credulity.

Gwendolen : Then you think we should forgive them ?

Cecily : Yes. I mean no.

Gwendolen : True ! I had forgotten. There are principles at stake that one cannot surrender. Which of us should tell them ? The task is not a pleasant one.

Cecily : Could we not both speak at the same time ?

Gwendolen : An excellent idea ! I always speak at the same time as other people. Will you take the time from me ?

Cecily : Certainly.

GWENDOLEN *beats time with uplifted finger.*

Gwendolen and Cecily (speaking together) : Your

Christian names are still an insuperable barrier. That is all !

Jack and Algernon (speaking together) : Our Christian names ! Is that all ? But we are going to be christened this afternoon.

Gwendolen (to JACK) *:* For my sake you are prepared to do this terrible thing ?

Jack : I am.

Cecily (to ALGERNON) *:* To please me you are ready to face this fearful ordeal ?

Algernon : I am !

Gwendolen : How absurd to talk of the equality of the sexes ! Where questions of self-sacrifice are concerned, men are infinitely beyond us.

Jack : We are. (*Clasps hands with* ALGERNON.)

Cecily : They have moments of physical courage of which we women know absolutely nothing.

Gwendolen (to JACK) *:* Darling.

Algernon (to CECILY) *:* Darling !

> *They fall into each other's arms.*
> *Enter* MERRIMAN. *When he enters he coughs loudly, seeing the situation.*

Merriman : Ahem ! Ahem ! Lady Bracknell !

Jack : Good heavens !

> *Enter* LADY BRACKNELL. *The couples separate in alarm. Exit* MERRIMAN.

Lady Bracknell : Gwendolen ! What does this mean ?

Gwendolen : Merely that I am engaged to be married to Mr. Worthing, mamma.

Lady Bracknell : Come here. Sit down. Sit down immediately. Hesitation of any kind is a sign of mental decay in the young, of physical weakness in the old. (*Turns to* JACK.) Apprised, sir, of my daughter's sudden flight by her trusty maid, whose confidence I

purchased by means of a small coin, I followed her at
once by a luggage train. Her unhappy father is, I am
glad to say, under the impression that she is attending
a more than usually lengthy lecture by the University
Extension Scheme on the Influence of a permanent
income on Thought. I do not propose to undeceive
him. Indeed I have never undeceived him on any
question. I would consider it wrong. But, of course,
you will clearly understand that all communication
between yourself and my daughter must cease immediately from this moment. On this point, as indeed
on all points, I am firm.

Jack : I am engaged to be married to Gwendolen,
Lady Bracknell !

Lady Bracknell : You are nothing of the kind, sir.
And now, as regards Algernon ! . . . Algernon !

Algernon : Yes, Aunt Augusta.

Lady Bracknell : May I ask if it is in this house that
your invalid friend Mr. Bunbury resides ?

Algernon (stammering) : Oh ! No ! Bunbury doesn't
live here. Bunbury is somewhere else at present. In
fact, Bunbury is dead.

Lady Bracknell : Dead ! When did Mr. Bunbury
die ? His death must have been extremely sudden.

Algernon (airily) : Oh ! I killed Bunbury this afternoon. I mean poor Bunbury died this afternoon.

Lady Bracknell : What did he die of ?

Algernon : Bunbury ? Oh, he was quite exploded.

Lady Bracknell : Exploded ! Was he the victim of a
revolutionary outrage ? I was not aware that Mr.
Bunbury was interested in social legislation. If so, he
is well punished for his morbidity.

Algernon : My dear Aunt Augusta, I mean he was
found out ! The doctors found out that Bunbury
could not live, that is what I mean—so Bunbury died.

Lady Bracknell : He seems to have had great
confidence in the opinion of his physicians. I am glad,
however, that he made up his mind at the last to

some definite course of action, and acted under proper medical advice. And now that we have finally got rid of this Mr. Bunbury, may I ask, Mr. Worthing, who is that young person whose hand my nephew Algernon is now holding in what seems to me a peculiarly unnecessary manner ?

Jack : That lady is Miss Cecily Cardew, my ward.

LADY BRACKNELL *bows coldly to* CECILY.

Algernon : I am engaged to be married to Cecily, Aunt Augusta.

Lady Bracknell : I beg your pardon ?

Cecily : Mr. Moncrieff and I are engaged to be married, Lady Bracknell.

Lady Bracknell (with a shiver, crossing to the sofa and sitting down) : I do not know whether there is any-thing peculiarly exciting in the air of this particular part of Hertfordshire, but the number of engagements that go on seems to me considerably above the proper average that statistics have laid down for our guidance. I think some preliminary inquiry on my part would not be out of place. Mr. Worthing, is Miss Cardew at all connected with any of the larger railway stations in London ? I merely desire information. Until yesterday I had no idea that there were any families or persons whose origin was a Terminus.

JACK *looks perfectly furious, but restrains himself.*

Jack (in a clear, cold voice) : Miss Cardew is the grand-daughter of the late Mr. Thomas Cardew of 149 Belgrave Square, S.W. ; Gervase Park, Dorking, Surrey ; and the Sporran, Fifeshire, N.B.

Lady Bracknell : That sounds not unsatisfactory. Three addresses always inspire confidence, even in tradesmen. But what proof have I of their authenticity?

Jack : I have carefully preserved the Court Guides of the period. They are open to your inspection, Lady Bracknell.

Lady Bracknell (grimly) : I have known strange errors in that publication.

Jack : Miss Cardew's family solicitors are Messrs. Markby, Markby, and Markby.

Lady Bracknell : Markby, Markby, and Markby ? A firm of the very highest position in their profession. Indeed I am told that one of the Mr. Markby's is occasionally to be seen at dinner parties. So far I am satisfied.

Jack (very irritably) : How extremely kind of you, Lady Bracknell ! I have also in my possession, you will be pleased to hear, certificates of Miss Cardew's birth, baptism, whooping cough, registration, vaccination, confirmation, and the measles ; both the German and the English variety.

Lady Bracknell : Ah ! A life crowded with incident, I see ; though perhaps somewhat too exciting for a young girl. I am not myself in favour of premature experiences. (*Rises, looks at her watch.*) Gwendolen ! the time approaches for our departure. We have not a moment to lose. As a matter of form, Mr. Worthing, I had better ask you if Miss Cardew has any little fortune ?

Jack : Oh ! about a hundred and thirty thousand pounds in the Funds. That is all. Good-bye, Lady Bracknell. So pleased to have seen you.

Lady Bracknell (sitting down again) : A moment, Mr. Worthing. A hundred and thirty thousand pounds ! And in the Funds ! Miss Cardew seems to me a most attractive young lady, now that I look at her. Few girls of the present day have any really solid qualities, any of the qualities that last, and improve with time. We live, I regret to say, in an age of surfaces. (*To* CECILY) : Come over here, dear. (CECILY *goes across.*) Pretty child ! your dress is sadly simple, and your hair seems almost as Nature might have left it. But we can soon alter all that. A thoroughly experienced French maid produces a really marvellous result in a very brief space of time. I remember recommending one to young Lady Lancing, and after three months her own husband did not know her.

Jack: And after six months nobody knew her.

Lady Bracknell (glares at JACK *for a few moments. Then bends, with a practised smile, to* CECILY*) :* Kindly turn round, sweet child. (CECILY *turns completely round.*) No, the side view is what I want. (CECILY *presents her profile.*) Yes, quite as I expected. There are distinct social possibilities in your profile. The two weak points in our age are its want of principle and its want of profile. The chin a little higher, dear. Style largely depends on the way the chin is worn. They are worn very high, just at present. Algernon !

Algernon: Yes, Aunt Augusta !

Lady Bracknell: There are distinct social possibilities in Miss Cardew's profile.

Algernon: Cecily is the sweetest, dearest, prettiest girl in the whole world. And I don't care twopence about social possibilities.

Lady Bracknell: Never speak disrespectfully of Society, Algernon. Only people who can't get into it do that. *(To* CECILY*) :* Dear child, of course you know that Algernon has nothing but his debts to depend upon. But I do not approve of mercenary marriages. When I married Lord Bracknell I had no fortune of any kind. But I never dreamed for a moment of allowing that to stand in my way. Well, I suppose I must give my consent.

Algernon: Thank you, Aunt Augusta.

Lady Bracknell: Cecily, you may kiss me !

Cecily (kisses her) : Thank you, Lady Bracknell.

Lady Bracknell: You may also address me as Aunt Augusta for the future.

Cecily: Thank you, Aunt Augusta.

Lady Bracknell : The marriage, I think, had better take place quite soon.

Algernon : Thank you, Aunt Augusta.

Cecily : Thank you, Aunt Augusta.

Lady Bracknell : To speak frankly, I am not in favour of long engagements. They give people the opportunity of finding out each other's character before marriage, which I think is never advisable.

Jack : I beg your pardon for interrupting you, Lady Bracknell, but this engagement is quite out of the question. I am Miss Cardew's guardian, and she cannot marry without my consent until she comes of age. That consent I absolutely decline to give.

Lady Bracknell : Upon what grounds may I ask ? Algernon is an extremely, I may almost say an ostentatiously, eligible young man. He has nothing, but he looks everything. What more can one desire ?

Jack : It pains me very much to have to speak frankly to you, Lady Bracknell, about your nephew, but the fact is that I do not approve at all of his moral character. I suspect him of being untruthful.

ALGERNON *and* CECILY *look at him in indignant amazement.*

Lady Bracknell : Untruthful ! My nephew Algernon ? Impossible ! He is an Oxonian.

Jack : I fear there can be no possible doubt about the matter. This afternoon during my temporary absence in London on an important question of romance, he obtained admission to my house by means of the false pretence of being my brother. Under an assumed name he drank, I've just been informed by my butler, an entire pint bottle of my Perrier-Jouet, Brut, '89 ; wine I was specially reserving for myself. Continuing his disgraceful deception, he succeeded in the course of the afternoon in alienating the affections of my only ward. He subsequently stayed to tea, and devoured every single muffin. And what makes his conduct all the more heartless is, that he was perfectly well aware from the first that I have no brother, that I never had a brother, and that I don't intend to have a brother, not even of any kind. I distinctly told him so myself yesterday afternoon.

Lady Bracknell : Ahem ! Mr. Worthing, after careful consideration I have decided entirely to overlook my nephew's conduct to you.

Jack : That is very generous of you, Lady Bracknell. My own decision, however, is unalterable. I decline to give my consent.

Lady Bracknell (to CECILY) *:* Come here, sweet child. (CECILY *goes over.*) How old are you, dear ?

Cecily : Well, I am really only eighteen, but I always admit to twenty when I go to evening parties.

Lady Bracknell : You are perfectly right in making some slight alteration. Indeed, no woman should ever be quite accurate about her age. It looks so calculating. . . . (*In a meditative manner.*) Eighteen, but admitting to twenty at evening parties. Well, it will not be very long before you are of age and free from the restraints of tutelage. So I don't think your guardian's consent is, after all, a matter of any importance.

Jack : Pray excuse me, Lady Bracknell, for interrupting you again, but it is only fair to tell you that according to the terms of her grandfather's will Miss Cardew does not come legally of age till she is thirty-five.

Lady Bracknell : That does not seem to me to be a grave objection. Thirty-five is a very attractive age. London society is full of women of the very highest birth who have, of their own free choice, remained thirty-five for years. Lady Dumbleton is an instance in point. To my own knowledge she has been thirty-five ever since she arrived at the age of forty, which was many years ago now. I see no reason why our dear Cecily should not be even still more attractive at the

660 THE IMPORTANCE OF BEING EARNEST

age you mention than she is at present. There will be
a large accumulation of property.

Cecily: Algy, could you wait for me till I was
thirty-five?

Algernon: Of course I could, Cecily. You know
I could.

Cecily: Yes, I felt it instinctively, but I couldn't
wait all that time. I hate waiting even five minutes
for anybody. It always makes me rather cross. I am
not punctual myself, I know, but I do like punctuality
in others, and waiting, even to be married, is quite
out of the question.

Algernon: Then what is to be done, Cecily?

Cecily: I don't know, Mr. Moncrieff.

Lady Bracknell: My dear Mr. Worthing, as Miss
Cecily states positively that she cannot wait till she is
thirty-five—a remark which I am bound to say seems
to me to show a somewhat impatient nature—I would
beg of you to reconsider your decision.

Jack: But my dear Lady Bracknell, the matter is
entirely in your own hands. The moment you consent
to my marriage with Gwendolen, I will most gladly
allow your nephew to form an alliance with my ward.

Lady Bracknell (rising and drawing herself up): You
must be quite aware that what you propose is out of
the question.

Jack: Then a passionate celibacy is all that any of
us can look forward to.

Lady Bracknell: That is not the destiny I propose
for Gwendolen. Algernon, of course, can choose for
himself. (*Pulls out her watch.*) Come, dear—(GWEN-
DOLEN *rises*)—we have already missed five, if not six,
trains. To miss any more might expose us to comment
on the platform.

Enter DR. CHASUBLE.

Chasuble: Everything is quite ready for the
christenings.

Lady Bracknell : The christenings, sir ! Is not that somewhat premature ?

Chasuble (looking rather puzzled, and pointing to JACK *and* ALGERNON*) :* Both these gentlemen have expressed a desire for immediate baptism.

Lady Bracknell : At their age ? The idea is grotesque and irreligious ! Algernon, I forbid you to be baptized. I will not hear of such excesses. Lord Bracknell would be highly displeased if he learned that that was the way in which you wasted your time and money.

Chasuble : Am I to understand then that there are to be no christenings at all this afternoon ?

Jack : I don't think that, as things are now, it would be of much practical value to either of us, Dr. Chasuble.

Chasuble : I am grieved to hear such sentiments from you, Mr. Worthing. They savour of the heretical views of the Anabaptists, views that I have completely refuted in four of my unpublished sermons. However, as your present mood seems to be one peculiarly secular, I will return to the church at once. Indeed, I have just been informed by the pew-opener that for the last hour and a half Miss Prism has been waiting for me in the vestry.

Lady Bracknell (starting) : Miss Prism ! Did I hear you mention a Miss Prism ?

Chasuble : Yes, Lady Bracknell. I am on my way to join her.

Lady Bracknell : Pray allow me to detain you for a moment. This matter may prove to be one of vital importance to Lord Bracknell and myself. Is this Miss Prism a female of repellent aspect, remotely connected with education ?

Chasuble (somewhat indignantly) : She is the most cultivated of ladies, and the very picture of respectability.

Lady Bracknell : It is obviously the same person. May I ask what position she holds in your household ?

Chasuble (severely) : I am a celibate, madam.

Jack (interposing) : Miss Prism, Lady Bracknell, has been for the last three years Miss Cardew's esteemed governess and valued companion.

Lady Bracknell : In spite of what I hear of her, I must see her at once. Let her be sent for.

Chasuble (looking off) : She approaches ; she is nigh.

Enter MISS PRISM *hurriedly.*

Miss Prism : I was told you expected me in the vestry, dear Canon. I have been waiting for you there for an hour and three-quarters. (*Catches sight of* LADY BRACKNELL, *who has fixed her with a stony glare.* MISS PRISM *grows pale and quails. She looks anxiously round as if desirous to escape.*)

Lady Bracknell (in a severe, judicial voice) : Prism ! (MISS PRISM *bows her head in shame.*) Come here, Prism ! (MISS PRISM *approaches in a humble manner.*) Prism ! Where is that baby ? (*General consternation. The* CANON *starts back in horror.* ALGERNON *and* JACK *pretend to be anxious to shield* CECILY *and* GWENDOLEN *from hearing the details of a terrible public scandal.*) Twenty-eight years ago, Prism, you left Lord Bracknell's house, Number 104, Upper Grosvenor Street, in charge of a perambulator that contained a baby of the male sex. You never returned. A few weeks later, through the elaborate investigations of the Metropolitan police, the perambulator was discovered at midnight standing by itself in a remote corner of Bayswater. It contained the manuscript of a three-volume novel of more than usually revolting sentimentality. (MISS PRISM *starts in involuntary indignation.*) But the baby was not there. (*Every one looks at* MISS PRISM.) Prism ! Where is that baby ? (*A pause.*)

Miss Prism : Lady Bracknell, I admit with shame that I do not know. I only wish I did. The plain facts of the case are these. On the morning of the day you mention, a day that is for ever branded on my memory, I prepared as usual to take the baby out in its perambulator. I had also with me a somewhat old, capacious hand-bag in which I had intended to place the manuscript of a work of fiction that I had written during my few unoccupied hours. In a moment of mental abstraction, for which I never can forgive myself, I deposited the manuscript in the basinette, and placed the baby in the hand-bag.

Jack (who has been listening attentively) : But where did you deposit the hand-bag?

Miss Prism : Do not ask me, Mr. Worthing.

Jack : Miss Prism, this is a matter of no small importance to me. I insist on knowing where you deposited the hand-bag that contained that infant.

Miss Prism : I left it in the cloak-room of one of the larger railway stations in London.

Jack : What railway station?

Miss Prism (quite crushed) : Victoria. The Brighton line. *(Sinks into a chair.)*

Jack : I must retire to my room for a moment. Gwendolen, wait here for me.

Gwendolen : If you are not too long, I will wait here for you all my life.

Exit JACK in great excitement.

Chasuble : What do you think this means, Lady Bracknell?

Lady Bracknell : I dare not even suspect, Dr. Chasuble. I need hardly tell you that in families of high position strange coincidences are not supposed to occur. They are hardly considered the thing.

Noises heard overhead as if some one was throwing trunks about. Every one looks up.

Cecily : Uncle Jack seems strangely agitated.

Chasuble : Your guardian has a very emotional nature.

Lady Bracknell : This noise is extremely unpleasant. It sounds as if he was having an argument. I dislike arguments of any kind. They are always vulgar, and often convincing.

Chasuble (looking up) : It has stopped now. (*The noise is redoubled.*)

Lady Bracknell : I wish he would arrive at some conclusion.

Gwendolen : This suspense is terrible. I hope it will last.

> *Enter* JACK *with a hand-bag of black leather in his hand.*

Jack (rushing over to MISS PRISM*) :* Is this the hand-bag, Miss Prism ? Examine it carefully before you speak. The happiness of more than one life depends on your answer.

Miss Prism (calmly) : It seems to be mine. Yes, here is the injury it received through the upsetting of a Gower Street omnibus in younger and happier days. Here is the stain on the lining caused by the explosion of a temperance beverage, an incident that occurred at Leamington. And here, on the lock, are my initials. I had forgotten that in an extravagant mood I had had them placed there. The bag is undoubtedly mine. I am delighted to have it so unexpectedly restored to me. It has been a great inconvenience being without it all these years.

Jack (in a pathetic voice) : Miss Prism, more is restored to you than this hand-bag. I was the baby you placed in it.

Miss Prism (amazed) : You ?

Jack (embracing her) : Yes . . . mother !

Miss Prism (recoiling in indignant astonishment) : Mr. Worthing, I am unmarried !

Jack : Unmarried ! I do not deny that is a serious blow. But after all, who has the right to cast a stone against one who has suffered ? Cannot repentance wipe out an act of folly ? Why should there be one law for men, and another for women ? Mother, I forgive you. (*Tries to embrace her again.*)

Miss Prism (*still more indignant*) *:* Mr. Worthing, there is some error. (*Pointing to* LADY BRACKNELL) *:* There is the lady who can tell you who you really are.

Jack (*after a pause*) *:* Lady Bracknell, I hate to seem inquisitive, but would you kindly inform me who I am ?

Lady Bracknell : I am afraid that the news I have to give you will not altogether please you. You are the son of my poor sister, Mrs. Moncrieff, and consequently Algernon's elder brother.

Jack : Algy's elder brother ! Then I have a brother after all. I knew I had a brother ! I always said I had a brother ! Cecily,—how could you have ever doubted that I had a brother ! (*Seizes hold of* ALGERNON.) Dr. Chasuble, my unfortunate brother. Miss Prism, my unfortunate brother. Gwendolen, my unfortunate brother. Algy, you young scoundrel, you will have to treat me with more respect in the future. You have never behaved to me like a brother in all your life.

Algernon : Well, not till to-day, old boy, I admit. I did my best, however, though I was out of practice. (*Shakes hands.*)

Gwendolen (*to* JACK) *:* My own ! But what own are you ? What is your Christian name, now that you have become some one else ?

Jack : Good heavens ! . . . I had quite forgotten that point. Your decision on the subject of my name is irrevocable, I suppose ?

Gwendolen : I never change, except in my affections.

Cecily : What a noble nature you have, Gwendolen !

Jack : Then the question had better be cleared up at once. Aunt Augusta, a moment. At the time when

Miss Prism left me in the hand-bag, had I been christened already?

Lady Bracknell: Every luxury that money could buy, including christening, had been lavished on you by your fond and doting parents.

Jack: Then I was christened! That is settled. Now, what name was I given? Let me know the worst.

Lady Bracknell: Being the eldest son you were naturally christened after your father.

Jack (irritably): Yes, but what was my father's Christian name?

Lady Bracknell (meditatively): I cannot at the present moment recall what the General's Christian name was. But I have no doubt he had one. He was eccentric, I admit. But only in later years. And that was the result of the Indian climate, and marriage, and indigestion, and other things of that kind.

Jack: Algy! Can't you recollect what our father's Christian name was?

Algernon: My dear boy, we were never even on speaking terms. He died before I was a year old.

Jack: His name would appear in the Army Lists of the period, I suppose, Aunt Augusta?

Lady Bracknell: The General was essentially a man of peace, except in his domestic life. But I have no doubt his name would appear in any military directory.

Jack: The Army Lists of the last forty years are here. These delightful records should have been my constant study. (*Rushes to bookcase and tears the books out.*) M. Generals . . . Mallam, Maxbohm, Magley, what ghastly names they have—Markby, Migsby, Mobbs, Moncrieff! Lieutenant 1840, Captain, Lieutenant-Colonel, Colonel, General 1869, Christian names, Ernest John. (*Puts book very quietly down and speaks quite calmly.*) I always told you, Gwendolen, my name was Ernest, didn't I? Well, it is Ernest after all. I mean it naturally is Ernest.

Lady Bracknell: Yes, I remember now that the

General was called Ernest. I knew I had some particular reason for disliking the name.

Gwendolen : Ernest ! My own Ernest ! I felt from the first that you could have no other name !

Jack : Gwendolen, it is a terrible thing for a man to find out suddenly that all his life he has been speaking nothing but the truth. Can you forgive me ?

Gwendolen : I can. For I feel that you are sure to change.

Jack : My own one !

Chasuble (to MISS PRISM) *:* Lætitia ! (*Embraces her.*

Miss Prism (enthusiastically) : Frederick ! At last !

Algernon : Cecily ! (*Embraces her.*) At last !

Jack : Gwendolen ! (*Embraces her.*) At last !

Lady Bracknell : My nephew, you seem to be displaying signs of triviality.

Jack : On the contrary, Aunt Augusta, I've now realised for the first time in my life the vital Importance of Being Earnest.

TABLEAU.

CURTAIN.

POEMS & ESSAYS

Newdigate Prize Poem

RAVENNA

Recited in the Sheldonian Theatre
Oxford
June 26th, 1878

TO MY FRIEND

GEORGE FLEMING

AUTHOR OF

" THE NILE NOVEL " AND " MIRAGE "

RAVENNA

I

A YEAR ago I breathed the Italian air,—
And yet, methinks this northern Spring is
     fair,—
These fields made golden with the flower of March,
The throstle singing on the feathered larch,
The cawing rooks, the wood-doves fluttering by,
The little clouds that race across the sky;
And fair the violet's gentle drooping head,
The primrose, pale for love uncomforted,
The rose that burgeons on the climbing briar,
The crocus-bed, (that seems a moon of fire
Round-girdled with a purple marriage-ring);
And all the flowers of our English Spring,
Fond snowdrops, and the bright-starred daffodil.
Up starts the lark beside the murmuring mill,
And breaks the gossamer-threads of early dew;
And down the river, like a flame of blue,
Keen as an arrow flies the water-king,
While the brown linnets in the greenwood sing.
A year ago!—it seems a little time
Since last I saw that lordly southern clime,
Where flower and fruit to purple radiance blow,
And like bright lamps the fabled apples glow.
Full Spring it was—and by rich flowering vines,
Dark olive-groves and noble forest-pines,
I rode at will; the moist glad air was sweet,
The white road rang beneath my horse's feet,
And musing on Ravenna's ancient name,
I watched the day till, marked with wounds of flame,
The turquoise sky to burnished gold was turned.

O how my heart with boyish passion burned,
When far away across the sedge and mere
I saw that Holy City rising clear,
Crowned with her crown of towers !—On and on
I galloped, racing with the setting sun,
And ere the crimson after-glow was passed,
I stood within Ravenna's walls at last !

II

How strangely still ! no sound of life or joy
Startles the air ; no laughing shepherd-boy
Pipes on his reed, nor ever through the day
Comes the glad sound of children at their play :
O sad, and sweet, and silent ! surely here
A man might dwell apart from troublous fear,
Watching the tide of seasons as they flow
From amorous Spring to Winter's rain and snow,
And have no thought of sorrow ;—here, indeed,
Are Lethe's waters, and that fatal weed
Which makes a man forget his fatherland.

Ay ! amid lotus-meadows dost thou stand,
Like Proserpine, with poppy-laden head,
Guarding the holy ashes of the dead.
For though thy brood of warrior sons hath ceased,
Thy noble dead are with thee !—they at least
Are faithful to thine honour :—guard them well,
O childless city ! for a mighty spell,
To wake men's hearts to dreams of things sublime,
Are the lone tombs where rest the Great of Time.

III

Yon lonely pillar, rising on the plain,
Marks where the bravest knight of France was slain,—

The Prince of chivalry, the Lord of war,
Gaston de Foix : for some untimely star
Led him against thy city, and he fell,
As falls some forest-lion fighting well.
Taken from life while life and love were new,
He lies beneath God's seamless veil of blue ;
Tall lance-like reeds wave sadly o'er his head,
And oleanders bloom to deeper red,
Where his bright youth flowed crimson on the ground.

Look farther north unto that broken mound—
There, prisoned now within a lordly tomb
Raised by a daughter's hand, in lonely gloom,
Huge-limbed Theodoric, the Gothic king,
Sleeps after all his weary conquering.
Time hath not spared his ruin,—wind and rain
Have broken down his stronghold ; and again
We see that Death is mighty lord of all,
And king and clown to ashen dust must fall.

Mighty indeed *their* glory ! yet to me
Barbaric king, or knight of chivalry,
Or the great queen herself, were poor and vain,
Beside the grave where Dante rests from pain.
His gilded shrine lies open to the air ;
And cunning sculptor's hands have carven there
The calm white brow, as calm as earliest morn,
The eyes that flashed with passionate love and scorn,
The lips that sang of Heaven and of Hell,
The almond-face which Giotto drew so well,
The weary face of Dante ;—to this day,
Here in his place of resting, far away
From Arno's yellow waters, rushing down
Through the wide bridges of that fairy town,
Where the tall tower of Giotto seems to rise
A marble lily under sapphire skies !
Alas ! my Dante ! thou hast known the pain
Of meaner lives,—the exile's galling chain,

How steep the stairs within kings' houses are,
And all the petty miseries which mar
Man's nobler nature with the sense of wrong.
Yet this dull world is grateful for thy song ;
Our nations do thee homage,—even she,
That cruel queen of vine-clad Tuscany,
Who bound with crown of thorns thy living brow,
Hath decked thine empty tomb with laurels now,
And begs in vain the ashes of her son.

O mightiest exile ! all thy grief is done :
Thy soul walks now beside thy Beatrice ;
Ravenna guards thine ashes : sleep in peace.

IV

How lone this palace is ; how grey the walls !
No minstrel now wakes echoes in these halls.
The broken chain lies rusting on the door,
And noisome weeds have split the marble floor :
Here lurks the snake, and here the lizards run
By the stone lions blinking in the sun.
Byron dwelt here in love and revelry
For two long years—a second Anthony,
Who of the world another Actium made !
Yet suffered not his royal soul to fade,
Or lyre to break, or lance to grow less keen,
'Neath any wiles of an Egyptian queen.
For from the East there came a mighty cry,
And Greece stood up to fight for Liberty,
And called him from Ravenna : never knight
Rode forth more nobly to wild scenes of fight !
None fell more bravely on ensanguined field,
Borne like a Spartan back upon his shield !
O Hellas ! Hellas ! in thine hour of pride,
Thy day of might, remember him who died
To wrest from off thy limbs the trammelling chain :

O Salamis ! O lone Platæan plain !
O tossing waves of wild Eubœan sea !
O wind-swept heights of lone Thermopylæ !
He loved you well—ay, not alone in word,
Who freely gave to thee his lyre and sword,
Like Æschylos at well-fought Marathon :

And England, too, shall glory in her son,
Her warrior-poet, first in song and fight.
No longer now shall Slander's venomed spite
Crawl like a snake across his perfect name,
Or mar the lordly scutcheon of his fame.

For as the olive-garland of the race,
Which lights with joy each eager runner's face,
As the red cross which saveth men in war,
As a flame-bearded beacon seen from far
By mariners upon a storm-tossed sea,—
Such was his love for Greece and Liberty !

Byron, thy crowns are ever fresh and green :
Red leaves of rose from Sapphic Mitylene
Shall bind thy brows ; the myrtle blooms for thee,
In hidden glades by lonely Castaly ;
The laurels wait thy coming : all are thine,
And round thy head one perfect wreath will twine.

V

The pine-tops rocked before the evening breeze
With the hoarse murmur of the wintry seas,
And the tall stems were streaked with amber bright ;—
I wandered through the wood in wild delight,
Some startled bird, with fluttering wings and fleet,
Made snow of all the blossoms ; at my feet,
Like silver crowns, the pale narcissi lay,
And small birds sang on every twining spray.

O waving trees, O forest liberty !
Within your haunts at least a man is free,
And half forgets the weary world of strife :
The blood flows hotter, and a sense of life
Wakes i' the quickening veins, while once again
The woods are filled with gods we fancied slain.
Long time I watched, and surely hoped to see
Some goat-foot Pan make merry minstrelsy
Amid the reeds ! some startled Dryad-maid
In girlish flight ! or lurking in the glade,
The soft brown limbs, the wanton treacherous face
Of woodland god ! Queen Dian in the chase,
White-limbed and terrible, with look of pride,
And leash of boar-hounds leaping at her side !
Or Hylas mirrored in the perfect stream.

O idle heart ! O fond Hellenic dream !
Ere long, with melancholy rise and swell,
The evening chimes, the convent's vesper bell,
Struck on mine ears amid the amorous flowers.
Alas ! alas ! these sweet and honied hours
Had whelmed my heart like some encroaching sea,
And drowned all thoughts of black Gethsemane.

VI

O lone Ravenna ! many a tale is told
Of thy great glories in the days of old :
Two thousand years have passed since thou didst see
Cæsar ride forth to royal victory.
Mighty thy name when Rome's lean eagles flew
From Britain's isles to far Euphrates blue ;
And of the peoples thou wast noble queen,
Till in thy streets the Goth and Hun were seen.
Discrowned by man, deserted by the sea,
Thou sleepest, rocked in lonely misery !
No longer now upon thy swelling tide,

Pine-forest-like, thy myriad galleys ride !
For where the brass-beaked ships were wont to float,
The weary shepherd pipes his mournful note ;
And the white sheep are free to come and go
Where Adria's purple waters used to flow.

O fair ! O sad ! O Queen uncomforted !
In ruined loveliness thou liest dead,
Alone of all thy sisters ; for at last
Italia's royal warrior hath passed
Rome's lordliest entrance, and hath worn his crown
In the high temples of the Eternal Town !
The Palatine hath welcomed back her king,
And with his name the seven mountains ring !

And Naples hath outlived her dream of pain.
And mocks her tyrant ! Venice lives again,
New risen from the waters ! and the cry
Of Light and Truth, of Love and Liberty,
Is heard in lordly Genoa, and where
The marble spires of Milan wound the air,
Rings from the Alps to the Sicilian shore,
And Dante's dream is now a dream no more.

But thou, Ravenna, better loved than all,
Thy ruined palaces are but a pall
That hides thy fallen greatness ! and thy name
Burns like a grey and flickering candle-flame
Beneath the noonday splendour of the sun
Of new Italia ! for the night is done,
The night of dark oppression, and the day
Hath dawned in passionate splendour : far away
The Austrian hounds are hunted from the land,
Beyond those ice-crowned citadels which stand
Girdling the plain of royal Lombardy,
From the far West unto the Eastern sea.

I know, indeed, that sons of thine have died
In Lissa's waters, by the mountain-side
Of Aspromonte, on Novara's plain,—

Nor have thy children died for thee in vain :
And yet, methinks, thou hast not drunk this wine
From grapes new-crushed of Liberty divine,
Thou hast not followed that immortal Star
Which leads the people forth to deeds of war.
Weary of life, thou liest in silent sleep,
As one who marks the lengthening shadows creep,
Careless of all the hurrying hours that run,
Mourning some day of glory, for the sun
Of Freedom hath not shewn to thee his face,
And thou hast caught no flambeau in the race.

Yet wake not from thy slumbers,—rest thee well,
Amidst thy fields of amber asphodel,
Thy lily-sprinkled meadows,—rest thee there,
To mock all human greatness : who would dare
To vent the paltry sorrows of his life
Before thy ruins, or to praise the strife
Of kings' ambition, and the barren pride
Of warring nations ! wert not thou the Bride
Of the wild Lord of Adria's stormy sea !
The Queen of double Empires ! and to thee
Were not the nations given as thy prey !
And now—thy gates lie open night and day,
The grass grows green on every tower and hall,
The ghastly fig hath cleft thy bastioned wall ;
And where thy mailèd warriors stood at rest
The midnight owl hath made her secret nest.
O fallen ! fallen ! from thy high estate,
O city trammelled in the toils of Fate,
Doth nought remain of all thy glorious days,
But a dull shield, a crown of withered bays !

Yet who beneath this night of wars and fears,
From tranquil tower can watch the coming years ;
Who can foretell what joys the day shall bring,
Or why before the dawn the linnets sing ?
Thou, even thou, mayst wake, as wakes the rose
To crimson splendour from its grave of snows ;

As the rich corn-fields rise to red and gold
From these brown lands, now stiff with Winter's cold
As from the storm-rack comes a perfect star !

O much-loved city ! I have wandered far
From the wave-circled island of my home ;
Have seen the gloomy mystery of the Dome
Rise slowly from the drear Campagna's way,
Clothed in the royal purple of the day :
I from the city of the violet crown
Have watched the sun by Corinth's hill go down,
And marked the " myriad laughter " of the sea
From starlit hills of flower-starred Arcady ;
Yet back to thee returns my perfect love,
As to its forest-nest the evening dove.

O poet's city ! one who scarce has seen
Some twenty summers cast their doublets green
For Autumn's livery, would seek in vain
To wake his lyre to sing a louder strain,
Or tell thy days of glory ;—poor indeed
Is the low murmur of the shepherd's reed,
Where the loud clarion's blast should shake the sky,
And flame across the heavens ! and to try
Such lofty themes were folly : yet I know
That never felt my heart a nobler glow
Than when I woke the silence of thy street
With clamorous trampling of my horse's feet,
And saw the city which now I try to sing,
After long days of weary travelling.

VII

Adieu, Ravenna ! but a year ago,
I stood and watched the crimson sunset glow
From the lone chapel on thy marshy plain :
The sky was as a shield that caught the stain

Of blood and battle from the dying sun,
And in the west the circling clouds had spun
A royal robe, which some great God might wear,
While into ocean-seas of purple air
Sank the gold galley of the Lord of Light

Yet here the gentle stillness of the night
Brings back the swelling tide of memory,
And wakes again my passionate love for thee :
Now is the Spring of Love, yet soon will come
On meadow and tree the Summer's lordly bloom ;
And soon the grass with brighter flowers will blow,
And send up lilies for some boy to mow.
Then before long the Summer's conqueror,
Rich Autumn-time, the season's usurer,
Will lend his hoarded gold to all the trees,
And see it scattered by the spendthrift breeze ;
And after that the Winter cold and drear.
So runs the perfect cycle of the year.
And so from youth to manhood do we go,
And fall to weary days and locks of snow.
Love only knows no winter ; never dies :
Nor cares for frowning storms or leaden skies
And mine for thee shall never pass away,
Though my weak lips may falter in my lay.

Adieu ! Adieu ! yon silent evening star,
The night's ambassador, doth gleam afar,
And bid the shepherd bring his flocks to fold.
Perchance before our inland seas of gold
Are garnered by the reapers into sheaves,
Perchance before I see the Autumn leaves,
I may behold thy city ; and lay down
Low at thy feet the poet's laurel crown.

Adieu ! Adieu ! yon silver lamp, the moon,
Which turns our midnight into perfect noon,
Doth surely light thy towers, guarding well
Where Dante sleeps, where Byron loved to dwell.

THE BALLAD OF READING GAOL

IN MEMORIAM

C. T. W.

SOMETIME TROOPER OF THE ROYAL HORSE GUARDS

OBIIT H.M. PRISON, READING, BERKSHIRE

JULY 7, 1896

THE BALLAD OF READING GAOL

I

HE did not wear his scarlet coat,
   For blood and wine are red,
   And blood and wine were on his hands
When they found him with the dead,
The poor dead woman whom he loved,
   And murdered in her bed.

He walked amongst the Trial Men
   In a suit of shabby grey ;
A cricket cap was on his head,
   And his step seemed light and gay ;
But I never saw a man who looked
   So wistfully at the day.

I never saw a man who looked
   With such a wistful eye
Upon that little tent of blue
   Which prisoners call the sky,
And at every drifting cloud that went
   With sails of silver by.

I walked, with other souls in pain,
   Within another ring,
And was wondering if the man had done
   A great or little thing,
When a voice behind me whispered low,
   " That fellow's got to swing."

Dear Christ ! the very prison walls
   Suddenly seemed to reel,
And the sky above my head became
   Like a casque of scorching steel ;
And, though I was a soul in pain,
   My pain I could not feel.

I only knew what hunted thought
    Quickened his step, and why
He looked upon the garish day
    With such a wistful eye ;
The man had killed the thing he loved,
    And so he had to die.

Yet each man kills the thing he loves,
    By each let this be heard,
Some do it with a bitter look,
    Some with a flattering word.
The coward does it with a kiss,
    The brave man with a sword !

Some kill their love when they are young,
    And some when they are old ;
Some strangle with the hands of Lust,
    Some with the hands of Gold :
The kindest use a knife, because
    The dead so soon grow cold.

Some love too little, some too long,
    Some sell, and others buy ;
Some do the deed with many tears,
    And some without a sigh :
For each man kills the thing he loves,
    Yet each man does not die.

He does not die a death of shame
    On a day of dark disgrace,
Nor have a noose about his neck,
    Nor a cloth upon his face,
Nor drop feet foremost through the floor
    Into an empty space.

He does not sit with silent men
  Who watch him night and day ;
Who watch him when he tries to weep,
  And when he tries to pray ;
Who watch him lest himself should rob
  The prison of its prey.

He does not wake at dawn to see
  Dread figures throng his room,
The shivering Chaplain robed in white,
  The Sheriff stern with gloom,
And the Governor all in shiny black,
  With the yellow face of Doom.

He does not rise in piteous haste
  To put on convict-clothes,
While some coarse-mouthed Doctor gloats, and
    notes
  Each new and nerve-twitched pose,
Fingering a watch whose little ticks
  Are like horrible hammer-blows.

He does not feel that sickening thirst
  That sands one's throat, before
The hangman with his gardener's gloves
  Comes through the padded door,
And binds one with three leathern thongs,
  That the throat may thirst no more.

He does not bend his head to hear
  The Burial Office read,
Nor, while the anguish of his soul
  Tells him he is not dead,
Cross his own coffin, as he moves
  Into the hideous shed.

He does not stare upon the air
  Through a little roof of glass :
He does not pray with lips of clay
  For his agony to pass ;
Nor feel upon his shuddering cheek
  The kiss of Caiaphas.

II

SIX weeks the guardsman walked the yard,
    In the suit of shabby grey :
  His cricket cap was on his head,
  And his step seemed light and gay,
But I never saw a man who looked
  So wistfully at the day.

I never saw a man who looked
  With such a wistful eye
Upon that little tent of blue
  Which prisoners call the sky,
And at every wandering cloud that trailed
  Its ravelled fleeces by.

He did not wring his hands, as do
  Those witless men who dare
To try to rear the changeling Hope
  In the cave of black Despair :
He only looked upon the sun,
  And drank the morning air.

He did not wring his hands nor weep,
  Nor did he peek or pine,
But he drank the air as though it held
  Some healthful anodyne ;
With open mouth he drank the sun
  As though it had been wine !

And I and all the souls in pain,
  Who tramped the other ring,
Forgot if we ourselves had done
  A great or little thing,
And watched with gaze of dull amaze
  The man who had to swing.

For strange it was to see him pass
  With a step so light and gay,
And strange it was to see him look
  So wistfully at the day,
And strange it was to think that he
  Had such a debt to pay.

❧

For oak and elm have pleasant leaves
  That in the spring-time shoot :
But grim to see is the gallows-tree,
  With its adder-bitten root,
And, green or dry, a man must die
  Before it bears its fruit !

The loftiest place is that seat of grace
  For which all worldlings try :
But who would stand in hempen band
  Upon a scaffold high,
And through a murderer's collar take
  His last look at the sky ?

It is sweet to dance to violins
  When Love and Life are fair :
To dance to flutes, to dance to lutes
  Is delicate and rare :
But it is not sweet with nimble feet
  To dance upon the air !

So with curious eyes and sick surmise
  We watched him day by day,
And wondered if each one of us
  Would end the self-same way,
For none can tell to what red Hell
  His sightless soul may stray.

At last the dead man walked no more
  Amongst the Trial Men,
And I knew that he was standing up
  In the black dock's dreadful pen,
And that never would I see his face
  For weal or woe again.

Like two doomed ships that pass in storm
  We had crossed each other's way:
But we made no sign, we said no word,
  We had no word to say;
For we did not meet in the holy night,
  But in the shameful day.

A prison wall was round us both,
  Two outcast men we were:
The world had thrust us from its heart,
  And God from out His care:
And the iron gin that waits for Sin
  Had caught us in its snare.

III

IN Debtors' Yard the stones are hard,
  And the dripping wall is high,
So it was there he took the air
Beneath the leaden sky,
And by each side a Warder walked,
  For fear the man might die.

Or else he sat with those who watched
  His anguish night and day ;
Who watched him when he rose to weep,
  And when he crouched to pray ;
Who watched him lest himself should rob
  Their scaffold of its prey.

The Governor was strong upon
  The Regulations Act :
The Doctor said that Death was but
  A scientific fact :
And twice a day the Chaplain called,
  And left a little tract.

And twice a day he smoked his pipe,
  And drank his quart of beer :
His soul was resolute, and held
  No hiding-place for fear ;
He often said that he was glad
  The hangman's day was near.

But why he said so strange a thing
  No warder dared to ask :
For he to whom a watcher's doom
  Is given as his task,
Must set a lock upon his lips
  And make his face a mask.

Or else he might be moved, and try
  To comfort or console :
And what should Human Pity do
  Pent up in Murderer's Hole ?
What word of grace in such a place
  Could help a brother's soul ?

With slouch and swing around the ring
   We trod the Fools' Parade !
We did not care : we knew we were
   The Devil's Own Brigade :
And shaven head and feet of lead
   Make a merry masquerade.

We tore the tarry rope to shreds
   With blunt and bleeding nails ;
We rubbed the doors, and scrubbed the floors,
   And cleaned the shining rails :
And, rank by rank, we soaped the plank,
   And clattered with the pails.

We sewed the sacks, we broke the stones,
   We turned the dusty drill :
We banged the tins, and bawled the hymns,
   And sweated on the mill :
But in the heart of every man
   Terror was lying still.

So still it lay that every day
   Crawled like a weed-clogged wave :
And we forgot the bitter lot
   That waits for fool and knave,
Till once, as we tramped in from work,
   We passed an open grave.

With yawning mouth the yellow hole
   Gaped for a living thing ;
The very mud cried out for blood
   To the thirsty asphalte ring :
And we knew that ere one dawn grew fair
   Some prisoner had to swing.

Right in we went, with soul intent
  On Death and Dread and Doom :
The hangman, with his little bag,
  Went shuffling through the gloom :
And I trembled as I groped my way
  Into my numbered tomb.

That night the empty corridors
  Were full of forms of Fear,
And up and down the iron town
  Stole feet we could not hear,
And through the bars that hide the stars
  White faces seemed to peer.

He lay as one who lies and dreams
  In a pleasant meadow-land,
The watchers watched him as he slept,
  And could not understand
How one could sleep so sweet a sleep
  With a hangman close at hand.

But there is no sleep when men must weep
  Who never yet have wept :
So we—the fool, the fraud, the knave—
  That endless vigil kept,
And through each brain on hands of pain
  Another's terror crept.

Alas! it is a fearful thing
  To feel another's guilt !
For, right, within, the Sword of Sin
  Pierced to its poisoned hilt,
And as molten lead were the tears we shed
  For the blood we had not spilt.

The warders with their shoes of felt
  Crept by each padlocked door,
And peeped and saw, with eyes of awe,
  Grey figures on the floor,
And wondered why men knelt to pray
  Who never prayed before.

All through the night we knelt and prayed,
  Mad mourners of a corse !
The troubled plumes of midnight shook
  The plumes upon a hearse :
And bitter wine upon a sponge
  Was the savour of Remorse.

❖

The grey cock crew, the red cock crew,
  But never came the day :
And crooked shapes of Terror crouched,
  In the corners where we lay :
And each evil sprite that walks by night
  Before us seemed to play.

They glided past, they glided fast,
  Like travellers through a mist :
They mocked the moon in a rigadoon
  Of delicate turn and twist,
And with formal pace and loathsome grace
  The phantoms kept their tryst.

With mop and mow, we saw them go,
  Slim shadows hand in hand :
About, about, in ghostly rout
  They trod a saraband :
And the damned grotesques made arabesques,
  Like the wind upon the sand !

With the pirouettes of marionettes,
  They tripped on pointed tread :
But with flutes of Fear they filled the ear,
  As their grisly masque they led,
And loud they sang, and long they sang,
  For they sang to wake the dead.

" *Oho !* " *they cried,* " *The world is wide,*
  But fettered limbs go lame !
And once, or twice, to throw the dice
  Is a gentlemanly game,
But he does not win who plays with Sin
  In the secret House of Shame."

No things of air these antics were,
  That frolicked with such glee :
To men whose lives were held in gyves,
  And whose feet might not go free,
Ah ! wounds of Christ ! they were living things.
  Most terrible to see.

Around, around, they waltzed and wound ;
  Some wheeled in smirking pairs ;
With the mincing step of a demirep
  Some sidled up the stairs :
And with subtle sneer, and fawning leer,
  Each helped us at our prayers.

The morning wind began to moan,
  But still the night went on :
Through its giant loom the web of gloom
  Crept till each thread was spun :
And, as we prayed, we grew afraid
  Of the Justice of the Sun.

The moaning wind went wandering round
  The weeping prison-wall :
Till like a wheel of turning steel
  We felt the minutes crawl :
O moaning wind ! what had we done
  To have such a seneschal ?

At last I saw the shadowed bars,
  Like a lattice wrought in lead,
Move right across the whitewashed wall
  That faced my three-plank bed,
And I knew that somewhere in the world
  God's dreadful dawn was red.

At six o'clock we cleaned our cells,
  At seven all was still,
But the sough and swing of a mighty wing
  The prison seemed to fill,
For the Lord of Death with icy breath
  Had entered in to kill.

He did not pass in purple pomp,
  Nor ride a moon-white steed.
Three yards of cord and a sliding board
  Are all the gallows' need :
So with rope of shame the Herald came
  To do the secret deed.

We were as men who through a fen
  Of filthy darkness grope :
We did not dare to breathe a prayer,
  Or to give our anguish scope :
Something was dead in each of us,
  And what was dead was Hope.

For Man's grim Justice goes its way,
   And will not swerve aside :
It slays the weak, it slays the strong,
   It has a deadly stride :
With iron heel it slays the strong,
   The monstrous parricide !

We waited for the stroke of eight :
   Each tongue was thick with thirst :
For the stroke of eight is the stroke of Fate
   That makes a man accursed,
And Fate will use a running noose
   For the best man and the worst.

We had no other thing to do,
   Save to wait for the sign to come :
So, like things of stone in a valley lone,
   Quiet we sat and dumb :
But each man's heart beat thick and quick,
   Like a madman on a drum !

With sudden shock the prison-clock
   Smote on the shivering air,
And from all the gaol rose up a wail
   Of impotent despair,
Like the sound that frightened marches hear
   From some leper in his lair.

And as one sees most fearful things
   In the crystal of a dream,
We saw the greasy hempen rope
   Hooked to the blackened beam,
And heard the prayer the hangman's snare
   Strangled into a scream.

And all the woe that moved him so
That he gave that bitter cry,
And the wild regrets, and the bloody sweats,
None knew so well as I :
For he who lives more lives than one
More deaths than one must die.

IV

THERE is no chapel on the day
On which they hang a man :
The Chaplain's heart is far too sick,
Or his face is far too wan,
Or there is that written in his eyes
Which none should look upon.

So they kept us close till nigh on noon,
And then they rang the bell,
And the warders with their jingling keys
Opened each listening cell,
And down the iron stair we tramped,
Each from his separate Hell.

Out into God's sweet air we went,
But not in wonted way,
For this man's face was white with fear,
And that man's face was grey,
And I never saw sad men who looked
So wistfully at the day.

I never saw sad men who looked
With such a wistful eye
Upon that little tent of blue
We prisoners called the sky,
And at every happy cloud that passed
In such strange freedom by.

But there were those amongst us all
  Who walked with downcast head,
And knew that, had each got his due,
  They should have died instead :
He had but killed a thing that lived,
  Whilst they had killed the dead.

For he who sins a second time
  Wakes a dead soul to pain,
And draws it from its spotted shroud,
  And makes it bleed again,
And makes it bleed great gouts of blood,
  And makes it bleed in vain !

❧

Like ape or clown, in monstrous garb
  With crooked arrows starred,
Silently we went round and round
  The slippery asphalte yard ;
Silently we went round and round,
  And no man spoke a word.

Silently we went round and round,
  And through each hollow mind
The Memory of dreadful things
  Rushed like a dreadful wind,
And Horror stalked before each man,
  And Terror crept behind.

❧

The warders strutted up and down,
  And watched their herd of brutes,
Their uniforms were spick and span,
  And they wore their Sunday suits,
But we knew the work they had been at,
  By the quicklime on their boots.

For where a grave had opened wide,
   There was no grave at all :
Only a stretch of mud and sand
   By the hideous prison-wall,
And a little heap of burning lime,
That the man should have his pall.

For he has a pall, this wretched man,
   Such as few men can claim :
Deep down below a prison-yard,
   Naked for greater shame,
He lies, with fetters on each foot,
   Wrapt in a sheet of flame !

And all the while the burning lime
   Eats flesh and bone away,
It eats the brittle bone by night,
   And the soft flesh by day,
It eats the flesh and bone by turns,
   But it eats the heart alway.

For three long years they will not sow
   Or root or seedling there :
For three long years the unblessed spot
   Will sterile be and bare,
And look upon the wondering sky
   With unreproachful stare.

They think a murderer's heart would taint
   Each simple seed they sow.
It is not true ! God's kindly earth
   Is kindlier than men know,
And the red rose would but blow more red,
   The white rose whiter blow.

Out of his mouth a red, red rose !
  Out of his heart a white !
For who can say by what strange way,
  Christ brings His will to light,
Since the barren staff the pilgrim bore
  Bloomed in the great Pope's sight ?

But neither milk-white rose nor red
  May bloom in prison-air ;
The shard, the pebble, and the flint,
  Are what they give us there :
For flowers have been known to heal
  A common man's despair.

So never will wine-red rose or white,
  Petal by petal, fall
On that stretch of mud and sand that lies
  By the hideous prison-wall,
To tell the men who tramp the yard
  That God's Son died for all.

Yet though the hideous prison-wall
  Still hems him round and round,
And a spirit may not walk by night
  That is with fetters bound,
And a spirit may but weep that lies
  In such unholy ground,

He is at peace—this wretched man—
  At peace, or will be soon :
There is no thing to make him mad,
  Nor does Terror walk at noon,
For the lampless Earth in which he lies
  Has neither Sun nor Moon.

They hanged him as a beast is hanged :
   They did not even toll
A requiem that might have brought
   Rest to his startled soul,
But hurriedly they took him out,
   And hid him in a hole.

The warders stripped him of his clothes,
   And gave him to the flies :
They mocked the swollen purple throat,
   And the stark and staring eyes :
And with laughter loud they heaped the shroud
   In which the convict lies.

The Chaplain would not kneel to pray
   By his dishonoured grave :
Nor mark it with that blessed Cross
   That Christ for sinners gave,
Because the man was one of those
   Whom Christ came down to save.

Yet all is well ; he has but passed
   To Life's appointed bourne :
And alien tears will fill for him
   Pity's long-broken urn,
For his mourners will be outcast men,
   And outcasts always mourn

V

I KNOW not whether Laws be right,
   Or whether Laws be wrong ;
   All that we know who lie in gaol
Is that the wall is strong ;
And that each day is like a year,
   A year whose days are long.

But this I know, that every Law
  That men have made for Man,
Since first Man took his brother's life,
  And the sad world began,
But straws the wheat and saves the chaff
  With a most evil fan.

This too I know—and wise it were
  If each could know the same—
That every prison that men build
  Is built with bricks of shame,
And bound with bars lest Christ should see
  How men their brothers maim.

With bars they blur the gracious moon,
  And blind the goodly sun :
And they do well to hide their Hell,
  For in it things are done
That Son of God nor son of Man
  Ever should look upon !

The vilest deeds like poison weeds,
  Bloom well in prison-air ;
It is only what is good in Man
  That wastes and withers there :
Pale Anguish keeps the heavy gate,
  And the Warder is Despair.

For they starve the little frightened child
  Till it weeps both night and day :
And they scourge the weak, and flog the fool,
  And gibe the old and grey,
And some grow mad, and all grow bad,
  And none a word may say.

Each narrow cell in which we dwell
   Is a foul and dark latrine,
And the fetid breath of living Death
   Chokes up each grated screen,
And all, but Lust, is turned to dust
   In Humanity's machine.

The brackish water that we drink
   Creeps with a loathsome slime,
And the bitter bread they weigh in scales
   Is full of chalk and lime,
And Sleep will not lie down, but walks
   Wild-eyed, and cries to Time.

          ❧

But though lean Hunger and green Thirst
   Like asp with adder fight,
We have little care of prison fare,
   For what chills and kills outright
Is that every stone one lifts by day
   Becomes one's heart by night.

With midnight always in one's heart,
   And twilight in one's cell,
We turn the crank, or tear the rope,
   Each in his separate Hell,
And the silence is more awful far
   Than the sound of a brazen bell.

And never a human voice comes near
   To speak a gentle word :
And the eye that watches through the door
   Is pitiless and hard :
And by all forgot, we rot and rot,
   With soul and body marred.

And thus we rust Life's iron chain
  Degraded and alone :
And some men curse, and some men weep,
  And some men make no moan :
But God's eternal Laws are kind
  And break the heart of stone.

And every human heart that breaks,
  In prison-cell or yard,
Is as that broken box that gave
  Its treasure to the Lord,
And filled the unclean leper's house
  With the scent of costliest nard.

Ah ! happy they whose hearts can break
  And peace of pardon win !
How else may man make straight his plan
  And cleanse his soul from Sin ?
How else but through a broken heart
  May Lord Christ enter in ?

�֍

And he of the swollen purple throat,
  And the stark and staring eyes,
Waits for the holy hands that took
  The Thief to Paradise ;
And a broken and a contrite heart
  The Lord will not despise.

The man in red who reads the Law
  Gave him three weeks of life,
Three little weeks in which to heal
  His soul of his soul's strife,
And cleanse from every blot of blood
  The hand that held the knife.

And with tears of blood he cleansed the hand,
   The hand that held the steel :
For only blood can wipe out blood,
   And only tears can heal :
And the crimson stain that was of Cain
   Became Christ's snow-white seal.

VI

IN Reading gaol by Reading town
   There is a pit of shame,
And in it lies a wretched man
   Eaten by teeth of flame,
In a burning winding-sheet he lies,
   And his grave has got no name.

And there, till Christ call forth the dead,
   In silence let him lie :
No need to waste the foolish tear,
   Or heave the windy sigh :
The man had killed the thing he loved,
   And so he had to die.

And all men kill the thing they love,
   By all let this be heard,
Some do it with a bitter look,
   Some with a flattering word,
The coward does it with a kiss,
   The brave man with a sword !

THE CRITIC AS ARTIST

WITH SOME REMARKS UPON THE IMPORTANCE OF DOING NOTHING

A DIALOGUE. Part I. Persons: Gilbert and Ernest. Scene: the library of a house in Piccadilly, overlooking the Green Park.

THE CRITIC AS ARTIST

GILBERT (at the piano): My dear Ernest, what are you laughing at?

Ernest (looking up): At a capital story that I have just come across in this volume of Reminiscences that I have found on your table.

Gilbert: What is the book? Ah! I see. I have not read it yet. Is it good?

Ernest: Well, while you have been playing, I have been turning over the pages with some amusement, though, as a rule, I dislike modern memoirs. They are generally written by people who have either entirely lost their memories, or have never done anything worth remembering; which, however, is, no doubt, the true explanation of their popularity, as the English public always feels perfectly at its ease when a mediocrity is talking to it.

Gilbert: Yes; the public is wonderfully tolerant. It forgives everything except genius. But I must confess that I like all memoirs. I like them for their form, just as much as for their matter. In literature mere egotism is delightful. It is what fascinates us in the letters of personalities so different as Cicero and Balzac, Flaubert and Berlioz, Byron and Madame de Sévigné. Whenever we come across it, and, strangely enough, it is rather rare, we cannot but welcome it, and do not easily forget it. Humanity will always love Rousseau for having confessed his sins, not to a priest, but to the world, and the couchant nymphs that Cellini wrought in bronze for the castle of King Francis, the green and gold Perseus, even, that in the open Loggia at Florence shows the moon the dead terror that once turned life to stone, have not given it more pleasure than has that autobiography in which the supreme scoundrel of the Renaissance relates the story

of his splendour and his shame. The opinions, the
character, the achievements of the man, matter very
little. He may be a sceptic like the gentle Sieur de
Montaigne, or a saint like the bitter son of Monica, but
when he tells us his own secrets he can always charm
our ears to listening and our lips to silence. The mode
of thought that Cardinal Newman represented—if
that can be called a mode of thought which seeks to
solve intellectual problems by a denial of the supremacy
of the intellect—may not, cannot, I think, survive.
But the world will never weary of watching that
troubled soul in its progress from darkness to darkness.
The lonely church at Littlemore, where " the breath
of the morning is damp, and worshippers are few,"
will always be dear to it, and whenever men see the
yellow snapdragon blossoming on the wall of Trinity
they will think of that gracious undergraduate who saw
in the flower's sure recurrence a prophecy that he
would abide for ever with the Benign Mother of his
days—a prophecy that Faith, in her wisdom or her
folly, suffered not to be fulfilled. Yes ; autobiography
is irresistible. Poor, silly, conceited Mr. Secretary
Pepys had chattered his way into the circle of the
Immortals, and, conscious that indiscretion is the
better part of valour, bustles about among them in
that " shaggy purple gown with gold buttons and
looped lace " which he is so fond of describing to us,
perfectly at his ease, and prattling, to his own and
our infinite pleasure, of the Indian blue petticoat that
he bought for his wife, of the " good hog's harslet,"
and the " pleasant French fricassee of veal " that he
loved to eat, of his game of bowls with Will Joyce,
and his " gadding after beauties," and his reciting of
Hamlet on a Sunday, and his playing of the viol on
week days, and other wicked or trival things. Even
in actual life egotism is not without its attractions.
When people talk to us about others they are usually
dull. When they talk to us about themselves they are

nearly always interesting, and if one could shut them up, when they become wearisome, as easily as one can shut up a book of which one has grown wearied, they would be perfect absolutely.

Ernest : There is much virtue in that If, as Touch-stone would say. But do you seriously propose that every man should become his own Boswell ? What would become of our industrious compilers of Lives and Recollections in that case ?

Gilbert : What has become of them ? They are the pest of the age, nothing more and nothing less. Every great man nowadays has his disciples, and it is always Judas who writes the biography.

Ernest : My dear fellow !

Gilbert : I am afraid it is true. Formerly we used to canonise our heroes. The modern method is to vulgarise them. Cheap editions of great books may be delightful, but cheap editions of great men are absolutely detestable.

Ernest : May I ask, Gilbert, to whom you allude ?

Gilbert : Oh ! to all our second-rate *littérateurs.* We are overrun by a set of people who, when poet or painter passes away, arrive at the house along with the undertaker, and forget that their one duty is to behave as mutes. But we won't talk about them. They are the mere body-snatchers of literature. The dust is given to one, and the ashes to another, and the soul is out of their reach. And now, let me play Chopin to you, or Dvorák ? Shall I play you a fantasy by Dvorák ? He writes passionate, curiously-coloured things.

Ernest : No ; I don't want music just at present. It is far too indefinite. Besides, I took the Baroness Bernstein down to dinner last night, and, though absolutely charming in every other respect, she insisted on discussing music as if it were actually written in the German language. Now, whatever music sounds like, I am glad to say that it does not sound in the smallest

THE CRITIC AS ARTIST

that are really quite degrading. No ; Gilbert, don't
play any more. Turn round and talk to me. Talk to
me till the white-horned day comes into the room.
There is something in your voice that is wonderful.

Gilbert (*rising from the piano*) : I am not in a mood
for talking to-night. How horrid of you to smile !
I really am not. Where are the cigarettes ? Thanks.
How exquisite these single daffodils are ! They seem
to be made of amber and cool ivory. They are like
Greek things of the best period. What was the story
in the confessions of the remorseful Academician that
made you laugh ? Tell it to me. After playing Chopin,
I feel as if I had been weeping over sins that I had
never committed, and mourning over tragedies that
were not my own. Music always seems to me to
produce that effect. It creates for one a past of which
one has been ignorant, and fills one with a sense of
sorrows that have been hidden from one's tears.
I can fancy a man who had led a perfectly commonplace life, hearing by chance some curious piece of
music, and suddenly discovering that his soul, without
his being conscious of it, had passed through terrible
experiences, and known fearful joys, or wild romantic
loves, or great renunciations. And so tell me this
story, Ernest. I want to be amused.

Ernest : Oh ! I don't know that it is of any importance. But I thought it a really admirable illustra-
tion of the true value of ordinary art-criticism. It
seems that a lady once gravely asked the remorseful
Academician, as you call him, if his celebrated picture
of " A Spring-Day at Whiteley's," or " Waiting for
the Last Omnibus," or some subject of that kind, was
all painted by hand ?

Gilbert : And was it ?

Ernest : You are quite incorrigible. But, seriously
speaking, what is the use of art-criticism ? Why cannot
the artist be left alone, to create a new world if he wishes

it, or, if not, to shadow forth the world which we already know, and of which, I fancy, we would each one of us be wearied if Art, with her fine spirit of choice and delicate instinct of selection, did not, as it were, purify it for us, and give to it a momentary perfection. It seems to me that the imagination spreads, or should spread, a solitude around it, and works best in silence and in isolation. Why should the artist be troubled by the shrill clamour of criticism ? Why should those who cannot create take upon themselves to estimate the value of creative work ? What can they know about it ? If a man's work is easy to understand, an explanation is unnecessary. . . .

Gilbert : And if his work is incomprehensible, an explanation is wicked.

Ernest : I did not say that.

Gilbert : Ah ! but you should have. Nowadays, we have so few mysteries left to us that we cannot afford to part with one of them. The members of the Browning Society, like the theologians of the Broad Church Party, or the authors of Mr. Walter Scott's Great Writers' Series, seem to me to spend their time in trying to explain their divinity away. Where one had hoped that Browning was a mystic they have sought to show that he was simply inarticulate. Where one had fancied that he had something to conceal, they have proved that he had but little to reveal. But I speak merely of his incoherent work. Taken as a whole the man was great. He did not belong to the Olympians, and had all the incompleteness of the Titan. He did not survey, and it was but rarely that he could sing. His work is marred by struggle, violence and effort, and he passed not from emotion to form, but from thought to chaos. Still, he was great. He has been called a thinker, and was certainly a man who was always thinking, and always thinking aloud ; but it was not thought that fascinated him, but rather the processes by which thought moves. It was the machine he loved, not what the machine makes. The method by which the fool arrives at his folly was as dear to him as the ultimate wisdom of the wise. So much, indeed, did the subtle mechanism of mind fascinate him that he despised language, or looked upon it as an incomplete instrument of expression. Rhyme, that exquisite echo which in the Muse's hollow hill creates and answers its own voice ; rhyme, which in the hands of the real artist becomes not merely a material element of metrical beauty, but a spiritual element of thought and passion also, waking a new mood, it may be, or stirring a fresh train of ideas, or opening by mere sweetness and suggestion of sound some golden door at which the Imagination itself had knocked in vain ; rhyme, which can turn man's utterance to the speech of gods ; rhyme, the one chord we have added to the Greek lyre, became in Robert Browning's hands a grotesque, misshapen thing, which at times made him masquerade in poetry as a low comedian, and ride Pegasus too often with his tongue in his cheek. There are moments when he wounds us by monstrous music. Nay, if he can only get his music by breaking the strings of his lute, he breaks them, and they snap in discord, and no Athenian tettix, making melody from tremulous wings, lights on the ivory horn to make the movement perfect, or the interval less harsh. Yet, he was great : and though he turned language into ignoble clay, he made from it men and women that live. He is the most Shakespearian creature since Shakespeare. If Shakespeare could sing with myriad lips, Browning could stammer through a thousand mouths. Even now, as I am speaking, and speaking not against him but for him, there glides through the room the pageant of his persons. There, creeps Fra Lippo Lippi with his cheeks still burning from some girl's hot kiss. There, stands dread Saul with the lordly male-sapphires gleaming in his turban. Mildred Tresham is there, and the Spanish monk, yellow with hatred, and Blougram, and Ben Ezra, and the Bishop of St. Praxed's. The spawn of Setebos gibbers in the corner, and Sebald, hearing Pippa pass by, looks on Ottima's haggard face, and loathes her and his own sin, and himself. Pale as the white satin of his doublet, the melancholy king watches with dreamy treacherous eyes too loyal Strafford pass forth to his doom, and Andrea shudders as he hears the cousins whistle in the garden, and bids his perfect wife go down. Yes, Browning was great. And as what will he be remembered? As a poet? Ah, not as a poet! He will be remembered as a writer of fiction, as the most supreme writer of fiction, it may be, that we have ever had. His sense of dramatic situation was unrivalled, and, if he could not answer his own problems, he could at least put problems forth, and what more should an artist do? Considered from the point of view of a creator of character he ranks next to him who made Hamlet. Had he been articulate, he might have sat beside him. The only man who can touch the hem of his garment is George Meredith. Meredith is a prose Browning, and so is Browning. He used poetry as a medium for writing in prose.

Ernest: There is something in what you say, but there is not everything in what you say. In many points you are unjust.

Gilbert: It is difficult not to be unjust to what one loves. But let us return to the particular point at issue. What was it that you said?

Ernest: Simply this: that in the best days of art there were no art-critics.

Gilbert: I seem to have heard that observation before, Ernest. It has all the vitality of error and all the tediousness of an old friend.

Ernest: It is true. Yes: there is no use your tossing your head in that petulant manner. It is quite true. In the best days of art there were no art-critics. The sculptor hewed from the marble block the great

white-limbed Hermes that slept within it. The waxers
and gilders of images gave tone and texture to the
statue, and the world, when it saw it, worshipped and
was dumb. He poured the glowing bronze into the
mould of sand, and the river of red metal cooled into
noble curves and took the impress of the body of a
god. With enamel or polished jewels he gave sight
to the sightless eyes. The hyacinth-like curls grew
crisp beneath his graver. And when, in some dim
frescoed fane, or pillared sunlit portico, the child of
Leto stood upon his pedestal, those who passed by,
διὰ λαμπροτάτου βαίνοντες ἁβρῶς ἀιθέρος, became
conscious of a new influence that had come across
their lives, and dreamily, or with a sense of strange
and quickening joy, went to their homes or daily
labour, or wandered, it may be, through the city
gates to that nymph-haunted meadow where young
Phædrus bathed his feet, and, lying there on the soft
grass, beneath the tall wind-whispering planes and
flowering *agnus castus*, began to think of the wonder
of beauty, and grew silent with unaccustomed awe.
In those days the artist was free. From the river
valley he took the fine clay in his fingers, and with a
little tool of wood or bone, fashioned it into forms so
exquisite that the people gave them to the dead as their
playthings, and we find them still in the dusty tombs
on the yellow hillside by Tanagra, with the faint gold
and the fading crimson still lingering about hair and
lips and raiment. On a wall of fresh plaster, stained
with bright sandyx or mixed with milk and saffron, he
pictured one who trod with tired feet the purple white-
starred fields of asphodel, one " in whose eyelids lay
the whole of the Trojan War," Polyxena, the daughter
of Priam ; or figured Odysseus, the wise and cunning,
bound by tight cords to the mast-step, that he might
listen without hurt to the singing of the Sirens, or
wandering by the clear river of Acheron, where the
ghosts of fishes flitted over the pebbly bed ; or showed

the Persian in trews and mitre flying before the Greek
at Marathon, or the galleys clashing their beaks of brass
in the little Salaminian bay. He drew with silver-point
and charcoal upon parchment and prepared cedar.
Upon ivory and rose-coloured terra-cotta he painted
with wax, making the wax fluid with juice of olives, and
with heated irons making it firm. Panel and marble
and linen canvas became wonderful as his brush swept
across them ; and life seeing her own image, was still,
and dared not speak. All life, indeed, was his, from
the merchants seated in the market-place to the
cloaked shepherd lying on the hill ; from the nymph
hidden in the laurels and the faun that pipes at noon,
to the king whom, in long green-curtained litter, slaves
bore upon oil-bright shoulders, and fanned with
peacock fans. Men and women, with pleasure or sorrow
in their faces, passed before him. He watched them,
and their secret became his. Through form and colour
he re-created a world.

All subtle arts belonged to him also. He held the
gem against the revolving disk, and the amethyst
became the purple couch for Adonis, and across the
veined sardonyx sped Artemis with her hounds. He
beat out the gold into roses, and strung them together
for necklace or armlet. He beat out the gold into
wreaths for the conqueror's helmet, or into palmates
for the Tyrian robe, or into masks for the royal dead.
On the back of the silver mirror he graved Thetis borne
by her Nereids, or love-sick Phædra with her nurse,
of Persephone, weary of memory, putting poppies in
her hair. The potter sat in his shed, and, flower-like
from the silent wheel, the vase rose up beneath his
hands. He decorated the base and stem and ears with
pattern of dainty olive-leaf, of foliated acanthus, or
curved and crested wave. Then in black or red he
painted lads wrestling, or in the race : knights in full
armour, with strange heraldic shields and curious
visors, leaning from shell-shaped chariot over rearing

steeds : the gods seated at the feast or working their
miracles : the heroes in their victory or in their pain.
Sometimes he would etch in thin vermilion lines upon
a ground of white the languid bridegroom and his
bride, with Eros hovering round them—an Eros like
one of Donatello's angels, a little laughing thing with
gilded or with azure wings. On the curved side he would
write the name of his friend. ΚΑΛΟΣ ΑΛΚΙΒΙΑΔΗΣ
or ΚΑΛΟΣ ΧΑΡΜΙΔΗΣ tells us the story of his
days. Again, on the rim of the wide flat cup he
would draw the stag browsing, or the lion at rest, as
his fancy willed it. From the tiny perfume-bottle
laughed Aphrodite at her toilet, and, with bare-
limbed Mænads in his train, Dionysus danced round
the wine-jar on naked must-stained feet, while, satyr-
like, the old Silenus sprawled upon the bloated skins,
or shook that magic spear which was tipped with a
fretted fir-cone, and wreathed with dark ivy. And no
one came to trouble the artist at his work. No irresponsible chatter disturbed him. He was not worried
by opinions. By the Ilyssus, says Arnold somewhere,
there was no Higginbotham. By the Ilyssus, my dear
Gilbert, there were no silly art congresses bringing
provincialism to the provinces and teaching the
mediocrity how to mouth. By the Ilyssus there were
no tedious magazines about art, in which the industrious prattle of what they do not understand. On
the reed-grown banks of that little stream strutted
no ridiculous journalism monopolising the seat of
judgment when it should be apologising in the dock.
The Greeks had no art-critics.

Gilbert : Ernest, you are quite delightful, but your
views are terribly unsound. I am afraid that you have
been listening to the conversation of some one older
than yourself. That is always a dangerous thing to do,
and if you allow it to degenerate into a habit you will
find it absolutely fatal to any intellectual development. As for modern journalism, it is not my business

to defend it. It justifies its own existence by the great Darwinian principle of the survival of the vulgarest. I have merely to do with literature.

Ernest : But what is the difference between literature and journalism ?

Gilbert : Oh ! journalism is unreadable, and literature is not read. That is all. But with regard to your statement that the Greeks had no art-critics, I assure you that is quite absurd. It would be more just to say that the Greeks were a nation of art-critics.

Ernest : Really ?

Gilbert : Yes, a nation of art-critics. But I don't wish to destroy the delightfully unreal picture that you have drawn of the relation of the Hellenic artist to the intellectual spirit of his age. To give an accurate description of what has never occurred is not merely the proper occupation of the historian, but the inalienable privilege of any man of parts and culture. Still less do I desire to talk learnedly. Learned conversation is either the affectation of the ignorant or the profession of the mentally unemployed. And, as for what is called improving conversation, that is merely the foolish method by which the still more foolish philanthropist feebly tries to disarm the just rancour of the criminal classes. No ; let me play to you some mad scarlet thing by Dvorák. The pallid figures on the tapestry are smiling at us, and the heavy eyelids of my bronze Narcissus are folded in sleep. Don't let us discuss anything solemnly. I am but too conscious of the fact that we are born in an age when only the dull are treated seriously, and I live in terror of not being misunderstood. Don't degrade me into the position of giving you useful information. Education is an admirable thing, but it is well to remember from time to time that nothing that is worth knowing can be taught. Through the parted curtains of the window I see the moon like a clipped piece of silver. Like gilded bees the stars cluster round her. The sky is a hard hollow sapphire. Let us go out into the night. Thought is wonderful, but adventure is more wonderful still. Who knows but we may meet Prince Florizel of Bohemia, and hear the fair Cuban tell us that she is not what she seems ?

Ernest : You are horribly wilful. I insist on your discussing this matter with me. You have said that the Greeks were a nation of art-critics. What art-criticism have they left us ?

Gilbert : My dear Ernest, even if not a single fragment of art-criticism had come down to us from Hellenic or Hellenistic days, it would be none the less true that the Greeks were a nation of art-critics, and that they invented the criticism of art just as they invented the criticism of everything else. For, after all, what is our primary debt to the Greeks ? Simply the critical spirit. And, this spirit, which they exercised on questions of religion and science, of ethics and metaphysics, of politics and education, they exercised on questions of art also, and, indeed, of the two supreme and highest arts, they have left us the most flawless system of criticism that the world has ever seen.

Ernest : But what are the two supreme and highest arts ?

Gilbert : Life and Literature, life and the perfect expression of life. The principles of the former, as laid down by the Greeks, we may not realise in an age so marred by false ideals as our own. The principles of the latter, as they laid them down, are, in many cases, so subtle that we can hardly understand them. Recognising that the most perfect art is that which most fully mirrors man in all his infinite variety, they elaborated the criticism of language, considered in the light of the mere material of that art, to a point to which we, with our accentual system of reasonable or emotional emphasis, can barely if at all attain ; studying, for instance, the metrical movements of a prose as scientifically as a modern musician studies harmony and counterpoint, and, I need hardly say, with much keener æsthetic instinct. In this they were right, as they were right in all things. Since the introduction of printing, and the fatal development of the habit of reading amongst the middle and lower classes of this country, there has been a tendency in literature to appeal more and more to the eye, and less and less to the ear which is really the sense which, from the standpoint of pure art, it should seek to please, and by whose canons of pleasure it should abide always. Even the work of Mr. Pater, who is, on the whole, the most perfect master of English prose now creating amongst us, is often far more like a piece of mosaic than a passage in music, and seems, here and there, to lack the true rhythmical life of words and the fine freedom and richness of effect that such rhythmical life produces. We, in fact, have made writing a definite mode of composition, and have treated it as a form of elaborate design. The Greeks, upon the other hand, regarded writing simply as a method of chronicling. Their test was always the spoken word in its musical and metrical relations. The voice was the medium, and the ear the critic. I have sometimes thought that the story of Homer's blindness might be really an artistic myth, created in critical days, and serving to remind us, not merely that the great poet is always a seer, seeing less with the eyes of the body than he does with the eyes of the soul, but he is a true singer also, building his song out of music, repeating each line over and over again to himself till he has caught the secret of its melody, chaunting in darkness the words that are winged with light. Certainly, whether this be so or not, it was to his blindness, as an occasion, if not as a cause, that England's great poet owed much of the majestic movement and sonorous splendour of his later verse. When Milton could no longer write he began to sing. Who would match the measures of *Comus* with

the measures of *Samson Agonistes*, or of *Paradise Lost*
or *Regained* ? When Milton became blind he composed,
as every one should compose, with the voice purely,
and so the pipe or reed of earlier days became that
mighty many-stopped organ whose rich reverberant
music has all the stateliness of Homeric verse, if it
seeks not to have its swiftness, and is the one im-
perishable inheritance of English literature sweeping
through all the ages, because above them, and abiding
with us ever, being immortal in its form. Yes : writing
has done much harm to writers. We must return to
the voice. That must be our test, and perhaps then
we shall be able to appreciate some of the subtleties of
Greek art-criticism.

As it now is, we cannot do so. Sometimes, when I
have written a piece of prose that I have been modest
enough to consider absolutely free from fault, a dreadful thought comes over me that I may have been
guilty of the immoral effeminacy of using trochaic and
tribrachic movements, a crime for which a learned
critic of the Augustan age censures with most just
severity the brilliant if somewhat paradoxical Hegesias.
I grow cold when I think of it, and wonder to myself
if the admirable ethical effect of the prose of that
charming writer, who once in a spirit of reckless
generosity towards the uncultivated portion of our
community proclaimed the monstrous doctrine that
conduct is three-fourths of life, will not some day be
entirely annihilated by the discovery that the pæons
have been wrongly placed.

Ernest : Ah ! now you are flippant.

Gilbert : Who would not be flippant when he is
gravely told that the Greeks had no art-critics ? I
can understand it being said that the constructive
genius of the Greeks lost itself in criticism, but not that
the race to whom we owe the critical spirit did not
criticise. You will not ask me to give you a survey of
Greek art-criticism from Plato to Plotinus. The night

is too lovely for that, and the moon, if she heard us, would put more ashes on her face than are there already. But think merely of one perfect little work of æsthetic criticism, Aristotle's *Treatise on Poetry*. It is not perfect in form, for it is badly written, consisting perhaps of notes dotted down for an art lecture, or of isolated fragments destined for some larger book, but in temper and treatment it is perfect, absolutely. The ethical effect of art, its importance to culture, and its place in the formation of character, had been done once for all by Plato ; but here we have art treated, not from the moral, but from the purely æsthetic point of view. Plato had, of course, dealt with many definitely artistic subjects, such as the importance of unity in a work of art, the necessity for tone and harmony, the æsthetic value of appearances, the relation of the visible arts to the external world, and the relation of fiction to fact. He first perhaps stirred in the soul of man that desire that we have not yet satisfied, the desire to know the connection between Beauty and Truth, and the place of Beauty in the moral and intellectual order of the Kosmos. The problems of idealism and realism, as he sets them forth, may seem to many to be somewhat barren of result in the metaphysical sphere of abstract being in which he places them, but transfer them to the sphere of art, and you will find that they are still vital and full of meaning. It may be that it is as a critic of Beauty that Plato is destined to live, and that by altering the name of the sphere of his speculation we shall find a new philosophy. But Aristotle, like Goethe, deals with art primarily in its concrete manifestations, taking Tragedy, for instance, and investigating the material it uses, which is language, its subject-matter, which is life, the method by which it works, which is action, the conditions under which it reveals itself, which are those of theatric presentation, its logical structure, which is plot, and its final æsthetic appeal, which is to the sense of beauty realised through the passions of pity and awe. That purification and spiritualising of the nature which he calls κάθαρσις is, as Goethe saw, essentially æsthetic, and is not moral, as Lessing fancied. Concerning himself primarily with the impression that the work of art produces, Aristotle sets himself to analyse that impression, to investigate its source, to see how it is engendered. As a physiologist and psychologist, he knows that the health of a function resides in energy. To have a capacity for a passion and not to realise it, is to make oneself incomplete and limited. The mimic spectacle of life that Tragedy affords cleanses the bosom of much " perilous stuff," and by presenting high and worthy objects for the exercise of the emotions purifies and spiritualises the man ; nay, not merely does it spiritualise him, but it initiates him also into noble feelings of which he might else have known nothing, the word κάθαρσις having, it has sometimes seemed to me, a definite allusion to the rite of initiation, if indeed that be not, as I am occasionally tempted to fancy, its true and only meaning here. This is of course a mere outline of the book. But you see what a perfect piece of æsthetic criticism it is. Who indeed but a Greek could have analysed art so well ? After reading it, one does not wonder any longer that Alexandria devoted itself so largely to art-criticism, and that we find the artistic temperaments of the day investigating every question of style and manner, discussing the great Academic schools of painting, for instance, such as the school of Sicyon, that sought to preserve the dignified traditions of the antique mode, or the realistic and impressionist schools, that aimed at reproducing actual life, or the elements of ideality in portraiture, or the artistic value of the epic form in an age so modern as theirs, or the proper subject-matter for the artist. Indeed, I fear that the inartistic temperaments of the day busied themselves also in matters of literature and art, for the accusations of plagiarism were endless, and such accusations proceed either from the thin colourless lips of impotence, or from the grotesque mouths of those who, possessing nothing of their own, fancy that they can gain a reputation for wealth by crying out that they have been robbed. And I assure you, my dear Ernest, that the Greeks chattered about painters quite as much as people do nowadays, and had their private views, and shilling exhibitions, and Arts and Crafts guilds, and Pre-Raphaelite movements, and movements towards realism, and lectured about art, and wrote essays on art, and produced their art-historians, and their archæologists, and all the rest of it. Why, even the theatrical managers of travelling companies brought their dramatic critics with them when they went on tour, and paid them very handsome salaries for writing laudatory notices. Whatever, in fact, is modern in our life we owe to the Greeks. Whatever is an anachronism is due to mediævalism. It is the Greeks who have given us the whole system of art-criticism, and how fine their critical instinct was, may be seen from the fact that the material they criticised with most care was, as I have already said, language. For the material that painter or sculptor uses is meagre in comparison with that of words. Words have not merely music as sweet as that of viol and lute, colour as rich and vivid as any that makes lovely for us the canvas of the Venetian or the Spaniard, and plastic form no less sure and certain than that which reveals itself in marble or in bronze, but thought and passion and spirituality are theirs also, are theirs indeed alone. If the Greeks had criticised nothing but language, they would still have been the great art-critics of the world. To know the principles of the highest art is to know the principles of all the arts.

But I see that the moon is hiding behind a sulphur-coloured cloud. Out of a tawny mane or drift she gleams like a lion's eye. She is afraid that I will talk to you of Lucian and Longinus, of Quinctilian and Dionysius, of Pliny and Fronto and Pausanias, of all those who in the antique world wrote or lectured upon art matters. She need not be afraid. I am tired of my expedition into the dim, dull abyss of facts. There is nothing left for me now but the divine μονόχρονος ἡδονή of another cigarette. Cigarettes have at least the charm of leaving one unsatisfied.

Ernest : Try one of mine. They are rather good, I get them direct from Cairo. The only use of our *attachés* is that they supply their friends with excellent tobacco. And as the moon has hidden herself, let us talk a little longer. I am quite ready to admit that I was wrong in what I said about the Greeks. They were, as you have pointed out, a nation of art-critics. I acknowledge it, and I feel a little sorry for them. For the creative faculty is higher than the critical. There is really no comparison between them.

Gilbert : The antithesis between them is entirely arbitrary. Without the critical faculty, there is no artistic creation at all, worthy of the name. You spoke a little while ago of that fine spirit of choice and delicate instinct of selection by which the artist realises life for us, and gives to it a momentary perfection. Well, that spirit of choice, that subtle tact of omission, is really the critical faculty in one of its most characteristic moods, and no one who does not possess this critical faculty can create anything at all in art. Arnold's definition of literature as a criticism of life was not very felicitous in form, but it showed how keenly he recognised the importance of the critical element in all creative work.

Ernest : I should have said that great artists work unconsciously, that they were " wiser than they knew," as, I think, Emerson remarks somewhere.

Gilbert : It is really not so, Ernest. All fine imaginative work is self-conscious and deliberate. No poet sings because he must sing. At least, no great poet

does. A great poet sings because he chooses to sing.
It is so now, and it has always been so. We are sometimes apt to think that the voices that sounded at the
dawn of poetry were simpler, fresher, and more natural
than ours, and that the world which the early poets
looked at, and through which they walked, had a kind
of poetical quality of its own, and almost without
changing could pass into song. The snow lies thick
now upon Olympus, and its steep scarped sides are
bleak and barren, but once, we fancy, the white feet of
the Muses brushed the dew from the anemones in the
morning, and at evening came Apollo to sing to the
shepherds in the vale. But in this we are merely
lending to other ages what we desire, or think we desire,
for our own. Our historical sense is at fault. Every
century that produces poetry is, so far, an artificial
century, and the work that seems to us to be the most
natural and simple product of its time is always the
result of the most self-conscious effort. Believe me,
Ernest, there is no fine art without self-consciousness,
and self-consciousness and the critical spirit are one.

Ernest : I see what you mean, and there is much in
it. But surely you would admit that the great poems
of the early world, the primitive, anonymous collective
poems, were the result of the imagination of races,
rather than of the imagination of individuals ?

Gilbert : Not when they became poetry. Not when
they received a beautiful form. For there is no art
where there is no style, and no style where there is
no unity, and unity is of the individual. No doubt
Homer had old ballads and stories to deal with, as
Shakespeare had chronicles and plays and novels from
which to work, but they were merely his rough material.
He took them, and shaped them into song. They
become his, because he made them lovely. They were
built out of music,

And so not built at all,
And therefore built for ever.

The longer one studies life and literature, the more strongly one feels that behind everything that is wonderful stands the individual, and that it is not the moment that makes the man, but the man who creates the age. Indeed, I am inclined to think that each myth and legend that seems to us to spring out of the wonder, or terror, or fancy of tribe and nation, was in its origin the invention of one single mind. The curiously limited number of the myths seems to me to point to this conclusion. But we must not go off into questions of comparative mythology. We must keep to criticism. And what I want to point out is this. An age that has no criticism is either an age in which art is immobile, hieratic, and confined to the reproduction of formal types, or an age that possesses no art at all. There have been critical ages that have not been creative, in the ordinary sense of the word, ages in which the spirit of man has sought to set in order the treasures of his treasure-house, to separate the gold from the silver, and the silver from the lead, to count over the jewels, and to give names to the pearls. But there has never been a creative age that has not been critical also. For it is the critical faculty that invents fresh forms. The tendency of creation is to repeat itself. It is to the critical instinct that we owe each new school that springs up, each new mould that art finds ready to its hand. There is really not a single form that art now uses that does not come to us from the critical spirit of Alexandria, where these forms were either stereotyped or invented or made perfect. I say Alexandria, not merely because it was there that the Greek spirit became most self-conscious, and indeed ultimately expired in scepticism and theology, but because it was to that city, and not to Athens, that Rome turned for her models, and it was through the survival, such as it was, of the Latin language that culture lived at all. When, at the Renaissance, Greek literature dawned upon Europe, the soil had been in

some measure prepared for it. But, to get rid of the
details of history, which are always wearisome and
usually inaccurate, let us say generally, that the forms
of art have been due to the Greek critical spirit. To
it we owe the epic, the lyric, the entire drama in every
one of its developments, including burlesque, the idyll,
the romantic novel, the novel of adventure, the essay,
the dialogue, the oration, the lecture, for which perhaps
we should not forgive them, and the epigram, in all
the wide meaning of that word. In fact, we owe it
everything, except the sonnet, to which, however,
some curious parallels of thought-movement may be
traced in the Anthology, American journalism, to which
no parallel can be found anywhere, and the ballad
in sham Scotch dialect, which one of our most industrious writers has recently proposed should be
made the basis for a final and unanimous effort on the
part of our second-rate poets to make themselves really
romantic. Each new school, as it appears, cries out
against criticism, but it is to the critical faculty in
man that it owes its origin. The mere creative instinct
does not innovate, but reproduces.

Ernest : You have been talking of criticism as an
essential part of the creative spirit, and I now fully
accept your theory. But what of criticism outside
creation ? I have a foolish habit of reading periodicals,
and it seems to me that most modern criticism is
perfectly valueless.

Gilbert : So is most modern creative work also.
Mediocrity weighing mediocrity in the balance, and
incompetence applauding its brother—that is the
spectacle which the artistic activity of England affords
us from time to time. And yet, I feel I am a little
unfair in this matter. As a rule, the critics—I speak,
of course, of the higher class, of those, in fact, who
write for the sixpenny papers—are far more cultured
than the people whose work they are called upon to
review. This is, indeed, only what one would expect,

for criticism demands infinitely more cultivation than
creation does.

Ernest : Really ?

Gilbert : Certainly. Anybody can write a three-
volumed novel. It merely requires a complete ignorance
of both life and literature. The difficulty that I should
fancy the reviewer feels is the difficulty of sustaining
any standard. Where there is no style a standard must
be impossible. The poor reviewers are apparently
reduced to be the reporters of the police-court of
literature, the chroniclers of the doings of the habitual
criminals of art. It is sometimes said of them that they
do not read all through the works they are called upon
to criticise. They do not. Or at least they should not.
If they did so, they would become confirmed mis-
anthropes, or if I may borrow a phrase from one of the
pretty Newnham graduates, confirmed womanthropes
for the rest of their lives. Nor is it necessary. To know
the vintage and quality of a wine one need not drink
the whole cask. It must be perfectly easy in half an
hour to say whether a book is worth anything or worth
nothing. Ten minutes are really sufficient, if one has
the instinct for form. Who wants to wade through a
dull volume ? One tastes it, and that is quite enough
—more than enough, I should imagine. I am aware
that there are many honest workers in painting as well
as in literature who object to criticism entirely. They
are quite right. Their work stands in no intellectual
relation to their age. It brings us no new element of
pleasure. It suggests no fresh departure of thought,
or passion, or beauty. It should not be spoken of.
It should be left to the oblivion that it deserves.

Ernest : But, my dear fellow—excuse me for interrupting you—you seem to me to be allowing your
passion for criticism to lead you a great deal too far.
For, after all, even you must admit that it is much
more difficult to do a thing than to talk about it.

Gilbert : More difficult to do a thing than to talk

about it ? Not at all. That is a gross popular error.
It is very much more difficult to talk about a thing
than to do it. In the sphere of actual life that is of
course obvious. Anybody can make history. Only a
great man can write it. There is no mode of action, no
form of emotion, that we do not share with the lower
animals. It is only by language that we rise above
them, or above each other—by language, which is
the parent, and not the child, of thought. Action,
indeed, is always easy, and when presented to us in its
most aggravated, because most continuous form, which
I take to be that of real industry, becomes simply the
refuge of people who have nothing whatsoever to do.
No, Ernest, don't talk about action. It is a blind thing
dependent on external influences, and moved by an
impulse of whose nature it is unconscious. It is a thing
incomplete in its essence, because limited by accident,
and ignorant of its direction, being always at variance
with its aim. Its basis is the lack of imagination. It is
the last resource of those who know not how to dream.

Ernest : Gilbert, you treat the world as if it were a
crystal ball. You hold it in your hand, and reverse
it to please a wilful fancy. You do nothing but re-write
history.

Gilbert : The one duty we owe to history is to re-
write it. That is not the least of the tasks in store for
the critical spirit. When we have fully discovered
the scientific laws that govern life, we shall realise that
the one person who has more illusions than the dreamer
is the man of action. He, indeed, knows neither the
origin of his deeds nor their results. From the field in
which he thought that he had sown thorns, we have
gathered our vintage, and the fig-tree that he planted
for our pleasure is as barren as the thistle, and more
bitter. It is because Humanity has never known where
it was going that it has been able to find its way.

Ernest : You think, then, that in the sphere of
action a conscious aim is a delusion ?

Gilbert : It is worse than a delusion. If we lived long enough to see the results of our actions it may be that those who call themselves good would be sickened with a dull remorse, and those whom the world calls evil stirred by a noble joy. Each little thing that we do passes into the great machine of life which may grind our virtues to powder and make them worthless, or transform our sins into elements of a new civilisation, more marvellous and more splendid than any that has gone before. But men are the slaves of words. They rage against Materialism, as they call it, forgetting that there has been no material improvement that has not spiritualised the world, and that there have been few, if any, spiritual awakenings that have not wasted the world's faculties in barren hopes, and fruitless aspirations, and empty or trammelling creeds. What is termed Sin is an essential element of progress. Without it the world would stagnate, or grow old, or become colourless. By its curiosity Sin increases the experience of the race. Through its intensified assertion of individualism, it saves us from monotony of type. In its rejection of the current notions about morality, it is one with the higher ethics. And as for the virtues ! What are the virtues ? Nature, M. Renan tells us, cares little about chastity, and it may be that it is to the shame of the Magdalen, and not to their own purity, that the Lucretias of modern life owe their freedom from stain. Charity, as even those of whose religion it makes a formal part have been compelled to acknowledge, creates a multitude of evils. The mere existence of conscience, that faculty of which people prate so much nowadays, and are so ignorantly proud, is a sign of our imperfect development. It must be merged in instinct before we become fine. Self-denial is simply a method by which man arrests his progress, and self-sacrifice a survival of the mutilation of the savage, part of that old worship of pain which is so terrible a factor in the history of the world, and which even

now makes its victims day by day, and has its altars
in the land. Virtues! Who knows what the virtues
are? Not you. Not I. Not any one. It is well for our
vanity that we slay the criminal, for if we suffered him
to live he might show us what we had gained by his
crime. It is well for his peace that the saint goes to
his martyrdom. He is spared the sight of the horror
of his harvest.

Ernest : Gilbert, you sound too harsh a note. Let
us go back to the more gracious fields of literature.
What was it you said? That it was more difficult to
talk about a thing than to do it?

Gilbert (after a pause) : Yes ; I believe I ventured
upon that simple truth. Surely you see now that I
am right? When man acts he is a puppet. When he
describes he is a poet. The whole secret lies in that.
It was easy enough on the sandy plains by windy Ilion
to send the notched arrow from the painted bow, or to
hurl against the shield of hide and flame-like brass
the long ash-handled spear. It was easy for the
adulterous queen to spread the Tyrian carpets for her
lord, and then, as he lay couched in the marble bath,
to throw over his head the purple net, and call to her
smooth-faced lover to stab through the meshes at the
heart that should have broken at Aulis. For Antigone
even, with Death waiting for her as her bridegroom,
it was easy to pass through the tainted air at noon,
and climb the hill, and strew with kindly earth the
wretched naked corse that had no tomb. But what of
those who wrote about these things? What of those
who gave them reality, and made them live for ever?
Are they not greater than the men and women they
sing of? " Hector that sweet knight is dead," and
Lucian tells us how in the dim underworld Menippus
saw the bleaching skull of Helen, and marvelled that
it was for so grim a favour that all those horned ships
were launched, those beautiful mailed men laid low,
those towered cities brought to dust. Yet, every day the

swan-like daughter of Leda comes out on the battle-
ments, and looks down at the tide of war. The grey-
beards wonder at her loveliness, and she stands by the
side of the king. In his chamber of stained ivory lies
her leman. He is polishing his dainty armour, and
combing the scarlet plume. With squire and page, her
husband passes from tent to tent. She can see his bright
hair, and hears, or fancies that she hears, that clear
cold voice. In the courtyard below, the son of Priam
is buckling on his brazen cuirass. The white arms of
Andromache are around his neck. He sets his helmet
on the ground, lest their babe should be frightened.
Behind the embroidered curtains of his pavilion sits
Achilles, in perfumed raiment, while in harness of gilt
and silver the friend of his soul arrays himself to go
forth to the fight. From a curiously carven chest that
his mother Thetis had brought to his ship-side, the
Lord of the Myrmidons takes out that mystic chalice
that the lip of man had never touched, and cleanses it
with brimstone, and with fresh water cools it, and,
having washed his hands, fills with black wine its
burnished hollow, and spills the thick grape-blood upon
the ground in honour of Him whom at Dodona bare-
footed prophets worshipped, and prays to Him, and
knows not that he prays in vain, and that by the hands
of two knights from Troy, Panthous' son, Euphorbus,
whose love-locks were looped with gold, and the
Priamid, the lion-hearted, Patroklus, the comrade of
comrades, must meet his doom. Phantoms, are they ?
Heroes of mist and mountain ? Shadows in a song ?
No ; they are real. Action ! What is action ? It dies at
the moment of its energy. It is a base concession to
fact. The world is made by the singer for the dreamer.

    Ernest : While you talk it seems to me to be so.

    Gilbert : It is so in truth. On the mouldering citadel
of Troy lies the lizard like a thing of green bronze.
The owl has built her nest in the palace of Priam.
Over the empty plain wander shepherd and goatherd

with their flocks, and where, on the wine-surfaced, oily sea, οἰνοψ πόντος as Homer calls it, copper-prowed and steaked with vermilion, the great galleys of the Danaoi came in their gleaming crescent, the lonely tunny-fisher sits in his little boat and watches the bobbing corks of his net. Yet, every morning the doors of the city are thrown open, and on foot, or in horse-drawn chariot, the warriors go forth to battle, and mock their enemies from behind their iron masks. All day long the fight rages, and when night comes the torches gleam by the tents, and the cresset burns in the hall. Those who live in marble or on painted panel, know of life but a single exquisite instant, eternal indeed in its beauty, but limited to one note of passion or one mood of calm. Those whom the poet makes live have their myriad emotions of joy and terror, of courage and despair, of pleasure and of suffering. The seasons come and go in glad or saddening pageant, and with winged or leaden feet the years pass by before them. They have their youth and their manhood, they are children, and they grow old. It is always dawn for St. Helena, as Veronese saw her at the window. Through the still morning air the angels bring her the symbol of God's pain. The cool breezes of the morning lift the gilt threads from her brow. On that little hill by the city of Florence, where the lovers of Giorgione are lying, it it always the solstice of noon, of noon made so languorous by summer suns that hardly can the slim naked girl dip into the marble tank the round bubble of clear glass, and the long fingers of the lute-player rest idly upon the chords. It is twilight always for the dancing nymphs whom Corot set free among the silver poplars of France. In eternal twilight they move, those frail diaphanous figures, whose tremulous white feet seem not to touch the dew-drenched grass they tread on. But those who walk in epos, drama, or romance, see through the labouring months the young moons wax and wane, and watch the night from

evening unto morning star, and from sunrise unto
sunsetting can note the shifting day with all its gold
and shadow. For them, as for us, the flowers bloom
and wither, and the Earth, that Green-tressed Goddess,
as Coleridge calls her, alters her raiment for their
pleasure. The statue is concentrated to one moment
of perfection. The image stained upon the canvas
possesses no spiritual element of growth or change.
If they know nothing of death, it is because they know
little of life, for the secrets of life and death belong to
those, and those only, whom the sequence of time
affects, and who possess not merely the present but the
future, and can rise or fall from a past of glory or of
shame. Movement, that problem of the visible arts,
can be truly realised by Literature alone. It is Literature
that shows us the body in its swiftness and the soul in
its unrest.

Ernest: Yes; I see now what you mean. But,
surely, the higher you place the creative artist, the
lower must the critic rank.

Gilbert: Why so?

Ernest: Because the best that he can give us will
be but an echo of rich music, a dim shadow of clear-
outlined form. It may, indeed, be that life is chaos,
as you tell me that it is; that its martyrdoms are mean
and its heroisms ignoble; and that it is the function
of Literature to create, from the rough material of
actual existence, a new world that will be more marvellous, more enduring, and more true than the world
that common eyes look upon, and through which
common natures seek to realise their perfection. But
surely, if this new world has been made by the spirit
and touch of a great artist, it will be a thing so complete
and perfect that there will be nothing left for the
critic to do. I quite understand now, and indeed admit
most readily, that it is far more difficult to talk about
a thing than to do it. But it seems to me that this
sound and sensible maxim, which is really extremely

soothing to one's feelings, and should be adopted as its motto by every Academy of Literature all over the world, applies only to the relations that exist between Art and Life, and not to any relations that there may be between Art and Criticism.

Gilbert : But, surely, Criticism is itself an art. And just as artistic creation implies the working of the critical faculty, and, indeed, without it cannot be said to exist at all, so Criticism is really creative in the highest sense of the word. Criticism is, in fact, both creative and independent.

Ernest : Independent ?

Gilbert : Yes ; independent. Criticism is no more to be judged by any low standard of imitation or resemblance than is the work of poet or sculptor. The critic occupies the same relation to the work of art that he criticises as the artist does to the visible world of form and colour, or the unseen world of passion and of thought. He does not even require for the perfection of his art the finest materials. Anything will serve his purpose. And just as out of the sordid and sentimental amours of the silly wife of a small country doctor in the squalid village of Yonville-l'Abbaye, near Rouen, Gustave Flaubert was able to create a classic, and make a masterpiece of style, so, from subjects of little or of no importance, such as the pictures in this year's Royal Academy, or in any year's Royal Academy for that matter, Mr. Lewis Morris's poems, M. Ohnet's novels, or the plays of Mr. Henry Arthur Jones, the true critic can, if it be his pleasure so to direct or waste his faculty of contemplation, produce work that will be flawless in beauty and instinct with intellectual subtlety. Why not ? Dulness is always an irresistible temptation for brilliancy, and stupidity is the permanent *Bestia Trionfans* that calls wisdom from its cave. To an artist so creative as the critic, what does subject-matter signify ? No more and no less than it does to the novelist and the painter. Like them, he can find his motives everywhere. Treatment is the test. There is nothing that has not in it suggestion or challenge.

Ernest : But is Criticism really a creative art ?

Gilbert : Why should it not be ? It works with materials, and puts them into a form that is at once new and delightful. What more can one say of poetry ? Indeed, I would call criticism a creation within a creation. For just as the great artists, from Homer and Æschylus, down to Shakespeare and Keats, did not go directly to life for their subject-matter, but sought for it in myth, and legend, and ancient tale, so the critic deals with materials that others have, as it were, purified for him, and to which imaginative form and colour have been already added. Nay, more, I would say that the highest Criticism, being the purest form of personal impression, is in its way more creative than creation, as it has least reference to any standard external to itself, and is, in fact, its own reason for existing, and, as the Greeks would put it, in itself, and to itself, an end. Certainly, it is never trammelled by any shackles of verisimilitude. No ignoble considerations of probability, that cowardly concession to the tedious repetitions of domestic or public life, effect it ever. One may appeal from fiction unto fact. But from the soul there is no appeal.

Ernest : From the soul ?

Gilbert : Yes, from the soul. That is what the highest criticism really is, the record of one's own soul. It is more fascinating than history, as it is concerned simply with oneself. It is more delightful than philosophy, as its subject is concrete and not abstract, real and not vague. It is the only civilised form of autobiography, as it deals not with the events, but with the thoughts of one's life ; not with life's physical accidents of deed or circumstance, but with the spiritual moods and imaginative passions of the mind. I am always amused by the silly vanity of those

writers and artists of our day who seem to imagine
that the primary function of the critic is to chatter
about their second-rate work. The best that one can
say of most modern creative art is that it is just a little
less vulgar than reality, and so the critic, with his fine
sense of distinction and sure instinct of delicate
refinement, will prefer to look into the silver mirror
or through the woven veil, and will turn his eyes away
from the chaos and clamour of actual existence, though
the mirror be tarnished and the veil be torn. His sole
aim is to chronicle his own impressions. It is for him
that pictures are painted, books written, and marble
hewn into form.

Ernest : I seem to have heard another theory of
Criticism.

Gilbert : Yes ; it has been said by one whose gracious
memory we all revere, and the music of whose pipe
once lured Proserpina from her Sicilian fields, and
made those white feet stir, and not in vain, the Cumnor
cowslips, that the proper aim of Criticism is to see
the object as in itself it really is.   But this is a very
serious error, and takes no cognizance of Criticism's
most perfect form, which is in its essence purely
subjective, and seeks to reveal its own secret and
not the secret of another.   For the highest Criticism
deals with art not as expressive but as impressive
purely.

Ernest : But is that really so ?

Gilbert : Of course it is. Who cares whether Mr.
Ruskin's views on Turner are sound or not ? What
does it matter ? That mighty and majestic prose of
his, so fervid and so fiery-coloured in its noble eloquence,
so rich in its elaborate symphonic music, so sure and
certain, at its best, in subtle choice of word and epithet,
is at least as great a work of art as any of those wonderful sunsets that bleach or rot on their corrupted
canvases in England's Gallery ; greater indeed, one is
apt to think at times, not merely because its equal

beauty is more enduring, but on account of the fuller
variety of its appeal, soul speaking to soul in those
long-cadenced lines, not through form and colour
alone, though through these, indeed, completely and
without loss, but with intellectual and emotional
utterance, with lofty passion and with loftier thought,
with imaginative insight, and with poetic aim ; greater,
I always think, even as Literature is the greater art.
Who, again, cares whether Mr. Pater has put into the
portrait of Monna Lisa something that Lionardo never
dreamed of ? The painter may have been merely the
slave of an archaic smile, as some have fancied, but
whenever I pass into the cool galleries of the Palace
of the Louvre, and stand before that strange figure
" set in its marble chair in that cirque of fantastic rocks,
as in some faint light under sea," I murmur to myself,
" She is older than the rocks among which she sits ;
like the vampire, she has been dead many times, and
learned the secrets of the grave ; and has been a diver
in deep seas, and keeps their fallen day about her :
and trafficked for strange webs with Eastern merchants;
and, as Leda, was the mother of Helen of Troy, and, as
St. Anne, the mother of Mary ; and all this has been
to her but as the sound of lyres and flutes, and lives
only in the delicacy with which it has moulded the
changing lineaments, and tinged the eyelids and the
hands." And I say to my friend, " The presence that
thus so strangely rose beside the waters is expressive
of what in the ways of a thousand years man had come
to desire ; " and he answers me, " Hers is the head
upon which all ' the ends of the world are come,' and
the eylids are a little weary."
 And so the picture becomes more wonderful to us
than it really is, and reveals to us a secret of which,
in truth, it knows nothing, and the music of the
mystical prose is as sweet in our ears as was that
flute-player's music that lent to the lips of La Gioconda
those subtle and poisonous curves. Do you ask me what

Lionardo would have said had any one told him of this picture that " all the thoughts and experience of the world had etched and moulded therein that which they had of power to refine and make expressive the outward form, the animalism of Greece, the lust of Rome, the reverie of the Middle Age with its spiritual ambition and imaginative loves, the return of the Pagan world, the sins of the Borgias ? " He would probably have answered that he had contemplated none of these things, but had concerned himself simply with certain arrangements of lines and masses, and with new and curious colour-harmonies of blue and green. And it is for this very reason that the criticism which I have quoted is criticism of the highest kind. It treats the work of art simply as a starting-point for a new creation. It does not confine itself—let us at least suppose so for the moment—to discovering the real intention of the artist and accepting that as final. And in this it is right, for the meaning of any beautiful created thing is, at least, as much in the soul of him who looks at it, as it was in his soul who wrought it. Nay, it is rather the beholder who lends to the beautiful thing its myriad meanings, and makes it marvellous for us, and sets it in some new relation to the age, so that it becomes a vital portion of our lives, and a symbol of what we pray for, or perhaps of what, having prayed for, we fear that we may receive. The longer I study, Ernest, the more clearly I see that the beauty of the visible arts is, as the beauty of music, impressive primarily, and that it may be marred, and indeed often is so, by any excess of intellectual intention on the part of the artist. For when the work is finished it has, as it were, an independent life of its own, and may deliver a message far other than that which was put into its lips to say. Sometimes, when I listen to the overture to *Tannhäuser*, I seem indeed to see that comely knight treading delicately on the flower-strewn grass, and to hear the voice of Venus calling to him

from the caverned hill. But at other times it speaks
to me of a thousand different things, of myself, it
may be, and my own life, or of the lives of others
whom one has loved and grown weary of loving,
or of the passions that man has known, or of the
passions that man has not known, and so has sought
for. To-night it may fill one with that ΕΡΩΣ ΤΩΝ
ΑΔΥΝΑΤΩΝ, that *Amour de l'Impossible*, which
falls like a madness on many who think they live
securely and out of reach of harm, so that they sicken
suddenly with the poison of unlimited desire, and,
in the infinite pursuit of what they may not obtain,
grow faint and swoon or stumble. To-morrow, like the
music of which Aristotle and Plato tell us, the noble
Dorian music of the Greek, it may perform the office
of a physician, and give us an anodyne against pain,
and heal the spirit that is wounded, and " bring the
soul into harmony with all right things." And what
is true about music is true about all the arts.
Beauty has as many meanings as man has moods.
Beauty is the symbol of symbols. Beauty reveals
everything, because it expresses nothing. When
it shows us itself, it shows us the whole fiery-coloured
world.

Ernest : But is such work as you have talked
about really criticism ?

Gilbert : It is the highest Criticism, for it criticises
not merely the individual work of art, but Beauty
itself, and fills with wonder a form which the artist may
have left void, or not understood, or understood
incompletely.

Ernest : The highest Criticism, then, is more creative
than creation, and the primary aim of the critic is to
see the object as in itself it really is not ; that is your
theory, I believe ?

Gilbert : Yes, that is my theory. To the critic the
work of art is simply a suggestion for a new work of
his own, that need not necessarily bear any obvious

resemblance to the thing it criticises. The one characteristic of a beautiful form is that one can put into it
whatever one wishes, and see in it whatever one chooses
to see ; and the Beauty, that gives to creation its
universal and æsthetic element, makes the critic a
creator in his turn, and whispers of a thousand different
things which were not present in the mind of him who
carved the statue or painted the panel or graved the
gem.

It is sometimes said by those who understand
neither the nature of the highest Criticism nor the
charm of the highest Art, that the pictures that the
critic loves most to write about are those that belong
to the anecdotage of painting, and that deal with
scenes taken out of literature or history. But this is
not so. Indeed, pictures of this kind are far too
intelligible. As a class, they rank with illustrations,
and even considered from this point of view are
failures, as they do not stir the imagination, but set
definite bounds to it. For the domain of the painter
is, as I suggested before, widely different from that of
the poet. To the latter belongs life in its full and
absolutely entirety ; not merely the beauty that men
look at, but the beauty that men listen to also ; not
merely the momentary grace of form or the transient
gladness of colour, but the whole sphere of feeling, the
perfect cycle of thought. The painter is so far limited
that it is only through the mask of the body that he
can show us the mystery of the soul ; only through
conventional images that he can handle ideas ; only
through its physical equivalents that he can deal with
psychology. And how inadequately does he do it
then, asking us to accept the torn turban of the Moor
for the noble rage of Othello, or a dotard in a storm for
the wild madness of Lear ! Yet it seems as if nothing
could stop him. Most of our elderly English painters
spend their wicked and wasted lives in poaching upon
the domain of the poets, marring their motives by

clumsy treatment, and striving to render, by visible
form or colour, the marvel of what is invisible, the
splendour of what is not seen. Their pictures are, as
a natural consequence, insufferably tedious. They have
degraded the invisible arts into the obvious arts, and
the one thing not worth looking at is the obvious.
I do not say that poet and painter may not treat of
the same subject. They have always done so, and
will always do so. But while the poet can be pictorial
or not, as he chooses, the painter must be pictorial
always. For a painter is limited, not to what
he sees in nature, but to what upon canvas may be
seen.

And so, my dear Ernest, pictures of this kind will
not really fascinate the critic. He will turn from them
to such works as made him brood and dream and
fancy, to works that possess the subtle quality of
suggestion, and seem to tell one that even from them
there is an escape into a wider world. It is sometimes
said that the tragedy of an artist's life is that he cannot
realise his ideal. But the true tragedy that dogs the
steps of most artists is that they realise their ideal
too absolutely. For, when the ideal is realised, it is
robbed of its wonder and its mystery, and becomes
simply a new starting-point for an ideal that is other
than itself. This is the reason why music is the perfect
type of art. Music can never reveal its ultimate secret.
This, also, is the explanation of the value of limitations
in art. The sculptor gladly surrenders imitative colour,
and the painter the actual dimensions of form, because
by such renunciations they are able to avoid too
definite a presentation of the Real, which would be
mere imitation, and too definite a realisation of the
Ideal, which would be too purely intellectual. It is
through its very incompleteness that Art becomes
complete in beauty, and so addresses itself, not to
the faculty of recognition nor to the faculty of reason,
but to the æsthetic sense alone, which, while accepting

both reason and recognition as stages of apprehension, subordinates them both to a pure synthetic impression of the work of art as a whole, and, taking whatever alien emotional elements the work may possess, uses their very complexity as a means by which a richer unity may be added to the ultimate impression itself. You see, then, how it is that the æsthetic critic rejects these obvious modes of art that have but one message to deliver, and having delivered it become dumb and sterile, and seeks rather for such modes as suggest reverie and mood, and by their imaginative beauty make all interpretations true, and no interpretation final. Some resemblance, no doubt, the creative work of the critic will have to the work that has stirred him to creation, but it will be such resemblance as exists, not between Nature and the mirror that the painter of landscape or figure may be supposed to hold up to her, but between Nature and the work of the decorative artist. Just as on the flowerless carpets of Persia, tulip and rose blossom indeed and are lovely to look on, though they are not reproduced in visible shape or line ; just as the pearl and purple of the sea-shell is echoed in the church of St. Mark at Venice ; just as the vaulted ceiling of the wondrous chapel at Ravenna is made gorgeous by the gold and green and sapphire of the peacock's tail, though the birds of Juno fly not across it ; so the critic reproduces the work that he criticises in a mode that is never imitative, and part of whose charm may really consist in the rejection of resemblance, and shows us in this way not merely the meaning but also the mystery of Beauty and, by transforming each art into literature, solves once for all the problem of Art's unity.

But I see it is time for supper. After we have discussed some Chamertin and a few ortolans, we will pass on to the question of the critic considered in the light of the interpreter.

Ernest : Ah ! you admit, then, that the critic may occasionally be allowed to see the object as in itself it really is.

Gilbert : I am not quite sure. Perhaps I may admit it after supper. There is a subtle influence in supper.

DE PROFUNDIS

DE PROFUNDIS

. . . SUFFERING is one very long moment. We cannot divide it by seasons. We can only record its moods, and chronicle their return. With us time itself does not progress. It revolves. It seems to circle round one centre of pain. The paralysing immobility of a life every circumstance of which is regulated after an unchangeable pattern, so that we eat and drink and lie down and pray, or kneel at least for prayer, according to the inflexible laws of an iron formula : this immobile quality, that makes each dreadful day in the very minutest detail like its brother, seems to communicate itself to those external forces the very essence of whose existence is ceaseless change. Of seed-time or harvest, of the reapers bending over the corn, or the grape gatherers threading through the vines, of the grass in the orchard made white with broken blossoms or strewn with fallen fruit : of these we know nothing and can know nothing.

For us there is only one season, the season of sorrow. The very sun and moon seem taken from us. Outside, the day may be blue and gold, but the light that creeps down through the thickly-muffled glass of the small iron-barred window beneath which one sits is grey and niggard. It is always twilight in one's cell, as it is always twilight in one's heart. And in the sphere of thought, no less than in the sphere of time, motion is no more. The thing that you personally have long ago forgotten, or can easily forget, is happening to me now, and will happen to me again to-morrow. Remember this, and you will be able to understand a little of why I am writing, and in this manner writing. . . .

A week later, I am transferred here. Three more months go over and my mother dies. No one knew how deeply I loved and honoured her. Her death was terrible to me ; but I, once a lord of language, have no words in which to express my anguish and my shame. She and my father had bequeathed me a name they had made noble and honoured, not merely in literature, art, archæology, and science, but in the public history of my own country, in its evolution as a nation. I had disgraced that name eternally. I had made it a low byword among low people. I had dragged it through the very mire. I had given it to brutes that they might make it brutal, and to fools that they might turn it into a synonym for folly. What I suffered then, and still suffer, is not for pen to write or paper to record. My wife, always kind and gentle to me, rather than that I should hear the news from indifferent lips, travelled, ill as she was, all the way from Genoa to England to break to me herself the tidings of so irreparable, so irremediable, a loss. Messages of sympathy reached me from all who had still affection for me. Even people who had not known me personally, hearing that a new sorrow had broken into my life, wrote to ask that some expression of their condolence should be conveyed to me. . . .

Three months go over. The calendar of my daily conduct and labour that hangs on the outside of my cell door, with my name and sentence written upon it, tells me that it is May. . . .

Prosperity, pleasure and success, may be rough of grain and common in fibre, but sorrow is the most sensitive of all created things. There is nothing that stirs in the whole world of thought to which sorrow does not vibrate in terrible and exquisite pulsation. The thin beaten-out leaf of tremulous gold that chronicles the direction of forces the eye cannot see is in comparison coarse. It is a wound that bleeds when any hand but that of love touches it, and even then must bleed again, though not in pain.

Where there is sorrow there is holy ground. Some day people will realise what that means. They will know nothing of life till they do. —— and natures like his can realise it. When I was brought down from my prison to the Court of Bankruptcy, between two policemen, —— waited in the long dreary corridor that, before the whole crowd, whom an action so sweet and simple hushed into silence, he might gravely raise his hat to me, as, handcuffed and with bowed head, I passed him by. Men have gone to heaven for smaller things than that. It was in this spirit, and with this mode of love, that the saints knelt down to wash the feet of the poor, or stooped to kiss the leper on the cheek. I have never said one single word to him about what he did. I do not know to the present moment whether he is aware that I was even conscious of his action. It is not a thing for which one can render formal thanks in formal words. I store it in the treasure-house of my heart. I keep it there as a secret debt that I am glad to think I can never possibly repay. It is embalmed and kept sweet by the myrrh and cassia of many tears. When wisdom has been profitless to me, philosophy barren, and the proverbs and phrases of those who have sought to give me consolation as dust and ashes in my mouth, the memory of that little, lovely, silent act of love has unsealed for me all the wells of pity : made the desert blossom like a rose, and brought me out of the bitterness of lonely exile into harmony with the wounded, broken, and great heart of the world. When people are able to understand, not merely how beautiful ——'s action was, but why it meant so much to me, and always will mean so much, then, perhaps, they will realise how and in what spirit they should approach me. . . .

The poor are wise, more charitable, more kind, more

sensitive than we are. In their eyes prison is a tragedy in a man's life, a misfortune, a casuality, something that calls for sympathy in others. They speak of one who is in prison as of one who is "in trouble" simply. It is the phrase they always use, and the expression has the perfect wisdom of love in it. With people of our own rank it is different. With us, prison makes a man a pariah. I, and such as I am, have hardly any right to air and sun. Our presence taints the pleasures of others. We are unwelcome when we reappear. To revisit the glimpses of the moon is not for us. Our very children are taken away. Those lovely links with humanity are broken. We are doomed to be solitary, while our sons still live. We are denied the one thing that might heal us and keep us, that might bring balm to the bruised heart, and peace to the soul in pain. . . .

I must say to myself that I ruined myself, and that nobody great or small can be ruined except by his own hand. I am quite ready to say so. I am trying to say so, though they may not think it at the present moment. This pitiless indictment I bring without pity against myself. Terrible as was what the world did to me, what I did to myself was far more terrible still.

I was a man who stood in symbolic relations to the art and culture of my age. I had realised this for myself at the very dawn of my manhood, and had forced my age to realise it afterwards. Few men hold such a position in their own lifetime, and have it so acknowledged. It is usually discerned, if discerned at all, by the historian, or the critic, long after both the man and his age have passed away. With me it was different. I felt it myself, and made others feel it. Byron was a symbolic figure, but his relations were to the passion of his age and its weariness of passion. Mine were to something more noble, more permanent, of more vital issue, of larger scope.

The gods had given me almost everything. But I let myself be lured into long spells of senseless and sensual ease. I amused myself with being a *flâneur*, a dandy, a man of fashion. I surrounded myself with the smaller natures and the meaner minds. I became the spendthrift of my own genius, and to waste an eternal youth gave me a curious joy. Tired of being on the heights, I deliberately went to the depths in the search for new sensation. What the paradox was to me in the sphere of thought, perversity became to me in the sphere of passion. Desire, at the end, was a malady, or a madness, or both. I grew careless of the lives of others. I took pleasure where it pleased me, and passed on. I forgot that every little action of the common day makes or unmakes character, and that therefore what one has done in the secret chamber one has some day to cry aloud on the housetop. I ceased to be lord over myself. I was no longer the captain of my soul, and did not know it. I allowed pleasure to dominate me. I ended in horrible disgrace. There is only one thing for me now, absolute humility.

I have lain in prison for nearly two years. Out of my nature has come wild despair ; an abandonment to grief that was piteous even to look at ; terrible and impotent rage ; bitterness and scorn ; anguish that wept aloud ; misery that could find no voice ; sorrow that was dumb. I have passed through every possible mood of suffering. Better than Wordsworth himself I know what Wordsworth meant when he said—

> " Suffering is permanent, obscure, and dark,
> And has the nature of infinity."

But while there were times when I rejoiced in the idea that my sufferings were to be endless, I could not bear them to be without meaning. Now I find hidden somewhere away in my nature something that tells me that nothing in the whole world is meaningless, and suffering least of all. That something hidden away in my nature, like a treasure in a field, is Humility.

It is the last thing left in me, and the best : the ultimate discovery at which I have arrived, the starting-point for a fresh development. It has come to me right out of myself, so I know that it has come at the proper time. It could not have come before, nor later. Had any one told me of it, I would have rejected it. Had it been brought to me, I would have refused it. As I found it, I want to keep it. I must do so. It is the one thing that has in it the elements of life, of a new life, a *Vita Nuova* for me. Of all things it is the strangest. One cannot acquire it, except by sur-rendering everything that one has. It is only when one has lost all things, that one knows that one pos-sesses it.

Now I have realised that it is in me, I see quite clearly what I ought to do ; in fact, must do. And when I use such a phrase as that, I need not say that I am not alluding to any external sanction or command. I admit none. I am far more of an individualist than I ever was. Nothing seems to me of the smallest value except what one gets out of oneself. My nature is seeking a fresh mode of self-realisation. That is all I am concerned with. And the first thing that I have got to do is to free myself from any possible bitterness of feeling against the world.

I am completely penniless, and absolutely homeless. Yet there are worse things in the world than that. I am quite candid when I say that rather than go out from this prison with bitterness in my heart against the world, I would gladly and readily beg my bread from door to door. If I got nothing from the house of the rich I would get something at the house of the poor. Those who have much are often greedy ; those who have little always share. I would not a bit mind sleeping in the cool grass in summer, and when winter came on sheltering myself by the warm close-thatched rick, or under the penthouse of a great barn, provided I had love in my heart. The external things of life seem to me now of no importance at all. You can see to what intensity of individualism I have arrived—or am arriving rather, for the journey is long, and " where I walk there are thorns."

Of course I know that to ask alms on the highway is not to be my lot, and that if ever I lie in the cool grass at night-time it will be to write sonnets to the moon. When I go out of prison, R—— will be waiting for me on the other side of the big iron-studded gate, and he is the symbol, not merely of his own affection, but of the affection of many others besides. I believe I am to have enough to live on for about eighteen months at any rate, so that if I may not write beautiful books, I may at least read beautiful books ; and what joy can be greater ? After that, I hope to be able to recreate my creative faculty.

But were things different : had I not a friend left in the world ; were there not a single house open to me in pity ; had I to accept the wallet and ragged cloak of sheer penury : as long as I am free from all resentment, hardness and scorn, I would be able to face the life with much more calm and confidence than I would were my body in purple and fine linen, and the soul within me sick with hate.

And I really shall have no difficulty. When you really want love you will find it waiting for you.

I need not say that my task does not end there. It would be comparatively easy if it did. There is much more before me. I have hills far steeper to climb, valleys much darker to pass through. And I have to get it all out of myself. Neither religion, morality, nor reason can help me at all.

Morality does not help me. I am a born antinomian. I am one of those who are made for exceptions, not for laws. But while I see that there is nothing wrong

in what one does, I see that there is something wrong
in what one becomes. It is well to have learned that.

Religion does not help me. The faith that others
give to what is unseen, I give to what one can touch,
and look at. My gods dwell in temples made with
hands ; and within the circle of actual experience is
my creed made perfect and complete : too complete,
it may be, for like many or all of those who have
placed their heaven in this earth, I have found in it
not merely the beauty of heaven, but the horror of
hell also. When I think about religion at all, I feel
as if I would like to found an order for those who
cannot believe : the Confraternity of the Faithless,
one might call it, where on an altar, on which no taper
burned, a priest, in whose heart peace had no dwelling,
might celebrate with unblessed bread and a chalice
empty of wine. Every thing to be true must become
a religion. And agnosticism should have its ritual
no less than faith. It has sown its martyrs, it should
reap its saints, and praise God daily for having hidden
Himself from man. But whether it be faith or agnosticism, it must be nothing external to me. Its
symbols must be of my own creating. Only that is
spiritual which makes its own form. If I may not
find its secret within myself, I shall never find it · if
I have not got it already, it will never come to
me.

Reason does not help me. It tells me that the laws
under which I am convicted are wrong and unjust
laws, and the system under which I have suffered a
wrong and unjust system. But, somehow, I have
got to make both of these things just and right to me.
And exactly as in Art one is only concerned with
what a particular thing is at a particular moment to
oneself, so it is also in the ethical evolution of one's
character. I have got to make everything that has
happened to me good for me. The plank bed, the
loathsome food, the hard ropes shredded into oakum

till one's finger-tips grow dull with pain, the menial offices with which each day begins and finishes, the harsh orders the routine seems to necessitate, the dreadful dress that makes sorrow grotesque to look at, the silence, the solitude, the shame—each and all of these things I have to transform into a spiritual experience. There is not a single degradation of the body which I must not try and make into a spiritualising of the soul.

I want to get to the point when I shall be able to say quite simply, and without affectation, that the two great turning-points in my life were when my father sent me to Oxford, and when society sent me to prison. I will not say that prison is the best thing that could have happened to me: for that phrase would savour of too great bitterness towards myself. I would sooner say, or hear it said of me, that I was so typical a child of my age, that in my perversity, and for that perversity's sake, I turned the good things of my life to evil, and the evil things of my life to good.

What is said, however, by myself or by others, matters little. The important thing, the thing that lies before me, the thing that I have to do, if the brief remainder of my days is not to be maimed, marred, and incomplete, is to absorb into my nature all that has been done to me, to make it part of me, to accept it without complaint, fear, or reluctance. The supreme vice is shallowness. Whatever is realised is right.

When first I was put into prison some people advised me to try and forget who I was. It was ruinous advice. It is only by realising what I am that I have found comfort of any kind. Now I am advised by others to try on my release to forget that I have ever been in a prison at all. I know that would be equally fatal. It would mean that I would always be haunted by an intolerable sense of disgrace, and that those things that are meant for me as much as for anybody else—the beauty of the sun and moon, the pageant of the seasons, the music of daybreak and the silence of great nights, the rain falling through the leaves, or the dew creeping over the grass and making it silver—would all be tainted for me, and lose their healing power, and their power of communicating joy. To regret one's own experiences is to arrest one's own development. To deny one's own experiences is to put a lie into the lips of one's own life. It is no less than a denial of the soul.

For just as the body absorbs things of all kinds, things common and unclean no less than those that the priest or a vision has cleansed, and converts them into swiftness or strength, into the play of beautiful muscles and the moulding of fair flesh, into the curves and colours of the hair, the lips, the eye ; so the soul in its turn has its nutritive functions also, and can transform into noble moods of thought and passions of high import what in itself is base, cruel and degrading ; nay, more, may find in these its most august modes of assertion, and can often reveal itself most perfectly through what was intended to desecrate or destroy.

The fact of my having been the common prisoner of a common gaol I must frankly accept, and, curious as it may seem, one of the things I shall have to teach myself is not to be ashamed of it. I must accept it as a punishment, and if one is ashamed of having been punished, one might just as well never have been punished at all. Of course there are many things of which I was convicted that I had not done, but then there are many things of which I was convicted that I had done, and a still greater number of things in my life for which I was never indicted at all. And as the gods are strange, and punish us for what is good and humane in us as much as for what is evil and perverse, I must accept the fact that one is punished for the good as well as for the evil that one does. I have no doubt that it is quite right one should be. It helps one, or should help one, to realise both, and not to be too conceited about either. And if I then am not ashamed of my punishment, as I hope not to be, I shall be able to think, and walk, and live with freedom.

Many men on their release carry their prison about with them into the air, and hide it as a secret disgrace in their hearts, and at length, like poor poisoned things, creep into some hole and die. It is wretched that they should have to do so, and it is wrong, terribly wrong, of society that it should force them to do so. Society takes upon itself the right to inflict appalling punishment on the individual, but it also has the supreme vice of shallowness, and fails to realise what it has done. When the man's punishment is over, it leaves him to himself; that is to say, it abandons him at the very moment when its highest duty towards him begins. It is really ashamed of its own actions, and shuns those whom it has punished, as people shun a creditor whose debt they cannot pay, or one on whom they have inflicted an irreparable, an irremediable wrong. I can claim on my side that if I realise what I have suffered, society should realise what it has inflicted on me; and that there should be no bitterness or hate on either side.

Of course I know that from one point of view things will be made different for me than for others; must indeed, by the very nature of the case, be made so. The poor thieves and outcasts who are imprisoned here with me are in many respects more fortunate than I am. The little way in grey city or green field that saw their sin is small; to find those who know nothing of what they have done they need go no further than a bird might fly between the twilight and the dawn; but for me the world is shrivelled to a handsbreadth, and everywhere I turn my name is

written on the rocks in lead. For I have come, not
from obscurity into the momentary notoriety of crime,
but from a sort of eternity of fame to a sort of eternity
of infamy, and sometimes seem to myself to have
shown, if indeed it required showing, that between
the famous and the infamous there is but one step,
if as much as one.

Still, in the very fact that people will recognise me
wherever I go, and know all about my life, as far
as its follies go, I can discern something good for
me. It will force on me the necessity of again asserting
myself as an artist, and as soon as I possibly can.
If I can produce only one beautiful work of art I
shall be able to rob malice of its venom, and cowardice
of its sneer, and to pluck out the tongue of scorn
by the roots.

And if life be, as it surely is, a problem to me, I
am no less a problem to life. People must adopt
some attitude towards me, and so pass judgment
both on themselves and me. I need not say I am
not talking of particular individuals. The only people
I would care to be with now are artists and people
who have suffered : those who know what beauty is,
and those who know what sorrow is : nobody else
interests me. Nor am I making any demands on life.
In all that I have said I am simply concerned with
my own mental attitude towards life as a whole ;
and I feel that not to be ashamed of having been
punished is one of the first points I must attain to,
for the sake of my own perfection, and because I
am so imperfect.

Then I must learn how to be happy. Once I knew
it, or thought I knew it, by instinct. It was always
springtime once in my heart. My temperament was
akin to joy. I filled my life to the very brim with
pleasure, as one might fill a cup to the very brim
with wine. Now I am approaching life from a completely new standpoint, and even to conceive happi-

ness is often extremely difficult for me. I remember during my first term at Oxford reading in Pater's *Renaissance*—that book which has had such strange influence over my life—how Dante places low in the Inferno those who wilfully live in sadness ; and going to the college library and turning to the passage in the *Divine Comedy* where beneath the dreary marsh lie those who were " sullen in the sweet air," saying for ever and ever through their sighs :

> "Tristi fummo
> Nell aer dolce che dal sol s'allegra."

I knew the church condemned *accidia*, but the whole idea seemed to me quite fantastic, just the sort of sin, I fancied, a priest who knew nothing about real life would invent. Nor could I understand how Dante, who says that " sorrow remarries us to God," could have been so harsh to those who were enamoured of melancholy, if any such there really were. I had no idea that some day this would become to me one of the greatest temptations of my life.

While I was in Wandsworth prison I longed to die. It was my one desire. When after two months in the infirmary I was transferred here, and found myself growing gradually better in physical health, I was filled with rage. I determined to commit suicide on the very day on which I left prison. After a time that evil mood passed away, and I made up my mind to live, but to wear gloom as a king wears purple : never to smile again : to turn whatever house I entered into a house of mourning : to make my friends walk slowly in sadness with me : to teach them that melancholy is the true secret of life : to maim them with an alien sorrow : to mar them with my own pain. Now I feel quite differently. I see it would be both ungrateful and unkind of me to pull so long a face that when my friends came to see me they would have to make their faces still longer in order to show their sympathy ; or, if I desired to entertain them, to invite them to sit down silently to bitter herbs and funeral baked meats. I must learn how to be cheerful and happy.

The last two occasions on which I was allowed to see my friends here, I tried to be as cheerful as possible, and to show my cheerfulness, in order to make them some slight return for their trouble in coming all the way from town to see me. It is only a slight return, I know, but it is the one, I feel certain, that pleases them most. I saw R—— for an hour on Saturday week, and I tried to give the fullest possible expression of the delight I really felt at our meeting. And that, in the views and ideas I am here shaping for myself, I am quite right is shown to me by the fact that now for the first time since my imprisonment I have a real desire for life.

There is before me so much to do that I would regard it as a terrible tragedy if I died before I was allowed to complete at any rate a little of it. I see new developments in art and life, each one of which is a fresh mode of perfection. I long to live so that I can explore what is no less than a new world to me. Do you want to know what this new world is ? I think you can guess what it is. It is the world in which I have been living. Sorrow, then, and all that it teaches one, is my new world.

I used to live entirely for pleasure. I shunned suffering and sorrow of every kind. I hated both. I resolved to ignore them as far as possible : to treat them, that is to say, as modes of imperfection. They were not part of my scheme of life. They had no place in my philosophy. My mother, who knew life as a whole, used often to quote to me Goethe's lines —written by Carlyle in a book he had given her years ago, and translated by him, I fancy, also :

" Who never ate his bread in sorrow,
 Who never spent the midnight hours
Weeping and waiting for the morrow,—
 He knows you not, ye heavenly powers."

They were the lines which that noble Queen of
Prussia, whom Napoleon treated with such coarse
brutality, used to quote in her humiliation and exile ;
they were the lines my mother often quoted in the
troubles of her later life. I absolutely declined to
accept or admit the enormous truth hidden in them.
I could not understand it. I remember quite well
how I used to tell her that I did not want to eat my
bread in sorrow, or to pass any night weeping and
watching for a more bitter dawn.

I had no idea that it was one of the special things
that the Fates had in store for me : that for a whole
year of my life, indeed, I was to do little else. But
so has my portion been meted out to me ; and during
the last few months I have, after terrible difficulties
and struggles, been able to comprehend some of the
lessons hidden in the heart of pain. Clergymen and
people who use phrases without wisdom sometimes
talk of suffering as a mystery. It is really a revelation.
One discerns things one never discerned before. One
approaches the whole of history from a different
standpoint. What one had felt dimly, through instinct,
about art, is intellectually and emotionally realised
with perfect clearness of vision and absolute intensity
of apprehension.

I now see that sorrow, being the supreme emotion
of which man is capable, is at once the type and test
of all great art. What the artist is always looking
for is the mode of existence in which soul and body
are one and indivisible : in which the outward is
expressive of the inward : in which form reveals. Of
such modes of existence there are not a few : youth
and the arts preoccupied with youth may serve as a

model for us at one moment : at another we may
like to think that, in its subtlety and sensitiveness of
impression, its suggestion of a spirit dwelling in external things and making its raiment of earth and air,
of mist and city alike, and in its morbid sympathy of
its moods, and tones, and colours, modern landscape
art is realising for us pictorially what was realised in
such plastic perfection by the Greeks. Music, in which
all subject is absorbed in expression and cannot be
separated from it, is a complex example, and a flower
or a child a simple example, of what I mean ; but
sorrow is the ultimate type both in life and art.

Behind joy and laughter there may be a temperament, coarse, hard and callous. But behind sorrow
there is always sorrow. Pain, unlike pleasure, wears
no mask. Truth in art is not any correspondence
between the essential idea and the accidental existence ;
it is not the resemblance of shape to shadow, or of
the form mirrored in the crystal to the form itself ;
it is no echo coming from a hollow hill, any more
than it is a silver well of water in the valley that
shows the moon to the moon and Narcissus to Narcissus.
Truth in art is the unity of a thing with itself : the
outward rendered expressive of the inward : the soul
made incarnate : the body instinct with spirit. For
this reason there is no truth comparable to sorrow.
There are times when sorrow seems to me to be the
only truth. Other things may be illusions of the eye
or the appetite, made to blind the one and cloy the
other, but out of sorrow have the worlds been built,
and at the birth of a child or a star there is pain.

More than this, there is about sorrow an intense,
an extraordinary reality. I have said of myself that
I was one who stood in symbolic relations to the art
and culture of my age. There is not a single wretched
man in this wretched place along with me who does
not stand in symbolic relation to the very secret of
life. For the secret of life is suffering. It is what is

hidden behind everything. When we begin to live, what is sweet is so sweet to us, and what is bitter so bitter, that we inevitably direct all our desires towards pleasures, and seek not merely for a " month or twain to feed on honeycomb," but for all our years to taste no other food, ignorant all the while that we may really be starving the soul.

I remember talking once on this subject to one of the most beautiful personalities I have ever known : a woman, whose sympathy and noble kindness to me, both before and since the tragedy of my imprisonment, have been beyond power and description ; one who has really assisted me, though she does not know it, to bear the burden of my troubles more than any one else in the whole world has, and all through the mere fact of her existence, through her being what she is—partly an ideal and partly an influence : a suggestion of what one might become as well as a real help towards becoming it ; a soul that renders the common air sweet, and makes what is spiritual seem as simple and natural as sunlight or the sea ; one for whom beauty and sorrow walk hand in hand, and have the same message. On the occasion of which I am thinking I recall distinctly how I said to her that there was enough suffering in one narrow London lane to show that God did not love man, and that wherever there was any sorrow, though but that of a child, in some little garden weeping over a fault that it had or had not committed, the whole face of creation was completely marred. I was entirely wrong. She told me so, but I could not believe her. I was not in the sphere in which such belief was to be attained to. Now it seems to me that love of some kind is the only possible explanation of the extraordinary amount of suffering that there is in the world. I cannot conceive of any other explanation. I am convinced that there is no other, and that if the world has indeed, as I have said, been built of sorrow, it has been built by the hands of love, because in no other way could the soul of man, for whom the world was made, reach the full stature of its perfection. Pleasure for the beautiful body, but pain for the beautiful soul.

When I say that I am convinced of these things I speak with too much pride. Far off, like a perfect pearl, one can see the City of God. It is so wonderful that it seems as if a child could reach it in a summer's day. And so a child could. But with me and such as me it is different. One can realise a thing in a single moment, but one loses it in the long hours that follow with leaden feet. It is so difficult to keep " heights that the soul is competent to gain." We think in eternity, but we move slowly through time ; and how slowly time goes with us who lie in prison I need not tell again, nor of the weariness and despair that creep back into one's cell, and into the cell of one's heart, with such strange insistence that one has, as it were, to garnish and sweep one's house for their coming, as for an unwelcome guest, or a bitter master, or a slave whose slave it is one's chance or choice to be.

And, though at present my friends may find it a hard thing to believe, it is true none the less, that for them living in freedom and idleness and comfort it is more easy to learn the lessons of humility than it is for me, who begin the day by going down on my knees and washing the floor of my cell. For prison life with its endless privations and restrictions makes one rebellious. The most terrible thing about it is not that it breaks one's heart—hearts are made to be broken—but that it turns one's heart to stone. One sometimes feels that it is only with a front of brass and a lip of scorn that one can get through the day at all. And he who is in a state of rebellion cannot receive grace, to use the phrase of which the Church is so fond—so rightly fond, I dare say—for in life as in art the mood of rebellion closes up the channels of the soul, and shuts out the airs of heaven. Yet I must learn these lessons here, if I am to learn them anywhere, and must be filled with joy if my feet are on the right road and my face set towards " the gate which is called beautiful," though I may fall many times in the mire and often in the mist go astray.

This New Life, as through my love of Dante I like sometimes to call it, is of course no new life at all, but simply the continuance, by means of development and evolution, of my former life. I remember when I was at Oxford saying to one of my friends as we were strolling round Magdalen's narrow bird-haunted walks one morning in the year before I took my degree, that I wanted to eat of the fruit of all the trees in the garden of the world, and that I was going out into the world with that passion in my soul. And so, indeed, I went out, and so I lived. My only mistake was that I confined myself so exclusively to the trees of what seemed to me the sunlit side of the garden, and shunned the other side for its shadow and its gloom. Failure, disgrace, poverty, sorrow, despair, suffering, tears even, the broken words that come from lips in pain, remorse that makes one walk on thorns, conscience that condemns, self-abasement that punishes, the misery that puts ashes on its head, the anguish that chooses sackcloth for its raiment and into its own drink puts gall—all these were things of which I was afraid. And as I had determined to know nothing of them, I was forced to taste each of them in turn, to feed on them, to have for a season, indeed, no other food at all.

I don't regret for a single moment having lived for pleasure. I did it to the full, as one should do everything that one does. There was no pleasure I did not experience. I threw the pearl of my soul into a cup of wine. I went down the primrose path to the sound of flutes. I lived on honeycomb. But to have

continued the same life would have been wrong, because it would have been limiting. I had to pass on.
The other half of the garden had its secrets for me
also. Of course all this is foreshadowed and prefigured
in my books. Some of it is in *The Happy Prince*, some
of it in *The Young King*, notably in the passage where
the bishop says to the kneeling boy, " Is not He,
who made misery, wiser than thou art ? " a phrase
which when I wrote it seemed to me little more than
a phrase ; a great deal of it is hidden away in the note
of doom that like a purple thread runs through the
texture of *Dorian Gray* ; in *The Critic as Artist* it is
set forth in many colours ; in *The Soul of Man* it is
written down, and in letters too easy to read ; it is
one of the refrains whose recurring *motifs* make *Salomé*
so like a piece of music and bind it together as a
ballad ; in the prose poem of the man who from the
bronze of the image of the " Pleasure that liveth for
a moment " has to make the image of the " Sorrow
that abideth for ever " it is incarnate. It could not
have been otherwise. At every single moment of one's
life one is what one is going to be no less than what
one has been. Art is a symbol, because man is a
symbol.

It is, if I can fully attain to it, the ultimate realisation of the artistic life. For the artistic life is simply
self-development. Humility in the artist is his frank
acceptance of all experiences, just as love in the artist
is simply the sense of beauty that reveals to the world
its body and its soul. In *Marius the Epicurean* Pater
seeks to reconcile the artistic life with the life of religion, in the deep, sweet, and austere sense of the word.
But Marius is little more than a spectator : an ideal
spectator indeed, and one to whom it is given " to
contemplate the spectacle of life with appropriate
emotions," which Wordsworth defines as the poet's
true aim ; yet a spectator merely, and perhaps a little
too much occupied with the comeliness of the benches

of the sanctuary to notice that it is the sanctuary of sorrow that he is gazing at.

I see a far more intimate and immediate connection between the true life of Christ and the true life of the artist ; and I take a keen pleasure in the reflection that long before sorrow had made my days her own and bound me to her wheel I had written in *The Soul of Man* that he who would lead a Christ-like life must be entirely and absolutely himself, and had taken as my types not merely the shepherd on the hillside and the prisoner in his cell, but also the painter to whom the world is a pageant and the poet for whom the world is a song. I remember saying once to André Gide, as we sat together in some Paris *café*, that while metaphysics had but little real interest for me, and morality absolutely none, there was nothing that either Plato or Christ had said that could not be transferred immediately into the sphere of Art and there find its complete fulfilment.

Nor is it merely that we can discern in Christ that close union of personality with perfection which forms the real distinction between the classical and romantic movement in life, but the very basis of his nature was the same as that of the nature of the artist —an intense and flamelike imagination. He realised in the entire sphere of human relations that imaginative sympathy which in the Sphere of Art is the sole secret of creation. He understood the leprosy of the leper, the darkness of the blind, the fierce misery of those who live for pleasure, the strange poverty of the rich. Some one wrote to me in trouble, " When you are not on your pedestal you are not interesting." How remote was the writer from what Matthew Arnold calls " the Secret of Jesus." Either would have taught him that whatever happens to another happens to oneself, and if you want an inscription to read at dawn and at night-time, and for pleasure or for pain, write up on the walls of your house in letters for the sun to gild and the moon to silver, " Whatever happens to oneself happens to another."

Christ's place indeed is with the poets. His whole conception of Humanity sprang right out of the imagination and can only be realised by it. What God was to the pantheist, man was to Him. He was the first to conceive the divided races as a unity. Before his time there had been gods and men, and, feeling through the mysticism of sympathy that in himself each had been made incarnate, he calls himself the Son of the one or the Son of the other, according to his mood. More than any one else in history he wakes in us that temper of wonder to which romance always appeals. There is still something to me almost in-credible in the idea of a young Galilean peasant imagining that he could bear on his own shoulders the burden of the entire world ; all that had already been done and suffered, and all that was yet to be done and suffered : the sins of Nero, of Cæsar Borgia, of Alexander VI., and of him who was Emperor of Rome and Priest of the Sun : the sufferings of those whose names are legion and whose dwelling is among the tombs : oppressed nationalities, factory children, thieves, people in prison, outcasts, those who are dumb under oppression and whose silence is heard only of God ; and not merely imagining this but actually achieving it, so that at the present moment all who come in contact with his personality, even though they may neither bow to his altar nor kneel before his priest, in some way find that the ugliness of their sin is taken away and the beauty of their sorrow revealed to them.

I had said of Christ that he ranks with the poets. That is true. Shelley and Sophocles are of his com-pany. But his entire life also is the most wonderful of poems. For " pity and terror " there is nothing in the entire cycle of Greek tragedy to touch it. The absolute purity of the protagonist raises the entire

scheme to a height of romantic art from which the
sufferings of Thebes and Pelops' line are by their
very horror excluded, and shows how wrong Aristotle
was when he said in his treatise on the drama that it
would be impossible to bear the spectacle of one
blameless in pain. Nor in Æschylus nor Dante, those
stern masters of tenderness, in Shakespeare, the most
purely human of all the great artists, in the whole of
Celtic myth and legend, where the loveliness of the
world is shown through a mist of tears, and the life
of a man is no more than the life of a flower, is there
anything that, for sheer simplicity of pathos wedded
and made one with sublimity of tragic effect, can be
said to equal or even approach the last act of Christ's
passion. The little supper with his companions, one
of whom has already sold him for a price ; the anguish
in the quiet moonlit garden ; the false friend coming
close to him so as to betray him with a kiss ; the
friend who still believed in him, and on whom as on
a rock he had hoped to build a house of refuge for Man,
denying him as the bird cried to the dawn ; his own
utter loneliness, his submission, his acceptance of
everything ; and along with it all such scenes as the
high priest of orthodoxy rending his raiment in wrath,
and the magistrate of civil justice calling for water
in the vain hope of cleansing himself of that stain of
innocent blood that makes him the scarlet figure of
history ; the coronation ceremony of sorrow, one of
the most wonderful things in the whole of recorded
time ; the crucifixion of the Innocent One before the
eyes of his mother and of the disciple whom he loved ;
the soldiers gambling and throwing dice for his clothes ;
the terrible death by which he gave the world its
most eternal symbol ; and his final burial in the tomb
of the rich man, his body swathed in Egyptian linen
with costly spices and perfumes as though he had
been a king's son. When one contemplates all this
from the point of view of art alone one cannot but be

grateful that the supreme office of the Church should be the playing of the tragedy without the shedding of blood : the mystical presentation, by means of dialogue and costume and gesture even, of the Passion of her Lord ; and it is always a source of pleasure and awe to me to remember that the ultimate survival of the Greek chorus, lost elsewhere to art, is to be found in the servitor answering the priest at Mass.

Yet the whole life of Christ—so entirely may sorrow and beauty be made one in their meaning and manifestation—is really an idyll, though it ends with the veil of the temple being rent, and the darkness coming over the face of the earth, and the stone rolled to the door of the sepulchre. One always thinks of him as a young bridegroom with his companions, as indeed he somewhere describes himself ; as a shepherd straying through a valley with his sheep in search of green meadow or cool stream ; as a singer trying to build out of the music the walls of the City of God ; or as a lover for whose love the whole world was too small. His miracles seem to me to be as exquisite as the coming of spring, and quite as natural. I see no difficulty at all in believing that such was the charm of his personality that his mere presence could bring peace to souls in anguish, and that those who touched his garments or his hands forgot their pain ; or that as he passed by on the highway of life people who had seen nothing of life's mystery, saw it clearly, and others who had been deaf to every voice but that of pleasure heard for the first time the voice of love and found it as " musical as Apollo's lute " ; or that evil passions fled at his approach, and men whose dull unimaginative lives had been but a mode of death rose as it were from the grave when he called them ; or that when he taught on the hill-side the multitude forgot their hunger and thirst and the cares of this world, and that to his friends who listened to him as he sat at meat the coarse food seemed delicate, and the water had the taste of good wine, and the whole house became full of the odour and sweetness of nard.

Renan in his *Vie de Jesus*—that gracious fifth gospel, the gospel according to St. Thomas, one might call it—says somewhere that Christ's great achievement was that he made himself as much loved after his death as he had been during his lifetime. And certainly, if his place is among the poets, he is the leader of all the lovers. He saw that love was the first secret of the world for which the wise men had been looking, and that it was only through love that one could approach either the heart of the leper or the feet of God.

And, above all, Christ is the most supreme of individualists. Humility, like the artistic acceptance of all experiences, is merely a mode of manifestation. It is man's soul that Christ is always looking for. He calls it "God's Kingdom," and finds it in every one. He compares it to little things, to a tiny seed, to a handful of leaven, to a pearl. That is because one realises one's soul only by getting rid of all alien passions, all acquired culture, and all external possessions, be they good or evil.

I bore up against everything with some stubbornness of will and much rebellion of nature, till I had absolutely nothing left in the world but one thing. I had lost my name, my position, my happiness, my freedom, my wealth. I was a prisoner and a pauper. But I still had my children left. Suddenly they were taken away from me by the law. It was a blow so appalling that I did not know what to do, so I flung myself on my knees, and bowed my head, and wept, and said, "The body of a child is as the body of the Lord: I am not worthy of either." That moment seemed to save me. I saw then that the only thing for me was to accept everything. Since then—curious as it will no doubt sound—I have been happier. It

was of course my soul in its ultimate essence that I
had reached. In many ways I had been its enemy,
but I found it waiting for me as a friend. When one
comes in contact with the soul it makes one simple
as a child, as Christ said one should be.

It is tragic how few people ever " possess their souls "
before they die. " Nothing is more rare in any man,"
says Emerson, " than an act of his own." It is quite
true. Most people are other people. Their thoughts
are some one else's opinions, their lives a mimicry,
their passions a quotation. Christ was not merely the
supreme individualist, but he was the first individualist
in history. People have tried to make him out an
ordinary philanthropist, or ranked him as an altruist
with the unscientific and sentimental. But he was
really neither one nor the other. Pity he has, of
course, for the poor, for those who are shut up in
prisons, for the lowly, for the wretched ; but he has
far more pity for the rich, for the hard hedonists, for
those who waste their freedom in becoming slaves to
things, for those who wear soft raiment and live in
kings' houses. Riches and pleasure seemed to him to
be really greater tragedies than poverty or sorrow. And
as for altruism, who knew better than he that it is
vocation not volition that determines us, and that one
cannot gather grapes of thorns or figs from thistles ?

To live for others as a definite self-conscious aim
was not his creed. It was not the basis of his creed.
When he says, " Forgive your enemies," it is not for
the sake of the enemy, but for one's own sake that
he says so, and because love is more beautiful than
hate. In his own entreaty to the young man, " Sell
all that thou hast and give to the poor," it is not of
the state of the poor that he is thinking, but of the
soul of the young man, the soul that wealth was
marring. In his view of life he is one with the artist
who knows that by the inevitable law of self-perfec-
tion, the poet must sing, and the sculptor think in

bronze, and the painter make the world a mirror for his moods, as surely and as certainly as the hawthorn must blossom in spring, and the corn turn to gold at harvest-time, and the moon in her ordered wanderings change from shield to sickle, and from sickle to shield.

But while Christ did not say to men, " Live for others," he pointed out that there was no difference at all between the lives of others and one's own life. By this means he gave to man an extended, a Titan personality. Since his coming the history of each separate individual is, or can be made, the history of the world. Of course, culture has intensified the personality of man. Art has made us myriad-minded. Those who have the artistic temperament go into exile with Dante and learn how salt is the bread of others, and how steep their stairs ; they catch for a moment the serenity and calm of Goethe, and yet know but too well that Baudelaire cried to God :

" O Seigneur, donnez moi la force et le courage
    De contempler mon corps et mon cœur sans
      dégoût."

Out of Shakespeare's sonnets they draw, to their own hurt it may be, the secret of his love and make it their own ; they look with new eyes on modern life, because they have listened to one of Chopin's nocturnes, or handled Greek things, or read the story of the passion of some dead man for some dead woman whose hair was like threads of fine gold, and whose mouth was as a pomegranate. But the sympathy of the artistic temperament is necessarily with what has found expression. In words or in colours, in music or in marble, behind the painted masks of an Æschylean play, or through some Sicilian shepherds' pierced and jointed reeds, the man and his message must have been revealed.

To the artist, expression is the only mode under which he can conceive life at all. To him what is dumb is dead. But to Christ it was not so. With a width and wonder of imagination that fills one almost with awe, he took the entire world of the inarticulate, the voiceless world of pain, as his kingdom, and made of himself its eternal mouthpiece. Those of whom I have spoken, who are dumb under oppression, and " whose silence is heard only of God," he chose as his brothers. He sought to become eyes to the blind, ears to the deaf, and a cry in the lips of those whose tongues had been tied. His desire was to be to the myriads who had found no utterance a very trumpet through which they might call to heaven. And feeling, with the artistic nature of one to whom suffering and sorrow were modes through which he could realise his conception of the beautiful, that an idea is of no value till it becomes incarnate and is made an image, he made of himself the image of the Man of Sorrows, and as such has fascinated and dominated art as no Greek god ever succeeded in doing.

For the Greek gods, in spite of the white and red of their fair fleet limbs, were not really what they appeared to be. The curved brow of Apollo was like the sun's disc crescent over a hill at dawn, and his feet were as the wings of the morning, but he himself had been cruel to Marsyas and had made Niobe childless. In the steel shields of Athena's eyes there had been no pity for Arachne ; the pomp and peacocks of Hera were all that was really noble about her ; and the Father of the Gods himself had been too fond of the daughters of men. The two most deeply suggestive figures of Greek Mythology were, for religion, Demeter, an Earth Goddess, not one of the Olympians, and for art, Dionysus, the son of a mortal woman to whom the moment of his birth had proved also the moment of her death.

But Life itself from its lowliest and most humble

sphere produced one far more marvellous than the mother of Proserpina or the son of Semele. Out of the Carpenter's shop at Nazareth had come a personality infinitely greater than any made by myth and legend, and one, strangely enough, destined to reveal to the world the mystical meaning of wine and the real beauties of the liles of the field as none, either on Cithaeron or at Enna, had ever done.

The song of Isaiah, " He is despised and rejected of men, a man of sorrows and acquainted with grief : and we hid as it were our faces from him," had seemed to him to prefigure himself, and in him the prophecy was fulfilled. We must not be afraid of such a phrase. Every single work of art is the fulfilment of a prophecy : for every work of art is the conversion of an idea into an image. Every single human being should be the fulfilment of a prophecy : for every human being should be the realisation of some ideal, either in the mind of God or in the mind of man. Christ found the type and fixed it, and the dream of a Virgilian poet, either at Jerusalem or at Babylon, became in the long progress of the centuries incarnate in him for whom the world was waiting.

To me one of the things in history the most to be regretted is that the Christ's own renaissance, which has produced the Cathedral at Chartres, the Arthurian cycle of legends, the life of St. Francis of Assisi, the art of Giotto, and Dante's *Divine Comedy*, was not allowed to develop on its own lines, but was interrupted and spoiled by the dreary classical Renaissance that gave us Petrarch, and Raphael's frescoes, and Palladian architecture, and formal French tragedy, and St. Paul's Cathedral, and Pope's poetry, and everything that is made from without and by dead rules, and does not spring from within through some spirit informing it. But wherever there is a romantic movement in art there somehow, and under some form, is Christ, or the soul of Christ. He is in *Romeo and Juliet,* in the *Winter's Tale,* in Provencal poetry, in the *Ancient Mariner,* in *La Belle Dame sans merci,* and in Chatterton's *Ballad of Charity.*

We owe to him the most diverse things and people. Hugo's *Les Misérables,* Baudelaire's *Fleurs du Mal,* the note of pity in Russian novels, Verlaine and Verlaine's poems, the stained glass and tapestries and the quattrocento work of Burne-Jones and Morris, belong to him no less than the tower of Giotto, Lancelot and Guinevere, Tannhäuser, the troubled romantic marbles of Michael Angelo, pointed architecture, and the love of children and flowers—for both of which, indeed, in classical art there was but little place, hardly enough for them to grow or play in, but which, from the twelfth century down to our own day, have been continually making their appearances in art, under various modes and at various times, coming fitfully and wilfully, as children, as flowers, are apt to do : spring always seeming to one as if the flowers had been in hiding, and only came out into the sun because they were afraid that grown-up people would grow tired of looking for them and give up the search ; and the life of a child being no more than an April day on which there is both rain and sun for the narcissus.

It is the imaginative quality of Christ's own nature that makes him this palpitating centre of romance. The strange figures of poetic drama and ballad are made by the imagination of others, but out of his own imagination entirely did Jesus of Nazareth create himself. The cry of Isaiah had really no more to do with his coming than the song of the nightingale has to do with the rising of the moon—no more, though perhaps no less. He was the denial as well as the affirmation of prophecy. For every expectation that he fulfilled there was another that he destroyed. " In all beauty," says Bacon, " there is some strangeness of proportion," and of those who are born of the spirit—of those, that is to say, who like himself are dynamic forces—Christ says that they are like the wind that "bloweth where it listeth, and no man can tell whence it cometh and whither it goeth." That is why he is so fascinating to artists. He has all the colour elements of life : mystery, strangeness, pathos, suggestion, ecstasy, love. He appeals to the temper of wonder, and creates that mood in which alone he can be understood.

And to me it is a joy to remember that if he is " of imagination all compact," the world itself is of the same substance. I said in *Dorian Gray* that the great sins of the world take place in the brain ; but it is in the brain that everything takes place. We know now that we do not see with the eyes or hear with the ears. They are really channels for the transmission, adequate or inadequate, of sense impressions. It is in the brain that the poppy is red, that the apple is odorous, that the skylark sings.

Of late I have been studying with diligence the four prose poems about Christ. At Christmas I managed to get hold of a Greek Testament, and every morning, after I had cleaned my cell and polished my tins, I read a little of the Gospels, a dozen verses taken by chance anywhere. It is a delightful way of opening the day. Every one, even in a turbulent, ill-disciplined life, should do the same. Endless repetition, in and out of season, has spoiled for us the freshness, the naïveté, the simple romantic charm of the Gospels. We hear them read far too often and far too badly, and all repetition is anti-spiritual. When one returns to the Greek, it is like going into a garden of lilies out of some narrow and dark house.

And to me, the pleasure is doubled by the reflection that it is extremely probable that we have the actual terms, the *ipsissima verba*, used by Christ. It was always supposed that Christ talked in Aramaic. Even Renan thought so. But now we know that the Galilean peasants, like the Irish peasants of our own day, were bilingual, and that Greek was the ordinary language of intercourse all over Palestine, as indeed all over the Eastern world. I never liked the idea that we knew of Christ's own words only through a translation of a translation. It is a delight to me to think that as far as his conversation was concerned, Charmides might have listened to him, and Socrates reasoned with him, and Plato understood him : that he really said ἐγώ εἰμι ὁ ποιμήν ὁ καλός, that when he thought of the lilies of the field and how they neither toil nor spin, his absolute expression was κατα-μάθετε τὰ κρίνα τοῦ αγροῦ πῶς αὐξάνει· οὐ κοπιᾷ οὐδὲ νήθει, and that his last word when he cried out, " My life has been completed, has reached its fulfilment, has been perfected," was exactly as St. John tells us it was : τετέλεσται —no more.

While in reading the Gospels—particularly that of St. John himself, or whatever early Gnostic took his name and mantle—I see the continual assertion of the imagination as the basis of all spiritual and material life, I see also that to Christ imagination was simply a form of love, and that to him love was lord in the fullest meaning of the phrase. Some six weeks ago I was allowed by the doctor to have white bread to eat instead of the coarse black or brown bread of ordinary prison fare. It is a great delicacy. It will sound strange that dry bread could possibly be a delicacy to any one. To me it is so much so that at the close of each meal I carefully eat whatever crumbs may be left on my tin plate, or have fallen on the rough towel that one uses as a cloth so as not to soil one's table ; and I do so not from hunger—I get now quite sufficient food — but simply in order that nothing should be wasted of what is given to me. So one should look on love.

Christ, like all fascinating personalities, had the power of not merely saying beautiful things himself, but of making other people say beautiful things to him ; and I love the story St. Mark tells us about the Greek woman who, when as a trial of her faith he said to her that he could not give her the bread of the children of Israel, answered him that the little dogs— (κυνάρια, "little dogs," it should be rendered)—who are under the table eat of the crumbs that the children let fall. Most people live for love and admiration. But it is by love and admiration that we should live. If any love is shown us we should recognise that we are quite unworthy of it. Nobody is worthy to be loved. The fact that God loves man shows us that in the divine order of ideal things it is written that eternal love is to be given to what is eternally unworthy. Or if that phrase seems to be a bitter one to bear, let us say that every one is worthy of love, except him who thinks that he is. Love is a sacrament that should be taken kneeling, and *Domine, non sum dignus* should be on the lips and in the hearts of those who receive it.

If ever I write again, in the sense of producing artistic work, there are just two subjects on which and through which I desire to express myself : one is " Christ as the precursor of the romantic movement in life " ; the other is " The artistic life considered in its relation to conduct." The first is, of course, intensely fascinating, for I see in Christ not merely the essentials of the supreme romantic type, but all the accidents, the wilfulnesses even, of the romantic temperament also. He was the first person who ever said to people that they should live " flower-like lives." He fixed the phrase. He took children as the type of what people should try to become. He held them up as examples to their elders, which I myself have always thought the chief use of children, if what is perfect should have a use. Dante describes the soul of a man as coming from the hand of God " weeping and laughing like a little child," and Christ also saw that the soul of each one should be *a guisa di fanciulla che pian-*

gendo e ridendo pargoleggia. He felt that life was changeful, fluid, active, and that to allow it to be stereotyped into any form was death. He saw that people should not be too serious over material, common interests : that to be unpractical was to be a great thing : that one should not bother too much over affairs. The birds didn't, why should man ? He is charming when he says, " Take no thought for the morrow ; is not the soul more than meat ? Is not the body more than raiment ? " A Greek might have used the latter phrase. It is full of Greek feeling. But only Christ could have said both, and so summed up life perfectly for us.

His morality is all sympathy, just what morality should be. If the only thing that he ever said had been, " Her sins are forgiven her because she loved much," it would have been worth while dying to have said it. His justice is all poetical justice, exactly what justice should be. The beggar goes to heaven because he has been unhappy. I cannot conceive a better reason for his being sent there. The people who work for an hour in the vineyard in the cool of the evening receive just as much reward as those who have toiled there all day long in the hot sun. Why shouldn't they ? Probably no one deserved anything. Or perhaps they were a different kind of people. Christ had no patience with the dull lifeless mechanical systems that treat people as if they were things, and so treat everybody alike ; for him there were no laws : there were exceptions merely, as if anybody, or anything, for that matter, was like aught else in the world !

That which is the very keynote of romantic art was to him the proper basis of natural life. He saw no other basis. And when they brought him one taken in the very act of sin and showed him her sentence written in the law, and asked him what was to be done, he wrote with his finger on the ground as though he did not hear them, and finally, when they pressed him again, looked up and said, " Let him of you who has never sinned be the first to throw the stone at her." It was worth while living to have said that.

Like all poetical natures, he loved ignorant people. He knew that in the soul of one who is ignorant there is always room for a great idea. But he could not stand stupid people, especially those who are made stupid by education : people who are full of opinions not one of which they even understand, a peculiarly modern type, summed up by Christ when he describes it as the type of one who has the key of knowledge, cannot use it himself, and does not allow other people to use it, though it may be made to open the gate of God's Kingdom. His chief war was against the Philistines. That is the war every child of light has to wage. Philistinism was the note of the age and community in which he lived. In their heavy inaccessibility to ideas, their dull respectability, their tedious orthodoxy, their worship of vulgar success, their entire preoccupation with the gross materialistic side of life, and their ridiculous estimate of themselves and their importance, the Jews of Jerusalem in Christ's day were the exact counterpart of the British Philistine of our own. Christ mocked at the " whited sepulchre " of respectability, and fixed that phrase for ever. He treated worldly success as a thing absolutely to be despised. He saw nothing in it at all. He looked on wealth as an encumbrance to a man. He would not hear of life being sacrificed to any system of thought or morals. He pointed out that forms and ceremonies were made for man, not man for forms and ceremonies. He took sabbatarianism as a type of the things that should be set at nought. The cold philanthropies, the ostentatious public charities, the tedious formalisms so dear to the middle-class mind, he exposed with utter and relentless scorn. To us, what is termed orthodoxy is merely a facile unintelligent acquiescence ; but to them, and in their hands, it was a terrible and paralysing tyranny. Christ swept it aside. He showed that the spirit alone was of value. He took a keen pleasure in pointing out to them that though the were always reading the law and the prophets, they had not really the smallest idea of what either of them meant. In opposition to their tithing of each separate day into the fixed routine of prescribed duties, as they tithe mint and rue, he preached the enormous importance of living completely for the moment.

Those whom he saved from their sins are saved simply for beautiful moments in their lives. Mary Magdalen, when she sees Christ, breaks the rich vase of alabaster that one of her seven lovers had given her, and spills the odorous spices over his tired dusty feet, and for that one moment's sake sits for ever with Ruth and Beatrice in the tresses of the snow-white rose of Paradise. All that Christ says to us by the way of a little warning is that every moment should be beautiful, that the soul should always be ready for the coming of the bridegroom, always waiting for the voice of the lover, Philistinism being simply that side of man's nature that is not illumined by the imagination. He sees all the lovely influences of life as modes of light : the imagination itself is the world of light. The world is made by it, and yet the world cannot understand it : that is because the imagination is simply a manifestation of love, and it is love and the capacity for it that distinguishes one human being from another.

But it is when he deals with a sinner that Christ is most romantic, in the sense of most real. The world had always loved the saint as being the nearest possible approach to the perfection of God. Christ, through some divine instinct in him, seems to have always loved the sinner as being the nearest possible approach to the perfection of man. His primary desire was not to reform people, any more than his primary desire was to relieve suffering. To turn an interesting thief into a tedious honest man was not his aim. He would have thought little of the Prisoners' Aid Society and other modern movements of the kind. The conversion of a publican into a Pharisee would not have seemed to him a great achievement. But in a manner not yet understood of the world he regarded sin and suffering as being in themselves beautiful holy things and modes of perfection.

It seems a very dangerous idea. It is—all great ideas are dangerous. That it was Christ's creed admits of no doubt. That it is the true creed I don't doubt myself.

Of course the sinner must repent. But why? Simply because otherwise he would be unable to realise what he had done. The moment of repentance is the moment of initiation. More than that: it is the means by which one alters one's past. The Greeks thought that impossible. They often say in their Gnomic aphorisms, " Even the Gods cannot alter the past." Christ showed that the commonest sinner could do it, that it was the one thing he could do. Christ, had he been asked, would have said—I feel quite certain about it—that the moment the prodigal son fell on his knees and wept, he made his having wasted his substance with harlots, his swine-herding and hungering for the husks they ate, beautiful and holy moments in his life. It is difficult for most people to grasp the idea. I dare say one has to go to prison to understand it. If so, it may be worth while going to prison.

There is something so unique about Christ. Of course just as there are false dawns before the dawn itself, and winter days so full of sudden sunlight that they will cheat the wise crocus into squandering its gold before its time, and make some foolish bird call to its mate to build on barren boughs, so there were Christians before Christ. For that we should be grateful. The unfortunate thing is that there have been none since. I make one exception, St. Francis of Assisi. But then God had given him at his birth the soul of a poet, as he himself when quite young had in mystical marriage taken poverty as his bride : and with the soul of a poet and the body of a beggar he found the way to perfection not difficult. He understood Christ, and so he became like him. We do not require the Liber Conformitatum to teach us that the life of St. Francis was the true *Imitatio Christi*, a poem compared to which the book of that name is merely prose.

Indeed, that is the charm about Christ, when all is said ; he is just like a work of art. He does not really teach one anything, but by being brought into his presence one becomes something. And everybody is predestined to his presence. Once at least in his life each man walks with Christ to Emmaus.

As regards the other subject, the Relation of the Artistic Life to Conduct, it will no doubt seem strange to you that I should select it. People point to Reading Gaol and say, " That is where the artistic life leads a man." Well, it might lead to worse places. The more mechanical people to whom life is a shrewd speculation depending on a careful calculation of ways and means, always know where they are going, and go there. They start with the ideal desire of being the parish beadle, and in whatever sphere they are placed they succeed in being the parish beadle and no more. A man whose desire is to be something separate from himself, to be a member of Parliament, or a successful grocer, or a prominent solicitor, or a judge, or something equally tedious, invariably succeeds in being what he wants to be. That is his punishment. Those who want a mask have to wear it.

But with the dynamic forces of life, and those in

whom those dynamic forces become incarnate, it is different. People whose desire is solely for self-realisation never know where they are going. They can't know. In one sense of the word it is of course necessary, as the Greek oracle said, to know oneself : that is the first achievement of knowledge. But to recognise that the soul of a man is unknowable, is the ultimate achievement of wisdom. The final mystery is oneself. When one has weighed the sun in the balance, and measured the steps of the moon, and mapped out the seven heavens star by star, there still remains oneself. Who can calculate the orbit of his own soul ? When the son went out to look for his father's asses, he did not know that a man of God was waiting for him with the very chrism of coronation, and that his own soul was already the soul of a king.

I hope to live long enough and to produce work of such a character that I shall be able at the end of my days to say, " Yes ! this is just where the artistic life leads a man ! " Two of the most perfect lives I have come across in my own experience are the lives of Verlaine and of Prince Kropotkin : both of them men who have passed years in prison : the first, the one Christian poet since Dante ; the other, a man with a soul of that beautiful white Christ which seems coming out of Russia. And for the last seven or eight months, in spite of a succession of great troubles reaching me from the outside world almost without intermission, I have been placed in direct contact with a new spirit working in this prison through man and things, that has helped me beyond any possibility of expression in words ; so that while for the first year of my imprisonment I did nothing else, and can remember doing nothing else, but wring my hands in impotent despair, and say, " What an ending, what an appalling ending ! " now I try to say to myself, and sometimes when I am not torturing myself do really and sincerely say, " What a beginning, what a wonderful beginning!" It may really be so. It may become so. If it does I shall owe much to this new personality that has altered every man's life in this place.

You may realise it when I say that had I been released last May, as I tried to be, I would have left this place loathing it and every official in it with a bitterness of hatred that would have poisoned my life. I have had a year longer of imprisonment, but humanity has been in the prison along with us all, and now when I go out I shall always remember great kindnesses that I have received here from almost everybody, and on the day of my release I shall give many thanks to many people, and ask to be remembered by them in turn.

The prison style is absolutely and entirely wrong. I would give anything to be able to alter it when I go out. I intend to try. But there is nothing in the world so wrong but that the spirit of humanity, which is the spirit of love, the spirit of the Christ who is not in churches, may make it, if not right, at least possible to be borne without too much bitterness of heart.

I know also that much is waiting for me outside that is very delightful, from what St. Francis of Assisi calls "my brother the wind, and my sister the rain," lovely things both of them, down to the shop-windows and sunsets of great cities. If I made a list of all that still remains to me, I don't know where I should stop, for, indeed, God made the world just as much for me as for any one else. Perhaps I may go out with something that I had not got before. I need not tell you that to me reformations in morals are as meaningless and vulgar as Reformations in theology. But while to propose to be a better man is a piece of unscientific cant, to have become a deeper man is the privilege of those who have suffered. And such I think I have become.

If after I am free a friend of mine gave a feast, and did not invite me to it, I should not mind a bit. I can be perfectly happy by myself. With freedom, flowers, books, and the moon, who could not be perfectly happy? Besides, feasts are not for me any more. I have given too many to care about them. That side of life is over for me, very fortunately, I dare say. But if after I am free a friend of mine had a sorrow and refused to allow me to share it, I should feel it most bitterly. If he shut the doors of the house of mourning against me, I would come back again and again and beg to be admitted, so that I might share in what I was entitled to share in. If he thought me unworthy, unfit to weep with him, I should feel it as the most poignant humiliation, as the most terrible mode in which disgrace could be inflicted on me. But that could not be. I have a right to share in sorrow, and he who can look at the loveliness of the world and share its sorrow, and realise something of the wonder of both, is in immediate contact with divine things, and has got as near to God's secret as any one can get.

Perhaps there may come into my art also, no less than into my life, a still deeper note, one of greater unity of passion, and directness of impulse. Not width but intensity is the true aim of modern art. We are no longer in art concerned with the type. It is with the exception that we have to do. I cannot put my sufferings into any form they took, I need hardly say. Art only begins where Imitation ends, but something must come into my work, of fuller memory of words perhaps, of richer cadences, of more curious effects, of simpler architectural order, of some aesthetic quality at any rate.

When Marsyas was " torn from the scabbard of his limbs "—*della vagina della membre sue*, to use one of Dante's most terrible Tacitean phrases—he had no more song, the Greek said. Apollo had been victor.

The lyre had vanquished the reed. But perhaps the Greeks were mistaken. I hear in much modern Art the cry of Marsyas. It is bitter in Baudelaire, sweet and plaintive in Lamartine, mystic in Verlaine. It is in the deferred resolutions of Chopin's music. It is in the discontent that haunts Burne-Jones's women. Even Matthew Arnold, whose song of Callicles tells of " the triumph of the sweet persuasive lyre," and the " famous final victory," in such a clear note of lyrical beauty, has not a little of it ; in the troubled undertone of doubt and distress that haunts his verses, neither Goethe nor Wordsworth could help him, though he followed each in turn, and when he seeks to mourn for *Thyrsis* or to sing of the *Scholar Gipsy*, it is the reed that he has to take for the rendering of his strain. But whether or not the Phrygian Faun was silent, I cannot be. Expression is as necessary to me as leaf and blossoms are to the black branches of the trees that show themselves above the prison walls and are so restless in the wind. Between my art and the world there is now a wide gulf, but between art and myself there is none. I hope at least that there is none.

To each of us different fates are meted out. My lot has been one of public infamy, of long imprisonment, of misery, of ruin, of disgrace, but I am not worthy of it—not yet, at any rate. I remember that I used to say that I thought I could bear a real tragedy if it came to me with purple pall and a mask of noble sorrow, but that the dreadful thing about modernity was that it put tragedy into the raiment of comedy, so that the great realities seemed commonplace or grotesque or lacking in style. It is quite true about modernity. It has probably always been true about actual life. It is said that all martyrdoms seemed mean to the looker on. The nineteenth century is no exception to the rule.

Everything about my tragedy has been hideous,

mean, repellent, lacking in style; our very dress
makes us grotesque. We are the zanies of sorrow. We
are clowns whose hearts are broken. We are specially
designed to appeal to the sense of humour. On November 13th, 1895, I was brought down here from London.
From two o'clock till half-past two on that day I
had to stand on the centre platform of Clapham Junc-
tion in convict dress, and handcuffed, for the world
to look at. I had been taken out of the hospital ward
without a moment's notice being given to me. Of all
possible objects I was the most grotesque. When
people saw me they laughed. Each train as it came
up swelled the audience. Nothing could exceed their
amusement. That was, of course, before they knew
who I was. As soon as they had been informed they
laughed still more. For half an hour I stood there in
the grey November rain surrounded by a jeering mob.

For a year after that was done to me I wept every
day at the same hour and for the same space of time.
That is not such a tragic thing as possibly it sounds
to you. To those who are in prison tears are a part
of every day's experience. A day in prison on which
one does not weep is a day on which one's heart is
hard, not a day on which one's heart is happy.

Well, now I am really beginning to feel more regret
for the people who laughed than for myself. Of course
when they saw me I was not on my pedestal, I was
in the pillory. But it is a very unimaginative nature
that only cares for people on their pedestals. A
pedestal may be a very unreal thing. A pillory is a
terrific reality. They should have known also how
to interpret sorrow better. I have said that behind
sorrow there is always sorrow. It were wiser still to
say that behind sorrow there is always a soul. And to
mock at a soul in pain is a dreadful thing. In the
strangely simple economy of the world people only
get what they give, and to those who have not enough
imagination to penetrate the mere outward of things,

and feel pity, what pity can be given save that of scorn ?

I write this account of the mode of my being transferred here simply that it should be realised how hard it has been for me to get anything out of my punishment but bitterness and despair. I have, however, to do it, and now and then I have moments of submission and acceptance. All the spring may be hidden in the single bud, and the low ground nest of the lark may hold the joy that is to herald the feet of many rose-red dawns. So perhaps whatever beauty of life still remains to me is contained in some moment of surrender, abasement, and humiliation. I can, at any rate, merely proceed on the lines of my own development, and, accepting all that has happened to me, make myself worthy of it.

People used to say of me that I was too individualistic. I must be far more of an individualist than ever I was. I must get far more out of myself than ever I got, and ask far less of the world than ever I asked. Indeed, my ruin came not from too great individualism of life, but from too little. The one disgraceful, unpardonable, and to all time contemptible action of my life was to allow myself to appeal to society for help and protection. To have made such an appeal would have been from the individualist point of view bad enough, but what excuse can there ever be put forward for having made it ? Of course once I had put into motion the forces of society, society turned on me and said, " Have you been living all this time in defiance of my laws, and do you now appeal to those laws for protection ? You shall have those laws exercised to the full. You shall abide by what you have appealed to." The result is I am in gaol. Certainly no man ever fell so ignobly, and by such ignoble instruments, as I did.

The Philistine element in life is not the failure to understand art. Charming people, such as fishermen, shepherds, ploughboys, peasants and the like, know nothing about art, and are the very salt of the earth. He is the Philistine who upholds and aids the heavy, cumbrous, blind, mechanical forces of society and who does not recognise dynamic force when he meets it either in a man or a movement.

People thought it dreadful of me to have entertained at dinner the evil things of life, and to have found pleasure in their company. But then, from the point of view through which I, as an artist in life, approach them they were delightfully suggestive and stimulating. The danger was half the excitement. . . . My business as an artist was with Ariel. I set myself to wrestle with Caliban. . . .

A great friend of mine—a friend of ten years' standing—came to see me some time ago, and told me that he did not believe a single word of what was said against me, and wished me to know that he considered me quite innocent, and the victim of a hideous plot. I burst into tears at what he said, and told him that while there was much amongst the definite charges that was quite untrue and transferred to me by revolting malice, still that my life had been full of perverse pleasures, and that unless he accepted that as a fact about me and realised it to the full I could not possibly be friends with him any more, or ever be in his company. It was a terrible shock to him, but we are friends, and I have not got his friendship on false pretences.

Emotional forces, as I say, somewhere in *Intentions*, are as limited in extent and duration as the forces of physical energy. The little cup that is made to hold so much can hold so much and no more, though all the purple vats of Burgundy be filled with wine to the brim, and the treaders stand knee-deep in the gathered grapes of the stony vineyards of Spain. There is no error more common than that of thinking that those who are the causes or occasions of great tragedies

share in the feelings suitable to the tragic mood :
no error more fatal than expecting it of them. The
martyr in his " shirt of flame " may be looking on
the face of God, but to him who is piling the faggots
or loosening the logs for the blast the whole scene is
no more than the slaying of an ox is to the butcher,
or the felling of a tree to the charcoal burner in the
forest, or the fall of a flower to one who is mowing
down the grass with a scythe. Great passions are for
the great of soul, and great events can be seen only
by those who are on a level with them.

. . . .

I know of nothing in all drama more incomparable
from the point of view of art, nothing more suggestive
in its subtlety of observation, than Shakespeare's
drawing of Rosencrantz and Guildenstern. They are
Hamlet's college friends. They have been his companions. They bring with them memories of pleasant
days together. At the moment when they come across
him in the play he is staggering under the weight of a
burden intolerable to one of his temperament. The
dead have come armed out of the grave to impose
on him a mission at once too great and too mean for
him. He is a dreamer, and he is called upon to act.
He has the nature of the poet, and he is asked to
grapple with the common complexity of cause and effect,
with life in its practical realisation, of which he knows
nothing, not with life in its ideal essence, of which
he knows so much. He has no conception of what
to do, and his folly is to feign folly. Brutus used madness as a cloak to conceal the sword of his purpose,
the dagger of his will, but the Hamlet madness is a
mere mask for the hiding of weakness. In the making
of fancies and jests he sees a chance of delay. He
keeps playing with action as an artist plays with a
theory. He makes himself the spy of his proper
actions, and listening to his own words knows them tc
be but " words, words, words." Instead of trying to

be the hero of his own history, he seeks to be the
spectator of his own tragedy. He disbelieves in everything, including himself, and yet his doubt helps
him not, as it comes not from scepticism, but from a
divided will.

Of all this Guildenstern and Rosencrantz realise
nothing. They bow and smirk and smile, and what
the one says the other echoes with sickliest intonation.
When at last, by means of the play within the play,
and the puppets in their dalliance, Hamlet " catches
the conscience " of the King, and drives the wretched
man in terror from his throne, Guildenstern and Rosencrantz see no more in his conduct than a rather painful
breach of Court etiquette. That is as far as they can
attain to in " the contemplation of the spectacle of
life with appropriate emotions." They are close to
his very secret and know nothing of it. Nor would
there be any use in telling them. They are the little
cups that can hold so much and no more. Towards
the close it is suggested that, caught in a cunning
spring set for another, they have met, or may meet,
with a violent and sudden death. But a tragic ending
of this kind, though touched by Hamlet's humour
with something of the surprise and justice of comedy,
is really not for such as they. They never die. Horatio,
who in order to " report Hamlet and his cause aright
to the unsatisfied,"

" Absents him from felicity a while,
And in this harsh world draws his breath in pain,"

dies, but Guildenstern and Rosencrantz are as immortal as Angelo and Tartuffe, and should rank with
them. They are what modern life has contributed
to the antique ideal of friendship. He who writes a
new *De Amicitia* must find a niche for them, and
praise them in Tusculan prose. They are types fixed
for all time. To censure them would show " a lack of

appreciation." They are merely out of their sphere—
that is all. In sublimity of soul there is no contagion.
High thoughts and high emotions are by their very
existence isolated.

I am to be released, if all goes well with me, towards
the end of May, and hope to go at once to some little
seaside village abroad with R—— and M——.
The sea, as Euripides says in one of his plays about
Iphigeneia, washes away the stains and wounds of
the world.
I hope to be at least a month with my friends, and
to gain peace and balance, and a less troubled heart,
and a sweeter mood. I have a strange longing for
the great simple primeval things, such as the sea, to
me no less of a mother than the Earth. It seems to
me that we all look at Nature too much, and live with
her too little. I discern great sanity in the Greek attitude. They never chattered about sunsets, or discussed whether the shadows on the grass were really
mauve or not. But they saw that the sea was for the
swimmer, and the sand for the feet of the runner. They
loved the trees for the shadow that they cast, and the
forest for its silence at noon. The vineyard-dresser
wreathed his hair with ivy that he might keep off the
rays of the sun as he stooped over the young shoots,
and for the artist and the athlete, the two types that
Greece gave us, they plaited with garlands the leaves
of the bitter laurel and of the wild parsley, which else
had been of no service to men.
We call ours a utilitarian age, and we do not know
the uses of any single thing. We have forgotten that
water can cleanse, and fire purify, and that the Earth
is mother to us all. As a consequence our art is of
the moon and plays with shadows, while Greek art
is of the sun and deals directly with things. I feel
sure that in elemental forces there is purification,
and I want to go back to them and live in their presence.

Of course to one so modern as I am, " Enfant de mon siècle," merely to look at the world will be always lovely. I tremble with pleasure when I think that on the very day of my leaving prison both the laburnum and the lilac will be blooming in the gardens, and that I shall see the wind stir into restless beauty the swaying gold of the one, and make the other toss the pale purple of its plumes so that all the air shall be Arabia for me. Linnæus fell on his knees and wept for joy when he saw for the first time the long heath of some English upland made yellow with the tawny aromatic blossoms of the common furze ; and I know that for me, to whom flowers are part of desire, there are tears waiting in the petals of some rose. It has always been so with me from my boyhood. There is not a single colour hidden away in the chalice of a flower, or the curve of a shell, to which, by some subtle sympathy with the very soul of things, my nature does not answer. Like Gautier, I have always been one of those " pour qui le monde visible existe."

Still, I am conscious now that behind all this beauty, satisfying though it may be, there is some spirit hidden of which the painted forms and shapes are but modes of manifestation, and it is with this spirit that I desire to become in harmony. I have grown tired of the articulate utterances of men and things. The Mystical in Art, the Mystical in Life, the Mystical in Nature, this is what I am looking for. It is absolutely necessary for me to find it somewhere.

All trials are trials for one's life, just as all sentences are sentences of death ; and three times have I been tried. The first time I left the box to be arrested, the second time to be led back to the house of detention, the third time to pass into a prison for two years. Society, as we have constituted it, will have no place for me, has none to offer ; but Nature, whose sweet rains fall on unjust and just alike, will have clefts in the rocks where I may hide, and secret valleys in whose silence I may weep undisturbed. She will hang the night with stars so that I may walk abroad in the darkness without stumbling, and send the wind over my footprints so that none may track me to my hurt : she will cleanse me in great waters, and with bitter herbs make me whole.